PRESERVING MINDS, SAVING LIVES

THE BEST CRYONICS WRITINGS FROM THE ALCOR LIFE EXTENSION FOUNDATION

Edited by Aschwin de Wolf and Stephen Bridge

This publication is designed to provide accurate and authoritative information in regard to the subject matter covered. It is published with the understanding that the publisher and author are not engaged in rendering legal, accounting or other professional service. If legal advice or other professional advice, including financial, is required, the services of a competent professional person should be sought.

While the author has made every effort to provide accurate telephone numbers and Internet addresses at the time of publication, neither the publisher nor the author assumes any responsibility for errors, or for changes that occur after publication.

Commercial Printers Inc. and Tiger Type Design are not affiliated or connected in any way with the Alcor Life Extension Foundation.

Published by Commercial Printers Inc.
6600 NW 15th Avenue
Ft. Lauderdale, FL 33309

Book design by Jill Grasse, Tiger Type Design
Scottsdale, AZ

Printed in the United States of America

FOREWORD

CRYONICS AND HOPE

BY GREGORY BENFORD, PH.D.

In the late 1980s I wrote a mainstream thriller about cryonics and published *Chiller* under a pseudonym, Sterling Blake. I had become interested in it through a visit with fellow science fiction writer Joe Haldeman, where the Alcor site in Riverside, California impressed us both. I modeled my *Chiller* characters on actual Alcor people and set it near UC Irvine, where I am a professor.

A quarter century later, *Chiller* is still in print, the Boomers are aging, and longevity is making major progress. Still, humanity's Great Problem, probably unique to us as a thinking species, is illness and death—what Terry Prachett called the Embuggerance, before it took him.

These decades give us cryonicists a chance to look back on what our efforts have made, and think forward. This anthology of the best writing on the field (except for fiction) gives us that perspective. Many of the writers here I used as models for my novel.

Ray Bradbury once said he was interested in any chance of seeing the future, but when he thought over cryonics, he realized that he would be torn away from everything he loved. What would the future be worth without his wife, his children, his friends? No, he told me, he wouldn't take the option at any price.

Still, he came into this world without all those associations. And further, why assume that nobody else would go with him? This is an example of the "neighborhood" argument, which says that mature people are so entwined with their surroundings, people and habits of mind, that to yank them out is a trauma worse than death. One is fond of one's own era, certainly. But it seems to me that ordinary immigrants often face similar challenges and manage to come through.

Still, if you truly feel this way, no arithmetic argument will dissuade you. For many, I suspect, the future isn't open to rational gambles, because it is too deeply embedded in emotional issues.

So it must be with any way of thinking quantitatively about our future. We cannot see the range of possibilities without imposing our own values and views, mired in our time, culture, and place. Often, these are the things we value most—our idiosyncratic angles on the world.

But there is one clear advantage to cryonics: It allows one to die with some sliver of hope.

In this volume you can learn what time has taught us, through these articles and projections. Then it's up to you to push the field forward, so we can all share a future up there in the Great Beyond.

Hope to see you there!

Gregory Benford
July 2015

INTRODUCTION

BY STEPHEN W. BRIDGE

We are offering to you an opportunity that you are likely to find in few other places— the chance to change the world. We have dreams that may seem beyond reach: the elimination of disease and old age, the end of hunger, biological adaptations that could allow us to live on other planets or travel to the stars, a greatly extended lifespan, even immortality. But we have the courage to stretch out our hands and minds toward those dreams. They are not impossible, which is a belief we hope you may come to share with us. We are the radicals, the outer fringe of the scientific world. We are the ultimate revolutionaries. What is the overthrow of a government or even the founding of a new nation compared to the elimination of death? Governments come and go, and one is pretty much the same as another. If you want to make a permanent change in the world, the human life span is where you must direct your attention. Some will call us mad; I say we have vision. This is your invitation to help us determine the future of the future.

Stephen W. Bridge
IABS Newsletter #1
September 1977

With those brave, youthful words, Mike Darwin and I started the Institute for Advanced Biological Studies, Inc., in Indianapolis, Indiana. This non-profit corporation was focused on cryonics; but our attorney advised us to give it a more generic scientific name, so we didn't have to attract attention until we were ready, and so we could still use the corporation for something else if the whole cryonics thing didn't work out. It didn't work out very well in Indianapolis, so in 1981, Mike decided to move to southern California to join forces with Jerry Leaf's Cryovita Laboratories. But before he left, he persuaded me that we should turn our occasional newsletter into a regular monthly magazine and name it CRYONICS. Yes, all CAPS. The first issue of CRYONICS came out in March, 1981; but we called it issue #8, following our seven issues of the IABS newsletter. (I have regretted ever since the confusion this has caused.)

That first issue was 6 pages, but it quickly grew to 36 pages as we gained more writers and readers who turned to us for cryonics news, philosophy, discussion, and arguments. Since we were willing to publish articles and letters from just about every cryonics activist, arguments were plentiful.

In May, 1981, the Alcor Life Extension Foundation joined IABS as a sponsor of *Cryonics*. In September, 1982, IABS and Alcor officially merged, keeping the Alcor name. Beginning with the November, 1982 issue, the magazine became the official publication of Alcor, and it has remained that way ever since. Eventually, Hugh Hixon replaced me as Mike's co-editor, and the two of them oversaw the first big growth of the magazine. In November, 1990, Ralph Whelan became the "Managing Editor" of *Cryonics*, eventually taking over full editorship.

Beginning with the first issue of 1994, *Cryonics* changed to a slicker look, quarterly format, a frequency it maintained (except for 6 issues in 2005) until the first issue of 2012. It is now published monthly after a brief experiment with a web-only bimonthly format. Brian Shock was the editor from 2nd Quarter, 1997 through 3rd Quarter, 1999. Alcor founders Fred and Linda Chamberlain took over editing the magazine for a while, then turned it over to Lisa Lock for the 2nd Quarter of 2000, a position she held through 2003. For two years the editor was simply listed as "The Alcor Staff" until Jennifer Chapman became the editor with the 1st Quarter of 2006. Aschwin de Wolf, the co-editor of this book, took over as editor of *Cryonics* with the 3rd Quarter of 2008 and remains so today.

247 issues and 33 years after we began *Cryonics*, I must admit to being both proud and surprised that it has endured so long. But it only became so through the efforts and inspiration of the dozens of Alcor staff and writers who have contributed to its pages. You hold the results in your hands. It was not easy to cut the 7 million or so words in 3 decades of *Cryonics* down to one book. We assume some of your favorite articles have missed the cut. We know some of ours are not here. (To read every issue of *Cryonics*, see: http://www.alcor.org/CryonicsMagazine/index.html)

In these pages you will learn about the history of cryonics and of Alcor. You will learn about the science and technology of cryonics. You will examine speculations as to which cryonics technologies are best, what developments might occur in the future, and how cryopreserved patients might someday be repaired and returned to consciousness. Most of all you will read about the great ideas that support cryonics and about the great thinkers and workers who have allowed us to get this far.

This book is not merely a selection of the best contributions to *Cryonics*. One of the important considerations that went into selecting the articles is that this volume should also double as a contemporary introduction to cryonics, and cryonics as practiced by Alcor in particular. Some articles that have triggered a lot of discussion have been omitted but lesser known contributions that reflect Alcor's current perspective on the rationale and practice of human cryopreservation have been included. In particular, our emphasis has been to select articles that present cryonics as an extension of critical care medicine and to (mostly) steer clear from philosophical treatments about transhumanism and immortality. In some cases we have asked the authors to update their contribution to reflect contemporary cryonics terminology and recent advances. For example, the article that outlines the case for whole body cryopreservation has been greatly expanded and improved.

Some of the articles in this book are quite technical but we believe that it is not possible to do justice to the technical feasibility of cryonics without including detailed expositions of the science that underpins Alcor's operations. In particular, we spent considerable time ensuring that all the major scientific and technological advances at Alcor are presented in a logical, chronological fashion.

Selecting the articles for this book was a non-trivial undertaking and this book would have been even bigger if we did not make some difficult decisions to omit a lot of quality writings. Since this book was years in the making it was also tempting to include very recent contributions; but at some point we had to draw the line. In the Afterword, current editor of *Cryonics*, Aschwin de Wolf, will further reflect on what it is like to edit the magazine today and where Alcor might be heading in the future.

It is not just ideas which propel this mission, it is also the hard work of hundreds of Alcor members, volunteers, and employees in many different capacities—scientists, engineers, doctors, nurses, paramedics, fabricators, writers, speakers, bookkeepers, office managers, fund-raisers, computer programmers, board members, and the many other people necessary to make any organization succeed. We are permanently (in the *longest* sense of that word) grateful to all who have given life to Alcor.

Ultimately, this book is dedicated to Alcor's patients, waiting in their cryopreserved state, especially those who contributed so much effort to Alcor's progress: Jerry Leaf, Paul Genteman, Thomas Munson, Paul Garfield, Fred Chamberlain III, etc. We anticipate that we will join them someday, and we invite—and expect—you to pick up the slack and provide the same energy and commitment for us. That's the world of cryonics. Welcome in.

CONTENTS

HISTORY OF ALCOR

RESEARCH IN CRYONICS

ALCOR PROCEDURES AND TECHNOLOGIES

RESUSCITATION OF CRYONICS PATIENTS

PERSPECTIVES ON CRYONICS

DEBATES WITHIN CRYONICS

WHAT IS CRYONICS?

WHY WE ARE CRYONICISTS

BY MICHAEL DARWIN
Cryonics, January, 1983

We are cryonicists because we choose to be optimistic rather than pessimistic about the future. We believe that human knowledge and medical technology will continue to expand and that even people who are considered "dead" today will someday be able to be restored to life, health, and youth. We understand that the state of "death" is nothing more than a physician admitting he is unable to restore a person to life; that this decision as to when a person dies will vary from doctor to doctor, place to place and most importantly from time to time. A person suffering a cardiac arrest in a hospital cafeteria will have a radically different prognosis than the same person with the same condition on the crowded streets of Bombay: in a hospital he might be resuscitated and live, but on the streets of Bombay a physician would pronounce him dead. We understand that as progress in our understanding of physiology and medicine is made and translated into improved medical technology, we are able to recover more and more people from so-called "death." We believe an explosion of biological technology is coming that will transform the world even more radically than the changes brought by the explosion of engineering and physical technology in this century. We believe that mankind will soon have control over living systems, allowing us to end all human illness, reverse and control the aging process, and solve the thorny ecological problems which seem so overwhelming to us today. We believe that this coming control over living systems will also allow us to fabricate new organisms for use in food and industrial production as well as for the repair and regeneration of patients currently waiting in cryonic suspension.

We are cryonicists because we know what we are doing is right. We don't know if what we are doing will work, but we know that it is the right action to take. When someone discovers a person lying on the ground with an apparent cardiac arrest, he does not enter into a debate with himself or other bystanders about whether or not his application of cardiopulmonary resuscitation will work for this particular individual, whether the victim will suffer brain damage, has another terminal illness, would have wanted CPR to be applied, or whether or not doctors will be able to treat the cause of his heart arrest successfully. Rather, the rescuer immediately applies CPR in order to stabilize the victim's condition and prevent any further deterioration from occurring until the victim can reach trained medical personnel who can make those decisions. It is not the rescuer's place to second guess medical capability. As cryonicists we feel that it is not our place to second guess future medical capabilities either. We know that the right thing for us to do is to move immediately to prevent the patient's condition from deteriorating further and to continue to exert maximum effort to get that patient to a time when it may be possible to treat him effectively. So just as the CPR rescuer seeks to stabilize his heart attack victim and move him over distance to medical assistance, the cryonics rescuer seeks to stabilize his patient and move him through time to an era when effective medical help will be available.

We are cryonicists because we love being alive and do not want our lives to ever end. We know that the most important things we have—the only things that really matter—are our lives and health. Where we differ from others is in our unwillingness to admit defeat because contemporary medical and social authority tells us that we should. We believe in fighting even when the odds against us may be very high and the certainty of success non-existent. We believe we should fight because some chance to hold on to our precious lives, even a minuscule chance, is better than no chance at all and certain death.

We are cryonicists because we refuse to let go of those we love and lose them forever. We are through closing black cuts in the earth and living with deeper ones in our hearts. We know that taking action to save the people we cherish, even if there is little chance that it will succeed, is infinitely superior to helpless inaction and smothering our grief and loss with worthless tears and dying flowers. We believe that action is better than inaction and that the psychological advantage to the dying person and his loved ones is reason enough to undertake cryonic suspension. We believe that it is better to fight than to surrender and we will not give up solely on the basis of someone else admitting their impotence.

Finally we are cryonicists because we know that each of us is responsible for our own lives and survival; that if we do not take action to defend our lives, no one else will. Being cryonicists puts us back in control of our lives: no longer are we under an absolute, inescapable death sentence. We are taking action to fight death and achieve indefinite extension of our lives. We are not helpless cattle being led to slaughter by an indifferent universe. This realization transforms us and lets us take joy in our lives because it frees us from the draining certainty that we are going to grow weak and disappear forever. We know that we have a chance because we are cryonicists and this awareness motivates us to be productive and to strive to maximize this chance that cryonics represents. If you would like learn more about cryonics, please write or call us at:

ALCOR LIFE EXTENSION FOUNDATION
7895 East Acoma Drive, Suite 110
Scottsdale, Arizona 85260
(480) 905-1906
1 (877) 462-5267 ■

CRYONICS: USING LOW TEMPERATURES TO CARE FOR THE CRITICALLY ILL

BY ASCHWIN DE WOLF
Cryonics, 4th Quarter, 2007

"We'll look back on this 50 to 100 years from now—we'll shake our heads and say, "What were people thinking? They took these people who were very nearly viable, just barely dysfunctional, and they put them in an oven or buried them under the ground, when there were people who could have put them into cryopreservation. I think we'll look at this just as we look today at slavery, beating women, and human sacrifice, and we'll say, "this was insane—a huge tragedy."—Alcor CEO Max More, Ph.D.

Introduction

In contemporary medicine terminally ill patients can be declared legally dead using two different criteria: whole brain death or cardiorespiratory arrest. Although many people would agree that a human being without any functional brain activity, or even without higher brain function, has ceased to exist as a person, not many people realize that most patients who are currently declared legally dead by cardiorespiratory criteria have not yet died as a person. Or to use conventional biomedical language, although the organism has ceased to exist as a functional, integrated whole, the neuroanatomy of the person is still intact when a patient is declared legally dead using cardiorespiratory criteria.

It might seem odd that contemporary medicine allows deliberate destruction of the properties that make us uniquely human (our capacity for consciousness), unless one considers the significant challenge of keeping a brain alive in a body that has ceased to function as an integrated whole. But what if we could put the brain "on pause" until a time when medical science has become advanced enough to treat the rest of the body, reverse aging, and restore the patient to health?

Metabolic Arrest

Putting the brain on pause is not as far fetched as it seems. The brain of a patient undergoing general anesthesia has ceased being conscious. But because we know that the brain that represents the person is still there in a viable body, we do not think of such a person as "temporarily dead."

One step further than general anesthesia is hypothermic circulatory arrest. Some medical procedures, such as complicated neurosurgical interventions, require not only cessation of consciousness but also complete cessation of blood flow to the brain. In these cases the temperature of the patient is lowered to such a degree ($\approx$16 degrees Celsius) that the brain can tolerate a period without any circulation at all. Considering the fact that parts of the human brain can become irreversibly injured after no more than five minutes without oxygen, the ability of the brain to survive for at least an hour at these temperatures without any oxygen is quite remarkable.

Again, because we know that in such cases the brain that represents the person is still there in a viable body, we do not think of such a person as "temporarily dead." These examples illustrate that the medical community already recognizes and accepts the fact that a medical procedure that produces loss of consciousness, and even loss of circulation, does not constitute irreversible death.

Unfortunately, general anesthesia and hypothermic circulatory arrest cannot be used to pause the brain long enough to find a treatment for a person who has been declared legally dead by cardiorespiratory criteria. Such a person under general anesthesia may require tens, if not hundreds, of years of artificial circulation to keep the brain viable until medical science is able to return him to health. Leaving financial considerations aside, artificial circulation of an organ, let alone such a vulnerable organ as the brain, will produce increasing brain injury over time, and ultimately, destruction of the person.

Hypothermic circulatory arrest eliminates the need for metabolic support of the brain, but only for a limited period of time. Current research into hypothermic circulatory arrest indicates that the brain might tolerate up to 3 hours of complete circulatory arrest if the temperature is lowered close to the freezing point of water (zero degrees Celsius). This is not nearly long enough to put the brain on pause to allow the patient to reach a time where his current medical condition may be treatable. In light of these limitations, it is understandable that no serious attempts are currently being made to continue long-term care for a patient whose body has stopped functioning as an integrated organism.

But if low temperatures can extend the period that the brain can survive without circulation, much lower temperatures should be able to extend this period even further. At -196 degrees Celsius (the temperature of a patient cryopreserved in liquid nitrogen) molecular activity has become so negligible that it can be said that the brain has been put on pause in the literal sense of the word. This allows the patient to be "transported" to a time when more advanced medical technologies are available, even if this would require hundreds of years. Advocates of human cryopreservation argue that long-term care at cryogenic temperatures offers a rational alternative to the current practice of burial or cremation of persons no longer treatable by contemporary medicine.

Contrary to popular views of cryonics, cryonics is not about preserving dead people but about *long-term* care of *critically ill patients*. The objection that cryonics is an attempt to resuscitate dead people reflects a misunderstanding of the rationale behind cryonics. The arguments supporting human cryopreservation are not radically different than the already established arguments behind general anesthesia and hypothermic circulatory arrest; it merely introduces *lower temperatures* and *longer care*. Therefore, the difference between contemporary medicine and cryonics is quantitative, not qualitative, in nature. Likewise, the relationship between cryonics and religion is not qualitatively different than that between contemporary medicine and religion. In both cases medical technology is used to preserve life.

Vitrification

But does the procedure of cooling a patient to cryogenic temperatures not cause injury in itself? Most of the human body consists of water and lowering the body below the freezing point of water will produce massive ice formation. For this reason, cryonics patients are protected from ice damage by using a *cryoprotective agent* to reduce, or even eliminate, ice formation. Conventional extracorporeal bypass technologies are used to circulate the solution throughout the body. When enough water is replaced with the cryoprotective agent, the patient is maintained at cryogenic temperatures for long-term care. Historically the cryoprotective agents that were used in cryonics are mainstream cryoprotective agents such as DMSO and glycerol. High concentrations of glycerol or DMSO can significantly reduce ice formation, but cannot eliminate it altogether, except at the cost of substantial toxicity.

A better alternative to conventional cryopreservation is *vitrification*. Vitrification offers the prospect of cooling an organ to cryogenic temperatures without ice formation. Although vitrification of pure water requires extremely high cooling rates, these cooling rates can be greatly reduced if high concentrations of cryoprotective agents and "ice blockers" are added. Ice blockers are synthetic variants of naturally occurring anti-freeze proteins used by hibernating animals to protect themselves from freezing injury. The vitrification agent is introduced within a so-called "carrier solution" which includes molecules to prevent cell swelling, support metabolism, maintain physiological pH, and prevent oxidative damage. The vitrification agent is introduced in a gradual fashion to prevent excessive volume changes in cells. During the final stages of cryoprotectant perfusion, the temperature is dropped below zero degrees Celsius to protect the cells from toxicity caused by high concentrations of the vitrification agent at higher temperatures.

The current generation of vitrification agents can preserve the fine details (ultrastructure) of the brain without requiring unfeasible cooling rates. Although electrical activity has recently been demonstrated in vitrified rabbit brain slices, reversible vitrification of the human brain without loss of viability is currently not possible. The current research objective, therefore, is to improve on these vitrification agents to allow for reproducible vitrification and recovery of organs with complete long-term viability. Such a breakthrough would not only lead to cryogenic organ banking for transplantation and research but would remove the most fundamental obstacle to suspended animation of humans.

Brain death and cryonics
Although a vitrified patient cannot be rewarmed and restored to health with contemporary technologies, the extremely low temperatures at which a patient is maintained permit possible resuscitation of a patient in the future without any risk of deterioration during long-term care. In this sense it compares favorably to procedures such as hypothermic circulatory arrest which allow for only a few hours to treat a patient. This not only offers the option to treat patients who cannot be treated with contemporary medical technologies, it also offers the possibility to treat medical conditions where successful resuscitation is possible but higher brain function will be lost if care is resumed at normal body temperature.

A good example of this is cardiac arrest. Patients who have suffered more than 5-7 minutes of cardiac arrest can often be resuscitated, *but* some of the most vulnerable cells in the brain (such as the hippocampal CA1 neurons) will die within days of the insult. There are currently no effective medical interventions or neuroprotective agents that will prevent such damage. As a result, today's medicine can restore viability to such patients, but only by losing some, or most, higher brain functions.

If one believes that the objective of medical care is not just to preserve life in the sense of integrated biological function, but also to preserve the *person*, then one would agree that such patients might be better served by interventions that place them under long-term care in the form of cryonics. Although there is no guarantee that such patients will be restored to full functionality in the future, the certainty of higher brain death is an alternative that many people would prefer to avoid.

The first minutes after "death"
As currently practiced, cryonics procedures can only be started *after* legal death has been pronounced by a medical professional. To prevent brain injury between pronouncement of legal death and long-term care in liquid nitrogen, all major cryonics organizations offer standby services to ensure that the time of circulatory arrest is minimized. In ideal circumstances the cryonics organization of which the patient is a member will deploy a *standby team* consisting of cryonics professionals to stabilize the patient immediately after pronouncement of legal death.

A mechanical device is used to restart blood circulation and ventilate the patient.

Because the objective of this intervention is not to resuscitate but to stabilize the patient this is called *cardiopulmonary support (CPS)*. At the same time the patient is lifted into a portable ice bath to induce hypothermia to slow metabolic rate. A number of medications are also given to support blood flow to the central organs, reverse and prevent blot clotting, restore physiological pH, prevent edema, and protect the brain from ischemic injury.

If the patient is pronounced legally dead at a remote location, an additional step to this protocol is added and the patient's blood is washed out and replaced with an organ preservation solution to preserve viability of the tissue during transport at low temperatures. The organ preservation solution that is currently used by cryonics organizations is similar to the cold organ preservation solutions that are used in mainstream medicine (such as *Viaspan*) to preserve organs for transplantation.

At the cryonics organization the patient's blood (or the organ preservation solution) is replaced with the vitrification agent to prevent ice formation during cooldown to liquid nitrogen temperature for long-term care.

Conclusion

Cryonics does not involve the freezing of dead people. Cryonics involves placing critically ill patients that cannot be treated with contemporary medical technologies in a state of long-term low temperature care to preserve the *person* until a time when treatments might be available. Similar to such common medical practices as general anesthesia and hypothermic circulatory arrest, cryonics does not require a fundamental paradigm shift in how conventional medicine thinks about biology, physiology, and brain function. Although current cryopreservation methods are not reversible, under ideal circumstances the fine structure that encodes a person's personality is likely to be preserved. Complete proof of reversible vitrification of human beings would be sufficient, but is not necessary, for acceptance of cryonics as a form of long-term critical care medicine. The current alternative is death or, for persons who are at risk of suffering extensive brain injury, loss of personhood.

For very old and fragile patients, meaningful resuscitation would require reversal of the aging process. Obviously, the objective of cryonics is not to resuscitate patients in a debilitated and compromised condition, but to rejuvenate the patient. Ongoing research in fields such as biogerontology, nanomedicine, and synthetic biology inspire optimism that such treatment will be available in the future. The fortunate thing for cryonics patients is that, even if fundamental breakthroughs in these fields will only happen after long and painstaking research, the cold temperatures allow them time—a lot of time. ■

MEDICAL TIME TRAVEL

BY BRIAN WOWK, PH.D.

Originally published in 2004 as a chapter from the book The Scientific Conquest of Death. *It is reproduced here with permission of the author and publisher.*

SUMMARY: Clinical medicine is now able to "turn off" people for more than an hour with no heartbeat or brain activity for certain surgical procedures. Scientists are on the verge of being able to preserve individual organs indefinitely by using a new technology called vitrification. Brain electrical activity has been detected in animals rewarmed after seven years of frozen storage. Could human life be preserved in an arrested state for years or decades instead of hours? The prospects are still distant, but some people are already betting that current preservation technology may be good enough to be reversible in the future. Whether they are correct is a legitimate scientific question.

Time travel is a solved problem. Einstein showed that if you travel in a spaceship for months at speeds close to the speed of light, you can return to earth centuries in the future. Unfortunately for would-be time travelers, such spacecraft will not be available until centuries in the future.

Rather than Einstein, nature relies on Arrhenius to achieve time travel. The Arrhenius equation of chemistry describes how chemical reactions slow down as temperature is reduced. Since life is chemistry, life itself slows down at cooler temperatures. Hibernating animals use this principle to time travel from summer to summer, skipping winters when food is scarce.

Medicine already uses this kind of biological time travel. When transplantable organs such as hearts or kidneys are removed from donors, the organs begin dying as soon as their blood supply stops. Removed organs have only minutes to live. However with special preservation solutions and cooling in ice, organs can be moved across hours of time and thousands of miles to waiting recipients. Cold slows chemical processes that would otherwise be quickly fatal.

Can whole people travel through time like preserved organs? Remarkably, the answer seems to be yes. Although it is seldom done, medicine sometimes does preserve people like organs awaiting transplant. Some surgeries on major blood vessels of the heart or brain can only be done if blood circulation through the entire body is stopped.[1,2] Stopped blood circulation would ordinarily be fatal within 5 minutes, but cooling to +16°C (60°F) allows the human body to remain alive in a "turned off" state for up to 60 minutes.[3] With special blood substitutes and further cooling to a temperature of 0°C (32°F), life without heartbeat or circulation can be extended as much as three hours.[4] Although there is currently no surgical use for circulatory arrest of several hours,[5] it may be used in the future to permit surgical repair of wounds before blood circulation is restored after severe trauma.[6]

While some biological processes are merely slowed by deep cooling, others are completely stopped. Brain activity is an important example. Brain electrical activity usually ceases at temperatures below +18°C (64°F), and disappears completely in all cases as freezing temperatures are approached.[7] Yet these temperatures can still be survived. In fact, not only can the brain survive being turned off, surgeons often use drugs to force the brain to turn off when temperature alone doesn't do the trick.[8] They do this because if the brain is active when blood circulation is stopped, vital energy stores can become depleted, later causing death. This reminds us that death is not when life turns off. Death is when the chemistry of life becomes irreversibly damaged.

Specialized surgeries are not the only cases in which the brain can stop working and later start again. Simple cardiac arrest (stopping of the heart) at normal body temperature also causes brain electrical activity to stop within 40 seconds.[9] Yet the heart can remain stopped for several times this long with no lasting harm. Anesthetic

1   Aebert H, Brawanski A, Philipp A, Behr R, Ullrich OW, Keyl C, Birnbaum DE, in: *European Journal of Cardiothoracic Surgery* (1998, vol. 13), "Deep hypothermia and circulatory arrest for surgery of complex intracranial aneurysms," pg. 223-229.

2   Ehrlich M, Grabenwoger M, Simon P, Laufer G, Wolner E, Havel M, in: *Texas Heart Institute Journal* (1995, vol. 22), "Surgical treatment of type A aortic dissections. Results with profound hypothermia and circulatory arrest," pg. 250-253.

3   Rosenthal E, in: *New York Times* (1990, Nov. 13), "Suspended Animation - Surgery's Frontier."

4   Haneda K, Thomas R, Sands MP, Breazeale DG, Dillard DH, in: *Cryobiology* (1986, vol. 23), "Whole body protection during three hours of total circulatory arrest: an experimental study," pg. 483-494.

5   Greenberg MS, in: *Handbook of Neurosurgery* (1997, 4th edition), "General technical considerations of aneurysm surgery."

6   Bellamy R, Safar P, Tisherman SA, Basford R, Bruttig SP, Capone A, Dubick MA, Ernster L, Hattler BG Jr, Hochachka P, Klain M, Kochanek PM, Kofke WA, Lancaster JR, McGowan FX Jr, Oeltgen PR, Severinghaus JW, Taylor MJ, Zar H, in: *Critical Care Medicine* (1996, vol. 24), "Suspended animation for delayed resuscitation," S24-47.

7   Stecker MM, Cheung AT, Pochettino A, Kent GP, Patterson T, Weiss SJ, Bavaria JE, in: *Annals of Thoracic Surgery* (2001, vol. 71), "Deep hypothermic circulatory arrest: I. Effects of cooling on electroencephalogram and evoked potentials," pg. 14-21.

8   Rung GW, Wickey GS, Myers JL, Salus JE, Hensley FA Jr, Martin DE, in: *Journal of Cardiothoracic and Vascular Anesthesia* (1991, vol. 5), "Thiopental as an adjunct to hypothermia for EEG suppression in infants prior to circulatory arrest," pg. 337-342.

9   Lind B, Snyder J, Kampschulte S, Safar P, in: *Resuscitation* (1975, vol. 4), "A review of total brain ischaemia models in dogs and original experiments on clamping the aorta," pg. 19-31.

drugs, such as barbiturates, can flatten EEG (brain electrical activity) readings for many hours while still permitting later recovery.[10] This prolonged drug-induced elimination of brain activity is sometimes used as a treatment for head injuries.[11] Patients do not emerge from these comas as blank slates. Evidently human beings don't require continuous operation like computer chips. Brains store long-term memories in physical structures, not fleeting electrical patterns.

Perhaps the most extreme example of brains completely stopping and later starting again are the experiments of Isamu Suda reported in the journal Nature[12] and elsewhere[13] in 1966 and 1974. Suda showed recovery of EEG activity in cat brains resuscitated with warm blood after frozen storage at -20°C (-4°F) for up to seven years.

Reversible experiments in which all electrical activity stops, and chemistry comes to a virtual halt, disprove the 19th-century belief that there is a "spark of life" inside living things. Life is chemistry. When the chemistry of life is adequately preserved, so is life. When the chemistry of a human mind is adequately preserved, so is the person.

Suda's frozen cat brains deteriorated with time. Brains thawed after five days showed EEG patterns almost identical to EEGs obtained before freezing. However brains thawed after seven years showed greatly slowed activity. At a temperature of -20°C, liquid water still exists in a concentrated solution between ice crystals. Chemical deterioration still slowly occurs in this cold liquid.

Preserving the chemistry of life for unlimited periods of time requires cooling below -130°C (-200°F).[14] Below this temperature, any remaining unfrozen liquid between ice crystals undergoes a "glass transition." Molecules become stuck to their neighbors with weak hydrogen bonds. Instead of wandering about, molecules just vibrate in one place. Without freely moving molecules, all chemistry stops.

For living cells to survive this process, chemicals called cryoprotectants must be added. Cryoprotectants, such as glycerol, are small molecules that freely penetrate inside cells and limit the percentage of water that converts into ice during cooling. This allows cells to survive freezing by remaining in isolated pockets of unfrozen solution between ice crystals[14]. Below the glass transition temperature, molecules inside these pockets lock into place, and cells remain preserved inside the glassy water-cryoprotectant mixture between ice crystals.

10   Bird TD, Plum F, in: *Neurology* (1968, vol. 18), "Recovery from barbiturate overdose coma with a prolonged isoelectric electroencephalogram," pg. 456-460.

11   Toyama, T, "Barbiturate Coma," in *Handbook of Head and Spine Trauma*, ed. Jonathan Greenberg, 1993, reproduced at: http://www.trauma.org/archive/anaesthesia/barbcoma.html

12   Suda I, Kito K, Adachi C, in: *Nature* (1966, vol. 212), "Viability of long term frozen cat brain in vitro," 268-270.

13   Suda I, Kito K, Adachi C, in: *Brain Research* (1974, vol. 70), "Bioelectric discharges of isolated cat brain after revival from years of frozen storage," pg. 527-531.

14   Mazur P, in: *American Journal of Physiology* (1984, vol. 247), "Freezing of living cells: mechanisms and implications," pg. C125-142.

This approach for preserving individual cells by freezing was first demonstrated half a century ago.[15] It is now used routinely for many different cell types, including human embryos. Preserving organized tissue by freezing has proven to be more difficult. While isolated cells can accommodate as much as 80% of the water around them turning into ice, organs are much less forgiving because there is no room between cells for ice to grow.[16] Suda's cat brains survived freezing because the relatively warm temperature of -20°C allowed modest quantities of glycerol to keep ice formation between cells within tolerable limits.

In 1984 cryobiologist Greg Fahy proposed a new approach to the problem of complex tissue preservation at low temperature.[17] Instead of freezing, Fahy proposed loading tissue with so much cryoprotectant that ice formation would be completely prevented at all temperatures. Below the glass transition temperature, entire organs would become a glassy solid (a solid with the molecular structure of a liquid), free of any damage from ice. This process was called "vitrification". Preservation by vitrification, first demonstrated for embryos,[18] has now been successfully applied to many different cell types and tissues of increasing complexity. In 2000, reversible vitrification of transplantable blood vessels was demonstrated.[19]

New breakthroughs in reducing the toxicity of vitrification solutions,[20] and in adding synthetic ice blocking molecules,[21,22] continue to push the field forward. In 2004, successful transplantation of rabbit kidneys after cooling to a temperature of -50°C (-58°F) was reported.[23] These kidneys were prevented from freezing by replacing more than half of the water inside them with vitrification chemicals. Amazingly, organs can survive this extreme treatment if the chemicals are introduced and removed quickly at low temperature.

Reversible vitrification of major organs is a reasonable prospect within this decade.

15   Polge C, Smith A, Parkes AS, in: *Nature* (1949, vol. 164), "Revival of Spermatozoa after Vitrification and Dehydration at Low Temperatures," pg. 666.

16   Fahy GM, Levy DI, Ali SE, in: *Cryobiology* (1987, vol. 24), "Some emerging principles underlying the physical properties, biological actions, and utility of vitrification solutions," pg. 196-213.

17   Fahy GM, MacFarlane DR, Angell CA, Meryman HT, in: *Cryobiology* (1984, vol. 21), "Vitrification as an approach to cryopreservation," pg. 407-426.

18   Rall WF, Fahy GM, in: *Nature* (1985, vol. 313), "Ice-free cryopreservation of mouse embryos at -196 degrees C by vitrification," pg. 573-575.

19   Song YC, Khirabadi BS, Lightfoot F, Brockbank KG, Taylor MJ, in: *Nature Biotechnology* (2000, vol. 18), "Vitreous cryopreservation maintains the function of vascular grafts," pg. 296-299.

20   Fahy GM, Wowk B, Wu J, Paynter S, in: *Cryobiology* (2004, vol. 48), "Improved vitrification solutions based on the predictability of vitrification solution toxicity," pg. 22-35.

21   Wowk B, Leitl E, Rasch CM, Mesbah-Karimi N, Harris SB, Fahy GM, in: *Cryobiology* (2000, vol. 40), "Vitrification enhancement by synthetic ice blocking agents," pg. 228-236.

22   Wowk B, Fahy GM, in: *Cryobiology* (2002, vol. 44), "Inhibition of bacterial ice nucleation by polyglycerol polymers," pg. 14-23.

23   Fahy GM, Wowk B, Wu J, Phan J, Rasch C, Chang A, Zendejas E, in: *Cryobiology* (2004, vol. 48), "Cryopreservation of Organs by Vitrification: Perspectives and Recent Advances," pg. 157-178.

What about vitrification of whole animals? This is a much more difficult problem. Some organs, such as the kidney and brain, are privileged organs for vitrification because of their high blood flow rate. This allows vitrification chemicals to enter and leave them quickly before there are toxic effects. Most other tissues would not survive the long chemical exposure time required to absorb a sufficient concentration to prevent freezing.

It is useful to distinguish between reversible vitrification and morphological vitrification. Reversible vitrification is vitrification in which tissue recovers from the vitrification process in a viable state. Morphological vitrification is vitrification in which tissue is preserved without freezing, with good structural preservation, but in which key enzymes or other biomolecules are damaged by the vitrification chemicals. Morphological vitrification of a kidney was photographically demonstrated in Fahy's original vitrification paper,[17] but 20 years later reversible kidney vitrification is still being pursued.

Given this background, what are the prospects of reversibly vitrifying a whole human being? It's theoretically possible, but the prospects are still distant. Morphological vitrification of most organs and tissues in the body may now be possible, but moving from morphological vitrification to reversible vitrification will require fundamental new knowledge of mechanisms of cryoprotectant toxicity, and means to intervene in those mechanisms.

If reversible vitrification of humans is developed in future decades, what would be the application of this "suspended animation"? Space travel is sometimes suggested as an application, but time travel—specifically, medical time travel—seems more likely to be the primary application. People, especially young people dying of diseases expected to be treatable in future years, would be most motivated to try new suspended animation technologies. Governments would probably not even allow anyone but dying people to undergo such an extreme process, especially in the early days. Applications like space travel would come much later.

Medical time travel, by definition, involves technological anticipation. Sometimes this anticipation goes beyond just cures for disease. After all, if people are cryopreserved in anticipation of future cures, what about future cures for imperfections of the preservation process itself? As the medical prospect of reversible suspended animation draws nearer, the temptation to cut this corner will become stronger. In fact, some people are already cutting this corner very wide.

In 1964, with the science of cryobiology still in its infancy, Robert Ettinger proposed freezing recently deceased persons until science could resuscitate them.[24] The proposal assumed that fatal injury/illness, the early stages of clinical death, and crude preservation

---

24   Ettinger RCW, in: *The Prospect of Immortality* (1964, 1st edition), Doubleday & Company.

would all be reversible in the future. Even aging was to be reversed. This proposal was made in absence of any detailed knowledge of the effects of stopped blood flow or freezing on the human body. The proposal later came to be known as "cryonics."

Cryonics was clever in that it circumvented legal obstacles to cryopreserving people by operating on the other side of the legal dividing line of death. However 40 years later, as measured by the number people involved and the scientific acceptance of the field, cryonics remains a fringe practice. Why? Probably because by operating as it does, cryonics is perceived as interment rather than medicine. Dictionaries now define cryonics as "freezing a dead human." Is it any wonder that cryonics is unpopular? It is a failure by definition!

Is this view biologically justified? In the 1980s another cryonics organization, the Alcor Life Extension Foundation, adopted a different approach to cryonics. Under the leadership of cardiothoracic surgery researcher, Jerry Leaf, and dialysis technician, Mike Darwin, Alcor brought methods of modern medicine into cryonics. Alcor sought to validate each step of their cryopreservation process as reversible, beginning with life support provided immediately after cardiac arrest, and continuing through hours of circulation with blood replacement solutions. Leaf and Darwin showed that large animals could be successfully recovered after several hours at near-freezing temperatures under conditions similar to those in the first hours of real cryonics cases.[25] Blood gas measurements and clinical chemistries obtained in real cryonics cases further demonstrated that application of life support techniques (mechanical CPR and heart-lung machines) could keep cryonics subjects biologically alive even in a state of cardiac arrest and legal death.[26]

This leaves cryonics today in an interesting situation. It is stigmatized as something that cannot work because the subjects are legally deceased. Yet under ideal conditions the subjects are apparently alive by all measurable criteria, except heartbeat. They are biologically the same as patients undergoing open heart surgery, legal labels notwithstanding. The cryopreservation phase of cryonics is of course not yet reversible. But cryonicists would argue that this does not imply death either, because death only happens when biochemistry becomes irreversibly damaged, and "irreversibility" is technology-dependent.

To clarify these issues, cryonicists have proposed the "information-theoretic criterion" for death.[27] According to this criterion, you are not dead when life stops (we already know that from clinical medicine), you are not dead when biochemistry is damaged, you are only dead when biochemistry is so badly damaged that no

---

25   Alcor Life Extension Foundation website: Alcor's Pioneering Total Body Washout Experiments.
26   Darwin M, in: *Biopreservation Tech Briefs* (1996, no. 18), "Cryopreservation of CryoCare Patient #C-2150."
27   Merkle RC, in: *Medical Hypotheses* (1992, vol. 39), "The technical feasibility of cryonics," pg. 6-16.

technology, not even molecular nanotechnology,[28] could restore normal biochemistry with your memories intact. By this criterion, someone who suffered cardiac arrest days ago in the wilderness is really dead. Someone who suffered only a few minutes of cardiac arrest and cryoprotectant toxicity during morphological vitrification may not be.

Whether one accepts this information-theoretic criterion or not, the modern cryonics practice of using life support equipment to resuscitate the brain after legal death raises important issues. Among them is the scientific issue that cryonics cannot be dismissed simply by calling its subjects "dead." Two minutes of cardiac arrest followed by restoration of blood circulation does not a skeleton make. There should be a rule that no one be allowed to say "dead" when discussing cryonics. It is usually a slur that communicates nothing scientific.

Whether cryonics can work depends on biological details of cerebral ischemic injury (brain injury during stopped blood flow), cryopreservation injury, and anticipated future technology. There is much published literature on cerebral ischemia, and a small, but growing body of writing on relevant future technologies.[29,30,31,32,33] There is, however, very little information on the quality of preservation achieved with cryonics.[34,35] It would seem logical to look to cryobiologists for this information.

Cryobiologists, professional scientists that study the effect of cold on living things, decided long ago that they didn't want their field associated with cryonics.[36] The Society for Cryobiology bylaws even provide for the expulsion of members that practice or promote "freezing deceased persons." The result has been the polarization of cryobiologists into either outspoken contempt or silence concerning cryonics. The contempt camp typically speaks of cryonics as if it hasn't changed in 40 years. The silent camp doesn't comment on the subject, and usually follows a "don't ask, don't tell" policy about cryonics sympathizers among them. This political environment, plus the fact that most cryobiologists work outside the specialty of

---

28   Drexler E, in: *Engines of Creation* (1986, 1st edition), Anchor Press/Doubleday.
29   Darwin M, in: *Life Extension Magazine* (1977, July/August), "The Anabolocyte: A Biological Approach to Repairing Cryoinjury," pg. 80-63.
30   Drexler KE, in: *Proceedings of the National Academy of Sciences* (1981, vol. 78), "Molecular engineering: An approach to the development of general capabilities for molecular manipulation," pg. 5275-5278.
31   Donaldson T, in: *Analog Science Fiction / Science Fact* (1988, Sept.), "24th Century Medicine."
32   Freitas RA, in: *Nanomedicine, Vol. I: Basic Capabilities* (1999, 1st edition), Landes Bioscience.
33   Freitas RA, in: *Nanomedicine, Vol. IIA: Biocompatibility* (2003, 1st edition), Landes Bioscience.
34   Alcor staff, in: *Cryonics* (1984, November), "Histological study of a temporarily cryopreserved human," pg. 13-32.
35   Darwin M, Russell R, Wood L, Wood C, in: *Biopreservation Tech Briefs* (1995, no. 16), "Effect of Human Cryopreservation Protocol on the Ultrastructure of the Canine Brain."
36   Darwin M, in: *Cryonics* (1991, June, July, August), "Cold War: The Conflict Between Cryonicists and Cryobiologists."

organ cryopreservation, makes obtaining informed cryobiological information about cryonics very difficult.

The most important cryobiological fact of cryonics (other than its current irreversibility) is that cryoprotectant chemicals can be successfully circulated through most of the major organs of the body if blood clots are not present. We can conclude this by simply considering that everything now known about long-term preservation of individual organs was learned by removing and treating those organs under conditions similar to ideal cryonics cases. It is generally observed that the quality of cell structure preservation (as revealed by light and electron microscopy) is very poor when there is no cryoprotectant, but steadily improves as the concentration of cryoprotectant is increased (provided toxicity thresholds are not exceeded). Recent years have seen a trend toward using higher cryoprotectant concentrations in cryonics, yielding structural preservation that is impressively similar to unfrozen tissue.[35]

Somewhere between freezing, morphological vitrification, reversible vitrification of the central nervous system, and reversible vitrification of whole people, there is technology that will lead medicine to take the idea of medical time travel seriously within this century. Whether what is now called cryonics will eventually become that technology remains to be seen. It will depend on whether cryonicists can manage to outgrow the stigma attached to their field, and develop methods that are validated by more biological feedback and less hand waving. It may also depend on whether critics of cryonics can manage to engage in more substantive discussion and less name calling. The ultimate feasibility of medical time travel is a question of science, not rhetoric. ■

THE BRICKS IN THE WALL

BY MICHAEL DARWIN
WITH CONTRIBUTIONS BY STEPHEN W. BRIDGE
Cryonics, November, 1981

Elsewhere in this issue (*Cryonics*, November 1981, p. 9-11) is reprint of an article by Laurie Mann on how the Cryonics Movement died. On my desk where I sit typing there is an article from the *Indianapolis Star* newspaper with the headline "Cryonics Now Only Involves Temporary Freezing of Parts." This article blithely informs us that "the heralded cryonicist movement of the '60s seems to have been no more than a passing fad. The scientists in whom the cryonicists invested their trust did not believe in cryonics." We are told elsewhere in the same article that "cryonics is dead, as dead as its thawed adherents." For a long time journalists have said that cryonics wouldn't work. Now some are already saying it didn't work. This lack of research and this matter-of-fact attitude toward something which seems so necessary to us is one of the main frustrations about pounding our heads against the wall of public indifference.

If we wish instead to dismantle the wall or find our way around it, we must educate ourselves about its construction. Why has the general public failed to accept cryonics as a logical idea? The first step toward an answer is the realization that there is no single or central reason for this failure. There is a host of reasons, some very small, others larger and more critical. In any individual the various reasons combine and act synergistically to create a determined barrier to understanding. Here is what we have to work against.

Another Crazy Sect

Before you even discuss cryonics with someone, you must deal with the commonly held notions that "enthusiasm denotes insanity" and "if I didn't already believe it, it can't be real." People are so inundated with supporters of philosophical cure-alls that they learn to block out automatically all new approaches to life. We all do that to some extent. I (Steve) was recently struck by the realization that, when I talk about cryonics, some people give me the same look that I reserve for people who want to tell me about the glories of Scientology or the Divine Light Mission. "Poor deluded fellow, he can't think for himself, so he must follow some bizarre sect." It is ironic to hear this line of reasoning used toward cryonics. It has been our experience that thinking for oneself is so common in cryonics groups that it is rare to get any three members to agree on anything (except the need for extended lifespan—and IABS once had a member who didn't really believe in that!). But it must be also admitted that cryonics has attracted more than a few undeniably bizarre characters in its history, and that these strange people could certainly appear to be cultists. Although we are not a cohesive group trying to run the lives of its members, we must be aware that our initial approach can make us seem that way. Since I have discovered that most people distrust fervor in anything, I try to encourage relaxed discussions about cryonics and wait for questions, rather than launching into an enthusiastic lecture.

Distraction and Denial

Once you get by the initial problem of being heard, there is an entire series of further barriers you must confront. The first of these is that it is a fundamental part of human nature to ignore unpleasant things. Death is one of the least pleasant aspects of existence, so people ignore it especially well. The supposed new openness in conversations about death has really not deeply affected most people. Life insurance still does not sell itself, even with huge television advertising campaigns about the need to "protect your family," etc. Ultimately, it takes the religious zeal of salesmen like Kurt Vonnegut's Fred Rosewater who "knew that lump in his throat had to be there and it had to be real, or he wouldn't sell any insurance." Since life insurance currently has the advantage of being a recognizable and socially acceptable product, it can use zeal more effectively than cryonics. However, if the social and cultural conditions ever become right for the freezer program, nothing short of the same zeal and tirelessness will sell it. Respectability for cryonics will not make it any easier for most people to think about death.

Protests that "freezing people sounds so unpleasant" (or "morbid" or "crazy") are not reasons, they are excuses to avoid the subject at all. Most of the immediate negative questions you will get are not asked so that the questioner can hear a logical answer. They are easy forms of denial of the subject of death, in an attempt to start a discussion of "definitions" or other trivia and avoid confronting the reality of death. Most of those accusing us of denying death have actually done a better job of avoidance than any cryonicists could possibly do.

Distraction is another form of denial. "If I don't have time to think about it, it isn't real." People who are good prospects for cryonics because of above-average intelligence tend to stay especially busy. People who are constantly distracted, with little time for reflection, are difficult to reach with matters of life and death.

Solved Problem Paradox

At some point in our lives each of us must confront the fact that we are going to die. Even involvement in cryonics does not obviate this necessity. Most people deal with death at an early age in terms of deciding its personal significance and forming working attitudes toward it. It would behoove Immortalist psychologists to find out what the average age is at which this process occurs. I (Mike) have the feeling that this is one of the most prominent barriers to penetration of cryonics into the culture. Once a child or young adult decides how to deal with death, then the matter is a closed subject, a solved problem. If someone decides that death isn't real, that Jesus Saves and Keeps, then he probably isn't interested in being frozen. If he decides that death isn't important, that it is inevitable or even beneficial, then once again he becomes closed off to cryonics. There are an almost limitless series of permutations of beliefs from reincarnation to Kubler-Ross. Anyone who has bought one of these belief packages is likely to stop questioning death, although later death experiences may weaken the person's grip on a particular attitude and again open him up to new ideas. At that time, a presentation of cryonics may have a chance to break through the emotional and intellectual armor. Still, we must remember that it had probably not been a pleasant experience for the person to have initially confronted his own mortality. Cryonics requires a lot from the individual, including the removal of a lot more defenses than this one. Cryonics will not sound easy and certain enough for most people to use as the quick replacement solution they may seek.

Worldview

In order for an idea to succeed, it must emerge as an extension of the culture's worldview. If an idea is very unusual and does not interface well with the rest of the culture, it will not come to wide acceptance. The idea of being frozen is an alien one to this culture. There are few precedents for such an act. We have an entire culture built on the principle of a changeover of generations, with young individuals as replacements for dead ones. The idea that people should not die is a difficult one for such a culture to absorb. Additionally, we do not have a religious structure such as the Egyptians', which emphasized immortality and strict physical preservation of the dead. We do not have good techniques for preserving organs or other animals, which could help prepare people for the idea of suspended animation. In the United States, where billions are spent combating cancer and cardiovascular diseases, there is a bitter irony in the blind spot which researchers and leaders have in the areas of aging and life-extension. Success in these two areas would provide cures for cancer, heart disease, and many other human killers. Comfortable existence is imaginable; continued existence is not.

Cryonics calls for a very different worldview of the nature of life and society. As resuscitation technology begins to erode the old idea that "Dead is dead," more people will become aware of the possibilities of continued existence. In the celebration of the United States Bicentennial, there was the assertion that 200 years is a long time. Compared to the time scales used by most people, it is an enormous time. Most people continue to define their lives on a very trivial time scale, brushing teeth, going to work, and dealing with the problems of the next few days. The upper limit for human planning is still retirement at age 65, and even that consideration takes up an immeasurably small fraction of a person's planning time. However, in a society of extremely long-lived individuals, 200 years would seem the equivalent of perhaps planning on where to go to college. The timescale perceptions of our society must start to become stretched to consider centuries-long planning for our world before many people will consider such planning for themselves.

Delayed Gratification

Cryonics isn't a product in the sense of food, automobiles, or even life insurance. The gratification we are selling won't come for possibly hundreds of years. Most people's time scales cannot conceive of anything happening in several hundred years and certainly cannot view themselves as part of it. Telling the individual that he won't feel it as hundreds of years, since he will be frozen, is completely beside the point. He can't see anything past his own death.

Few Social Benefits

Many religions promise delayed gratification, but they give their followers much current gratification as well. Religion is much more than the salvation business. It is the self-esteem business, the social club business, the professional club business, and the security-of-belonging business much more than it is the "save me from perdition" business. Cryonics offers fewer opportunities for business and social contacts. The self-esteem aspect of cryonics is also fairly low, since advocating it generally causes your friends to question your sanity. And it is hard to sell cryonics as security because of the few and widely-spread out current adherents.

Religion also offers promises and offers to take care of all of a person's decision making. The follower can follow the rules and be assured of success in the afterlife and here on Earth. Cryonics can offer no such relief from personal responsibility.

No Cosmic Truths

Cryonics does not offer any cosmic truths about the nature and purpose of existence. It doesn't tell people what their lives are for or why they should get up in the morning and go through another day. It doesn't tell people what to eat, how to dress, or how to interact with other human beings. Perhaps most importantly, cryonics does not offer answers to the seeming indifference of the universe or to the fundamental problem of human mortality. It is merely a piece of technology to give us more time to seek the answers. The social organizations which have grown out of cryonics stem from problems and inadequacies involved with the technology. They do not provide much in the way of philosophy. If suspended animation were a perfected technology, it is doubtful that there would be any participatory organizations built around it. (Does anyone belong to automobile repair clubs?) Because cryonics doesn't offer any answers to the deep questions which confront all thinking individuals, it has failed to gain any kind of following as a "movement" or a "cult."

Quality of Life

Life is not a pleasant thing for many people in this world, even for a number of them who would appear to be successful. Whether because of limited resources or lack of confidence or some missing joy in their life, these people see no reason to prolong existence. They will bear their burden as long as "nature" requires them to, but they ask for no extra time. They think of death as a long rest from the troubles of life. Existence of this sort seems quite hopeless and meaningless to these people, and it is pretty much a waste of time to sell them on cryonics (unless you have the time and resources to improve their lives first).

Lack of Scientific Credibility

Partially due to poor political handling and sensationalism, and partially due to the nature of the idea itself (based as it is on limited knowledge and insight, best guesses, and faith in the future), cryonics has not attracted the support of the scientific community. Indeed, it has generally attracted hostility and censure. Physicians and other health-care providers simply do not recognize a treatment until it has been given a scientific seal of approval. Dying patients and their families will generally not have confidence in a procedure unless it is recommended to them by the health-care provider.

Note: Scientific objections are often the most common excuses used to avoid serious discussion about the idea of future life or cryonics. When they are being used in this way, you will notice that your logical scientific responses are ignored.

Lack of Technical Confidence

No one frozen before 1973 (with the exception of James Bedford) remains in suspension. A variety of technical, financial, and logistic problems has resulted in the loss of all patients from the early days of cryonics. Although today's groups appear to be stable, the failure of one of them or of some group which does not yet exist could continue the process for several years. Each failure, especially highly publicized ones such as the collapse of Cryonic Interment, erodes people's confidence that they will remain frozen. In addition, our society's reliance on short time-scales makes it difficult for prospective donors to understand what kind of organization could continue for hundreds of years.

This fear is frequently combined with a general lack of confidence in the future of this society. Bombs, economic collapse, repressive governments—you've heard it all before. All you can do is remind these people that there is no guarantee of anything in life; we can only keep trying to do our best to survive. The world may indeed end tonight—but I think I'll go ahead and buy groceries just in case it doesn't. Playing to win doesn't guarantee you will win; but playing to lose guarantees you will not win.

Loss of Others

Many people who believe that cryonics may work from a technical standpoint are not afraid so much of physical compromise as they are of alienation from family and friends. The science fiction writer (and former cryonics spokesperson) Fred Pohl typifies this attitude when he states that a good part of what he is flows from his daily relationships with friends, colleagues, and loved ones. Cryonics offers the prospect of a profound uprooting. It guarantees that the individual will be thrust into a completely different time and place. It means the possibility of permanent separation from loved ones and friends or, maybe even worse, reunion with loved ones and friends whose values and personalities may have changed beyond recognition.

If one reads Kubler-Ross and other psychologists of death and dying, it is apparent that much of the emotional turmoil people feel over their impending deaths stems not from a realization of their own non-existence, but from grief over the loss of important relationships. Cryonics offers no magic or religious plan to solve the kinks in human relationships that the passage of time could create. The prospect of awakening alone in a different and alien world remains a terrifying one for most people. The improvement of technical and financial odds will make little difference to these people. Simply, they are being asked to take on an immense challenge, and most people hate even minor challenges.

Loss of Self

As Robert Ettinger has pointed out in *The Prospect of Immortality* (Chapter VIII), cryonics may bring us to the point where the question of "What is identity?" becomes a practical and legal matter, rather than one of philosophy. Debates on this will flourish like those on "What is the difference between life and death?" do today. A person contemplating being frozen may be frightened by the thought of his body becoming a zombie with no "soul," or by the question of "how much change in memory or personality can I undergo and still be me?"

Many cryonicists share my (Michael's) view that individuals are nothing more than dynamic rivers of information which can only be described statistically and approximately. However, many more cryonicists and the majority of all people appear to cling to nonrational sources of identity, either of a spiritual nature or of a physical nature. Most cryonicists insist on physical continuity with the resurrected self and refuse to consider bioduplication and memory transfer to be a valid recreation of self." Viewing human beings as just packages of information in flux raises questions about the very existence of identity. Indeed, as Ettinger concludes, we may be forced to accept the idea "that there is really no such thing as individuality in any profound sense. . . (Let us recognize) that identity, like morality, is man-made and relative, rather than natural and absolute. . . . It is only partly existent and partly invented. Instead of having identity, we have degrees of identity, measured by some criteria suitable to the purpose." (p. 142 of the British ed.) The concept of identity is so intricately intertwined with ideas about death, that this may be one of the most difficult barriers to overcome. While it may not directly be a hindrance to everyone's acceptance of cryonics (witness all of the cryonicists still debating the point), it is likely to be a hindrance to the acceptance of the less-than perfect procedures now existing, with their potential for greater damage and memory loss.

Loss of Position

This is closely related to the previous problems. As Robert Ettinger puts it, many people are afraid of "finding themselves little fish in a big pond." They have carved out their territory in this life and don't want to or don't have the confidence to do it again in the next life. They would rather be nothing than only a small something. "How could I adjust to a world completely different from today's?" is one of the most common complaints against cryonics.

Moral Objections

Some people are afraid that cryonics will work and believe that it is morally and socially wrong. They apparently have strong objections to any idea of a greatly expanded lifespan. They believe that old people should die and let a new generation take over. Often the reasons given for this belief are religious or in the form of "Death is natural." But more and more people are now objecting to the potential for over-population, lack of individual movement within society, and the stagnation of culture itself. They are unable to visualize positive results of a societal involvement with immortality. Isaac Asimov is one of the leaders of the "Death is an essential part of Nature" camp. Included are many of the writers of books on death and dying for colleges and even for children.

An even farther-out variation on this philosophy is that of Elisabeth Kubler-Ross, with the attitude that "Death is a very good thing." Kubler-Ross has actually stated that "Death will be your last and best experience." It is obviously very difficult to discuss cryonics with either of these groups.

Cost and Uncertainty

Cryonics costs a lot and gives no guarantees. We can't even tell a prospective donor that the odds are on his side. The odds for success are completely unknown. How can anyone evaluate the cost-effectiveness of such a proposal? And for this unknown, possibly minimal, chance of future life, we are asking this fellow to reduce his pleasure in the present life—to the tune of $28,000 to $60,000, depending on the company. Granted, if everything works out well, then the payoff will be incredibly rich. Unfortunately, it is the nature of reality that things often don't work at all. Results frequently fall short of expectations, especially in new and complex endeavors. Cryonics is a good deal more complex than adding a new room to your house or designing a new car. Whole areas of technology which we can scarcely imagine will have to come into existence and succeed before suspended animation is truly possible. And certain assumptions we already hold must be proven true, e.g., that memory is encoded in some stable and redundant form which can survive our particular perfusion and suspension techniques, as well as ischemia and freezing. There are some suggestive experiments on this need, but no hard evidence. These uncertainties make the cost appear even higher to many people.

Conclusion

We don't intend for this discussion to prevent you from trying to interest other people in cryonics. Obviously those walls can be broken in some people, or none of us would be involved. We want you to know what you are up against, to know what kinds of bricks make up the wall. Perhaps you won't be as discouraged about failures to persuade friends about the value of cryonics if you understand what motivates their resistance. And perhaps this understanding will help you get through to at least one. ∎

HISTORY OF CRYONICS

JOHN HUNTER, CRYONICS FORERUNNER

BY R. MICHAEL PERRY, PH.D.
Cryonics, November, 1990

Although the cryonics movement started in earnest in the 1960s, there are some fascinating anticipations of the central idea of freezing the newly deceased for possible later reanimation. The one I'm reporting on here didn't occur in the present century at all, or even the preceding century, but goes all the way back to the "Age of Enlightenment" in the mid-1700s. John Hunter (1728-1793) was a renowned British physiologist and surgeon who is credited with establishing surgery on a firm scientific footing. Among his many accomplishments was a study of the recovery of apparent drowning victims (*Philosophical Transactions*

John Hunter

of the Royal Society, 1776), an early milestone in the reversal of clinical death. He also made important contributions in understanding hibernation, demonstrating, for example, that metabolism largely ceases as the chilled organism enters a "holding pattern." What follows is his report of an experiment in the freezing of organisms (two fish) with some thoughts on the possibilities should such a process prove reversible.

"Experiment. In the year 1766 two carp were put in a glass vessel with common river water, and the vessel was put into a freezing-mixture. The water surrounding the fish froze very rapidly on the inside of the glass all round. When the freezing-process approached the fish it became, as it were, stationary; and the remaining water not freezing fast enough, in order to make it freeze sooner, I put in as much cold snow as made the whole thick. The snow round the carp melted. I put in more snow, which melted also. This was repeated several times, till I grew tired, and I left them covered up to freeze by the joint operation of the mixture and the atmosphere. After having exhausted the whole power of life in the production of heat, they froze; but that life was gone could not be known till we thawed the animals, which was done very gradually. But with their flexibility they did not recover action, so that they were really dead. Till this time I had imagined that it might be possible to prolong life to any period by freezing a person in the frigid zone, as I thought all action and waste would cease until the body was thawed. I thought that if a man would give up the last ten years of his life to this kind of alternate oblivion and action, it might be prolonged to a thousand years: and by getting himself thawed every hundred years, he might learn what had happened during his frozen condition. Like other schemers, I thought I should make my fortune by it; but this experiment undeceived me."[1]

Although Hunter's account ends on a note of discouragement, we should not overlook the significance of his experiment and his thinking on the possibilities of human life extension some two hundred years before the idea was popularized and a small knot of "true believers" began to take it seriously. (We hope, of course, that technology of the future can make up for deficiencies in the natural thawing process, and also reverse freezing damage, diseases, and aging so that those deep-frozen today can one day be restored to consciousness and health.) From a primitive vantage point, then, John Hunter saw and accomplished much. In the words of a commentator, "His doctrines were, necessarily, not those of his age: while lesser minds around him were still dim with the mists of ignorance and dogmatism of times past, his lofty intellect was illumined by the dawn of a distant day."[2] ■

---

1   *The Life of John Hunter,* F.R.S. by Drewry Ottley; Haswell, Barrington and Haswell, Philadelphia, 1841, quoted in *Life Extension Society Newsletter* #3, Aug. 1964, pp.1-2.
2   *Encyclopaedia Britannica,* 1948 ed., vol. 16, p. 921.

THE SOCIETY FOR THE RECOVERY OF PERSONS APPARENTLY DEAD

BY STEVEN B. HARRIS, M.D.
Cryonics, September, 1990

"The human mind treats a new idea the way the body treats a strange protein; it rejects it."

— Biologist P.B. Medawar

The history of technological innovation is the history of the torturous paths which advances often take to acceptance. It might seem at first, from the many well-known instances of simultaneous discoveries, that it is the nature of important ideas to spring up newly everywhere, independently, as soon as the world is ripe for them. But this is only the view at first glance. In actuality, the "synchronicity" of discovery usually turns out to be a late phenomenon, one that follows a prodrome in which the "new" idea in question has long been around in some form or another, but has been steadfastly ignored.

How long can an important idea be ignored? The model steam engine was demonstrated by Hero of Alexandria in the first century A.D., sixteen centuries before people started thinking along these lines again. Gregor Mendel published the basic principles of genetics in 1866, and was ignored until 1900. Oswald Avery published strong evidence that DNA was the principle of heredity in 1944, but no one really believed it until the time of Watson and Crick almost a decade later. The time varies, depending on circumstance.

Delayed acceptance of discovery happens in all areas of science, of course, but it always happens in the field of medicine with great poignancy, since there the human costs of dropping the technological ball are usually great. We may consider, for instance, the numbers of lives which might have been saved if not for the following delays:

— Leeuwenhoek invented the microscope in 1668 and saw animal cells and protozoa with it—but unfortunately for humanity, doctors weren't interested in that kind of thing in 1668, and wouldn't be for another couple of centuries. In the meantime they missed out on the germ theory of infectious disease, and thus, as late as 1850, when good Doctor Semmelweiss tried to get his Hungarian colleagues to curb the incidence of fatal "childbed fever" by washing their hands between dissecting diseased cadavers and examining patients, his colleagues responded by hounding him out of his job. Meanwhile diseases continued to spread on the hands of well-meaning doctors.

— Several explorers like Sir Richard Hawkins independently discovered the antiscorbutic properties of oranges and limes in the 18th century, and James Lind in 1754 even published the results of a controlled experiment in which he showed that citrus was superior to other folk methods for the curing of scurvy. The world, however, was not ready for the discovery, and sailors continued to suffer and die from this quite treatable nutritional disease for more than half a century after Lind's demonstration. Worse, scurvy was rampant among the troops of both North and South during the American Civil War, though the means was available to prevent it, and as late as 1912 the famous explorer Robert Falcon Scott died on his way back from the South Pole, probably as the result of scurvy.

— An investigator before the First World War discovered the curative powers of penicillium mold extracts on infected animals, but could not interest his colleagues, although he published the work. It remained for Alexander Fleming, ignorant of the earlier work, to rediscover the antibacterial effect of penicillium in a laboratory accident in 1928.

— Alexis Carrel, the French-American scientist who won the Nobel Prize in 1902 for techniques of suturing blood vessels, demonstrated in 1910 that a saphenous vein graft between aorta and main coronary artery in animals could bypass a blockage there, and speculated that the technique might be useful in the treatment of angina. Although Carrel (with aviator Charles Lindbergh) later went on to develop the heart-lung machines that would make such surgery possible, the medical community contented itself for the next half-century with ineffective treatments for severe coronary heart disease, and it was not until 1967 that the saphenous-graft coronary bypass operation was employed on humans.

To the historian, some medical fields seem more plagued with delays in the acceptance of new ideas than others (the medical study of infectious disease has been prominent in this dubious regard, as noted), and the above examples are sad enough. Still, there is possibly one field of medicine which is at least the equal of infectious disease in its record of ignoring proven lifesaving strategies for the longest time, and that is the area to which we will turn for the remainder of this essay. The medical field in question is that of resuscitation, which is the art of restoring clinically dead people to life. It will be of no surprise that many of the issues related to it which have been debated in history are also familiar to cryonicists. For example: when exactly is a person "dead," and how do you tell?

Cryonicists looking into the history of resuscitation may find themselves reading with a sense of déjà vu. We've seen these controversies already, and we'll see them again. Perhaps we can profit by exploring them further.

Resuscitation

Historically, the art of resuscitation turns out to be old. The idea of resuscitating a seemingly dead person by more or less physical means occurs in the Hebrew scriptures in the book of II Kings, as Elisha resuscitates a dead child by placing his mouth on the child's mouth (II Kings 4). Although the story appears a bit garbled, like the story of Elijah's [N.B.—Elijah and Elisha are different guys] resuscitation of the child before it in I Kings 17, both stories contain descriptive elements of chest compression, and there is clearly something more than mystical prayers and incantations going on. Perhaps the oral traditions which were later codified into these tales once contained descriptions of one or more real resuscitative events.

By a few millennia later, things were better defined. Italian writings of the 15th century indicated that midwives had, even then, long been using mouth-to-mouth breathing techniques to resuscitate newborns who did not spontaneously breathe. These techniques were soon to be imitated in the mechanical experiments of the Enlightenment. Paracelsus (1493-1541), an alchemist and perhaps the greatest physician of his age, was said to have attempted the resuscitation of a corpse using bellows, a trick he perhaps picked up from Arabic medical writings. And Andreas Vesalius (1514-1564), the father of modern anatomy, reported successfully using bellows to resuscitate asphyxiated dogs.

Bellows may not always have been available, but physicians eventually learned (possibly again from laymen) that simple mouth-to-mouth resuscitation sometimes worked on recently asphyxiated adults just as it did on newborns. By the 1740's, several cases of successful mouth-to-mouth resuscitation had been reported, the most famous of which was Tossach's 1744 report of the resuscitation of a clinically dead coal miner who had been suddenly overcome after descending into a burned-out mine. By the 1760s, in the wake of such reports, a number of groups advocating the resuscitation of drowned persons had sprung up in Europe. The thinking at this time in many places was strikingly modern. Here, by way of example, is a quote from a 1766 governmental edict from Zurich:

". . . Experience has shown that the drowned who are considered dead and that lay for some time under water have often been restored again and kept alive by proper maneuvers. From which one rightly concludes that life has not been completely suspended in the drowned, but that there is hope to save them from death if, as soon as they are withdrawn from the water, prompt and careful help is administered."

The Swiss may have been their usual regulation-happy selves about the subject, but in the rest of the Western world resuscitation was being pushed—typically by entirely private societies (voluntary clubs). In 1774, a society was founded in London to promulgate the idea of attempting to resuscitate the dead in some circumstances. Called, after a bit of experimentation, the Society for the Recovery of Persons Apparently Drowned, it quickly evolved into the Humane Society (and still later, with official patronage and funding, the Royal Humane Society).

The Humane Society advocated techniques which were highly advanced. Three months after the society's founding, as an example, a society member had the opportunity to minister to a 3-year-old child named Catherine Sophie Greenhill, who had fallen from an upper story window onto flagstones, and been pronounced dead. The society member, an apothecary named Squires, was on the scene within twenty minutes, and history records that he proceeded to give the clinically dead child several shocks through the chest with a portable electrostatic generator(!). This treatment caused her to regain pulse and respiration, and she eventually (after a time in coma) recovered fully.

[This story and other direct quotations, unless otherwise noted, are taken from *The History Of Anesthesia,* Richard S. Atkinson and Thomas V. Boulton, eds., International Congress and Symposium Series, #134, Parthenon Publishing Group, NJ, 1988. ISBN 0-929-858-18-2 (Parthenon)]

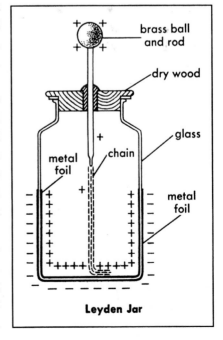

The resuscitation of little Catherine Greenhill was probably the first successful cardiac defibrillation of a human being, and it followed earlier suggestions by American scientist Benjamin Franklin and others that electricity might possibly be used to "revivify" the human body. And so it proved able to do in selected circumstances. In 1788, a silver medal was awarded to Humane Society member Charles Kite, who was by this time not only advocating the resuscitation of victims in cardiac arrest with bellows and both oropharyngeal and nasolaryngeal intubation, but had also developed his own electrostatic revivifying machine which used Leyden jar capacitors in a way exactly analogous to the DC capacitative countershock of the modern cardiac defibrillator. (I have to confess that to my mind all of these contraptions are as fantastic as the devices in a Flintstones cartoon, yet they actually existed. A time-traveling physician from the present could not have put together a better resuscitation kit, given the technology of the time.)

Dark Clouds

However amazing its progress was, the enlightened state of the late 18th century as regards resuscitation was not to last. From the very first, dark images from the human psyche began to gather in resistance to the new ideas. Technology never intervenes in a major way into the borderland between life and death without creating major anxieties and social backlash. Resuscitation had its problems.

To begin with, as the modern reader may guess, the 18th century discovery that "death" was not a sure and objective state did not exactly sit well in the public mind. Our historical friend Charles Kite was of the opinion that not even putrefaction was a sure sign of permanent death, since it might also be due to advanced scurvy(!). However conservative this view might have been for Kite and his medical agenda, the public had its own concerns. If one could be mistaken for dead when one was in fact resuscitatable, the public was wondering, just what else did that imply?

The answer, of course, is that it implied that you could be buried alive. Not long after the first word-of-mouth reports of adult resuscitations began surfacing in the 1730s, the French author Jacques Benigne Winslow published a book descriptively titled *The Uncertainty of the Signs of Death and the Danger of Precipitate Interments and Dissections.* Now the real problem with the difficulty of defining death in a technical age was out of the bag: What if you got the diagnosis wrong?

The result of this realization was a psychological terror perhaps made familiar to the reader by some of the works of Edgar Allan Poe. But Poe, popularizing the problem for early 19th century America, was late to the controversy. In 18th century Europe, the fear of premature burial and dissection was not just the preoccupation of macabre writers; whole classes of people were affected, albeit in different ways. Upper-class persons took to fitting coffins and crypts with special signaling devices which could be used to alert the outside world in case the occupant should inexplicably revive. The lower classes had their own special problems, too, since anatomical dissection (long a part of the punishment for heinous crimes because it denied the malefactor an intact bodily identity or a grave) had now taken on a special meaning. Here, as example, is what Ruth Richardson says of the dissection of criminals in her treatise *Death, Dissection, and the Destitute,* describing an incident in the 1820s in which one dissecting anatomist at Carlisle was killed, and another severely wounded, by the friends of an executed man:

". . .Although this was of course an extreme reaction, it was certainly the case that hanging the corpse in chains on a gibbet was popularly regarded as preferable to dissection. What later incredulous commentators seem to have missed or misunderstood was that in eighteenth and early nineteenth century popular belief, not only were the anatomists agents of the law, but they could be the agents of death. Genuine cases were known of incomplete hangings, in which the 'dead' were brought back to life, and plans for celebrated corpse-rescues centered on the possibility that the noose had not fully done its work. Folk-tales circulated about famous criminals revived by friends, and these ideas were fostered by the publicity which Humane Society resuscitations attracted after apparent drownings. Increased control over the body of the condemned rendered rescue and revival virtually impossible.

"It was popularly understood that the surgeon's official function and interest in a murderer's corpse was not to revive, but rather to destroy it. Dissection was a very final process. It denied hope of survival—even the survival of identity after death [!]. Above all, it threw into relief the collaborative role of the medical profession in the actual execution of death. The Carlisle surgeons bore the brunt of the resentment and frustration felt by the dead man's friends, for in their eyes the doctors had murdered him more surely than the hangman's rope."[1]

By the end of the first quarter of the 19th century, when the riot over the dissection of the hanged man at Carlisle took place, things had reached a fever pitch.

---

1   The denial of the body of the heinous criminal to the family has had a long history in law, and we see it historically employed in capital crimes which particularly outraged the public, even in relatively recent times. For instance, after execution in 1865 the bodies of the four Lincoln assassination conspirators were immediately buried in Army equipment boxes a few feet from the gallows in the prison yard in Washington's Old Penitentiary, the same institution where the body of John Wilkes Booth had been secretly buried a month earlier. In 1901, after anarchist Leon Czolgosz was electrocuted for the assassination of President McKinley, his body was dissolved in acid in the prison basement. One cannot read such accounts without a deeper appreciation for the psychological power of the freshly dead body in an era when resuscitation was still somewhat magic. Even as late as 1946, after the ten members of the Nazi high command were hanged at Nuremburg, the Surgeon General of the United States himself was turned down when he asked that the brains be removed, preserved, and sent to Washington for study. Instead, the bodies were cremated immediately at Dachau and the ashes secretly scattered, with the specific intent that nothing remain. One may read into official penal policy in all these cases a more or less unconscious desire to destroy what was perceived as the continuing identity of persons already pronounced dead.—S.B.H.

With scientific resuscitation, technology had intruded into the macabre. The horrific potential of the new electromechanical resuscitative technology had its influence on Mary Shelley, who in 1818 had first set out to write a ghost story, but instead ended up producing a cautionary tale of the technological resuscitation of a soulless corpse by a medical experimenter. Given the spirit of the times, the story touched a public nerve as though with one of the new electrical machines, and Frankenstein's monster was an instant sensation.

And then something strange happened. Shortly after the publication of Shelley's famous story, the new medicine began to go out of favor, and the science of resuscitation began to suffer on both the technical and mythological fronts. It happened for several reasons.

It is the propensity of all social movements to go too far. The Humane Society's problem was that, when it came to complicated biology, the late eighteenth century did not possess the experimental expertise necessary to separate the wheat from the chaff. Thus, within a few years after its founding, the Humane Society had gone from mouth-to-mouth resuscitation to the more impressive use of bellows. Following a number of instances of lung rupture with the bellows, however, these complicated and difficult-to-use devices were discarded early in the nineteenth century. Mouth-to-mouth resuscitation, unfortunately, was not reinstituted at that time, partly because of the new discovery of life-giving oxygen and the finding that expired air contained less of it (nobody bothered to find out if the difference was significant). For the next century and a quarter, therefore, resuscitative techniques centered around chest massage and armlift techniques, and mouth-to-mouth breathing did not return until the middle of the twentieth century.

Emergency electrical defibrillation fared no better. The new phenomenon of electricity had been transformed early-on into a quack cure by the practice of "galvanism" (passing mild shocks through the body in an attempt to cure disease), and its reputation accordingly tarnished. Later, and perhaps even more devastatingly, the charming new electricity was transmuted into a powerful and dangerous force by the giant transformers of Westinghouse (maligned from the first for their deadliness, in a PR campaign by rival industrialist-inventor Thomas Edison) and by the newfangled American electric chair. Technologies as well as people suffer from social stigmas. Mary Shelley had originally not specified the method of the revivification of her monster, but by 1930, in the new electrified America, Frankenstein's monster came into the movies electrically charged. The upshot of all these social transformations was that therapeutic electric shock, so full of promise in the 1790s, did not again come into its own for lifesaving purposes (or even for psychiatric purposes, for that matter) until about the same time resuscitative breathing was being reassessed, in the late 1950s.

Other resuscitative techniques like chest/cardiac compression had been used sporadically since the late 19th century as well, but they too did not see acceptance until the late 1950's, when almost inexplicably all of the "modern" techniques came together approximately simultaneously in what we know as "cardiopulmonary resuscitation (CPR)." The world, apparently, was not ready until the Space Age for any of these techniques, and simply rejected them when brilliant and well-meaning scientists invented them too early.

Some General Observations On History

What are we to make of all this? Is there anything to be learned? In looking at the history of resuscitation and medicine we might ask if there are any observations to be made about it which might apply as well to the medicine of today and tomorrow.

The first thing we notice is that there seem to be some themes in medical history which occur again and again. Important medical discoveries, like important philosophical discoveries, seem quite likely to be made by outsiders. In some cases, the "outsiders" in medicine have been doctors working outside the traditional groves of academe, and in others, the important medical discoveries have not been made by doctors at all. Leeuwenhoek, for instance, was a haberdasher, Pasteur a chemist, Fleming a bacteriologist. Recall that mouth-to-mouth resuscitation was the secret of midwives, and passed to medicine quite late. The original Humane Society, though founded by a doctor, was less a professional medical group than a group of ordinary and somewhat evangelistic citizens who (in exactly the manner of cryonicists) had banded together for humanitarian reasons and out of fear of being buried alive.

A second observation which can be made about the history of medicine and technology in general is that discoveries depend for acceptance upon a very complex social milieu which may have little to do with technology. A technological advance will not be accepted in a world which is not ready for it socially. The idea of using a steam engine to replace human muscle, for example, will not catch on in a world where human muscle power, because of slavery, is cheap. Conversely, a device like the cotton gin, which replaces delicate work with muscle work, will instantly be accepted in such a world.

For an analogous example of this phenomenon from medicine, we might consider the history of anesthesia. As we know from their writings, Muslim physicians practiced various forms of anesthesia during surgery back as far as the 8th century A.D. In Christendom, conversely, where the idea of redemptive suffering held sway, anesthesia took much longer to catch on. Thus, the anesthetic properties of nitrous oxide had been widely and publicly noted by Sir Humphrey Davy as early as 1798, yet it was not until the 1840s that an obscure general practitioner from Georgia and a couple of part-time dentists (remember our observation about outsiders) began to try out inhaled anesthetics for surgical purposes. Even at that, there was an ecclesiastical outcry when Queen Victoria requested chloroform for childbirth, soon after the first anesthetic demonstration in America. One prominent cleric complained that "travail and pain" in childbirth had been ordained by God in the Bible, and that therefore anesthesia was against the will of God. (Others pointed out *Genesis* 2:21 where Adam is put to sleep as the rib is taken for Eve. Scriptural wars can be quite inventive.)

What then held up full cardiopulmonary resuscitation until the late 1950s, even though the world had discovered all of its essential features before 1900? We can only speculate, but the answer may lie in the fundamental change in the way which people began to relate to and trust technology between 1900 and 1950—a social change which is as profound as any generation of humans has ever had to cope with. (See Frederick Lewis Allen's book *The Big Change: America from 1900 to 1950.*) Mythmaking, as ever, played a role. If technology first crept into our nightmares with *Frankenstein*, it later (redemptively) crept into our heroic myths and won some measure of acceptance. Thus, if the new 20th century technology of aviation was capable of creating a new kind of hero like Charles Lindbergh, the public was also willing to let him have a technological shot at Death with his new artificial heart machine. In any case, the mantle of Dr. Frankenstein had by the middle of the 20th century passed to the physicists and their atom bombs, and medicine for the time being, was at last back in the heroic mode. (See the book *Microbe Hunters.* This situation continued until the development of the modern ICU and "life support," at which time doctors and medical technology began taking heat once again.)

Cryonics

In the context of some of the foregoing observations, it is interesting to consider cryonics as an unaccepted technical idea. The study of history always offers perspective. Thus, if we cryonicists shudder with dread over the idea of a "premature" burial, or the idea of a viable person being destroyed by the autopsy knife, we may be a bit chastened to find that this conflict is already two centuries old, and not over concerns invented entirely by us.

As a practical matter, it might first be well to remind ourselves of the sources of danger in these situations. It takes only a change in point of view to regard a person in full cardiac arrest as being in a desperate and life-threatening situation for not just a few minutes, but (perhaps) days. This, in turn, may change the whole tenor of the game, for having a loved one in a desperate situation can engender the most desperate acts. Historically, as we have seen, men have committed violence over the question of dissecting a relative who might be viable, and as we have also seen, this very situation is a prime area of potential conflict between cryonicists and society. (We have seen cryonicists taken into custody over this question, though fortunately not yet for long.) All of this should re-emphasize the need to do tremendous amounts of prior legal preparation, if we are not eventually to be faced with the otherwise inevitable situation in which a cryonicist is charged with the assault of a coroner or pathologist.

Of course, the question of viability holds another danger specially for cryonicists, over and above our potential conflict with government. If a man in the throes of grief is capable of killing on behalf of a potentially viable "deanimated" loved one, then the refusal of "last-minute" cases (no matter the circumstances) places cryonics organizations in a potentially explosive confrontation with the public as well. Here, cryonicists are the potential targets. We have seen cases in the news where distraught relatives have killed ER physicians in the midst of grief and misplaced anger. Might not then the same violent action be directed at representatives of a cryonics organization which was in the position of being (technically) able to rescue a viable person, but (for necessary financial reasons) refused to do so? If history is not to be repeated, it is clear that security concerns are going to have to be paramount for cryonicists in the future.

What about wider concerns? Here, too, the past has something to teach, this time about groups of concerned people who began as outsiders to established medicine, yet later prevailed. Although the cry of "They laughed at the Wright Brothers, too!" has long been the defense of crackpots, even a cursory examination of the history of medicine shows that the initial non-acceptance of any important new idea by that profession is almost de rigueur. Thus, although the mere fact of medical non-acceptance does not prove the cryonicists' case, at the same time cryonicists certainly do not necessarily need to suffer embarrassment on that score. The long view of things is helpful. At present, it seems likely that cryonicists play the role of the midwives of old, practicing their own peculiar lifesaving ministrations in parallel with medicine. Medicine's recognition of cryonics, like its belated recognition of resuscitation, will come.

When? Unfortunately, history is not prophecy. The answer from the foregoing discussion, if there is one, is that it will come when society is ready for it. We know that humans are not naturally very good scientists (our brains weren't developed for that), and very primitive needs and fears drive both acceptance and rejection of new technologies. As we've noted, the fear of premature burial drove an entire series of electrical defibrillation experiments in the late 18th and early 19th centuries, all of which then were suppressed for more than a century partly because the idea of shocking people back to life had in turn been killed by a single well-placed monster myth. Human beings and their societies run on good stories, not scientific reports. Similarly, American society of the 1960s, gearing up for a holy war on cancer and heart disease and intoxicated with the Salk-myth of the all-powerful medical researcher, was not ready for cryonics. By the late 1980s, however, when it had begun to become apparent that heart disease and cancer (not to mention aging) were a lot more intractable than polio, there existed in this society at least a subculture that was now ready to listen to another idea for cheating death.

And so here we are. From a strictly technical view, cryonics as we know it might have been practiced 70 or 80 years ago. Technically we might have been ready for it, but culturally we were not. What is more (let's face it), American society as a whole is still not ready to listen to the idea of radically extended lifespans. The good news, however, is that with the publication of a number of popular gerontology books in the last decade, things are changing slowly. The social milieu (not to mention the age of the population) is changing, and scientific immortalists are getting ready for another try at the hearts of the public. As has been argued in previous essays, this change will require yet another set of new myths (hero stories) to counter Frankenstein's monster, just as our out-of-body experience stories now let us, as a society, deal with the ambiguity of complex resuscitations from clinical death (see the movie *Flatliners*). In the case of cryonics, the new myths will come, too. We can only hope for all our sakes that this necessary process doesn't take as long as it sometimes has in the past. ■

RIDING THE JAMESON SATELLITE

BY R. MICHAEL PERRY, PH.D.

Cryonics, November, 1991

It is always interesting to try to trace the origins of thinking that led to something significant, and this certainly applies to cryonics. In cryonics we find that major pioneer Robert Ettinger first got an inkling of the basic idea by reading a science fiction story, "The Jameson Satellite" by Neil R. Jones. The story appeared in the July, 1931 issue of *Amazing Stories*. It is worth remarking that magazine science fiction at this time was still in its infancy, having started, for most intents and purposes, with the April, 1926 issue of the same *Amazing*. (By 1931 *Amazing* had a rival known as *Astounding Stories of Super-science,* which eventually metamorphosed into *Analog*; both publications continue to this day.) Yes, there were good ideas around even in those early days, though this one was of such magnitude that (as I believe the future will confirm) it utterly transcends our poor efforts to explore through the medium of fiction.

The plot of the story concerns the efforts of one Professor Jameson to have his body, at death, "preserved perfectly forever . . . while on earth millions of generations of mankind would live and die, their bodies to molder into the dust of the forgotten past." The solution the professor arrives at, by his demise in 1958, is to have his body launched into earth orbit:

"With the assistance of a nephew, who carried out his instructions and wishes following his death, Professor Jameson was sent upon his pilgrimage into space within the rocket he himself had built. The nephew and heir kept the secret forever locked in his heart."

It is not made clear how space was to preserve the body. With sufficient shielding from solar radiation, low temperature adequate for long-term storage should be possible at earth's distance from the sun; evidently this was achieved. (It is interesting too that 1958 was not a bad guess for the achievement of space travel; the first man was in fact orbited in 1961.) The professor in turn has no thought of eventual reanimation, just indefinite storage. The years pass after he is in orbit, some 40 million of them. The human race dies out, along with other species that evolve later. The sun is a dying red ball with the earth slowly spiraling in, when finally the solar system is invaded by an exploratory party of aliens, "the machine men of Zor." They are an advanced race who, sometime ago, traded in their flesh-and-blood housing for more durable metal.

There is an interesting twist when the aliens encounter Jameson's perfectly frozen remains in orbit. They decide to reanimate the Professor—by transplanting his brain to a machine body like their own. The old body is discarded, the mind reactivated. The transformation renders the professor immortal and super-strong, a near-equal among his rescuers. If there is any problem about him not feeling entirely "himself" or of a compromise of his identity, it is not stated, even though he must now communicate telepathically, has a circle of eyes for 360° viewing, four legs, six tentacles for arms, and is mostly metal. He adjusts quickly, and evidently finds the metallic body superior in every way. Among other things, it allows him, along with his extraterrestrial companions, to explore the earth, which by now has become an uninhabitable wasteland with little atmosphere.

All is not perfect with Jameson, however, and the last part of the story, subtitled "Eternity or Death," explores some of the problems of his new, immortal existence. When he manages to fall into the dark interior of an extinct volcano, wrecking much of his metal frame and losing contact with the others, he is dismayed by the prospect of endless imprisonment.

> *"He would remain in this deathless, monotonous state forever in the black hole of the volcano's interior unable to move. What a horrible thought! He could not starve to death; eating was unknown among the Zoromes, the machines requiring no food. He could not even commit suicide. The only way for him to die would be to smash the strong metal head, and in his present immovable condition, this was impossible."*

The professor is rescued, however, when the others detect his telepathic pleas for help (though, with his more primitive brain, he can't receive their communications at a distance). Fixing him is easy: "We shall merely remove your head and place it upon another machine body." That done, the Professor is to be accompanied for a while by one of the aliens until he is better adjusted. They are really quite considerate and compassionate, but he faces a difficult decision, when they want him to join them on a permanent basis.

"A great loneliness seized him. Would he be happy among these machine men of another far-off world ...? They were kindly and solicitous of his welfare. What better fate could he expect? Still, a longing for his own kind arose in him . . .It was irresistible. What could he do? Was it not in vain? Humanity had long since disappeared from the earth—millions of years ago. He wondered what lay beyond the pales of death—real death, where the body decomposed and wasted away to return to the dust of the earth and assume new atomic structures."

In despair Jameson, resolving to end his life, climbs to a high precipice and prepares to hurl himself down. His alien companion makes no attempt to restrain him but offers thoughts:

"Why jump? . . . The dying world holds your imagination within a morbid clutch. It is all a matter of mental condition. Free your mind of this fascinating influence and come with us to visit other worlds, many of them beautiful and new. . . ."

It is hardly necessary to point out how similar is this plea to what we cryonicists are trying to tell others, as they spurn freezing for the more usual and destructive alternatives when the reaper comes knocking. Apparently they do not wish to outlive the "dying world" they have inhabited for so long, and which they realize is passing into history. (At least this must account for some of the lack of enthusiasm for cryonics.) Unlike these many, however, the Professor in the end does choose life:

"He would become an immortal after all and join the Zoromes in their never-ending adventures from world to world. They hastened to the space ship to escape the depressing, dreary influence of the dying world, which had nearly driven Professor Jameson to take the fatal leap to oblivion."

"The Jameson Satellite" anticipates much of the cryonics premise, though there are some omissions—mainly, the idea that available technology can be used for the suspension (orbiting spacecraft being unknown in 1931) and most importantly, that humanity itself can carry out the entire operation, including resuscitation, given enough time. But these later refinements, however important, do not detract from the overall tone of optimism about the prospect of continued existence, or the sobering prospect of having to leave our past world behind to enjoy it. As cryonicists, our options are not altogether different. ■

Sources

Jones, Neil R. "The Jameson Satellite," *Amazing Stories* July 1931, 334.

Regis, Ed. *Great Mambo Chicken and the Transhuman Condition* Addison-Wesley, 1990, p. 85.

THE FIRST CRYONICIST

BY SAUL KENT
Cryonics, March, 1983

The cryonics movement did not begin with the publication of *The Prospect of Immortality* by Robert Ettinger in 1964. At the time there was already a cryonics organization in being, although the word "cryonics" had not yet been invented. That organization—The Life Extension Society (LES)—was started by Ev Cooper—a tall, softspoken man who also wrote the first book on cryonics: *Immortality, Physically, Scientifically, Now,* which was published privately.

Ev's role in launching the cryonics movement deserves a longer and more thoughtful piece than I have time for right now, but here are a few recollections of the man and the early days of the movement.

When I read *The Prospect of Immortality* in June of 1964, I was exhilarated to a degree I had never before experienced. Instantly, I knew—beyond a shadow of a doubt—that the most profound and powerful idea in history had been unleashed and that I would devote my life to it. But it wasn't until the following winter that I finally got around to writing a letter to Ettinger to initiate my involvement in the movement.

In that letter, I asked if there were any organizations working to promote the idea. He replied that there were two: The Immortality Records and Compilation Association (IRCA) in Panorama City, California, headed by Tom Tierney and The Life Extension Society in Washington, D.C., headed by Ev Cooper.

I wrote a brief note to both organizations and awaited their replies. From IRCA I heard nothing. Two years later, I was to experience hours of intensive questioning from police and the FBI in Las Vegas when Curtis Henderson and I tried to meet with Tierney, who had just been arrested for counterfeiting and gun fraud. When the police interrogator asked me if we were involved in either of these schemes, I replied: "No, officer, we only freeze dead bodies."

From Ev, on the other hand, I heard a great deal. Several days later I received a Special Delivery letter from him that was a bit overwhelming. Not only did Ev welcome me into his organization with open arms, he actually asked me if I wanted to represent LES in New York as a "Life Extension Coordinator." I wasn't quite ready for that yet and wondered what kind of man would make such an offer so quickly.

About a month later I met Ev Cooper and his wife Mildred for the first time at Grand Central Station in New York. Ev had just participated in a seminar on the freezing idea at Pace Institute in Brooklyn. Another participant in the seminar was Dr.

Benjamin Schloss, who had formed an organization—The Society for Anabiosis—to raise money for cryonics research. Dr. Schloss soon shifted his attention to aging research. He died from cancer in the late 1970's, while trying to launch a crash program to achieve immortality by 1989. He was not frozen.

One of the spectators at the seminar was Karl Werner, a Pratt student who would soon (July 1965) join with Jim Sutton, Harry Costello, Curtis Henderson, and myself to form the Cryonics Society of New York (CSNY); the first organization to compete with LES. Karl was the one who thought up the word "cryonics." He dropped out of the movement in 1968 to join the Church of Scientology. Although he soon left Scientology, he never rejoined cryonics.

From the beginning I found Ev to be warm, friendly, gracious, and generous. We carried on an exciting and highly stimulating conversation in his car as we drove out to a restaurant in Queens to meet (for the first time) with Jim Sutton and Harry Costello, who were to join with me in becoming coordinators for LES in New York. Three months later, we would resign from LES and six months after that would join with Curtis Henderson and Karl Werner to form the Cryonics Society of New York.

About 6 weeks later, Jim Sutton, Harry Costello, and I took a bus ride to Washington, D.C., to meet with Ev and the other members of LES. Once again, Ev and Mildred greeted us with warmth and good cheer. While Jim and Harry stayed at a local motel, I had the good fortune to be invited to stay with Ev and Mildred at their apartment—the home base of the Life Extension Society.

That evening Ev and I discussed the idea of achieving immortality with great excitement. It was particularly thrilling for me to discuss the idea with a man who had obviously given great thought to its implications. Ev was well read in philosophy, psychology, and literature. He greatly enjoyed discussing traditional ideas and then speculating about how they might change as the prospect of immortality became more imminent. LES, in fact, had evolved from a discussion group led by Ev that examined the greatest books of the 20th century. Ev and I continued our discussions until well after midnight.

The following day, Jim, Harry, and I were introduced by Ev to some of the other members including Vice President John Prince, a tall (6'7") black man who dressed in 3-piece suits; Bill Albaugh, who was about to run for Congress in Maryland on a "Freeze-Wait-Reanimate" program (the title of the LES newsletter); and Phil Carlson, who was intrigued with the concept of personal identity and how it might change in the future. In all, we met about a dozen local members all of whom clearly looked up to Ev as their leader.

Later in the day, Ev showed me his small, but graceful sailboat, the use of which occupied most of his leisure time. Both Jim and Harry, who were dressed in business suits, declined a ride in Ev's sailboat, but I decided to chance it in my light jacket and desert boots.

Ev took me out about half a mile from shore. It was quite windy and I was soon cold and wet and anxious to get back to dry land. But Ev wasn't about to take me back so quickly. He was truly in his element at sea and was determined to tell me all he could about the glories of sailing, whether I wanted to know or not.

Finally, after about 45 minutes of gliding through the waves, we returned to shore. That was the first and last time I ever saw Ev's sailboat.

The first major cryonics event I ever attended was the 2nd Annual LES Conference held on January 1, 1966.

The previous evening, Curtis Henderson and I drove down to attend a New Year's Eve party at Ev's apartment. It was extraordinarily warm (70 degrees by the time we reached D.C.) and we were delayed.

We arrived at Ev's place at about 11:50 PM. At the stroke of midnight, Ev announced that the party was over. "Time to go to sleep," he said. "Got to get up real early for the conference tomorrow."

And what a conference it was! Ev had sent out press releases about a frozen dog ("Belle") who would be displayed at the conference. He also made arrangements with Ed Hope of Cryo-Care Equipment Corporation to drive that company's prototype "Cryo-Capsule" to D.C. from Phoenix in order to exhibit the frozen dog.

Hope arrived that night, but Ev had neglected to make arrangements for a place to put the trailer with the capsule. So he had to leave it in a "no-parking" zone next to the restaurant where the conference was to be held.

The next morning, photos were taken of Belle in the capsule and then the dog was put into a freezer. The conference started bright and early, with the streets of the city deserted (It was New Year's Day, you remember).

At noon we wandered out of the restaurant to find a small crowd gathering around the capsule. The police were questioning Ed Hope about the strange machine in his van. They had perplexed looks upon their faces as they pondered the meaning of the "suspended animation" sign on the side of the van.

Suddenly, several frantic-looking men and women carrying pickets arrived on the scene with fire in their eyes. They were members of the Humane Society and were outraged at the idea of freezing a dog for future reanimation. "We want to see that dog brought back to life right now!" shouted a particularly enraged woman.

Then the press arrived. A camera crew from one of the local TV news shows was the prime attraction. One of D.C.'s most popular TV reporters was asking for the person in charge of the festivities. When Ev couldn't be located (he was apparently in the Men's Room), Bob Ettinger consented to an interview to explain what freezing people was all about.

As the interview proceeded, the crowd grew larger, the Humane Society protesters became more vocal, and the police moved in to break up the proceedings.

As soon as the TV interview was over, we returned to the restaurant to resume the conference. That night we watched the late news at Ev's place with a sense of growing excitement. It seemed as if the freezing idea was about to take off and that LES would be in the forefront of the movement.

That wasn't to be of course. By then (Jan. 1, 1966), Ev had already "lost control" of things in New York. After several disagreements over policy, we had broken loose from LES and formed the Cryonics Society of New York (in July of 1965).

Later in 1966, we began to publish *Cryonics Reports* and, in October of that year, Curtis Henderson and I set forth on a trip around the country that triggered some profound changes in the movement. During that trip, the Cryonics Society of Michigan was formed, with Ettinger as President; the Cryonics Society of California was formed, with Bob Nelson as President; and we ordered a Cryo-Capsule from Ed Hope's company in Phoenix (after spending two weeks there). On Jan 12, 1967, James H. Bedford was frozen by the Cryonics Society of California, which led to a great deal of publicity about the idea and firmly placed the various Cryonics Societies in the forefront of the movement.

By the end of 1967 LES was almost moribund. Its influence ended, for all means and purposes, when Ev suddenly called off his annual LES conference on very short notice. We rapidly stepped in to fill the void by organizing the First Annual Cryonics Conference at the New York Academy of Sciences on March 28, 1968.

Ev Cooper never attended that meeting or any subsequent meeting. He quietly dropped out of the movement and went off to a simpler life at sea. ■

Note: Cooper disappeared at sea in October 1982.

Robert Ettinger: Some Brief Historical and Personal Notes

By R. Michael Perry, Ph.D.

Cryonics, 4th Quarter, 2011, revised August 2014

The nineteenth and early twentieth centuries were a time of unprecedented advances in science and technology, which affected persons worldwide, though not always in positive ways. In fact the gargantuan violence of two world wars, the development of nuclear weapons and other horrible means of destruction, the obliteration of lives and property, and the attendant hatreds, fears, and other ill feelings poisoned the minds of many against technological innovations. It seemed indeed that the bad might outweigh the good, that humankind had gone too far and rashly down a fancied road toward godhood, that it would be better, if only we could, to return to a simpler time when our destructive tendencies were better confined. Not everyone succumbed to such pessimism, however, and some even saw in technology a road to salvation that was otherwise lacking. One such optimist was Robert C. W. Ettinger (1918-2011), who grew up around Detroit, Michigan. As a boy in his father's store he read the pioneering science fiction periodical, *Amazing Stories*. The July 1931 issue contained a story by Neil R. Jones, "The Jameson Satellite." In it, Professor Jameson's body is chilled at death and placed into Earth orbit, to be revived millions of years later by an alien race, which has also conquered aging and other ailments. To the twelve-year-old Robert, the resuscitation of a human in a postmortal future held a fascination that would not be forgotten in the decades to come.

In 1944 Ettinger was wounded, ironically, while fighting the Nazis in World War II Germany, and spent several years recuperating in an army hospital in Battle Creek, Michigan. This offered him the opportunity to write a science fiction story of his own. Published in the March 1948 *Startling Stories,* "The Penultimate Trump" is about a wealthy man, H. D. Haworth, who is frozen at death and eventually resuscitated, with youth and health restored. In two important respects Haworth's reanimation differs from Professor Jameson's: (1) it is planned for by Haworth himself (Jameson simply intended to be well-preserved, not eventually brought back to consciousness); and (2) it is carried out by humans and not through a chance encounter with aliens. To Ettinger this seemed a plausible, real-life approach to personal life extension and betterment. He expected that others with better scientific credentials would soon be working on the freezing idea. In fact work was ongoing, and actually had advanced to the point that single cells could be frozen to liquid nitrogen temperature and revived, and mammals such as hamsters could be partly frozen (at much higher temperature) and also revived. But beyond such initial success, progress was slow. Little serious attention was paid to the fantastic possibility that Ettinger and others more tentatively before him had envisioned, of cryogenic storage as a means of defeating death. So in 1960 Ettinger, who had by then earned master's degrees in both physics and mathematics and become a college professor, set to work again. His first, modest effort was to circulate a short summary of his ideas to a few hundred people in *Who's Who*. Response was minimal, so he set out to write a book.

The first version of *The Prospect of Immortality* was completed and privately published in 1962. Ettinger began to circulate his new book, hoping to spur some interest in what would later be known as cryonics. (Some earlier terms for the idea were "freeze and wait" and "Freeze-Wait-Reanimate.") That same year Evan Cooper, working independently (and writing under the pseudonym "N. Duhring," signifying "enduring"), completed his own book, *Immortality: Physically, Scientifically, Now,* with essentially the same idea. (Cooper actually advocated storage in permafrost or a conventional deep freeze but soon would agree with Ettinger that much colder storage in liquid nitrogen was preferred.) The two men corresponded during 1963, while Cooper especially focused on the problem of how to organize a movement, with a non-profit organization called the Life Extension Society, a newsletter, correspondents (in a "letters" column in the newsletter), conferences, and the like.

Cooper's and others' efforts that year culminated in the first formal gathering devoted to the freezing idea, a two-day event that began on Saturday, December 28. The location was Marty Laffal's Charcoal Steak House, 1801 H Street N.W., Washington, D.C., near Cooper's residence. One spinoff was the creation of the first cryonics-promotional organization (though again the word "cryonics" had not yet been invented), the Life Extension Society (LES), whose newsletter first appeared in January the following year, with a recounting of events written by Cooper himself: "The last weekend of 1963 rang down and out with perhaps the world's smallest conference and time's most imposing title: *The First International Conference on the Scientific Prospects for Physical Immortality.* The number [who attended] depends on how adept you are at counting shadows, waitresses, correspondents, and broadcast reporters. Twenty registered, eighteen paid, while fifteen were able to attend. ..."

The morning session opened with the recognition that "practical aging control, for all the promise of present research, lies in the distant future." As a consequence, "we should get down to business on a freezing program for those who wish a plan for preservation in the event of any immediate deaths." The speaker who started things off, Larry Jensen, "who teaches at Castleton College [Vermont], where they call him the ice man, is one of the original formulators of the freeze and wait theory. He has helped spread the idea on radio broadcasts, wrote to President Kennedy in May, gave a talk at Green Mt. College, where the response was highly positive, and has taken out $10,000 in extra insurance to guaranty [sic] a very cool resting place in the event of death." (Larry Jensen—Lawrence Neil Jensen—was an artist, author and professor who is listed repeatedly in the LES newsletter as a contact. But after the first conference and despite the insurance policy, he does not seem to have had much active involvement or longstanding interest in cryonics; he died in 2000, with no report of cryopreservation. Ev Cooper, for his part, was active for a few years but then dropped out and was lost at sea in 1982. Ettinger, of course, maintained his interest and involvement throughout and was finally cryopreserved at the age of 92 in July 2011.)

"Bob Ettinger led the afternoon session," Cooper goes on, "... primarily a continuation of the morning's attempt to find and agree on a program.... There were the usual differences of opinion on both days with such strong-minded individualists. However the name *Life Extension Society* was adopted until and unless a better one can be found." Cooper also mentions Ettinger's book, *The Prospect of Immortality,* whose expanded, commercial version was nearing publication. This would occur in June, 1964; the August issue of the LES newsletter has a report, reprinted below with minor corrections.

BIG NEWS OF THE SUMMER:

"Bob Ettinger's book *The Prospect of Immortality* was released by Doubleday June 5th, coinciding with a short serialization in *Cosmopolitan*, and a thoughtful article by Fred Pohl in *Playboy*. Quite a number of radio and TV stations carried and are continuing to carry interviews of Ettinger and discussions of the freeze-wait-resuscitate idea. Bob's book has been translated into French, and LES members report seeing it in paperback on Paris newsstands.

"The book itself is a marvel of lucidity and forceful writing. Among the many contributions, the emergency dry ice freezing and storage suggestion is of special interest because the next step [after vital signs cease] is the actual preservation by freezing of [the] person who has just "died." The dry ice method is an emergency method, for it is preferable that the lower temperatures of evaporating liquid gases be used, but the latter are not always available. Dry ice is in much more common supply, easier to handle, and the cost of cooling can be made less expensive with sufficient insulation. The temperature of dry ice (-78°C) is lower than any ordinary deep freeze. Depending on the insulation and the number stored, Ettinger estimates that the cost could run from $4 to 10¢ per frozen person per day. An inexpensive storage unit could be built with sufficient room for the person's body and a compartment for dry ice immediately above. The body would be transferred when a better storage system became available.

"Response to the book has been varied—from enthusiasm to irritation with anything so revolutionary. It has been reviewed by a number of the major mass media publications indicating they are considering the possibility that Ettinger's is a significant book.

"Jean Rostand wrote a preface stating that the idea is solid. Gerald Gruman with his extensive background knowledge of the history of the concept of immortality wrote a second preface noting how great ideas such as this have often taken considerable time in taking hold. Penicillin, for example, is said to have taken 16 years between its discovery and its use.

"Congratulations are more than in order. It is a great event toward the defeat of death."

Prospect would launch the cryonics movement, at least in the minds of most of the public, and Ettinger would go on to a long involvement, including such milestones as publication of other books and the founding of the Cryonics Institute in 1976, today one of the two largest cryonics organizations with over 100 patients. On the personal level, Bob was a longtime friend. His kindness and thoughtfulness were apparent when, for example, he would go to lengths to photocopy historical material I was interested in (though he told me he wasn't), or the time he wrote a nice, consoling letter when my mother died and was buried. He also had an appreciation of larger issues than merely extending life, important though it is, as shown when he became a board member of the Society for Venturism, a cryonics-promoting 501(c)(3) organization dedicated, among other things, to seeing that persons who are cryopreserved are eventually resuscitated. (It is a sticking point with some people that no one will care to resuscitate them, supposing cryonics would otherwise work. The Venturists, and some organizations more recently formed with a similar outlook, aim to address that possible problem by offering unconditional support if and when it should be needed.)

I'll close this little pastiche with some words from the man himself, a Cryonet message in the 1990s that hasn't lost its relevance and also recounts some earlier history. (Again I've made minor corrections. "Mae," is the former Mae Junod, who married Ettinger after his first wife Elaine was frozen in 1987.)

```
X-Message-Number: 4414
From: Ettinger@aol.com
Date: Thu, 18 May 1995 17:13:15 -0400
Subject: recruitment
```

Saul Kent says we (cryonicists) are different in psychology and that we should try to identify those who are interested but haven't done anything about it.

Of course we are different—but not, as far as I can see, in any visible and useful way. Who set it in motion originally, or tried to do so? I wrote a book (after previous fitful efforts over many years), Evan Cooper wrote a somewhat similar book, and Lawrence Jensen, an art professor (yes, a PAINTER) at Castleton State College in Vermont, was planning to do so (and maybe others of whom we haven't heard). Those who read my book and instantly responded included Saul, Curtis Henderson, Mike Darwin (a child of 12 at the time), Paul Segall, Harry Waitz, Art Quaife, Greg Fahy, my brother Alan, my son David (who explained it on TV at age 15), Jerry Leaf (I think), Jerry White (I think), and some others to whom I apologize for omission of names. But what do they have in common—not counting my relatives?

The writers or would-be writers of books—myself, Ev Cooper, and Larry Jensen—were very different people, with almost nothing in common, as far as I can see, or nothing that was not also shared by enormous numbers of people. The same goes for the instant responders. The conclusion, once more, is that the psychological and practical pivots are so subtle, or so dependent on elements of chance, that identifying them is hopeless.

Eugen Leitl says uploaders should be prime candidates for cryonics. Again, while the statistics may show a slight favorable bias, it isn't enough to be practically meaningful. It's a little bit like saying that rich people should be prime candidates, because "logically" they can easily spare the money, so what's to lose? But it's not the logical that rules—it's the psychological, and psychology is not an exact science (or even a "fuzzy" science).

Locate the interested people? We have drawers full of names of people who have sent queries over the years, but on our sporadic attempts to follow them up we get mostly no response or notice that they have moved to an unknown address. (Yes, we should have been and should be more systematic about this.)

My general impression, once more, is that only two things do much good in cryonics advertising or public relations: (1) Get as much free publicity as you can, provided it is dignified, and (2) Use as much personal contact and influence as practicable. (The average cost per successful recruitment is very high, and when you have someone definitely interested a lot of additional expense and effort may be justified.)

Finally, as Saul says, support for research is extremely important both directly, for improving the patients' chances, and indirectly in many ways including its effect on our credibility. And Saul (with Bill Faloon) has done much more than most in this area, as well as having been an important contributor to the growth of Alcor. But again, this is nothing new.

What is the point of all this rumination? Perhaps recruitment should focus on two strategies: (1) Use the shotgun and free publicity; (2) Keep a hard squeeze on those already in the vise. Mae occasionally gives money to the Republicans, and every donation is instantly followed by a flood of requests for more and larger donations. Of course, that doesn't work with her; the cost of the request mailings probably exceeds her total donations. But one supposes their technique must work, on average, since they keep doing it.

Robert Ettinger
Cryonics Institute
Immortalist Society ∎

NOTES ON THE FIRST HUMAN FREEZING

BY TED KRAVER, PH.D.

The text below was transcribed and then edited from a recording made by Ted Kraver, chief engineer for Cryocare Equipment Corporation in May of 1966, about two weeks after freezing the first human being in the hopes of future resuscitation.

To begin with a little history: For me, the idea of making storage units for cryogenic interment purposes dates back to September of 1965. Frank (Rick) Rickenbacker and I met with Ed Hope where we worked at the Technical Services Department of the AiResearch Manufacturing Company (Phoenix). The meeting was held after I got off work. I'd joined the Life Extension Society several months before from a small ad in the Mensa newsletter, and noticed in the LES newsletter that Mr. Hope was going to be building a "cryogenic interment facility in Phoenix"—and my interest was sparked.

With our engineering background I thought there might be some possibility of personal involvement and we decided to contact Mr. Hope. Rick and I had gotten together a couple of times to discuss ideas for businesses which we could start by ourselves. We were both interested in cryogenic interment; we thought it would be a tremendous thing. But neither one of us had really done anything about it, mainly because we just didn't have the financial backing, knowledge, or freedom to undertake such an enterprise. We had built a large cryogenic test facility for AiResearch and had just completed a year of testing of Saturn SIVB components. This had required massive use of liquid hydrogen and nitrogen, and very cold, high-pressure helium. We had designed, built, and used a dozen unique cryogenic test rigs for valves, hoses, and tanks.

So I gave Mr. Hope a call. I was able to locate him without difficulty because our temporary secretary at Technical Services at that time turned out to have a sister who worked for Mr. Hope and was very interested in cryonics. Mr. Hope came over to our place. It's hard to say what our first impressions were. Rick came down after work and we sat around and just talked over the idea. So Rick and I got together a couple of nights later at his house and laid out the first drawing of what we thought a single-person capsule would look like. We had a few ideas on insulation and engineering the vacuum system. We decided on glass matte-foil insulation. The horizontal inner tank would hang on thin rods with stacked flat washers for minimum heat flow. The inner aluminum tank would have a bolted lead gasket that was compressed as the tank cooled. The outer steel tank also had a bolted head. Copper-constantan thermocouples monitored temperature, a simple automotive gas tank gauge monitored liquid level, and vacuum was measured by a thermocouple gauge. A long, spiral fill line and long vent line with bellows for expansion minimized heat leakage. Our target was six months between fills (0.55 % per day).

We both did some reading and we got together at Ed's house over the course of the next couple of days, and spent an evening there going over what we would do. We decided to set up a corporation and build a human storage capsule. Ed would finance it, at least the first few thousands, and we would provide the engineering expertise and even carry out the fabrication. Rick and I were putting in a more or less equal amount of time, and $500 each, and a little more time than Ed was at this point. Ed was going to handle not only financing the venture, but also running the business end of it; handling marketing, sales, and that sort of thing. That's how Cryocare Equipment Corporation, the first company actually to manufacture human cryogenic storage units, came to be. Ed had a number of small businesses (oil delivery, night club) in the Philadelphia area. When he came to Phoenix, he opened several wig shops at the beginning of the wig fad, and owned and built industrial buildings. He built the first "do-it-yourself storage warehouse" two years before the industry started.

Prior to our first meeting, Ed had visited a number of places around the country including a fellow by the name of Leonard Gold back in Springfield, Illinois, who was also intending to manufacture and market cryogenic interment equipment. I don't think he had talked to Ettinger yet, but he had met with just about everyone else. Most of the other outfits that were supposed to be manufacturing equipment either weren't producing an item or just had the product developed to the point of an artist's conceptions. In short, there was no real product and no sign of any being developed soon.

Our intention upon starting Cryocare was to simply build a product and sell it if a market developed. We had no interest at all in getting involved with handling the actual freezing of patients. We intended to leave the processing aspect of the operation to Ettinger and his group or anyone else who wanted to do it: morticians, physicians, whoever and however it developed. We would just build the physical hardware. But life is almost never that simple.

About two or three months after we formed Cryocare, following the usual quota of design changes, we built our first cryocapsule. The outside was fabricated of high-carbon steel—we used a commercially available steel tank 32 inches in diameter and eight feet long as the starting point. We put a single compression gasket on the front, just a flat neoprene gasket. It turned out to be one of our biggest headaches. The inner tank we had custom-fabricated from aluminum.

We had the ends for the inner tank spun locally from a die one of the local people had for spinning something else. It was sort of jerry-built right from the start. Many nights were spent just hauling things around, getting this done, getting that done, working out myriads of small, unexpected snags that cropped up. We had a fair amount of custom machining which had to be done and that took some time. Finally we ran some pressure and leak checks on it—not very good ones—but we ran them and put the thing together.

We originally designed it for powder (perlite) insulation using low vacuum, but actual calculations proved this old technology not to be good enough at all. So we got some aluminum foil and glass

Vacuum flange of outer vessel being machined on large lathe.

matte insulation and wrapped the inner tank with it. This was an extremely touchy operation. We had everyone there: Barb (my wife), Rick's wife, and Mrs. Hope. We spent a couple of nights just wrapping the thing and an entire weekend was spent with the unit up on-end just wrapping the head. This involved interlacing over a hundred layers of foil and glass matte, a kind of "do it yourself" version of superinsulation. This presented a number of very difficult problems and the work was tedious and unpleasant.

Next we welded on some heat shields and wrapped many additional layers of insulation around it; we really insulated the devil out of the space between the inner and outer tanks. We decided we had to get a helium leak check on it. We didn't feel we had a chance of holding a high vacuum any other way, so I called about thirty places. During this time I was hospitalized for appendicitis and I missed a couple of weeks of the fabrication as a result! In any event, we called a number of places and finally found a firm, Dixon Electronics, with a helium leak detector we could use. So, we went over and leak-checked the inner and outer tank one Saturday morning. There were no leaks that we could find, so it worked out pretty well, better than we had expected. We were fairly confident our leak check was reliable, so we assembled the whole thing and then spent about a month debugging it. It was just before Christmas, 1965 when we got it all assembled.

There was supposed to be a demonstration of the capsule in January of 1966. This put a lot of pressure on since we had to be in Washington D.C., with the unit by January 1st. We worked nights until midnight and one o'clock in the morning getting it put together and tested. We didn't have too much luck with the initial vacuum system. Ultimately we had to tear it out and increase the vacuum line size to 1" and put in a larger vacuum pump. We ended up having to air-express some special valves out, get a bigger vacuum pump, and then we had a lot of trouble with the front outer gasket. We made several of them before we came up with a workable system. We settled on a lead gasket with a layer of silicone glue over it.

The inner cylinder had had a lead gasket from the beginning. We had tried to cast these gaskets, got nowhere on it, and finally we just got sheets of lead and cut the gaskets out, which worked well, compared to how we thought it would perform. We also had troubles with the aluminum bolts breaking on the inside. The system to suspend the inner cylinder within the outer one with a minimum of heat transfer worked very well. We had a lot of trouble with leaks on the outside, and extrusion of the outer lead gasket. We made a number of those and ruined them about every third time we'd tighten up on them. Despite the problems we got this thing in a semblance of order. We finally rolled it down to a paint shop and had it painted white and took pictures of it.

Shortly thereafter we loaded the capsule aboard a trailer and Ed drove it all the way to Washington. It was on display there for the Life Extension Society Conference on January 1st. There was a lot of to-do over it, then Ed brought it back here, and we worked on it again for another month or so and finally got it into a state of readiness where we felt that it actually would work. At this time John Flynn, a biophysicist who had started a company in New York to offer cryogenic interment services (called Biopreservation) had purchased the capsule and we more or less got it into working order and sent it off to him.

Open cryocapsule, showing inner capsule with aluminum bolts, superinsulation, dam for LN2, rails for body rack, liquid level sensor, and thermocouple in vent line.

We drove it over to L.A. and air-expressed it off. He wanted to use it on the Merv Griffin show. The capsule was on that show, just the capsule, with Ettinger. He showed it off, displayed it, showed quite a bit about it—it was a pretty good show. There were some arguments against cryogenic interment, but all in all it was a very interesting show. There were even some cuts to the audience with Ed in the audience chaperoning it. Then Flynn took it in and tested it and had all kinds of troubles with it. Flynn has it at this time which is May 6 or 7 [1966] and is working on it.

During that time—two to three weeks ago—Ed flew back to New York again, picked up the capsule, took it to Philadelphia and it was on the Mike Douglas Show. We had a very good show. Ed was on the show and they really showed off; and they had a guy climb inside and the audience loved it! Anyway, so much for the history of the first cryocapsule.

During that time we were designing and building our second capsule, which had many improvements over the first one. We cut the price on certain things. We modified the vacuum system to handle a bigger flow. We reduced the blowoff disks on it to one, which is all that is really necessary. We changed the insulation from this real pain which we had with fiberglass and aluminum insulation to aluminized mylar, which is more expensive but still quite a much better insulation. Not to mention a lot easier to handle. So we wrapped the inner tank with this. We leak-checked everything before we even wrapped it. We did a better job on the leak checking than we had on the other one: when we leak-checked the first unit we didn't use liquid nitrogen on the front end. There were no leaks so we feel this has a tightening effect on the lead gasket on the front. It turned out that it does.

Anyway, getting back to capsule number two; we finished it up, had it painted, ran some tests on it, and there was an amazingly small amount of leakage, practically none. It was more-or-less a couple orders of magnitude better than the other tank right from the start. We changed to a lead gasket on the outside seal, which I think was an excellent idea. On our next one there'll probably be an O-ring in it. Anyway, the lead gasket worked well on the outside, with some help from sealants, and the inner tank also had a lead gasket. We got it all together and vacuum-checked and everything looked fine.

This tank had been contracted for by a young man in L.A. who had wanted his mother frozen. She had died a couple of months earlier and was taken to Phoenix and kept in cold storage, just above freezing. She was embalmed after she'd been dead about 18 hours, and then lay there in the funeral home for awhile, and finally was refrigerated maybe four or five days later. So there was a certain amount of deterioration, and the hope of the young man was that there would be some intact DNA that would not have been destroyed by the embalming and post-mortem deterioration. So she was brought over and stored in a local mortuary until we got the capsule ready. Well, Friday night we got the capsule ready and things were getting sort of shook. The man came over from L.A. and Ed was not too happy about the whole situation, neither was Rick, they were both sort of queasy about it. Myself—I don't know what my feelings were—sort of, you know, another job to be done. A person was dead, and that was all there was to it.

We came in right after work, Friday night, and Barb (my wife) was with us, and we got the tank set up, and everything hooked up to it and ready to go. Ed went out and got the refrigerated truck and brought the casket in—it was surprisingly heavy. I guess you never realize it until you lift a casket and feel how heavy it is as you lift it out of a truck. At the time, there was an odor in the truck and everyone was imagining what she was going to look like after this time. So we put her in a small back room in the bay we had rented for our company. We put her off in a side room and we finally got things organized. The stretcher bed was set, the final instrumentation was all in, everything was all checked out, so we were ready to go. All the liquid nitrogen was there—we had about four or five 160 liter dewars—and by eight o'clock or that time everyone else had disappeared. Ed went out. Rick took Barb out to eat. We'd taken some pictures beforehand, before the young man came over to look at the tank.

So Ed was conveniently gone and Rick split, and I was there with the young man and I went in while they were gone, and opened up the casket, and it turned out she was very well preserved. There was no deterioration we could notice except for a little bit of discoloration in the fingers. So we went in there, the young man and I, and we opened it up for the second time, and he was of course much relieved. I didn't want to tell him I'd opened it up originally because if I had and she was very bad off I'd want to prepare him for it. But she wasn't, so it worked out pretty well.

We tried to see if we could lift her out onto the bed that went in the capsule, but she was much too heavy and we decided we would have to have Ed and the others. We called the restaurant and managed to reach them there. Ed had met the others there and in response to our call they came back over. Things went very smoothly from there on. We got a blanket under her and lifted her out onto the stretcher and put her inside the sleeping bag—a standard camping sleeping bag with aluminized mylar wrapped around it. We put her in there and taped her up very securely so she was completely surrounded by insulation. The reason for this was that given her condition we didn't feel that freezing really was going to cause too much additional damage. We weren't really interested in a rapid cooldown. Again, because there was no DMSO or other perfusion, just normal embalming fluid, we felt that very slow freezing would be best. The insulation was also wrapped around her so that if there was a failure in the tank it would provide some additional protection against warming. The sleeping bag slowed cooling down quite a bit, as we had hoped, and in the future it would seem like a good idea to wrap the person in one for additional protection.

She was put on the stretcher and we carried her back into the other room, set her down, and tried to lift her in. It turned out that there was a bar that we'd put in there to keep the bed from sliding around and it was preventing us from getting her in because she sat so much higher up on the stretcher than we'd suspected she would. So we had to take her off. We cut the bar out of the front end of the capsule and then slid her in. Her hands had slipped down to the sides and we had to push them back up over the top to get her in.

We put thermocouples—two of them—inside the sleeping bag to monitor the temperature of the body on the inside. This was around nine o'clock at night and all the instrumentation checked out. Then we tried to put the head on the inner tank, and it turned out that the last time we had bolted it on for some of our tests, the bolts had gone sideways slightly and the flange had distorted. As a result the bolts were cocked at an angle and we had to do quite a bit of work to straighten them out. We reamed out the holes, and finally bent the bolts back a little bit and eventually were able to slip the head on after about another half-hour.

Fortunately we had all the shop tools there, and when this was on we tightened it down and then waited for awhile, tightened it down again and then tightened it for the third time. After the head had been tightened down three times we put a basket with all this insulation over the end of it. (This isn't really satisfactory—we're going to have to change this.) Once this insulating end-cap was in place we put the outside head on, bolted it down and started pulling a vacuum on it.

The vacuum went down very quickly, much more rapidly than we thought it would. We then started adding liquid nitrogen. Immediately the vacuum started going up again to around 300 microns, which is completely unacceptable. This would be much too wasteful—we'd use about 10 to 100 times the liquid nitrogen that we would ordinarily use if we had a vacuum this high. So we were semi-panicked at the time. It turned out that the problem was due to the brass ferrules around the fill line, around the Swage-Loc fitting. The brass immediately contracted when chilled with liquid nitrogen during filling, breaking the compression seal and allowing atmosphere to leak into the vacuum jacket. Unfortunately, we didn't notice it at the time.

There was quite a bit of boiloff and billowing vapor from the vent line and the chamber on the inside cooled down to a pretty low level. When we stopped filling, the vacuum started coming down again because the fill lines started warming up and the ferrules expanded and started sealing again.

We filled it up to a level below the body so that it would cool down pretty slowly—and that was it. We left her that night about one o'clock with everything all buttoned up, and liquid nitrogen was outgassing quite a bit. The next morning we went around and the vacuum was way down—I'll take it back—it was still around 16 microns. That following night we went over and added one more dewar of liquid nitrogen and I took one slight turn on the Swage-Loc fitting—it was loose—so I took a turn on it. Immediately, the vacuum went right on down, so it was this fitting that was causing our leak and we went down to less than one micron.

All I can say about this test is that it is probably one of the most fabulous engineering feats I've ever pulled off. I—well, I shouldn't say I—Rick, Ed, and I—to have something like this second prototype work so extremely well under such adverse conditions with a minimal setup—sort of a back garage affair—to have something this vacuum-tight work in a liquid nitrogen environment with this large gasket, we really lucked out on this tank.

Our second design just proved itself tremendously. We've added a couple of dewars since then and if we look at the boiloff, it's maybe about 20 percent higher than we've calculated. We also feel we have a little higher vacuum than we had. We still have a slight leak of about two or three microns an hour. We can easily maintain a good vacuum with a vacuum pump. However, we think we may be able to track down the leaks if they are on the outside tank. In any event, this is where we sit now. We're starting to work on some new design concepts for our third and fourth capsules, and we need six more. Ed is building a building now to house Cryocare Corporation plus several other businesses. We'll have good facilities there. We're building up our machine shop. We now have a drill press, a small lathe, a band saw, and a heliarc welder, plus a regular welder. We're building our capabilities up to a level that will let us control our quality better. We're also looking at some freeze-drying equipment and small-project subcontract work.

So, that's what happened. It just happened. It was one engineering step after another. I would say there was quite an emotional response, as far as we're concerned, that we actually did freeze the first person. We wanted to keep it quiet because the young man requested this, but the news leaked out to Ev Cooper (Life Extension Society President) in Washington, D.C. He immediately called the United Press news service, and UP broadcasted over the wires. Then the *Arizona Republic* called Ed and he told them that we had frozen this woman and that she wasn't in the Phoenix area any more. He also told them that he didn't want them to print any more about it because of the family's wishes.

The *Arizona Republic* published a story stating that it had been done. We've been getting a number of contacts. We've maybe gotten a hundred letters from various people interested in cryogenic interment. Some are seriously interested. The problem is that our tank costs about thirty-eight hundred dollars. We have to charge this just to try to break even on some of our labor and development costs and get this organization on its feet so we can really start mass producing cryocapsules and get the cost down to a decent level.

The thing is that we initially never intended to go carry out a freezing ourselves. We figured someone else would do this. But it turned out we had to because there was no one else available to do the job. So we more or less fell into it and it worked out quite well. We've gone from equipment manufacturer to becoming the entire vertical structure, and we just don't know where it's going to carry us from here.

Right now we're designing a new capsule, a better capsule. We feel it will be better made with the object being a real long life and less work involved in manufacturing it and setting it up. If this thing catches on, fine, if it doesn't—well, we'll just have to see.

(Less than a year later, the first person ever frozen was removed from cryonic suspension and conventionally interred. Almost nothing else is known about her at the time of this writing.—Eds.) ∎

THE REALITIES OF PATIENT STORAGE

BY R. MICHAEL PERRY, PH.D.

Cryonics, 2nd Quarter, 1994

Cryonics, in addressing through technology the ages-old problem of death, acquires some problems all its own. Prominent among them is the fact that frozen patients must be stored for a very long time, safely, and as economically as possible. An early, simplistic proposal would have made the task relatively easy, namely, burial in permafrost.[1] Essentially, there would be no maintenance, and a "cryonics storage facility" would be mostly a record-keeping center! Unfortunately, however, reality didn't cooperate: the polar regions of the earth just aren't cold enough. A few are frozen in permafrost today anyway, and there has been talk of combining this technique with some form of chemical fixation to guarantee adequate preservation. However, until more is known and developed, storage in liquid nitrogen must remain the method of choice for long-term preservation. This sensible position has been the prevailing viewpoint in the cryonics movement since before the first person was frozen. Storage vessels and associated technology thus have been under consideration and in use for some three decades. On the other hand, cryonics is a very small movement and resources have been limited. It will not be a surprise, then, that the innovations contributed by cryonicists to low-temperature storage have not been the flashier sort. In fact, roughly the same basic vacuum-insulated container has been used all along. Still, developments have occurred that I think will be of interest. Along with these, I'd like to report on the related topic of patient transfers (from older to newer units).

First, a little prehistory. Much of it has to do with the liquefaction of gases, an obvious prerequisite to a cryonics operation. Most of the basic work was done in the nineteenth century. Air (about 80% nitrogen) was first liquefied in 1877 by Louis Cailletet. Nitrogen was first liquefied in 1885 by the Polish chemists Wroblewski and Olszewski. Around 1892 the British chemist and physicist Sir James Dewar created the first of the double-walled, evacuated flasks which bear his name, and which have proved so handy in containing cold materials. Commercial development of air liquefaction products (including nitrogen) is traced to a plant in Germany started in 1903 by C. Linde.[2,3,4]

1   Duhring, N. (E.Cooper). *Immortality: physically, scientifically, now.* Society for Venturism (1991 repr. 1962 ed., 20th. C. Books) 14.

2   "Liquefaction of gases," *Encyclopaedia Britannica* (1948) 14, 173.

3   "Liquid air," op. cit., 14, 190.

4   "Dewar, James," op. cit., 7, 295.

The exciting scientific quest that, one by one, reduced the "permanent gases" to unheard of liquids and solids, and the technical and commercial progress that, among other things, made cryonics possible, are stories well worth telling, but will have to wait for now. Instead we focus on matters of more direct concern to cryonics.

In one form or another, the dewar has been used to store cryonics patients since the first freezings in the '60s. Its use seems destined to continue, at least for several years and quite possibly much longer. Some highlights of this usage, and the philosophy behind it, can be briefly recounted.

A little more should be said about Sir James' famous container, since it is so basic to patient storage. The need for such a vessel will be clear enough if you ever find yourself handling liquid nitrogen. Put some of the clear, cold fluid in an ordinary cup and it will very quickly boil away—and may crack your cup in two! Use of a metal cup or bucket will eliminate the cracking, but the intense cold may cause leaks to develop around seams, and you will still have the rapid boiloff regardless. Clearly something more sophisticated is needed. The dewar or "thermos" is basically two airtight containers, an inner vessel with a closely-fitting outer shell that nowhere touches it—except at the neck or opening at the top, where the two containers are bonded together. The empty space between the containers is evacuated, which greatly reduces the heat flow from outside to inside (or vice versa, in the case, say, of a thermos bottle with hot coffee inside). By and large, the heat must flow up the wall of the outer container, over the neck, and down inside—a roundabout pathway that offers a great obstacle even if the two shells are made of highly-conductive material such as metal. Smaller dewars such as the lunchbox thermos are made of aluminized glass for ease of fabrication; for similar reasons, larger containers used for biologic samples or to store liquefied gases in bulk are generally of welded stainless steel, aluminum, or copper. (The evacuated space in these larger vessels also has layers of aluminized mylar or similar materials to further reduce heat flow.)

A short primer on human cryogenic storage by Ev Cooper[5] (May 1967) reads, in part:

"The most general principles of liquid nitrogen storage are quite simple. The job is merely to keep enough liquid nitrogen (-195°C) in sufficiently close proximity to the object to be stored. Any heat picked up by the liquid ... excites some of [its] molecules. If the excitement ... is sufficient they escape from the liquid taking heat with them. A person could remain frozen in a sufficiently large open bowl if enough liquid nitrogen was kept in supply. Liquid nitrogen is chosen as a refrigerant as it is the least expensive, safe manner of obtaining extreme low temperatures. ..."

The report goes on to discuss construction of vessels for practical storage:

"If we wish to improve the efficiency of our simple system of the object in a bowl

---

5   Cooper, E. *Freeze-Wait-Reanimate* (May 1967) 5.

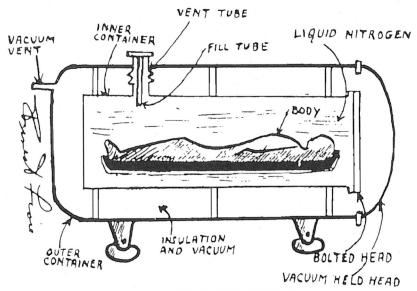

VENT TUBE

INNER CONTAINER

VACUUM VENT

FILL TUBE

LIQUID NITROGEN

BODY

INSULATION AND VACUUM

OUTER CONTAINER

BOLTED HEAD

VACUUM HELD HEAD

FREEZE-WAIT-REANIMATE 5-67:
Early horizontal cryonic storage container, sketched by Ernest Fiore.

of liquid nitrogen, we then insulate the walls of the bowl and bring them upward and over the object to be kept cold. But we always leave an opening for the evaporating liquid nitrogen so the heat can escape. One of the best ways of insulating the walls of our container is to arrange a vacuum within the walls. To increase the efficiency further, many layers of reflective foil between very thin layers of plastic or glass mat are placed within the vacuum to stop any radiant heat from getting in. ...”

At the time only one person had been frozen under controlled conditions. This was James Bedford, who entered cryonic suspension Jan. 12, 1967. There had also been a freezing the previous April. (The patient had previously spent weeks in a mortuary however, so the biological viability was very doubtful.) In both cases cylindrical, horizontal, metal capsules were used, manufactured by Cryo-Care Equipment Corporation in Phoenix, Arizona. In the second (Bedford) capsule the patient was welded inside the inner container, which further reduced nitrogen boiloff. In fact the capsule performed very well, only requiring a refill every 7 months. (It was actually filled at intervals of about three months.) The drawback was that the evacuated space was inadequately sealed so the vacuum had to be periodically “hardened” by pumping (a valve being provided for the purpose).[6] Horizontal capsules would continue in use for several years. Meanwhile, in 1969 a new, upright design was put in service for the suspension of Ann Deblasio by the Cryonics Society of New York. This proved

6   Perry, M. “For the record,” *Cryonics* 14 (7/8) 7 (1993).

Mike Perry, with Bedford's first capsule.

more practical than the earlier models, which in turn almost ceased to be used after 1981. (Unfortunately, most of the early suspensions had also terminated by then.) The lone exception was the Bedford capsule (a newer model, but still horizontal, manufactured in 1970 by Galiso of Fullerton, California). This durable vessel would remain in service for 21 years, a record.

By 1991, however, Bedford's old housing, now stored at Alcor's recent location in Riverside, was overdue for replacement. The cumbersome, sprawling, container occupied too much floor space. Worse, its vacuum had repeatedly softened over the years and had to be hardened again. This in turn was getting more difficult, apparently because of the buildup of oxidation products inside, which continually released small amounts of gas and prevented the desired hardening. (To eliminate this problem would have required heating, which was ruled out because the patient inside could not be easily removed and had to stay at liquid nitrogen temperature.) I remember a pump running *continuously* on this container for a year, sometime before the dewar was finally retired. This in turn was

Removing Dr. Bedford from his horizontal capsule

a dicey operation, carried out on May 25, 1991. Like Bedford's original capsule, this one was welded shut and had to be cut open—while it still had some liquid inside. On opening one end we found Dr. Bedford inside on a stretcher which, however, could not be removed so he had to be cut loose. He was lifted out—wrapped in a sleeping bag it turned out—and

The current state-of-the-art

quickly placed in a large, open foam box filled with liquid nitrogen. Sometime later we had an aluminum box or "pod" assembled, in this bath of cold liquid, around the good Doctor, now strapped inside, in an extra sleeping bag for good measure. (The pod was held together with rivets, which could be applied with a rivet gun at low temperature.) An overhead crane then quickly hoisted our patient up and then down into his new home, a nine-foot, upright, cylindrical "Bigfoot" dewar designed for four whole bodies.

Patient transfers, a little less laborious than this but still a workout (we could do about one per hour), were also needed to retire some of our older, upright containers. In a typical case we would lift the patient out of one container, in a sleeping bag tied to a stretcher, place them in the liquid nitrogen vat, cut them free of the stretcher, assemble a pod with them strapped in and seal it up, then hoist the pod up, and down again, into a waiting Bigfoot. (The Bigfoot would have to be rapidly positioned under the pendant patient by several strong backs, for the lowering operation. Typically a patient spent only about 90 seconds out of liquid during this operation, with the head in a "neurocan" full of liquid.)

I realize this history is a little haphazard; some of the more recent events I witnessed directly, while for the earlier ones I've relied on old newsletters and the like. In between I think there were long stretches when not much was happening, at least in the areas of patient storage. However there are some further items that deserve mention. Patients (whole-body that is) are generally now stored head-down, so their heads (the most important part, of course) will stay covered in liquid nitrogen in event of a long interruption in supply, as might happen in civil unrest or natural disasters. (In the early days they were stored upright.) Some years ago, in 1989, I visited the Cryonics Institute's facility in Oak Park, Michigan. They had an interesting alternative to the upright, steel capsules I'd seen at other facilities. Their containers were not of metal, but *epoxy*, reinforced with fiberglass. Not horizontal, *not vertical either,* but canted at about a 45-degree angle, supported in massive wooden frames. Patients (one or two to a cylindrical container, I believe) are sealed inside, much as with the old horizontal steel capsules, but with epoxy, which takes about 24 hours to harden. (They are of course maintained in liquid nitrogen during this time, which however does not touch the glued-on lid.) The vessels are insulated with a softer vacuum than your typical metal container and the evacuated space is filled with perlite. I understand CI now has larger, rectangular upright units of the same basic construction in use, that can store four or more patients each.

I also visited Trans Time's facility in Berkeley, California, around 1989. They had a rather varied assortment of upright, cylindrical metal containers, including one behemoth ("King Kong") able to hold ten whole bodies. I should mention, too, that not all containers are for whole bodies. The ones for neuros or heads only are, as expected, scaled down versions of their whole-body cousins (say about 4 feet in height). Neuros are easier to store and consequently, I think, not as much effort has gone into trying to find just the right container for them. I should mention, however, the concrete vaults encasing the neuro containers at Alcor, which have yet to be matched in whole body storage. Alcor's Bigfoots are actually for neuros too, being designed to hold several in a central well along with the whole bodies. (More ambitious plans call for dedicating an entire Bigfoot to neuros when the patient population is large enough.) Alcor's Bigfoot design, which is being "cloned" elsewhere, is arguably the most advanced to date for the purpose it serves. The dewar can be opened without cutting, through a large foam-lined lid on top. An attached fill line makes it convenient to replenish liquid nitrogen, without opening the container. Boiloff of the approximately 1,800-liter vessel is about 14 liters per day, or less than 1% (and this with the container nearly full, which increases the boiloff rate).

I understand CI's alternative technology also achieves a low boiloff rate, and has the advantage of being manufactured in-house, at a lower cost. (In the case of the Bigfoot, which requires a skilled, professional welding job, one manufacturer became squeamish about cryonics and another had to be found.) It is recognized, meanwhile, that the best storage technology available today is still not what one would like. A much larger unit or "cold room" would offer economies of scale and perhaps could help hold down cost if cryonics becomes widespread. This, however, is mostly in the dreaming stage still, and we must make do with a multiplicity of units designed for a few patients each. ■

SUSPENSION FAILURES:
LESSONS FROM THE EARLY YEARS

BY R. MICHAEL PERRY, PH.D.

Cryonics, February, 1992 and January/February, 2005. Last updated October, 2014

[Note: This article mainly concerns failures in early cryonics organizations that are unrelated to the Alcor Life Extension Foundation.]

In highlighting the history of any movement, one expects to find the good, the bad, and the outrageous: heroism, stupidity, perseverance, malfeasance, setbacks, suffering, and triumph. Cryonics is no exception, and if you are looking for a darker side you will not be disappointed. In fact a fair amount of early cryonics history is tragic, shocking, and gruesome. This is for the simple reason that patients can thaw out and have. It was not easy to get people frozen and keep them that way, particularly when cryonics organizations were first starting up and people didn't know just what they were getting into. A body that is not kept frozen is not a pleasant thing, even by non-cryonics standards, and the early failures were frequent.

Nevertheless these disasters need to be documented, if for no other reason than to make it less likely that such mistakes will happen again. The subject is complex and difficult to approach, and only a brief summary is possible. I will concentrate most on what happened—who was thawed, where, and when. Other issues such as who was at fault and by how much have their place but are not the main focus here. Another important issue is whether a suspension was viable in the sense of offering a realistic hope of eventual reanimation. Some of the early cases were done under adverse circumstances such as only after a long period of storage at above-freezing temperature. A suspension that was not viable from the start could not "fail" in the same sense as one that was, something which must temper our judgment on what happened. The issue of viability is another of those difficult matters that cannot be adequately addressed here, important though it is. (Critics of cryonics, of course, may doubt that any suspension even today could be "viable.") It should be kept in mind too that accurate information on suspension failures is often hard to come by. I have talked with most of the people who were involved and have studied records, but more research is needed. What follows is the best reconstruction I am able to make of basic events, and I believe the dates are accurate within a year or two at worst.

There were three public organizations in the early days (starting in the 1960s) that handled or sponsored freezings and patient storage. Cryo-Care Equipment Corporation in Phoenix, Arizona (not the same as a more recent California organization with similar name), was headed by Ed Hope and, unlike the others, built their own capsules, horizontal units on wheels for easy transport. Cryonics Society of New York (CSNY), New York City area, was headed by Curtis Henderson (and incidentally has the distinction of coining the term cryonics). Finally, there was Cryonics Society of California (CSC), Los Angeles area, a West-Coast imitator of CSNY that was headed by Robert Nelson, which actually did the first human freezing under cryonics-controlled (non-mortuary) conditions. Strictly speaking, CSNY and CSC, both non-profits, did not do freezings and patient storage directly, but handled these operations through sister for-profit organizations: Cryospan for CSNY and Cryonic Interment for CSC. (Late in CSC's life its cryonics services were handled through another company, General Fluidics.)

Cryo-Care did not use cryoprotectants or perfusion with their patients but only did straight freezes to liquid nitrogen temperature. These freezings were advertised as being for cosmetic purposes rather than eventual reanimation [1], though the cryonics issue did naturally arise. Their first case, in April 1966, was the first instance of a human being frozen with at least some thought of the cryonics premise of eventual reanimation, though conditions were adverse and prospects discouraging, as was admitted. The patient, a still-unidentified, middle-aged woman from the Los Angeles area, was placed in liquid nitrogen some two months after being embalmed and stored at slightly above-freezing temperature in a mortuary refrigerator [2]. Within a year she was thawed and buried by relatives [3]. But Cryo-Care would also store a person suspended elsewhere, as they did with James Bedford, who was frozen in January 1967 by Nelson's newly-formed organization and transferred by relatives. (Frozen quickly after death without embalming, with at least a crude attempt at cryoprotection by injections of perfusate and external heart massage, Bedford is often regarded as the first true cryonics case. Bedford also is still frozen today, unlike all the others frozen before 1974.)

Cryo-Care president Ed Hope was a wigmaker whose main interest in human freezing was financial. After some two years in the freezing business he saw it wasn't going to turn a profit and opted out, turning any remaining patients over to other organizations or to relatives. One individual who had been briefly stored by him was Eva Schulman who was autopsied prior to being frozen early in 1968, and whose son hauled her around in a truck for a time, on dry ice. (Dry ice—

Louis Nisco

solid carbon dioxide—is a far colder coolant than water ice but considerably warmer than liquid nitrogen which is commonly used for long-term storage of cryogenic specimens.) She was soon turned over to a mortuary by the son and buried. Another of his patients, Louis Nisco, was frozen in September 1967 after some damaging delay, and ended up at CSC because they offered the lowest storage rates. A third patient was Donald Kester, Sr., who committed suicide in July 1968. He was thawed and buried by his son a year or so later [4].

Robert Nelson meanwhile had frozen Bedford, who was promptly turned over to relatives, this being the reason he escaped eventual thawing (though relatives generally made poor prospects for long-term patient maintenance; Bedford's case was exceptional. His very devoted son stored him at a succession of locations over some two decades before transferring both his care and custody to Alcor [5], where he remains today.) Over the next year and a half Nelson froze three others: Marie Phelps-Sweet, Helen Kline, and Russ Stanley, who were kept in dry ice at a mortuary.

Marie Phelps-Sweet   *Helen Kline*   *Russ Stanley*

By March 1969 the mortician who assisted Nelson, Joseph Klockgether, was very uncomfortable having the three bodies in dry ice on his premises, and Nisco's capsule from Cryo-Care was on hand. So he and Nelson had the capsule cut open, removed Nisco and an interior support, then put Nisco and the other three back inside. I was told some were put in head first, some feet first, and "it was like putting together a Chinese puzzle." The placement took most of a night. The bodies were not deliberately thawed but must have suffered substantial warming, though according to Klockgether they were still frozen [6]. Then a welder resealed the capsule, which required a wait of several more hours, and it was refilled with liquid nitrogen. It remained at the mortuary another 14 months, tended by Klockgether, who refilled it periodically. This caused increasing problems, however, because of the liquid nitrogen delivery trucks which showed up frequently (a very unusual occurrence at a mortuary).

Nelson meanwhile purchased an underground vault at a cemetery in Chatsworth, a suburb on the northwest side of Los Angeles. The lid of the vault could be opened for placement of human cryogenic capsules; a smaller hatch allowed more limited access for periodic maintenance, including refilling with liquid nitrogen. Both the earlier-style, horizontal capsules and the later uprights could be accommodated. On May 15, 1970, the horizontal Nisco capsule with the four inside was lowered into the vault [7]. Nelson, in a court document, stated that despite the fact that funds to maintain the capsule were no longer being supplied by relatives, he maintained it "for an additional one-and-a-half years" [8]. It appears then that he quietly let the four bodies thaw, not later than around the end of 1971.

CSNY froze their first patient, Steven Mandell, in July 1968. His capsule, a horizontal, Cryo-Care unit like Nisco's, was eventually removed by his mother, who wanted to pay lower rates, and sent to Nelson. Their next, Andrew Mihok in November 1968, only remained frozen (at dry ice temperature) for two weeks before relatives refused

Stephen Mandell   *Andrew Mihok*   *Ann DeBlasio*

to pay and instead had him thawed [9, 10]. Their third freezing was of Ann DeBlasio in January 1969. Eventually (August 1971 [11]) she was removed from CSNY by her husband, Nicholas, and placed in an underground vault in New Jersey, which Nelson helped set up.

CSNY's fourth case, Paul Hurst (March 1969), would be terminated when his son who was funding it moved to Australia and no longer wanted to make payments. Before this another patient, Herman Greenberg (May 1970), would be stored in the same capsule.

Paul Hurst   *Herman Greenberg*   *Beverly Greenberg/ Gillian Cummings*

Greenberg's daughter Beverly, who used the stage name Gillian Cummings, was only in her teens when he suddenly died but fought vigorously to arrange his cryopreservation, which involved digging his newly-buried body out of the ground with the help of a backhoe. Beverly pursued a career in filmmaking as far as her meager finances allowed, while working at odd jobs and living frugally to make ends meet. Her free-lance lifestyle came to a tragic end in November 1973 when she died under mysterious circumstances at the CSNY facility, possibly a victim of hypothermia. She had been sleeping in her truck in the unheated building only a few feet from her father's capsule. At the time she had not made suspension arrangements, even though she was the vice president of CSNY and clearly wanted the procedure for herself. But none of her living relatives were interested in cryonics or making the payments; her father was reburied and she for her trouble was cremated [12].

CSNY's sixth case, Clara Dostal (December 1972), was maintained on dry ice for nearly two years. There were some overtures to Nelson during this time to arrange for permanent storage in liquid nitrogen; these came to naught. She remained in dry ice storage at CSNY's facility until November 1974, when her two children, by now unhappy with the cost and the emotional burden, had her buried [13].

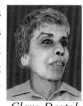

Clara Dostal

Meanwhile, in April 1974 CSNY did its last freezing, that of Michael Baburka, Sr., who was then stored privately by his son for several years before being thawed and, still in his capsule, buried [14].

CSNY stored their patients above ground and they were reasonably well-cared-for. Moreover, although relatives funded the suspensions, they were also required to furnish the storage capsules, and would receive these capsules back if funding terminated. CSNY did not take direct responsibility for thawing a patient, but physical custody would be transferred first, usually to a relative, a policy that protected against the sort of legal action that would later be brought against CSC.

Mildred Harris   *Genevieve de la Poterie*

Robert Nelson meanwhile had frozen two individuals, Mildred Harris (September 1970), and an 8-year-old girl, Genevieve de la Poterie (January 1972).

Both were kept on dry ice for awhile. When Steven Mandell arrived (see above), his capsule was opened and these two were placed inside along with the original patient. (Possibly the capsule arrived before the freezing of the little girl.) The capsule was then stored in the Chatsworth crypt with the now-abandoned Nisco capsule. As was generally true with these early capsules, this one had problems with the vacuum insulation; frequent pumping was needed to harden the vacuum and keep the boiloff of liquid nitrogen to a reasonable rate. Evidently the capsule was not checked nearly as often as it should have been. Sometime around mid-1974 it was found to have failed and been without liquid nitrogen for "a long interval" [15]. I would date the termination of its three suspensions from this time (or possibly earlier, if there were earlier failures of this sort), although the capsule was refilled and maintained, according to Nelson's testimony, for several more years [16].

In October 1974 Nelson froze a six-year-old boy (name withheld), who had died of leukemia. Nelson handled the maintenance at first, then turned the task over to the boy's father, who dealt directly with the liquid nitrogen supplier [17]. When the capsule was opened it was still functional and in good condition. The body overall was in a good state of preservation but showed cracking damage which has been reported as evidence it was thawed and refrozen; instead the cause was likely the rapid quenching with LN2 that occurred initially, at the time of suspension [18]. The body was placed in a casket and prepared for viewing by the family prior to burial [19].

In July 1976 Nelson froze a man, Pedro Ledesma, who had died the previous year and been kept by a relative in a mortuary refrigerator. Some ten months elapsed between death and freezing, so clearly the suspension was severely compromised from the start. Ledesma, however, was placed in the capsule in the crypt with the boy, and removed from suspension at the same time. (This capsule stood upright, with a removable lid; the two other, horizontal units were welded shut when in use.)

Nelson's freezing operations ended with the thawing of Ledesma and the boy in April 1979. The local press became interested, and, it was said, forced open the crypt and, though finding no bodies in the areas they were able to access, made much of the general ruin and offensive conditions. "The stench near the crypt is disarming," wrote one reporter, "strips away all defenses, spins the stomach into a thousand dizzying somersaults" [20]. Nelson defended his actions, however. "I haven't done anything criminal, anything wrong other than a lot of bad decisions. It didn't work. It failed. There was no money. Who can guarantee that you're going to be suspended for 10 or 15 years" [21].

A lawsuit, meanwhile, had been started by children of Mrs. Dostal. They had paid Nelson over $2,000 for what was to be the transfer of their mother to his facility. When this didn't occur they terminated the freezing and demanded reimbursement; Nelson's offer to pay back the greater part in small monthly installments was rejected [22]. At this point relatives of some of the patients that were stored in the crypt joined in the suit. In the five-week trial that followed, the court found against Nelson for fraud and against both Klockgether and Nelson for intentional infliction of emotional distress; a fine of nearly a million dollars was assessed [23]. Klockgether's insurance paid his share, amounting to $400,000. Nelson, who lacked insurance or substantial wealth, was able to negotiate the judgment based on procedural irregularities, and never paid anything [24] beyond attorney fees amounting to about $18,000. Some others, however, were peripherally involved and had nothing to do with the loss of the patients, yet also paid thousands of dollars in attorney fees.

In all there were nine frozen people stored—and thawed—at the Chatsworth site. Chatsworth became a byword for disaster in cryonics, and Nelson was excoriated as a liar, cheat, and even mass-murderer by some in cryonics, though others viewed him and his meagerly-funded operation more sympathetically. The kindly Klockgether, hurt by and rejecting the claim he had intentionally caused distress, was seen as mainly a victim of circumstance and did, in fact, provide valuable services in later cryonics cases not connected with Nelson.

Nicholas DeBlasio was living in the vicinity of New York City when his wife Ann died in January 1969. I understand his being a gun-toting policeman helped in prodding reluctant hospital officials to cooperate quickly in her freezing, which was carried out under sponsorship of CSNY. His wife was stored for a time on their New York premises, but Nelson convinced DeBlasio she could be maintained at a self-constructed facility more economically, and helped him set one up, a Chatsworth-style vault on a smaller scale, in a cemetery in Butler, New Jersey. The site, which became operational in August 1971, was tended by DeBlasio himself under an arrangement with CSC which allowed them to claim this East Coast location as an additional facility [25].

In November 1972 CSC froze a middle-aged California woman (name withheld) who was transferred to the New Jersey site. She and Mrs. DeBlasio were stored for several years in an upright capsule which was checked only at intervals of seven weeks, when the previously filled capsule would have been nearly empty and in need of a major fill. The capsule had a two-piece, removable lid or neck plug, but an arrangement of steel fill pipes allowed liquid nitrogen to be added without opening the capsule, to facilitate the large volume of high-pressure, bulk-delivered liquid nitrogen that was required to complete filling the unit in a reasonable time. The uninsulated fill pipes had a drawback, however, in that heat conduction from the outside to the interior was greatly increased. One consequence besides increasing the boiloff of liquid nitrogen was icing of the lid which made it difficult to open the capsule for periodic inspections of the interior. These in turn were needed since the capsule had no instrumentation to indicate liquid nitrogen levels or interior temperature. (DeBlasio also had a personal motive to look inside since the patients were stored upright so he was able to see his frozen wife in an approximately lifelike pose.) CSC meanwhile folded and DeBlasio continued alone.

For several years, it appears, things went well despite the potential for trouble. Then in August 1978 a problem developed. A hammer or other heavy object was used to break the ice so half of the lid could be removed, and the rough handling caused a leak in the vacuum jacket. DeBlasio's friend John Bull helped get it fixed. The patients inside were safely removed and stored on dry ice then returned to the repaired capsule and all was well. Unfortunately, there was more trouble of this sort and a partial meltdown and decomposition of the bodies occurred about May 1979. The decision was made to continue with the suspensions, but first the bodies had to be fully thawed out to remove them, which took about two days. This time Curtis Henderson assisted Bull and DeBlasio with the attempted salvage. The capsule again was repaired and the bodies again placed inside. But in July 1980, after another capsule failure with further decomposition, it was decided to terminate the suspensions and bury the patients. Mike Darwin, Joe Allen, and personnel from a nearby mortuary were called in to dispose of the bodies and also reclaim the still-valuable capsule. Again many hours were needed; Mike used a breathing apparatus when the capsule on its side had to be entered to remove the remains which had fallen to the bottom and frozen in place in a plug of body fluids. Mike commented: "The agonizing thing for me about this most recent loss is that it represents the first time to my knowledge that two people have thawed out and lost their chances not because of lack of money, but because of lack of sense." [26]

It is worth noting that in most of the above cases funding was limited and inadequate; usually relatives were expected to meet the continued expenses of maintenance but didn't. The relatives in turn were not signed up for the procedure themselves. The last suspension failure of this sort was of Samuel Berkowitz, who was frozen in July 1978 and stored at Trans Time's facility in northern California. I understand that, as the relatives who were funding the suspension (again lacking arrangements themselves) began to lose interest and/or wherewithal, an offer was made to continue the suspension as a neuro (head-only) free of charge, but it was turned down. Instead in October 1983 they had Berkowitz thawed, submerged in formaldehyde, and buried that way [27]. No attempt was made specifically to preserve the brain.

Capsule failure. Ann DeBlasio's dewar being hoisted out of the vault in Mt. Holiness Cemetery, Butler, New Jersey, July 1980. The two decomposed and refrozen bodies inside were thawed one last time then removed and buried and the capsule was cleaned out and sent to Trans Time. From left: John Bull, Nick DeBlasio, and the two cemetery workers who operated the backhoe. Photo by Mike Darwin.

One important lesson to be drawn from this tale of woe is that cryonic suspensions should only be maintained by those who have a strong personal interest in being cryopreserved themselves and have made arrangements. This includes the financial backers as well as those in charge of daily care. Those who are personally committed generally have superior judgment and realize the advisability of the neuro option (head-only preservation) in cases where funds are limited. Such people will fight hard to maintain even someone they hardly knew, who is not a relative, as happened at Alcor during the Dora Kent crisis for instance. They are not afraid to take measures others squeamishly shun, when a patient's survival is at stake. Neuroconversions carried out by such people have saved several patients whose funding ran out [28]. Not one of the many suspension failures was a neuro.

Of seventeen documented freezings through 1973, all but one ended in failure, while maybe five or six later cases, some of them privately maintained, were later terminated (or were continued under questionable circumstances, such as attempted permafrost interment). In most of these cases, finances were a factor. One notable exception involved a woman frozen in 1990 at Alcor (name withheld), whose will, it was later discovered, stated she did not want to be frozen. Her cryonicist husband fought the case through the (California) courts, arguing that the will, which survived only in photocopy, had been revoked, but the decision went against him, and her body was committed to burial under court order in 1994 [29].

If there is a silver lining in this, it is shown in overall trends. Suspension failures once were tragically much the rule but now are quite rare. A failure involving a patient stored at a public facility seems unlikely, except in cases where the patient's last wishes are disputed. (This is a good reason, of course, for those desiring cryopreservation for someone who may have little time left for making arrangements, to at least obtain that person's informed consent in a clear, documented form.) Cryonics cases in turn have dramatically increased, even though absolute numbers remain small (roughly a dozen cases per year). There are still lessons to be learned, possibly quite painful ones, but cryonics seems to have entered a new era of strength, stability, and continued growth. Let's hope this trend continues. ■

References

1. Chicago Daily News Jan. 29, 1968, 4, reprinted in *Freeze-Wait-Reanimate*, Feb. 1968, 3.

2. *Freeze-Wait-Reanimate*, May 1966, 1-2; Ted Kraver, "Notes on the First Human Freezing," *Cryonics* Mar. 1989, 11-21; Robert F. Nelson and Sandra Stanley, *We Froze the First Man*, New York: Dell, 1968, 14, 17-20.

3. *Freeze-Wait-Reanimate*, Feb. 1967, 4.

4. *Cryonics Reports* Sep. 1968, 166; *CFDA Newsbulletin* Nov.-Dec. 1969, 2.

5. Mike Darwin (Michael Federowicz), "Dear Dr. Bedford (and those who will care for you after I do)," *Cryonics* Jul. 1991, 15-22.

6. Joseph Klockgether, Interview (part 1), *Venturist Monthly* News, Feb. 1996, 6.

7. Los Angeles Superior Court case C-161229, records of Oakwood Memorial Park Cemetery, Chatsworth, Calif.

8. Los Angeles Superior Court case C-161229, 2nd civil no. 63721; Appellant Robert F. Nelson's settled statement ..., 10-12 (20 May 1982).

9. Mike Doll, "Vestal Man is 10th 'Frozen' by Cryonics," *The Sun-Bulletin*, Binghamton, N.Y. Thurs. Nov. 21, 1968.

10. "Family Bars Freezing for Heart Victim," *The Suffolk Sun*, Thurs. Dec. 5, 1968.

11. "New Storage Facilities," *The Outlook*, Sep. 1971, 1; "New East Coast Facility Opened," *Cryonics Review*, Sep. 1971, 1.

12. R. Michael Perry, "Remembering Beverly Greenberg," *The Venturist* 4 Qtr 1998, 3-6; earlier version R. Michael Perry, "For the Record," *Cryonics* 2 Qtr 1998, 41-44.

13. Los Angeles Superior Court case C-161229, Deposition of Claire Halpert esp. 58, 71-72 (Aug. 4, 1978); Deposition of Richard Dostal esp. 64 (Mar. 22, 1979).

14. *The Immortalist*, Nov. 1977, 2; *Cryonics*, Jun. 1981, 2; private sources.

15. Los Angeles Superior Court case C-161229; Supplemental answers to interrogatories ..., 14 (July 22, 1980).

16. Ibid.

17. Robert Nelson, interview, *Physical Immortality* 2 Qtr 2004, 18.

18. Robert Nelson, private communication Apr. 7, 2008; Joseph Klockgether, private communication Jun. 19, 2009.

19. Joseph Klockgether, Interview (part 3), *Venturist Monthly* News, Apr. 1996, 3.

20. David Walker, "Valley Cryonic Crypt Desecrated, Untended," *The Valley News* Sun. Jun. 10, 1979, Sec. 1, 11; quoted in Art Quaife, "Cryonic Interment Patients Abandoned," *The Cryonicist!* Oct. 1979, 2.

21. Quoted in David Walker, "Former Head of Cryonics Society Defends Actions," *The Valley News* Wed. Jun. 13, 1979, 1.

22. Los Angeles Superior Court case C-161229, promissory note of Robert Nelson and related material. David Walker, "Cryonic Sleep Remains Afloat in a Sea of Mystery," *The Valley News* Sun. Jun. 10, 1979, Sec. 1, 1, 10.

23. Los Angeles Superior Court case C-161229, Judgment on Verdict in Open Court (Long Form) D-14 (Jun. 5, 1981).

24. Robert Nelson, interview, *Physical Immortality* 2 Qtr 2004, 20. Nelson says he filed an appeal, then dropped it in return for an agreement that the case against him would not be pursued. In the introduction to the interview I reported Nelson "lost" his appeal, but court documents actually show that the appeal was "dismissed," apparently as part of a voluntary agreement.

25. "New East Coast Facility Opened," *Cryonics Review*, Sep. 1971, 1.; see also "New Storage Facilities," *The Outlook*, Sep. 1971, 1; "Genevieve de la Poterie Suspended in Los Angeles," *Cryonics Review*, Feb. 1972, 2; and *The Outlook* "directory" issues: Jan. 1973, 12; Jan. 1974, 11; Jan. 1975, 8.

26. Michael Darwin (Federowicz), "A Question of Time," *Cryonics* Mar. 1981, 4-6.

27. Michael Darwin (Federowicz) and Stephen Bridge, "Berkowitz Removed from Suspension: Lawsuit Settled," *Cryonics*, Dec. 1983, 1-2.

28. Michael Federowicz, Hugh Hixon, and Jerry Leaf, "Postmortem Examination of Three Cryonic Suspension Patients," *Cryonics*, Sep. 1984, 16-28.

29. Carlos Mondragón, "Paperwork Counts!," *Cryonics*, 3rd Qtr 1994, 13.

See also R. Michael Perry, "For the Record," *Cryonics*, 4th Qtr 1998, 35-39 (includes additional references).

I am also indebted to those who, in one way or another, contributed other verbal or unpublished written material used in this article, mainly: Fred and Linda Chamberlain, Mike Darwin, Paul Genteman, Claire Halpert (Claire Branand), Curtis Henderson, Saul Kent, Joseph Klockgether, Ted Kraver, and Robert Nelson.

Photo Credits

Capsule failure. "Thus Spake Curtis Henderson, Part 6," *Chronosphere* [accessed August 2014], photo by Mike Darwin.

de la Poterie, Genevieve: *The Outlook*, Feb. 1972, cover page; The Outlook, Aug. 1971, cover page.

DeBlasio, Ann: *Immortality*, Apr. 1970, 4.

Dostal, Clara: Author's rendering based on photographs from Mike Darwin, private communication, 23 Mar. 2011.

Greenberg, Beverly ("Gillian Cummings"): Cryo-Span Corp. brochure, about 1973, author's personal collection; *The Outlook,* Aug. 1973, cover page.

Greenberg, Herman: Author's rendering based photographs from Curtis Henderson, private communication 5 Oct. 2008; Mike Darwin, private communication 23 Mar. 2011; and images captured at showing of *The Icemen Cometh*, 10 Jan. 2010 at Suspended Animation, Inc., Deerfield Park, Fla.

Harris, Mildred: Robert Nelson, private communication, 25 Mar. 2007.

Hurst, Paul (Sr.): *Pandora* (Washington and Jefferson College, Washington, Penn. Yearbook) 1916, 57, listed as Paul Mitchell Hurst.

Kline, Helen: Photo from Robert Nelson, private communication 10 Oct. 2008.

Mandell, Stephen: *Cryonics Reports* (3) 9 (Sep. 1968) 162.

Mihok, Andrew: Binghamton, *New York Evening Press*, 21 Nov. 1968, 1-B.

Nisco, Louis: *The Detroit News Magazine*, 13 Jul. 1969, 33.

Phelps-Sweet, Marie (Mrs. Russ Le Croix Van Norden): *Freeze-Wait-Reanimate* (3) 38 (Sep. 1967) 1.

Stanley, C. Russell: Sargasso (Earlham College, Richmond, Ind. *Yearbook*), 1932, 59, listed as Stanley, R. Verified by Robert Nelson, private communication (email) 31 Dec. 2013.

DEAR DR. BEDFORD
(AND THOSE WHO WILL CARE FOR YOU AFTER I DO)

BY MICHAEL DARWIN
Cryonics, July, 1991

Twenty-four years ago a twelve-year-old boy with waxed-down hair and a clip-on tie stood in a long line of other youngsters at Butler University's Hinkle Fieldhouse in Indianapolis, Indiana. His father, dressed in a long, navy-blue overcoat, stood by his side. It was sometime in March or April and the first signs of Spring were in the air, although it was still a bit of a chilly day. Spring was welcome and full of promise. It had been a bitterly cold winter, and the memory of the boy's first Science Fair Presentation one frigid night late in February was vividly in his mind. There too his father had helped him, bringing his project into the basement auditorium of the school. The memory of that night came back him: of his father unloading the folding pegboard display, white clouds of breath billowing from man and boy. . . .

Despite the morning chill in the air, the day was bright and the old steel skeleton of the stadium was alive with a thousand voices full of hushed enthusiasm and fidgety anticipation. The boy was quiet, hardly exchanging a word with his father. He was lost in thought, full of excitement and nervous fear—and pride.

The boy had won first place at the cadet level in the local Science Fair and was now at the regional level competing against youngsters from all over the State of Indiana. He was very young compared to most of the other students who had progressed this far in the competition, and he was filled with a mixture of emotions: elation, pride and fear. His mouth was more than a little dry and his knees more than a little shaky as he began setting up his exhibit and rehearsing in his mind what he would say to the judges who would soon be making the rounds.

His project was entitled "Suspended Animation in Plants and Animals." The boy was an imaginative child with a rich (and some would say over-active) fantasy life. He had great hopes that he would win the competition and that this science fair was the beginning of a wonderful adventure for him. His teachers were very proud of him and offered much encouragement. Just as importantly they told him that he was special, different, and that his project was very original. Perhaps doors would open that would let him achieve what he most wanted and was very sure was his destiny: to become an astronaut and live and work in space. One thing he was secretly sure of: this science fair was going to change his life.

In having this vision of his future the boy was not alone. The American space program was running full-tilt towards the moon, and every popular science book, newspaper supplement, and NASA handout predicted with complete confidence that by the time the boy was a young man, space, the last frontier, would be wide open. The boy was very confident he would be raising his family on one of the first lunar colonies.

It was 1967. Lyndon Johnson was President. The Beatles were very much the rage. The Vietnam war was in full swing and the college campuses were beginning to become places of antiwar foment. Ronald Reagan had just taken office for his first term as Governor of California. The "hot" car was the Ford Mustang. The political and social focus of the country was on the "Great Society"—the notion that poverty and social ills could be overcome by government programs as successfully as the pull of gravity was being overcome by the government space program. The United States was at the cross-roads of a heady period of power and self-confidence and the beginning of another period, marked as much by uncertainty, pessimism, conflict, doubt, and shame as the previous period had been by optimism, vitality, enthusiasm and, can-do spirit.

"Made in Japan" was still largely a joke; an unknown company called Toyota had made a grossly unsuccessful attempt to introduce an automobile into the U.S. market. Another Japanese company named Sony introduced an amazingly small portable television with a six-inch screen and, of all things, a ten or fifteen pound rechargeable battery pack to run it with! The TV was a great success.

During the course of the Science Fair weekend, the boy explained the details of his project many times. He was excited by the many favorable comments he received and by the general hubbub and excitement around him. There were probably well over a thousand competitors on various levels; science, in 1967, was very "in."

Sometime during the course of that weekend a woman, perhaps one of the judges, made a remark to the boy that was both a question and a statement of fact: "Did you know they've frozen a man in California who died of cancer so that he can be revived when they find a cure?"

The boy hardly knew what to say. Was it true? It seemed so outrageous! How could they hope to do such a thing when he could not freeze a turtle to more than a few degrees below zero centigrade for more than half and hour without killing it? Had someone solved the suspended animation problem? Was the boy's project a waste of time and, much more important, was there now a way for astronauts to get to the stars?

The lady returned the next day with the newspaper article from the *Indianapolis Star*. The article chronicled how one James H. Bedford, a psychology professor from Glendale, California, had been frozen to await resurrection when medicine found a cure for cancer and, incidentally, for the freezing damage inflicted on him by unperfected preservation techniques.

The boy felt a rush of excitement—and a rush of contempt and skepticism. He was intrigued, but the whole thing seemed so fantastic. And the boy knew about freezing damage; he had seen enough of it in fifty cent, red-eared slider turtles, purchased at the dimestore, who were frozen too long to recover. . . .

That boy, needless to say, was me. That science fair did change my life, but not in the way I expected. My registration was somehow lost and as a consequence my project, while reviewed by all the judges, was never formally JUDGED. I did not win. But I did not know why until later, when several of the judges who were impressed with my project unraveled the whole mess and tried to set things right. I was given an honorable mention and an apology by the Regional Science Fair Committee. It was a bitter disappointment. I do not know if I would have won, and I will probably never know.

But there was a consolation prize: the newspaper clipping the woman had handed me. My life was about to change, and in a way I could hardly have been prepared, even in my wildest imaginings, to comprehend.

While I was preparing for my Science Fair project, busily freezing turtles, insects, and plants, and experimenting with trying to protect them from freezing injury with glycerol, you were busy dying. The passage of 24 years and my long involvement in both cryonics and medicine has given me a very good idea of what that must have been like for you. Your cancer was completely untreatable then (and is still largely so now) and while I have never seen your medical records, I have a pretty good idea of what your clinical course was like. The shortness of breath near the end as the cancer (metastatized from your kidney) consumed the air space in your lungs must have brought you to the edge of panic, and perhaps beyond.

I know very little about you personally. I know less about you than about most of the patients who entered cryonic suspension after you. I have met your son, Norman, on a number of occasions, but actually know his second wife Cecelia, whom you never met, much better than I know him. What I know of you as a man has been gleaned from bits and pieces of conversations and overheard remarks. All of it has been good. I know that you were a reflective man who pondered your purpose here in life and the meaning of death. I have been told that you were a gentle, quiet, decent, and responsible man. Your career and the recollections of several of your former students whom I have encountered testifies to the fact that you had a fine intellect and a genuine love of teaching.

Recently, I have learned a little bit more about you. I have been pleasantly surprised to discover that you authored at least six books on vocational training and career counseling. And that—despite your quiet demeanor—you had a real sense of adventure, setting for an African safari in 1958, a wilderness tour of the Amazon rain forests, and extensive travels in Greece, Turkey, Spain, England, Scotland, Germany, and Switzerland. You were also one of the first to drive the Alcan Highway to the

Canadian Northwest and Alaska. Perhaps that explains why you chose to take an even more fantastic and uncertain journey, the one upon which you are now embarked.

You, of course, do not know me at all. It is more than a little strange that two people who know almost nothing of each other, could find their lives so entwined and their prospects for survival so heavily dependent upon the actions of each other.

Your courage and your decision to undertake cryonic suspension, to be the FIRST "cryonaut," in the jargon of the times, had a profound effect on my life. Over the course of 1967 I gradually became more interested in cryonics, and sometime in 1968 I sent away to the Cryonics Society of New York for literature and later visited what was left of Ed Hope's Cryo-Care facility in Phoenix, where you briefly resided following your suspension on 12 January, 1967. Thereafter, I quickly became deeply involved in cryonics. But that is not the purpose of this letter. This is hardly the place for the complete narrative of my life story; besides, I doubt it would interest you very much.

I'm writing to tell you about how you were suspended and how you came into Alcor's care. My narrative will necessarily be brief and largely confined to issues and events which are not documented elsewhere. It is not my intention to repeat or summarize what has been covered in detail before or is part of the historical record (i.e., the media). Regrettably, my own struggle to survive leaves me neither the time nor the inclination to undertake such a daunting task. I could have accomplished this with dry technical prose: "The patient, a 73 year old caucasian male. . . ." And in fact, a technical account of your condition at this time is in your file. However, communicating the technical facts about what has happened would not tell the story I want to tell. Because, you see, it was not just the dry technical facts which caused events to unfold as they did, and in any event those could be just as easily gleaned from the pages of logbooks and your case notes. Rather, it is the human story I want to tell because that is the real story of how you came to be at Alcor and perhaps a big part of why you may have survived to read these words.

Since it is unclear how much of your short-term memory will survive cryonic suspension (it is no longer called cryogenic interment) I will begin this narrative at the beginning . . . .

At 1:15 P.M. on 12 January, 1967 you experienced cardiorespiratory arrest in a nursing home operated by a Seventh Day Adventist couple, Raymond and Mildred Vest. You had apparently known the Vests for over 16 years (they rented the property they operated their nursing home in from you and your wife). The immediate cause of your legal death was inadequate oxygenation due to your kidney cancer, which had metastasized to your lungs. Robert F. Nelson (a.k.a. Robert Buccelli), President of the Cryonics Society of California, was nowhere to be found. Mr. Vest and your physician, Dr. B. Renault Able, began CPR, packed you in ice on the hospital bed in which you had deanimated, and began a frantic search for Nelson. An hour or so later he was located.

The Cryonics Society of California "suspension team" was woefully unprepared. From testimony taken from Nelson and Robert Prehoda it appears that your "perfusion," so glowingly detailed to the news media, consisted of multiple injections with either pure DMSO or a DMSO-containing solution of a composition which was unknown to Nelson. (Prehoda recalls that pure DMSO from Matheson Scientific was employed[1]). Attempts were made to introduce the cryoprotectant into your carotid arteries bilaterally and to circulate it by performing manual chest compressions coupled with bag-valve respirator ventilations. According to Nelson, within approximately two hours of your deanimation you were transferred to a foam-insulated box, still wrapped in the bed sheet on which you deanimated (with some crushed water ice still on you) and covered over with one-inch-thick slabs of dry ice.

Over the next few days you were shuttled from place to place as a wild series of events began to unfold. Most of this story is chronicled (reportedly—and surprisingly—with some degree of accuracy) in Nelson's book about your suspension, *We Froze the First Man,* a copy of which accompanies this letter in your Alcor file.

It may shock you, but it is something of an understatement to describe Nelson as a pathological liar and an outright fraud.[2] It is a testimony to the good judgment and determination of your wife and son that you were removed from his clutches only six days after your suspension and shipped to Cryo-Care Equipment Corporation in Phoenix, Arizona. Had this not happened, you would certainly have perished at Chatsworth with the nine patients whom Nelson allowed to thaw out and decompose. Two days after your suspension, the following press release (written by Robert Ettinger and read by Nelson) was given to the media:

"The first reported freezing of a human at death, under controlled conditions, occurred Thursday, January 12, 1967, in Los Angeles. A patient was frozen immediately after his death from cancer in the hope of eventual revival and rejuvenation by future techniques. The next of kin concurred in the patient's wishes.

"Special freezing procedures were applied by Dr. B. Renault Able, a local physician, Dr. Dante Brunol, Scientific Advisor to the Cryonics Society of California, Robert Prehoda, author and scientist, and Robert Nelson, President of the Cryonics Society of California, 1019 Gayley Avenue, West Los Angeles. In consultation were Robert C.W. Ettinger, author of *The Prospect of Immortality*, the book which proposed the current L.T.A. (Low Temperature Anabiosis) program, Curtis Henderson, attorney and President of the Cryonics Society of New York, 306 Washington Avenue, Brooklyn,

---

[1] In his 1969 book, *Suspended Animation*, Prehoda says it was 15% DMSO in Ringer's solution, confirmed in other sources; see "Nelson and the Bedford Freezing: a Comment" by R. Michael Perry, included in this volume.

[2] A more positive assessment of Nelson is offered in Mike Perry's article on the Bedford Freezing.

and other members of the Cryonics Societies, coordinated by Mr. Nelson.

"When clinical death occurred, Dr. Able was present and at once began artificial respiration and external heart massage, to keep the brain alive while cooling the patient with ice. Heparin was injected to prevent coagulation of the blood.

"Later, the team of Dr. Brunol, Robert Prehoda and Robert Nelson, perfused the body with a protective solution of DMSO (Dimethylsulfoxide) using a Westinghouse Iron Heart sent by the Cryonics Society of Michigan.

"The patient is now frozen with dry ice, -79°C., and will soon be stored in liquid nitrogen, -196°C., when a cryocapsule is supplied by Cryo-Care Equipment Corporation of Phoenix, Arizona. He will be kept frozen indefinitely until such time as medical science may be able to cure cancer, any freezing damage that may have occurred, and perhaps old age as well.

"The patient's family has requested complete privacy; consequently no personal questions will be answered. All of those involved in the effort hope that this will lead to a massive biomedical effort on research into the prolongation of life."

A year later, Nelson, in conjunction with writer Sandra Stanley, published a book detailing your suspension and the events surrounding it (the aforementioned *We Froze The First Man*). This book, along with Ettinger's *The Prospect of Immortality,* had a very powerful effect on me. I became convinced not only that cryonics was a workable idea, but that it should be my life's work as well. Your suspension, as recounted in Nelson's and Stanley's book, was a mixture of revolutionary ideals and high drama, and I wanted to be a part of it.

By 1973 my perception had changed a great deal. I had discovered that the situation with cryonics was anything but how Nelson had depicted it. By this time I had heard rumors that your suspension was not the elaborate procedure employing blood washout and cryoprotective perfusion which Nelson described in his book and in subsequent media interviews. And by this time as well our paths had crossed for the first time.

While at Cryo-Care, the first "cryocapsule" you were in, a prototype unit with a bolt-on inner head, was performing badly (see your Alcor file for additional details on this unit). A decision was made to transfer you to a new unit, a Cryo-Care CC-101 with a welded inner head. This transfer was done sometime early in 1967.

Your stay at Cryo-Care was brief, and within approximately two years of your arrival there you were moved again, this time back to Southern California to the facilities of a small cryogenics and test equipment manufacturing and repair company by the name of Galiso, Inc. The Cryo-Care unit you were in was performing very badly. It had in fact developed a leak in the inner vessel and it was determined by all involved that it was time to transfer you to a newer, more reliable unit. The Cryo-Care unit was in such poor shape that the only way to tell if there was liquid nitrogen in it was to check the vent tube for frost (the thermocouples had all stopped working)! Galiso undertook to build such a unit, completing it late in March or early in April of 1970. During April of 1970 you were transferred from the Cryo-Care dewar to the Galiso unit.

During the interval in which you were cut-out of and removed from the Cryo-Care unit and welded into the new Galiso unit, you were not refrigerated by submersion in liquid nitrogen; you were wrapped in a Dacron polyester sleeping bag and sprayed with liquid nitrogen. A temperature probe placed on your chest during the transfer recorded the maximum temperature reached as 130°K (-143°C).

In the summer of 1973 I set out to California from Indianapolis by train (the Superchief) in the company of a young graduate student in cryobiology named Greg Fahy. A major purpose of that trip was to investigate Nelson and determine if he really was the fraud that I, and others in the cryonics community at that time, were rapidly becoming convinced he was. Another purpose of that trip was to verify that you were still safely in cryogenic storage at Galiso.

Greg Fahy, my guide in this, could not have been better chosen, since it was he who located you at Galiso after your "disappearance" from Cryo-Care circa 1969 and put to rest the rumors circulating that you had been quietly thawed and buried. Greg was president of the Cryonics Youth Association (CYA) and had stumbled across your location quite by accident sometime in 1971. This happened when he took the CYA newsletter, *Cryonics Vistas,* in for printing and one of the counter girls at the shop on Jamboree Boulevard in Irvine remarked that she knew about a frozen body being kept at a company called Galiso. Apparently a friend of hers who worked there had told her about your presence there. A call to Directory Assistance resulted in Greg locating Galiso and ultimately going out to visit you. The story of your continued care appeared initially in *Cryonics Vistas* and then in the newsletter of the Cryonics Society of New York, *Immortality*. I can well remember reading those articles and feeling very reassured that "the first man was still frozen!"

Sometime in June of 1973 I walked into the cavernous industrial bay of Galiso, Inc., in Anaheim, California. The unit containing you sat out on the shop floor amid the clutter of uncompleted dewars and test equipment in various stages of manufacture, covered with a heavy layer of ubiquitous Southern California dust. This was our first "meeting." It made a great impression on me. Above all, I was impressed that you were still apparently frozen after all this time and despite the vigorous legal challenges from your relatives. The archives of the Los Angeles County Courthouse contain the complete (and sordid) story of the greed that was unleashed by your suspension and your $100,000 bequest for cryobiological research; a bequest which was used up nearly two and half times over just to defend and maintain your suspension up to that time!

Whatever else may be said of your son Norman and your wife, one thing that is clear and incontestable is their fierce loyalty to you and your wish at a second chance at life. I never met your wife, but I have been told via Norman that while neither she nor he really "believed" in the workability of cryonics (Norman had apparently held a more optimistic position early on) they were totally committed to carrying out your wishes "come hell or high water." This they did, and they did so in the face of vituperative and hateful opposition from almost all around them. And they did it even without the support or encouragement of cryonicists.

Sometime early in 1976, Galiso notified Norman and your wife Ruby that they could no longer continue caring for you. Their liability insurer had gotten wind of your presence in the facility and was threatening to withdraw coverage if you were not moved. On 31 July, 1976 you were transferred to the facilities of Trans Time, Inc., a commercial cryonics service provider in Emeryville, California (Emeryville is a suburb of Berkeley). Norman drove you up himself on a rented U-Haul trailer. You remained at Trans Time until 1 June, 1977 and were then picked up by Norman and again transported by U-Haul trailer to Southern California. The reason for this transfer was reportedly unhappiness at the "escalating billing and high cost of storage with Trans Time." I don't know where you were cared for after 1 June of 1977; my questions about this to Norman and Cecelia were politely but firmly deflected.

Late in 1981 or early in 1982 my curiosity and my worry about what had happened to you began to get the better of me. By that time it had become clear that no one placed into cryonic suspension before 1973 had survived. Every patient had either been lost at Chatsworth or been conventionally disposed of by the relatives who placed them into suspension. With one possible exception.

With greater ease than I anticipated, I located your son and daughter-in-law. I inquired about your status and explained that we might be able to help them pursue continued care for you in a more secure environment, and perhaps even at lower cost, since we were getting some economies of scale in storing several patients.

It was also my bet that if they were caring for you themselves they were faced with major logistic problems which they must be very weary of. I was correct in this surmise. Cryogenic liquid suppliers don't "set appointments" to deliver liquid. The best they can usually do is tell you if they will be coming by in the morning or in the afternoon. They will virtually never deliver to a residence since the LS-160 liquid containers are heavy and must be carted or rolled; liability is another major concern. I realized that your family must be doing what we had to do, namely spend two or possibly three days a month waiting all day long for a delivery, and occasionally sitting all of the next day as well if you ended up at the end of the driver's day and he had one too many deliveries to make. . . .

As it turned out, the situation was worse than I imagined. Not only was your family having the problems I imagined, they were being gouged by the cryogenics company as well. The company had figured out what was in the tank they were pulling up to service twice a month, and they tacked on a $60.00 delivery charge for every fill—in addition to the fifty cents or so a liter they were charging for the liquid nitrogen. While it is true that a 1967 dollar went a lot further than a 1982 dollar (a 1967 dollar was worth 2.5 times what a 1982 dollar was worth) those amounts of money were non-trivial. In short they were starting to feel real economic as well as personal pressure.

However, they were very wary of us. Their past experiences with everyone from family members to cryonics organizations had apparently been uniformly bad where your suspension was concerned. Nevertheless, they decided to take the chance and pursue storage with us. An agreement was worked out, and at 1:30 P.M. on 14 February you and the Galiso dewar were loaded onto the Cryovita van from a "self storage miniwarehouse" in Burbank. What's a miniwarehouse, you may be wondering? I won't attempt to try to explain the cultural and economic changes which created such a thing; there should be other sources of information available to you there. Suffice it to say that by the 1980's large complexes of rental storage space in garage-sized slots were widely available and widely used by average people who had too much chattel to store in their own garages or apartments. It was in one such 10' by 10' or so slot that you were being kept when we picked you up. It is my impression that you had been cared for at that location for some time.

So, on a sunny, smoggy day in 1982, our paths crossed for a second time. Our care for you was provided through Cryovita Laboratories, a "for-profit" cryonics service provider similar to Trans Time. The difference was that Jerry Leaf, who headed Cryovita, was deeply concerned that your suspension continue and he, like me, just wanted to see the liquid nitrogen bills paid and you remain in storage.

In 1982 Alcor was very small, with almost no assets and only four patients in suspension. We were operating out of the rented facilities housing Cryovita. Our whole operation was crammed, and I do mean crammed, into a 1,600-square-foot industrial bay located at 4030 North Palm, Unit #304, in Fullerton, California. There you remained in the back of the building, just inside the roll-up, steel curtain door. Your dewar was serviced by myself and Hugh Hixon.

Cryonics began to grow again, after a long hiatus resulting in no small part from the actions of Nelson at Chatsworth. More importantly, we began to lay down what we hoped was a more solid base than had ever been present before.

So much happened between 1982 and now. The first years you were at Cryovita were very calm. I look back on that time as a quiet, yet highly productive period. Alcor and Cryovita were definitely out of the limelight, and the few of us then working on cryonics were able to focus our energy and attention on laying down basic policies and procedures that would serve us well in the coming years. It was also a time when we were doing research. On the other side of the flimsy "wood" panelled wall (there were open studs on the side where you rested) from where your dewar sat, we were washing out the blood of dogs and cooling them down to a few degrees above freezing using a completely "defined," artificial perfusate. This was path-breaking research, being done on a shoestring; the very kind of work you and Norman envisioned the Bedford Foundation undertaking.

During this period we also did a suspension, although certainly not the way you would have envisioned. A new method of cryonic suspension, neurosuspension (brain or head only) had been introduced in 1976. Alcor also completed a series of demanding studies on the effects of then-in-use cryonic suspension procedures. It was a happy, productive period in my life.

By 1986 we had grown to the point that we were able to afford our own facility. Indeed, we had little choice. Cryovita and Alcor soon lost liability insurance as a result of being a cryonics business, and we were told by our landlord that we would be evicted unless we moved out immediately. We raised almost all of the money needed to buy a facility in cash and moved. On 17 February, 1987 you were moved to our brand new facility at Riverside, California. The events which have occurred in the years intervening between 1987 and the time this letter is being written would take hundreds of pages to document. We will soon have back issues of *Cryonics* magazine on microfilm, and we will add a copy of those issues to the patient record files. Hopefully you'll be able to read that history for yourself.

Your wife Ruby died in 1987, and in September Norman, acting on instructions from Ruby, transferred your care directly and irrevocably to Alcor. It was Ruby's wish that your care be taken over by an organization that had a real chance of seeing you through the distance. The five years of care that we provided, and provided both lovingly and fairly, was the evidence that she needed. Ruby was cremated a few days after her death. As of now, it appears that where immediate family is concerned, you will be making the journey into tomorrow alone.

In a little over six months you will have been in uninterrupted cryonic suspension for 25 years. You were the first man ever frozen and you are still frozen. That is an incredible accomplishment, and one in which we (Alcor and Cryovita) take no small measure of pride in having contributed to. The two-decade-long legal battle over your suspension long ago exhausted the money you had set aside for your care. You are now Alcor's responsibility financially as well as morally. Alcor Director Jerry Leaf has personally absorbed most of the cost of providing your care and has provided additional insurance on his own life to cover your continued suspension. This is an incredibly generous act on his part.

On Saturday, 25 May 1991, we removed you from the Galiso unit which, like all "sealed-in-the-field" units, was failing. We wrapped you in an additional sleeping bag, secured you in an aluminum "pod" and transferred you to one of our new, state-of-the-art dewars, which boils off about what the Galiso unit did, but holds four patients, including yourself. Other advantages are no more careening around the freeway every year or so to Galiso or elsewhere for a re-vac, and we now have two vertical units, each capable of storing four patients, sitting where your single patient, horizontal unit once rested.

I was very anxious about what we would find when we opened the Galiso unit. You had been enclosed and shielded from view in that dewar for just over 21 years; indeed you were welded into it. What were the odds that you had never been allowed to warm up during the years of storage in the badly malfunctioning Cryo-Care unit? What were the odds that your dewar had been faithfully serviced during the years you were at Galiso and subsequently when you were being cared for by your son and daughter-in-law? Never letting a dewar run dry is not an easy thing to accomplish. Deliveries must be carefully scheduled around holidays and so on. . . . I must confess, pessimist that I am, I felt the odds that your condition was "good" were pretty slim (if good is ever an adjective to use to describe a straight-frozen patient!).

I cannot describe the feeling of elation I had when I peeled back the sleeping bag that enclosed you and saw that you appeared intact and well cared for. What's more, that the water ice that Nelson had said was left on you when you were transferred to dry ice was still there and unmelted. Whatever else has happened, you have remained frozen all these years. Few things in my life have satisfied and elated me more completely than has that knowledge.

I would like to think that my actions have been important in getting you to the tomorrow that you (and we) so hope for. History will be the judge of that.

Above all, I want to thank you for starting me on an incredible adventure. You really did change my life, and both directly and indirectly your actions may have vastly lengthened my life as well! I hope I have returned the favor with the actions I have taken.

I am well aware as I write this that the struggle is far from over. Now our opponents are the State of California, which seems bent on ending your suspension—as well as that of the other cryonics patients in this State. The battle is far from over and far from won.

Dr. Bedford, I hope we really meet someday. I am not sure we will have much in common, save perhaps for the heritage of the culture and era which we both shared. We will both have lost friends and family who chose not to accompany us; that sadness we will also have in common. But far more importantly, we will have the joy, the sheer, unbounded joy of being alive in a universe where we can move freely, unchained from the bonds of gravity, earth, and time. And your dream, the dream of reaching a tomorrow where you can resume living, will have been realized.

So too, the passionate dream of that 12 year-old boy from Indianapolis, Indiana, will also have come true. At long last, via a path at least as strange and convoluted as the one you have followed, he will be able to live and work in space, and walk on other worlds.

Until then, au revoir. ■

Robert Nelson and the Bedford Freezing: A Comment

By R. Michael Perry

2015

Robert Nelson was a controversial figure and opinions about him have varied widely. Mike Darwin denounces him as "a pathological liar and an outright fraud," [1] while Robert Ettinger is considerably more sympathetic: "I am convinced, based on information both public and private, that the worst he was guilty of was poor judgment. Certainly he reaped no personal profit from any of his activities, and suffered much personal harm."[2] My own opinions on Nelson have also varied over the years. I am sure that in certain ways he deeply hurt and angered a number of people and was seen by them as malfeasant, particularly as a consequence of the terrible events in which cryonics patients were lost at Chatsworth. After as careful a study as possible and feedback from various sources, however, I am in basic agreement with Ettinger and convinced Nelson was not malfeasant in any substantial, willful sense, though he did, of course, make serious mistakes with bad consequences which he did not wish to happen.

In any case, regarding the Bedford freezing, there is some uncertainty about the details and the available sources must be used with care. Inaccuracies are commonplace and judgment must be exercised. What follows is my current best estimate as to what likely happened. I will say too that I think Mike Darwin's reporting is for the most part accurate, even though I have disagreement with some of the details, in various of his articles which are reprinted in this book, plus a little to add.

A number of people were involved in the freezing, but the only ones who were present throughout were Raymond and Mildred Vest, who were personal friends of Dr. Bedford and were caring for him at their nursing home along with another terminally ill patient. Sensing on the morning of Jan. 12, 1967 that Bedford was very weak and the end was near, they called his physician, Dr. B. Renault Able, who arrived just minutes before Bedford's arrest at 1:15 p.m. After pronouncing the patient, Able injected heparin to inhibit clotting for the later, intended perfusion of cryoprotectant, and started packing the body in ice. He and Mr. Vest also began giving artificial respiration and chest compressions for metabolic support while the patient cooled. For nearly two hours they kept this up, then Dr. Able left, satisfied that the patient was reasonably stabilized for what would follow. Soon Robert Nelson and Dante Brunol arrived and

From left: Dante Brunol and Robert Nelson at the Bedford freezing, showing Bedford packed in ice with the Iron Heart piston poised over his chest, oxygen cylinder right. Photo credit: Robert Nelson, private communication (email), 2 Oct. 2014; reprinted (cropped slightly) in The Immortalist, Nov.-Dec. 2005, 14. A cropping showing Brunol but omitting most other details including the oxygen cylinder was used in Mike Darwin's article, "History of DMSO and Glycerol in Cryonics," Cryonics 3rd Quarter, 2007, 9, reprinted in this volume.

hooked up a Westinghouse Iron Heart—an automatic chest compressor and lung oxygenator—to continue the metabolic support while Brunol readied his perfusion apparatus. The Iron Heart had been sent by Robert Ettinger a few days before, along with a (full) compressed oxygen cylinder to power the apparatus and also provide oxygen to the patient through a face mask for metabolic support. Ettinger was in contact by telephone with Nelson and Brunol as they now put the equipment to use.[3]

The perfusion protocol called for replacement of the patient's blood with a cryoprotective agent, much as in a modern cryopreservation. In this case the agent or perfusate consisted of 15% DMSO in Ringer's solution, as confirmed from various sources, including Robert Prehoda's recounting of the incident in his 1969 book, *Suspended Animation*. [4] Thus it was not the more toxic pure DMSO, despite impressions that appear to have been created by later retellings. Brunol, however, was unable to get his perfusion apparatus working (he said he had been called on too short notice, only a few days before) and was thinking of giving up when Robert Prehoda arrived for what he thought would be just observation of the procedure as requested by the Bedford family. To resolve the impasse and get some cryoprotectant into the patient Prehoda suggested just injecting the perfusate with a syringe, and this is the choice that was made.[5]

Thus the blood was not removed as the perfusion apparatus would have done, so cryoprotection would have to depend on the limited effect of dilution of the blood by the cryoprotectant. Additionally, though, there must have been some actual removal and replacement of the blood in view of the extensive bleeding which occurred during the procedure (verified by Mike Darwin when Bedford's frozen body was examined 24 years later). Bedford had died of liver cancer which had metastasized to the lungs, leaving the lungs especially vulnerable. The constant pounding of the Iron Heart's piston on the chest (sternum), alternately compressing and relaxing the heart to induce blood circulation, also considerably stressed the surrounding tissues and, it appears, produced extensive internal and also external bleeding (from the mouth in particular). The heparinization of the blood to inhibit clotting would also have promoted bleeding.[6]

The perfusate was repeatedly injected into the body, maybe fifty to a hundred or so infusions of a few tens of cc's each, while the blood was circulated after a fashion and also leaked out as noted. The internal carotid arteries in the neck which supply the brain (or one of them) were special targets of injection. Just how much perfusate got in and how much reached the brain and where it reached in the brain and elsewhere are unknown. Each injection left a puncture track through which the heparinized blood mixed with perfusate could leak. Many such leakages may have accounted for the large "bruised" area noted on the upper torso and throat, during Darwin's examination, without assuming any special lysing effect or destructive activity on the part of the cryoprotectant.[7] The body did not swell up appreciably, so arguably the amount of induced perfusate was minimal in any case and Bedford's treatment would not have been very different from a straight freeze, despite all the pains that were taken. (DMSO-based perfusate was in fact found consistently to cause edema in other early cases in which it was used, where blood was also removed in a more usual way and a substantial amount of perfusate was pumped in.[8]) According to Nelson, the metabolic support of the Iron Heart continued, following instructions of Ettinger, until the cryoprotection was deemed adequate[9] and Bedford was then further cooled with dry ice.

Bedford is still with us, and more should be learned about his freezing in the attempt to restore him to healthy consciousness. ∎

Sources:

AD. Aaron Drake, NREMT-P, CCT, Alcor Medical Response Director, private communication, 8 Jan. 2014.

AW. Aschwin de Wolf, private communication (email) 8 Feb. 2009.

DB1. Dante Brunol, "What to Do If You Want to Be Frozen," *Freeze-Wait-Reanimate* **3**(40) 2 (Nov. 1967), http://www.foreverforall.org/, accessed 2 Aug. 2013. .

DB2. Dante Brunol, letter to Saul Kent, 19 Oct. 1967, Alcor archives.

GA. Gladys Piatt Ansley, "Drama of the 'Frozen Professor'," *The Youth's Instructor*, 20 Jun., 1967, 9-11. http://docs.adventistarchives.org/docs/YI/YI19670620-V115-25__C.pdf, accessed 11 Jan. 2014.

MD1. Mike Darwin, "Dear Dr. Bedford (and Those Who Will Care for You after I do)," *Cryonics*, Jul. 1991, 15-22, http://www.alcor.org/cryonics/cryonics9107.txt, accessed 13 Nov. 2014 and reprinted in this book.

MD2. Mike Darwin, "Evaluation of the Condition of Dr. James H. Bedford after 24 Years of Cryonic Suspension," *Cryonics*, Aug. 1991, http://www.alcor.org/Library/html/BedfordCondition.html, accessed 11 Jan. 2014 and reprinted in this book.

MP. Mike Perry, "For the Record," *Cryonics* **34**(9) (Sep. 2013) 33-37.

RA. B. Renault Able, M.D., *Give Us Tomorrow*, New York, Vantage Press, 1969, 43. (Novella with background relating to the Bedford case and Dr. Able's involvement.)

RE1. Robert Ettinger, "How the Nonfuneral Was Arranged," *Life* **62**(5) 21 (3 Feb. 1967, first version).

RE2. Robert Ettinger, quotation from "CIYG Digest," *Long Life*, Mar.-Apr. 2008, 24; originally appeared at https://groups.yahoo.com/neo/groups/Cryonics_Institute/conversations/messages/2884 , accessed 12 Nov. 2014.

RE3. Robert Ettinger, private communication (email), 5 Oct. 2008.

RN1. Robert Nelson with Sandra Stanley, *We Froze the First Man*, New York: Dell, 1968, 57-59. Note: pseudonyms used in this volume include Harold Greene (James Bedford), Junior Greene (Norman Bedford, son of James Bedford), Don Bickerson (Robert Prehoda), Alden Fox (B. Renault Able), Mario Satini (Dante Brunol), and the Baldwins (Vests).

RN2. "Robert Nelson Speaks: An Interview with David Pizer and Mike Perry," *Physical Immortality* 4(2) (2Q 2004) 8-22, esp. 15.

RN3. Robert Nelson, private communication (email) 10 Sep. 2008.

RN4. Robert Nelson, private communication (email) 8 Jan. 2014.

RN5. Robert Nelson, private communication (email) 12 Nov. 2014.

RP1. Robert Prehoda, *Suspended Animation: The Research Possibility That May Allow Man to Conquer the Limiting Chains of Time*, Philadelphia: Chilton, 1969, 115-16.

RP2. Robert Prehoda, interview with Mike Perry, 24 Oct. 1991 (audiotape), unpublished, available from the author.

WI. J. F. Wilkinson, "The Deep Freeze Scheme for Immortality," *True Man's Magazine*, Oct. 1967, 54-55; 79-81.

References:

1. MD1.

2. RE2.

3. GA; RN1; WI.

4. RP1; RP2; RA; RN3; RE3.

5. AW; DB1; DB2; RN1; RN2; RN4.

6. MD2; RE1; AD.

7. RN2; AD.

8. MP.

9. RN5.

For an earlier version of this report with some additional details, see R. Michael Perry, "For the Record," *Cryonics*, Feb. 2014, 10-14.

COLD WAR: THE CONFLICT BETWEEN CRYONICISTS AND CRYOBIOLOGISTS

BY MICHAEL DARWIN

Cryonics, June-August, 1991

Upon a two-thirds vote of the Governors in office, the Board of Governors may refuse membership to applicants, or suspend or expel members (including both individual and institutional members), whose conduct is deemed detrimental to the Society, including applicants or members engaged in or who promote any practice or application which the Board of Governors deems incompatible with the ethical and scientific standards of the Society or as misrepresenting the science of cryobiology, including any practice or application of freezing deceased persons in anticipation of the reanimation..."

Introduction

For 25 years cryonicists and cryobiologists have been doing battle in the public eye. Some might scoff and call it hyperbole to dignify the verbal exchanges and skirmishes between cryonicists and cryobiologists as "war." But war it is; for as in any war the cost has been the loss of lives, reputations, and fortunes. And as in war, the driving forces are envy, hatred, and a deeply-held belief that each side threatens the others' survival.

Twenty-five years is a long time for a war to continue. An entire generation has been born, and an older one died, since it began. Many of the early combatants are nearing the end of their lives. . . and still the battle goes on.

It is the purpose of this article to examine in detail the causes of the war, its history to date, and the likely outcome. The reader should be warned that this is a history written with a special set of prejudices: it is being written by one of the "generals" many years before the last shot is to be fired. As such, it must be scrutinized carefully and perhaps ultimately be set aside to await the passage of time and the objectivity and clarification that passing into history brings with it.

The Beginning

Cryobiologists and cryonicists were not always at war with each other. Indeed, many might question why there is a war at all between two groups of people with similar objectives and a common purpose: the development of mammalian suspended animation, or at least suspended animation for mammalian organs via cryopreservation.

The desire of cryonicists is to have available a technology which will allow them access to medical time travel (albeit one-way time travel) and cryobiologists are the most logical group of scientists capable of delivering that technology. At first glance these two groups should be natural allies, not enemies.

Logically, cryobiologists should have looked to cryonicists as a possible strong and unwavering source of support in achieving their research objectives, just as they have looked to the organ transplant community for such support. Certainly there are many examples in other areas of society and science where special interest groups have worked with researchers to develop technologies for which they have a deep need—even technologies which have theoretical problems standing in the way of their development.

Several examples of this kind of symbiosis between special interest groups and researchers come to mind. Consider the case of people who have suffered spinal cord injuries. Medical dogma was (and in some quarters still is) that spinal cords do not regenerate, cannot regenerate, and will NEVER be induced to regenerate. Many individuals who were paralyzed as a result of cord injuries (wisely) refused to accept this and began to watch the medical literature closely for any work that might offer some hope. Naturally, there was some research which indicated that the situation was not as cut-and-dried as the establishment projected. By the early 1970s a number of research support groups founded by cord-injured patients came into being with one overriding objective: find a cure for spinal cord injuries.

These groups had names like the American Paralysis Cure Foundation and the Spinal Cord Society. They set about raising money to support research into methods for achieving regeneration and repair of the spinal cord that would lead to a cure. Overall, they found the relative handful of researchers working in this area very receptive to their concerns and more than willing to take their money. What they did NOT find was a group of researchers who were hostile, jeering, polarized, and ridiculing of their desire to walk again or of their belief in the potential of scientific research to unearth mechanisms of repair for central nervous system injury. And this despite the fact that decades of medical dogma asserted a contrary opinion.

Similarly, a variety of governments (both totalitarian and democratic) have shown a willingness to underwrite extremely costly research into areas which can even at best be described as "speculative" and fraught with theoretical as well as technical problems. Perhaps the best example of this is the four-decade-long commitment of both the United States and the Soviet Union to the development of thermonuclear or so-called "fusion" power. This undertaking, which is by no means merely an exercise in solving technical problems (there are many thorny theoretical problems here as well) has cost 20 billion dollars (worldwide expenditures) over a time course of 40 years and still has not yielded any clear answers as to whether it will ever be practical to generate even one watt of controlled power using this approach. Indeed, earlier this year, the American fusion community requested 700 million dollars per year (to continue more or less indefinitely) for more work on this problem (Business Week Oct. 15, 1990, pg. 62).

Perhaps an even more stunning example of governments' willingness to work on projects which present substantial theoretical and technical obstacles and face strong opposition on theoretical grounds from a large body of establishment scientists is the Strategic Defense Initiative or "Star Wars" program. Six billion dollars per year has been spent on this project for over five years, despite the vigorous objections of a plurality of well-informed and well-credentialed scientists in a variety of relevant disciplines—not to mention a vocal and well organized segment of the American public.

What happened between the cryobiologists and the cryonicists to cause such unreasoning enmity and a state of virtual war? What is different about the relationship of the cord-injured patient and researchers working on understanding central nervous system repair and cryobiologists and cryonicists? Why, if entities as conservative as governments are willing to underwrite multi-billion dollar projects in speculative science (and establishment physicists are willing to take such money), do cryobiologists run screaming from cryonicists? In short, what went wrong?

Enmeshed as I am in the heat of the battle on the opposing side, and given my life-long history of involvement as a cryonicist, I am distanced somewhat from the minds of the cryobiologists. Also, the critical first few years of the encounter between cryonicists and cryobiologists occurred before I entered the fray, indeed occurred from 1963 to 1967 when I was between 8 and 12 years old and hardly in a position to evaluate it. Nevertheless, that period of time is not without its "historical record," fragmented and anecdotal as it is.

Perhaps the first contact cryobiologists had with cryonicists was receiving, for review, copies of Robert Ettinger's manuscript for *The Prospect of Immortality,* circa 1963. Reaction to Ettinger's manuscript (and to the book which was published in 1964) was reportedly divided, but by no means universally hostile. Several cryobiologists who later became some of the most vocal critics of cryonics were not only not hostile, but actually demonstrated interest in and support of cryonics; particularly with an eye towards getting money to pursue cryobiological research.

LETTER FROM ARTHUR W. ROWE TO R.C.W. ETTINGER:

THE NEW YORK BLOOD CENTER
310 East 67th Street
New York, NY 10021

November 12, 1968

Dr. R.C.W. Ettinger
Cryonics Society of Michigan, Inc.
24041 Stratford
Oak Park, Michigan 48237

Dear Dr. Ettinger:

I wish to thank you for your letter of July 22, inviting me to join the Cryonics Society of America and to become a member of the Scientific Advisory Council. Please forgive me for the long delay in answering your letter as I have been on vacation, traveling, and I have also taken some time to deliberate seriously over your offer.

After careful and serious consideration of your proposals I find that it would be inopportune at this time for me to join and participate actively in the Cryonics Society. As Treasurer-Elect of the Society for Cryobiology, I must admit that my decision was strongly influenced by Dr. Arthur P. Rinfret, President-Elect of the Cryobiology Society, who advised against joining and participating in the Cryonics Society.

Please believe that I have the greatest respect and admiration for you and your efforts in organizing the Society. I should appreciate very much being put on your mailing list and receiving correspondence pertaining to developments of the Scientific Advisory Council and the Society.

Sincerely yours,

Arthur W. Rowe, Ph.D.

* *

Chief amongst these was Arthur Rowe (editor of *Cryobiology* and past President of the Society for Cryobiology), frequent repeater of the quote: "Believing cryonics could reanimate somebody who has been frozen is like believing you can turn hamburger back into a cow," and one of contemporary cryobiology's sternest critics of cryonics. (The origin of this quote is usually attributed to cryobiologist Peter Mazur.) In a letter to Robert C.W. Ettinger dated 4 December, 1968, Rowe expresses interest in cryonics and wishes Ettinger "continued success in your endeavors." But perhaps more amazing still is the fact that in the summer of 1968, during the cryonic suspension of Steven Mandel by the Cryonic Society of New York (CSNY), Arthur Rowe was called by Saul Kent (then Secretary of the CSNY) and asked for cryobiological recommendations on how to better suspend Mandel. Not only was Rowe friendly and supportive during this conversation, he provided a considerable amount of advice (Saul Kent, personal communication).

As Saul Kent recounts:

"We were really unprepared to freeze Steven in that he was the first patient CSNY ever had and we had absolutely no warning whatsoever that he was terminally ill, let alone dying. When the call came in it was totally unexpected. The call came in the 28th of July, 1968. It was Sunday morning, and many of the people who were to participate were still asleep. Freezing someone was the last thing we were really prepared to do.

"I called Art Rowe to ask for basic advice. He had been friendly to cryonics in the past and I was hoping he might be able to make some recommendations or suggestions about what cryoprotectives to use, best temperature to perfuse at and so on. He (Rowe) was surprisingly forthcoming and friendly. He provided a fair amount of practical advice on just those issues, although now, with the passage of over 20 years, I don't recall the specifics.

"Rowe continued to subscribe to *Cryonics Reports* and I believe there are several warm and supportive communications from him in the CSNY correspondence files."

Similarly, John Baust, past president of the Society for Cryobiology, had no deep objections to the program. Indeed, Baust even accepted grant money in the late 1960's from Texas millionaires Harlan Lane and Don Yarborough to support cryonics-related cryobiological research (John Baust, personal communication). Cryobiologist and heart-lung machine pioneer Richard Lillehei was also favorable toward cryonics and offered public support on at least one occasion (*Life Extension Society Newsletter*, Oct., 1964.)

LETTER FROM RICHARD C. LILLEHEI TO SAUL KENT:

UNIVERSITY OF MINNESOTA
MEDICAL SCHOOL
DEPARTMENT OF SURGERY
MINNEAPOLIS, MINNESOTA 55455

August 23, 1965

Mr. Saul Kent
2083 Creston Avenue
Bronx, NY 10453

Dear Mr. Kent:

Thank you for your note of August 8, 1965. I still cannot agree with you that the way to drum up interest in this area of research is to freeze humans at this time. While this may take advantage of the "sensational" aspects of the work, it is not in the long term the best way. Rather, I think we should go ahead, as I have said before, with continued research in the freezing of warm-blooded animals. I know that when we are able to freeze a warm-blooded animal and thaw him successfully, there will be few, if any, problems remaining for freezing humans. Thus, it would seem to me premature to freeze humans at this time until we are able to revive some of the warm-blooded animals.

We do desperately need more funds for research in this area, not only from the Government, but from private sources as well. I hope that your Society, in its own way, can stir up interest in this area, although I do not agree that the path you have taken is necessarily the correct one. However, I do respect your point of view, as, I am sure, you do mine.

With regards,

Richard C. Lillehei, M.D.
Associate Prof. of Surgery

**

FROM RICHARD LILLEHEI TO SAUL KENT:

UNIVERSITY OF MINNESOTA
MEDICAL SCHOOL
DEPARTMENT OF SURGERY
MINNEAPOLIS, MINNESOTA 55455

March 20, 1967

Mr. Saul Kent
Corresponding Secretary
Cryonics Society of New York, Inc.
306 Washington Avenue
Brooklyn, NY 11205

Dear Mr. Kent:

Thank you for sending me a copy of "Description of the Method of Freezing Humans," by Dante Brunol, M.D. I found his descriptive method quite interesting, yet I cannot help but return to the theme which I have previously written to you about. That is, these techniques, as described, are all "armchair" techniques which should be worked out in the laboratory on experimental animals.

On page 2, Dr. Bruno makes a statement which I certainly agree with. "In my opinion, it has never been successfully done (referring to the freezing of a large animal) not because of the impossibility, but merely because of lack of financing." This is certainly true. I would think that your Cryonic Society could make much more progress toward the eventual successful freezing of man, if they would devote their efforts to fund raising for support of laboratories engaged in research on the freezing of organs and animals. There is presently an acute shortage of funds, with no agency of the Public Health Service funding such studies at the moment. Thus your Societies could provide the impetus not only to raise funds but to bring to the public's attention the lack of support for research in this area. I am certain that with the proper funding in the next 10 years, it will be no longer necessary to indulge in "armchair" speculation about how a person should be frozen, but that it will be done with a good scientific background that successful thawing can also be done.

Again, many thanks for sending me your protocol for freezing.

Sincerely,

Richard C. Lillehei, M.D.
Professor of Surgery

* *

Other evidence of the ambivalence and even the support of cryobiologists for cryonicists' objectives can be had by looking over the list of scientists present on the Scientific Advisory Council to the Cryonics Societies of America (CSA) as late as March of 1969. Present on that list are cryobiologists Hendrick B. Barner, M.D., Armand M. Karow, Jr., Ph.D., William G. Manax, M.D., James A. Miller, Jr., Ph.D. and Richard D. Rink, Ph.D.

Armand Karow early in his career not only accepted grant money from the Cryonics Society of New York (CSNY), but even wrote a regular column for CSNY's newsletter entitled "Scientifically Speaking" for nearly two years (cf. *Cryonics Reports* vols. 1 & 2, 1966-1967).

While it would be unfair to say that cryobiologists as a group were ever supportive of cryonics, it is very clear that they were not uniformly hostile, either.

Outside of the cryobiological community the response to cryonics, while equivocal, was considerably warmer. The CSNY archives contain letters expressing interest and support from the likes of Willem Kolff, M.D. (the inventor of the artificial kidney machine and the father of modern hemodialysis) (letter from W.J. Kolff to Saul Kent dated 26 August, 1965) and Adrian Kantrowitz, a leading innovator in early cardiac surgery and heart transplantation (letter from A. Kantrowitz to Saul Kent dated 27 August, 1965).

LETTER FROM W.J. KOLFF TO SAUL KENT:

```
CLEVELAND CLINIC
DEPARTMENT OF ARTIFICIAL ORGANS
WILLEM J. KOLFF, M.D.
2020 East 93rd Street
CLEVELAND, OHIO
```

August 26, 1965

```
Mr. Saul Kent
Cryonics Society of New York, Inc.
103-55 97th Street
Ozone Park, New York 11317
```

Dear Mr. Kent:

I have enjoyed previous publications that you have sent to me. Good luck. Please keep me informed and keep sending me your other publications.

Sincerely yours,

W.J. Kolff, M.D.

**

LETTER FROM ADRIAN KANTROWITZ TO SAUL KENT:

```
ADRIAN KANTROWITZ, M.D.
4802 TENTH AVENUE
BROOKLYN 19, NEW YORK
```

```
DIRECTOR OF SURGICAL SERVICES
MAIMONIDES HOSPITAL OF BROOKLYN
PROFESSOR OR SURGERY
STATE UNIVERSITY OF NEW YORK
COLLEGE OF MEDICINE
```

August 27, 1965

Mr. Saul Kent
Cryonics Society of New York, Inc.
2083 Creston Avenue
Bronx, New York 10453

Dear Mr. Kent:

Thank you for your note of August 20th with the enclosed
material. It seems to me that the aims of your Society are
indeed worthy. However, I do not know at the present time
of any method which has been demonstrated to achieve your
purpose. There are in fact enormous difficulties that must
be overcome before it will be possible to store a complete
organism. Indeed there are great difficulties in storing
individual cells, although this has been accomplished for
long periods of time. Our own experiences in the laboratory
have been attempts at storing a single organ, such as a
kidney or a heart, and we have successfully done this for
as long as 12 hours. However, to do it indefinitely would
raise enormous problems. In the long run I am not quite
sure that this is a reasonable solution to the problems of
disease. At any rate I admire your courage and wish you
the best of luck.

Sincerely yours,

Adrian Kantrowitz, M.D.

**

Polarization

Apparently, though, over the course of a few years cryobiologists became, as a group,
increasingly polarized against cryonics. Initially this polarization was expressed
simply in terms of more and more vocal and extreme anti-cryonics statements to the
media. By late 1969 or early 1970 all of the cryobiologists on the CSA Scientific
Advisory Board had been approached by one or more of their colleagues in the Society
for Cryobiology and pressured to resign their positions. In particular, Armand Karow
was chastised for listing the Cryonics Society of New York as a financial supporter

of his research on rat heart freezing, as well as his involvement with CSNY. Karow once expressed his opinion to the author that he "was passed over for a position on the Editorial Board of the Society's Journal *Cryobiology* because of his association with cryonics." Karow followed these remarks with an observation to the effect that he had "learned his lesson" and did not intend to get tangled up with cryonicists again (Armand Karow, personal communication).

War

By the late 1970's and early 1980's, prominent individuals within the cryobiological community began to take steps to destroy cryonics. Perhaps the first effort in this regard was made by Harold Meryman, then President of the Society. Meryman reportedly approached Minnesota Valley Engineering (MVE), the cryogenic engineering company and manufacturer of the custom storage vessels for whole body patients, and threatened them with loss of their institutional membership and refusal of their advertising in the Society's journal, as well as a boycott of purchase of their equipment unless they stopped supplying patient storage vessels to cryonicists. MVE complied, and for nearly a decade there was no reliable commercial source of whole body cryogenic equipment available to any cryonics organization anywhere (this information was supplied to the author in the late 1970s by an individual in MVE management who wishes to remain anonymous). Indeed, it was in part as a result of this storage unit embargo that Robert Ettinger and the Cryonics Institute launched their program to build patient dewars in-house so as to be protected from such manufacturer black-listing.

LETTER FROM HAROLD T. MERYMAN TO SAUL KENT:

Mr. Saul Kent:

As you can see, I have no particular quarrel with your ambitions other than that you are more optimistic than the facts warrant. The goal of freezing and resuscitating intact mammals is certainly the natural ultimate of applied cryobiology, although this does not necessarily imply that it is also achievable. In particular, the preservation of the labile constituents of cerebral function, particularly memory, poses a challenge many orders greater than the freezing and thawing of any other tissue in which millions of cells perform identical functions and where substitution, repair, and replacement make injury and partial loss tolerable.

I do have one major apprehension and this is the probability of exploitation of this proposal by commercial interests at the expense of a gullible public, mesmerized by the apparent ability of science to work miracles. The opportunities for profit in the provision of cryogenic burial facilities are enormous, exceeded only by the temptation of fraud. Your society will face opposition from many sides and will also attract its share of unstable personalities. I hope that in your enthusiasm and your need for support you will not find yourself supporting questionable commercial practices and organizations on the premise that any ally is better than none.

Very sincerely yours,

H.T. Meryman, M.D.
Biophysics Division

**

LETTER FROM J.K. SHERMAN TO SAUL KENT:

UNIVERSITY OF ARKANSAS
MEDICAL CENTER
LITTLE ROCK

14 November 1967

Mr. Saul Kent
Cryonics Society of New York
306 Washington Avenue
Brooklyn, New York 11205

Dear Mr. Kent:

I am a cryobiologist whose long research experience has imposed a continued skepticism of the purposes of the Cryonic

Society and Life Extension movements, based upon available research information, not theoretical possibility. Lately, I have noted statements like "Cryonic research is the key to the growth of cryonics" (*Cryonics Reports* Vol. 2, No. 7, p. 5, July '67) which stress research as an aim or better, the foundation of progress in cryonics.

The purpose of my letter is to test the sincerity of your society's attitude toward research. The federal government, especially NIH and the Navy, has severely cut back support for the growth of basic research. This has affected all areas including cryobiology. My own research program has been hurt by it, as supplements have been approved and left dormant because of no funds.

Now, if your society really has interest in research in cryonics, it should be ready to provide it with support. How much financial support can the Cryonics Society grant to me and to others who are pursuing research on the very problems vital to answering questions of technique in Cryonic Society movements?

As a founding member of the Society for Cryobiology and former member of its Board of Governors, I am most anxious to receive your reply.

Sincerely yours,

J.K. Sherman, Ph.D.
Professor

**

In April of 1980, cryobiologist Maxim Persidsky wrote a letter to the California Board of Funeral Directors and Embalmers urging the destruction of cryonics (letter from M. Persidsky to Kathleen Callanan dated 21 April, 1980). Persidsky's letter is interesting in that it shows the mind of a hostile cryobiologist at work in a way rarely publicly seen. Persidsky's letter lay undiscovered for 10 years until it was obtained, and then only with great difficulty, under the California Freedom of Information Act during litigation with the California Department of Health Services to establish the legality of cryonics in California. The letter is reproduced in full elsewhere in this article, but the following quote is instructive:

"I can't find the proper words to express my indignation about this gruesome practice, or rather cult, which has continued to persist for more than a decade. There is absolutely no scientific justification to expect that these frozen corpses can ever be resurrected regardless of any future scientific achievements. With our present knowledge we can clearly realize the extent of the irreparable damage that could be inflicted on the human body if it were subjected to freezing even under the most sophisticated conditions that current science can offer. However, even before freezing there will be irreversible damage to the brain and other vital body organs resulting shortly after death. This damage will be further amplified during the inevitable slow processes of perfusion with cryoprotective agents and cooling. Very soon after death there will be a breakdown of lysosomes in the different cells and tissues of the body, resulting in the release of their harmful enzymes which will digest all the cellular structures and macromolecules upon which life of the cell depends."

It is interesting and more than a little ironic to note that fifteen years prior to the time that Persidsky wrote the words above, a large and growing body of evidence was already present in the scientific literature to discredit the "suicide-bag concept" of lysosomal rupture resulting in destruction of cells shortly after so-called death. I cite below three papers debunking this notion:

Trump, B.F., P.J. Goldblatt, and R.E. Stowell, "Studies of necrosis in vitro of mouse hepatic parenchymal cells; ultrastructural and cytochemical alterations of cytosomes, cytosegresomes, multivesicular bodies, and microbodies and their relation to the lysosome concept," *Lab. Invest.*, 14, 1946 (1965).

Ericsson, J.L.E., P. Biberfeld, and R. Seljelid, "Electron microscopic and cytochemical studies of acid phosphates and aryl sulfatase during autolysis," *Acta Patho Microbio Scand*, 70, 215 (1967).

Trump, B.F. and R.E. Bulger, "Studies of cellular injury in isolated flounder tubules. IV. Electron microscopic observations of changes during the phase of altered hemostasis in tubules treated with cyanide," *Lab Invest*, 18, 731 (1968).

LETTER FROM MAXIM PERSIDSKY TO KATHLEEN CALLANAN:

2200 Webster Street
San Francisco, CA 94115
415 563-2333

April 21, 1980

Ms. Kathleen Callanan
Executive Secretary
Board of Funeral Directors and Embalmers
Department of Consumer Affairs
State of California
1021 O Street
Sacramento, California 95814

Dear Ms. Callanan:

I am responding to your letter of April 9, 1980, in which
you asked for my opinion as a cryobiologist concerning the
practice of cryonics involving freezing and low temperature
storage of dead human bodies, and the claims that revival
of these bodies in a distant future may be possible.

I can't find proper words to express my indignation about
this gruesome practice, or rather cult, which has continued
to persist for more than a decade. There is absolutely no
scientific justification to expect that these frozen corpses
can ever be resurrected regardless of any future scientific
achievements. With our present knowledge we can clearly
realize the extent of irreparable damage that could be
inflicted on the human body if it were subjected to freezing
even under the most sophisticated conditions that current
science can offer. However, even before freezing there
will be irreversible damage to the brain and other vital
organs resulting shortly after death. This damage will be
further amplified during the inevitably slow processes of
perfusion with cryoprotective agents and cooling. Very soon
after death there will be a breakdown of lysosomes in the

different cells and tissues of the body, resulting in the release of their harmful enzymes which will digest all the cellular structures and macromolecules upon which life of the cell depends. No future improvements in the techniques of thawing could ever repair disintegrated cells or the denatured or digested proteins and DNA molecules.

Prompted by success in cryopreservation of certain single cells in suspension, there have been numerous attempts during the past two decades to preserve organs such as kidneys at low temperatures. So far all have ended in total failure. In the early seventies we were optimistic in our predictions that it would take not more than a decade to resolve this problem, and that banking of frozen organs would become a routine practice. Today, after we have exhausted testing of most of the known experimental conditions and variables, we have come to realize how enormous are the problems associated with the preservation of organs alone. It is my belief that the attempts to preserve corpses in anticipation of possible future revival are completely futile scientifically and totally immoral in view of anguish, false expectations and useless monetary losses by relatives of the deceased.

Recently, an attorney, Michael Worthington, has informed me of corrupt practices by the Southern California groups at a cemetery facility at Chatsworth. Here are quotations from his letter to me:

"On March 3, 1980 I personally observed the desecration that was left by the defunct Southern California groups at a cemetery facility in Chatsworth. The occasion was my inspection of human remains that were left to thaw in the 'cryotorium' at Oakwood Memorial Park. Dr. Gen Niyama of the Glenview Pathologists Group at David Brotman Memorial Hospital in Culver City accompanied me on this investigation. He related to me on the trip out to Chatsworth that he was formerly a member of the Society for Cryobiology. You might telephone Dr. Niyama (213) 836-7000 ext. 2816 for further details on the grisly scene that he observed. . . .

"Each of the bodies that we inspected had been perfused or embalmed in a different manner, indicating that they were used for purely experimental purposes. This reckless type of experimentation cannot be tolerated in a civilized society. . . .

"The Northern California organization has formed a life insurance program whereunder payments of Fifty Thousand Dollars ($50,000.00) or more are made directly to them in the event one of their so-called 'suspension members' dies. There are well over One Hundred (100) such members in California alone. There are numerous similar groups in other states, but Trans Time, Inc., in Berkeley is the only entity that actually performs human suspensions. The longer this goes on, the more likely it is that the cryonics organizations will abscond with all of the money and abandon human remains entrusted to their care."

In conclusion, I would like to see these organizations thoroughly investigated and their illicit activities quickly brought to a stop.

Sincerely,

Maxim Persidsky, M.Sc.
Director, Department of Cryobiology
Heart Research Institute

**

Eight years before Persidsky pronounced the situation hopeless due to lysosome rupture after death, an excellent and exhaustive paper appeared, entitled "Lysosome and phagosome stability in lethal cell injury" (Hawkins, H.K., et al., *Amer. Jour Path.*, 68, 255 (1972)). The authors subjected human liver cells in tissue culture to lethal insults such as cyanide poisoning and then evaluated them for lysosomal rupture. They state: "In conclusion, the findings do not indicate that the suicide bag mechanism of lysosomal rupture prior to cell death was operative in the two systems studied.

On the contrary, the lysosomes appeared to be relatively stable organelles which burst only in the post-mortem phase of cellular necrosis." And when does this "post-mortem phase of cellular necrosis" occur? Again, to quote from the Hawkins paper: "As late as four hours after potassium cyanide and iodoacetic acid poisoning, where irreversible structural changes were uniformly seen, it was clear that the great majority of lysosomes continued to retain the ferritin marker within a morphologically intact membrane . . ." To translate: even four hours after poisoning with drugs that mimic complete ischemia, the cells had stable lysosomes.

Perhaps even more to the point, in the decade prior to Persidsky's statements to the California Board of Funeral Directors and Embalmers, there was a veritable explosion of studies on the effects of complete ischemia (completely absent blood flow) on the mammalian brain. These studies documented not only the persistence of brain ultrastructure right down to the macromolecular level of which Persidsky speaks, but also of the preservation of brain function even after as much as an hour of no blood flow at normal body temperature. Even a cursory review of the literature would have revealed papers documenting the persistence of brain cell structure over the time-course of an hour or more of cardiac arrest. Here are two of the best of many papers that appeared over a time course of more than a decade before Persidsky wrote the words above:

Kalimo, H., et al., "The ultrastructure of brain death II. Electron microscopy of the feline cerebral cortex after complete ischemia," *Virchow's Arch. B Cell Path.*, 25, 207 (1977).

Karlsson, U., and R.L. Schultz, "Fixation of the central nervous system for electron microscopy by aldehyde perfusion. III. Structural changes after exsanguination and delayed perfusion," *Ultrastruc. Res.*, 14, 47 (1966).

The same is also true for papers documenting the preservation of the ability of the brain to recover metabolism after up to an hour of total cerebral ischemia. Largely beginning with the publication of a paper by Hossman and Sato in *Science* on 17 April, 1970 (Hossman, R.A. and K. Sato, "Recovery of neuronal function after prolonged cerebral ischemia," *Science*, 168, 375 (1970)) which documented that so-called cell death did not occur until long after the return of circulation following a period of one hour of absent blood flow at normal body temperature, the literature exploded with papers on the effects of cerebral ischemia and the field of cerebral resuscitation was born. A small sampling of papers published in the preceding decade giving the lie to Persidsky's claims is cited below:

Okada, Y., "Recovery of neuronal activity and high energy compound level after complete and prolonged brain ischemia." *Brain Research,* 72, 346 (1974).

Hinzen, D.H. et al, "Metabolism and function of dog's brain recovering from long-time ischemia." *Amer. J. Phys.,* 223, 1158 (1972).

Hossman, K.A., and V. Zimmerman, "Resuscitation of the monkey brain after 1 hour complete ischemia. I. Physiological and morphological observations," *Brain Research,* 81, 59 (1974).

Rehncrona, S., et al, "Recovery of brain mitochondrial function in the rat after complete and incomplete cerebral ischemia," *Stroke,* 10, 437 (1979).

Hossman, K., and P. Kleihues, "Reversibility of ischemic brain damage," *Arch. Neurol.,* 29, 375 (1973).

Apparently Persidsky, like his colleagues, felt no need to get the facts before speaking out and urging that ". . . I would like to see these [cryonics] organizations thoroughly investigated and their illicit activities brought to a halt." Nowhere in his letter does he provide any references or other documentary evidence for his claims of "irreparable damage" as a result of freezing, let alone for his statements about the rapid post-mortem disintegration of cell structure.

Persidsky's scandalous statements reflect a total lack of respect for cryonics and are evidence of an out-of-hand dismissal based on personal prejudices without any recourse to the scientific literature which existed years before his statements were made. Nor is Persidsky alone in this kind of remark. Even today it is not uncommon to hear cryobiologists and medical and scientific "experts" make the same kind of statements. It is extremely unlikely that Persidsky or his colleagues would make statements regarding claims or assertions they considered in the realm of the "scientific mainstream" without careful recourse to the scientific literature first.

No doubt Persidsky never dreamed his letter would see the light of day. And, but for the California Freedom of Information Act and the efforts of Alcor Member Keith Henson, it would not have.

By October of 1981, the Society as a whole had developed a very hard attitude toward cryonics and was even willing to commit it to print, as evidenced by their denial of membership in the Society to cryonicists and/or cryonics related organizations simply because of their involvement in or association with cryonics (letter to Jerry Leaf from Harold Meryman, 5 October, 1981). By April of 1982 the Society was actively investigating ways to formally exclude cryonicists from its ranks (letter from Mary Douglas to Terrance J. Leahy, 20 April, 1982).

Word that an effort was underway to ban cryonicists, principally by the mechanism of revising the Society's bylaws, was leaked from the Society to cryonicists. Many of the internal communications which provide the documentation for this article were made available to the editors of cryonics publications, and thus passed into the hands of the leaders of the cryonics community.

Jerry Leaf, a member of the Society for Cryobiology, a cryonicist, president of Cryovita Laboratories (a major cryonics service provider) and a Research Associate at the University of California at Los Angeles (UCLA) made an effort to derail these proposed bylaw changes. He attended the Society's annual business meeting on 1 July, 1982 in Houston, Texas where it was anticipated the new bylaws would be enacted. Despite the fact that there was not a quorum of the Society's Directors present, Harold Meryman (then the Society's President) moved that the new bylaws be enacted, stating that "since we are all friends the absence of a quorum is not important." Jerry Leaf objected to this and argued against adoption of the new bylaws and the "Policy Statement On Cadaver Freezing." Jerry pointed out that the new bylaws would strip the membership of many rights they held under the old bylaws and the Policy Statement was premature, since the results were still not in on the issue of the workability of cryonics.

Jerry's efforts resulted in the Society deciding to mail out ballots for approval of the new bylaws; in effect giving the Society's entire membership the opportunity to decide the issue. On 3 August, 1982, a communication written by Jerry Leaf was mailed to the membership of the Society for Cryobiology explaining the unfairness of the proposed actions and urging them to vote "no" on the new bylaws and Policy Statement.

On 15 September, 1982, section 2.04 of the Society's bylaws took effect, denying membership and allowing expulsion of any existing member who is engaged or engages in "any practice or application of freezing deceased persons in anticipation of their reanimation." The bylaws passed by an overwhelming majority, confirming that the desire to exclude cryonicists from membership in the Society was broadly held, and did not represent the arbitrary imposition of the will of the Society's leadership on its membership.

Why?

I have talked with two cryobiologists unfriendly to cryonics about this issue and neither of them are able to pinpoint with certainty what the specific reasons were for this hardening of attitude.

One cryobiologist sympathetic to cryonics does have an opinion about what caused the formal polarization of cryobiologists against cryonicists. In particular, this cryobiologist feels that formal, administrative attempts to exclude cryonicists from the Society and attempt to publicly distance themselves from cryonics came about as a result of something this author did.

During 14-18 June, 1981, this author attended the Society for Cryobiology's meeting in St. Louis, Missouri. During the course of that meeting I had occasion to speak with Jerome K. Sherman, a cryobiologist who was at that time active and influential in the Society, and who was chairing a session on gamete preservation at the meeting. Since we had corresponded briefly in the past, he knew who I was, and the course of our discussion turned to cryonics. Sherman was fascinated by what I had to say and, much to my surprise, at the end of one of the sessions he chaired, he announced my presence and solicited a presentation on cryonics. Since I was giving cryonics presentations to others (not associated with the Society) in the area, I had a slide presentation documenting cryonics procedures. Sherman encouraged me to return to my room and retrieve it so that it could be used to accompany my presentation.

The 15 or so attendees were fascinated by the presentation I gave, which included a detailed series of slides showing how cryonic suspension was done; surgical approach used, cryoprotective protocol, and so on. The presentation seemed well received, and Sherman as well as half a dozen or so other cryobiologists stayed for nearly an hour afterward asking questions about every aspect of cryonics.

However, according to the cryobiologist informant who attributes to this episode the formal hardening of the Society for Cryobiology against cryonics, the repercussions from this incident were far-reaching. Rumors about the presentation—often wildly distorted rumors—began to circulate. One particularly pernicious rumor, according to this informant, was that my presentation had included graphic photos of "corpses' heads being cut off." This was not the case. Surgical photos which were shown were of thoracic surgery to place cannulae and would be suitable for viewing by any audience drawn from the general public.

This informant also indicates that it was his perception that this presentation caused real fear and anger amongst the Officers and Directors of the Society. They felt as if they had been "invaded" and that such a presentation given during the course of, and thus under the aegis of, their meeting could cause them to be publicly associated with cryonics. Comments such as "what if the press got wind of this," or "what if a reporter had been there" were reported to have circulated.

Also, the presentation may have brought into sharper focus the fact that cryonicists existed, were really freezing people, and that they were using sophisticated procedures borrowed from medicine, and yes, even from cryobiology, which could cause confusion between the "real" science of cryobiology and the "fraud" of cryonics in the public eye. More to the point, it was clear that cryonicists were not operating in some back room and mumbling inarticulately; they were now right there in the midst of the cryobiologists and they were anything but inarticulate, bumbling back-room fools.

The Enemy Within

In the informant's mind this made taking some action a real priority. I might also add my own perception that it was around this time, or shortly thereafter, that many of the Society's Officers and Directors became aware of something even more potentially threatening: namely that several of their own number were "closet" cryonicists, and what's more, were influential and active in the cryonics community.

Two cryobiologists in particular (one of them the informant I have previously cited) posed a special concern in this regard. For not only were these individuals cryonicists as well as cryobiologists; they were path-breaking, high-profile cryobiologists who were beginning to contribute enormously to cryobiology in general and, even more alarmingly, were beginning to become influential in the leadership of the Society.

The attitude of the Society and some of the reasons for it can perhaps be put into perspective best by examining what occurred in June of 1985, when the Society sponsored a panel on "Ethical Considerations and Applications of Cryobiology" at its annual meeting in Madison, Wisconsin. A major focus of this session was a rabid attack on cryonics, using as "evidence" of cryonicists' wrong-doing and incompetence a number of newspaper stories which had been copied onto transparencies and projected for the attendees to see. John Baust chaired the session and Harold Meryman of the Red Cross Blood Research Laboratory (Bethesda, MD) delivered the most vituperative attack. Meryman cited the newspaper articles as evidence of fraud and wrongdoing by cryonicists and further indicated that the activity of cryonicists was damaging not only the public, but the discipline of cryobiology as well. That these articles might be inflammatory and inaccurate was never considered as a possibility.

A number of cryonicists were in the audience for part or all of this presentation including Paul Segall, Jerry Leaf, Hugh Hixon and myself. Segall, Leaf, and I vigorously defended cryonics against the half-truths of the media articles (the worst of which had been selected by Meryman for presentation) and attempted to set the record straight. This was to no avail, with many of the younger members of the Society lashing out at the cryonicists and accusing them of wild fantasies and "science fiction schemes." In response to a statement by the author to the effect that "cryonicists are counting on repair capabilities, on the ability to engineer at the molecular level," one nameless cryobiologist jeeringly shouted "that will never happen; pure science fiction!"

The rest of the meeting was made as unpleasant as possible for cryonicists attending it, with most of the delegates refusing even to speak to or sit with (at dinner) the cryonicist attendees. One notable exception was cryobiologist Locksley McGann, who had the courage to approach Jerry Leaf and myself and express his regret for the way in which his colleagues handled themselves and the issue of cryonics at the "bioethics" session at the opening of the meeting. McGann was at pains to point out that he did not consider cryonics workable. But he also stated that he felt that we were sincere in our beliefs and that no one, including the Society, benefited from the kind of exchanges that had occurred earlier or the kind of treatment we were receiving at the meeting. Similar sentiments were expressed by J.K. Sherman.

The Madison meeting made clear that cryobiologists were not only not interested in establishing a dialogue with cryonicists, they were not interested in becoming even marginally informed about how cryonics works and why cryonicists think it a rational thing to do.

But beyond this particular incident, it is clear that the Society had a long history of less focused enmity toward cryonics. What was responsible for this enmity and lack of cooperation between cryonicists and cryobiologists? The answer is: a lot of things.

One major difference between the examples of speculative scientific research cited previously (spinal cord repair, fusion power, and SDI research) is that none of these undertakings involve commitment to taking any action now beyond paying for the research. As for example, researching the problem of how to fix spinal cords doesn't mean that cord-injured patients should be treated differently today.

(This is not strictly the case, as many cord-injured patients and the researchers and support groups driving them have recently begun to emphasize the need to protect such patients from muscle atrophy and tendon contracture which will occur; the rationale being that such changes cause permanent damage to limbs which may limit or prevent recovery if and/or when a paralysis cure is discovered.)

Need For Action Now

Cryonics involves altering the care of terminally ill patients now, today, in a very radical way; a way that challenges a variety of deeply held convictions and assumptions about matters of life and death. It also involves considerable expenditures and inconvenience for the person deciding on suspension, as well as for his/her family or friends.

Such bold action, which breaks with conventional mores on fundamental issues and challenges accepted medical criteria, is bound to provoke strong emotional reactions and much knee-jerk criticism. To take a position of advocacy for cryonics thus implies the need not only for foresight, but for courage.

As with any fundamental shift in world-view, early acceptance is not very likely. The history of science and technology is littered with the broken hearts and broken minds of individuals and groups who challenged the accepted "paradigm." Many examples come to mind; Robert Goddard was publicly ridiculed for his rocketry research and for his assertion that travel to the moon should be technically feasible

(*Robert H. Goddard: Pioneer of Space Research* by Milton Lehman, DaCapo Press, Inc., New York, 1963). The work of Semmelweis and Lister with antisepsis was vilified, and it was over two decades after Lister introduced the concept of antisepsis in England before it was widely practiced in the United States (*The Biography of Medicine* by Sherwin B. Nuland, Alfred Knopf, Inc. New York, 1988).

Need For Courage and Foresight

For cryobiologists to have taken a position of advocacy for cryonics, or even for them to have accepted money from cryonicists (and suffer guilt by association) would have required enormous moral courage in addition to enormous foresight. Or it would have required enormous financial/professional benefit as compensation. Several cryonicists who have been around since the inception of the program in the mid-1960s are convinced that either support from—or at least the critical silence of—cryobiologists could have been had if only the program had grown large enough to generate significant revenue to support mainstream cryobiological research (Saul Kent and Robert Ettinger, personal communication).

Certainly a number of mainstream cryobiologists, some of whom were then or are now in influential positions in the Society for Cryobiology, were willing to accept research dollars from cryonicists for cryonics-related objectives and even to provide advice or lend their name to support the program (i.e., John Baust, Armand Karow, and Arthur Rowe). Some cryobiologists, such as Jerome K. Sherman, even offered complex research proposals to cryonicists to evaluate the efficacy of current suspension techniques and work on ways to improve them (research proposal of J.K. Sherman to Robert Ettinger, as reported in *The Outlook,* p. 5, September, 1974). Unfortunately, the small size of the cryonics movement and the lack of research dollars prevented such support, causing the proposal to be turned down (*The Outlook,* p.5, October, 1974).

(*The Outlook* was the newsletter of the Cryonics Society of Michigan (CSM). It has had several titles since its inception in January 1970, and is now published as *Long Life* magazine by CSM's successor, The Immortalist Society in Clinton Township, Michigan, affiliated with but separate from The Cryonics Institute.—Eds.)

All of the Disadvantages

This situation left cryobiologists in a very interesting position; they were faced with all of the disadvantages of cryonics with no perceived or actual benefit. And there were plenty of disadvantages.

First there was the problem of the media. Cryonics, even under the best of circumstances, was bound to attract plenty of attention and not all of it favorable. Many people, both inside and outside of the medical and scientific establishments, find the very notion of cryonics macabre and gruesome (even leaving neurosuspension out of it). Further complicating the situation was the crude state of cryonics in the 1960s. Suspensions were hardly comparable to medical procedures and the image of most of the cryonics organizations in existence at that time was a non-professional and amateurish one at best.

Since cryobiologists and cryonicists do have similar objectives, there is often confusion in the public mind between the two. It has been our experience here at Alcor that members of the public often first contact the Society for Cryobiology or individual cryobiologists seeking information on cryonics. This puts cryobiologists in the position of frequently having to clarify and distance themselves from the activities of the "body freezers" whom they consider pseudoscientific, irrational, and possibly fraudulent, and thus with whom they have no desire to be associated.

There is also the problem of the defiance and challenge to authority that cryonics represents. In the early days cryonicists came to cryobiologists in a friendly, open way looking for support, and asking for advice and help. Within the space of a few years cryobiologists began to tell cryonicists in no uncertain terms that they should not be doing what they were doing (i.e., freezing people using unperfected techniques). Several cryobiologists were even forthright enough to say that they would cease to have a problem with cryonicists if we would "just stop freezing people and instead work on the problem of developing suspended animation by supporting basic cryobiological research."

But cryonicists didn't listen. They continued to place themselves into suspension and vigorously pursue a program of public education aimed at expanding their program. In short, they failed to obey the authorities.

Counterattack

During the late 1960s to mid-1970s, criticism by cryonicists of the attacks of cryobiologists on cryonics was very mild and never ad hominem. Cryonicists adopted an exclusively defensive posture and tried a program of appeasement and quiet reason in dealing with the increasingly hostile attacks of cryobiologists. This approach did not work, and in fact even seemed to contribute to the heat of the public denunciations issued by cryobiologists.

Cryobiologists increasingly began to use the words "fraud" and "quackery" to describe cryonics and its advocates. They also began the practice (which continues to this day) of representing to the public as "facts" a welter of misinformation about their own discipline (principally involving the mechanisms and extent of cryoinjury) in order to prove their point that cryonics could not work (see the television show exchanges between the author and A. Trounson, reproduced later in this article). All dialogue and exchange of information between the groups broke down.

"Peace Talks"

In the late 1970s a renewed effort was begun, largely by Alcor's Jerry Leaf, to establish a dialogue with the Society and to educate them about cryonics. It was felt that much of the misunderstanding between cryobiologists and cryonicists may have been the result of lack of communication. These efforts at opening dialogue by Jerry Leaf, Thomas Donaldson, Paul Segall, the author, and others were rebuffed. The Institute for Cryobiological Extension (a cryonics-associated cryobiology research support group) was denied institutional membership in the Society because of its (and its President Jerry Leaf's) association with cryonics (Letter from H.T. Meryman, President of the Society to J.D. Leaf dated 5 October, 1981). These efforts at dialogue apparently resulted in further polarization of the Society against cryonicists (see the letter from Mazur to Carr quoted below) and resulted in escalation of the conflict.

On 4 September, 1981 Society President Harold Meryman wrote, and circulated within the Society, a "Policy Draft: Cadaver Freezing" the purpose of which was to inform the media of the "truth" about cryonics and separate the Society for Cryobiology from the activities of the "cadaver freezers." This "Policy Draft" is reproduced here. Note that it contains the following statement: ". . . to encourage individuals to invest many tens of thousands of dollars in post-mortem freezing with the implication of ultimate reanimation borders more on fraud than either faith or science." As was previously noted, a modified version of this Policy Statement was adopted at the same time the Society changed its Bylaws in 1982.

POLICY DRAFT: CADAVER FREEZING

The Board of Governors of the Society for Cryobiology has received inquiries regarding the policy of the Society toward individuals and organizations engaged in long-term, low temperature storage of human cadavers in anticipation of eventual reanimation.

The Board recognizes and respects the well-established freedom of individuals to hold and express their opinions and to act, within lawful limits, according to their beliefs. Preference regarding the disposition of the dead are clearly a matter of personal belief and, therefore, inappropriate subjects of Society policy.

The Board also recognizes that the goals of cryobiology include not only achieving an understanding of freezing injury and its avoidance but also applying this knowledge to the preservation of cells, tissues, organs, and organisms.

A future achievement may well be successful mammalian cryopreservation. However complex the social consequences of such a development might be, this is not basis for discouraging research in cryobiology. The cryopreservation of biological systems remains a legitimate scientific endeavor which the Society for Cryobiology is chartered to support.

Current understanding in cryobiology is at best fragmentary. Many cells and tissues are refractory to cryopreservation by the best available techniques. There is no confirmed report of successful cryopreservation of an intact animal organ. It can be stated unequivocally that mammalian cryopreservation cannot be achieved by current technology.

Nonetheless, certain organizations and individuals are advocating that persons be frozen subsequent to death on the premise that science may ultimately develop the capability both to reverse the injury of freezing and to revive the cadaver. The Board does not choose to involve itself in a discussion of the degree of remoteness of this possibility. The Board does, however, take the position that cadaver freezing is not science. Freezing and indefinitely storing a cadaver is not an experimental procedure from which anything can be learned. The knowledge necessary for revival of whole animals following freezing and for reviving the dead will come not by freezing cadavers but from conscientious and patient research in cryobiology, biology, chemistry, and medicine. The sole motivation for freezing cadavers today is the remote hope on the part of individuals that it may be a means of avoiding death. It is an exercise in faith, not of science. Furthermore, to encourage individuals to invest many tens of thousands of dollars in post-mortem freezing with the implication of ultimate reanimation borders more on fraud than either faith or science.

The Board finds human cadaver freezing to be at this time a practice devoid of scientific or social value and inconsistent with the ethical and scientific standards of the Society. The Board recommends to the Society that

membership be denied to organizations or individuals
actively engaged in this practice.

4 September 1981

**

In 1985 (after the previously mentioned Society meeting in Madison) a research abstract and paper on subjects unrelated to cryonics (i.e., canine bloodless perfusion and deep hypothermia) were rejected for publication after presentation at the Society's 1985 annual meeting, solely because the work was sponsored and conducted by cryonicists and cryonics-related organizations (Dr. Gregory M. Fahy, personal communication). Despite the fact that the paper was well-received and was "defended" by both Society President Stanley Leibo and Society Treasurer Greg Fahy (Letter from G.M. Fahy to J.D. Leaf dated 26 July, 1986), and further, despite the fact that the authors agreed to the extraordinary request by Leibo and Fahy to have the paper appear without any indication of the (cryonics) institutional affiliation or sources of funding support (Letter from J.D. Leaf to S.P. Leibo dated 15 July, 1985).

The intensity of the animosity and hatred of cryonicists by cryobiologists can perhaps best be gauged by a remark reported to have been made by John Baust (then the Society's President-elect) at the 20 June, 1985 Society Board Meeting (which followed the paper's presentation) to the effect that accepting such work for publication from cryonicists, even valid, scientifically sound work, was like accepting for publication human hypothermia studies done on Jewish concentration camp victims by Nazi war criminal Josef Mengele. The final verdict as reported in the Minutes of the Society's 20 June annual Board Meeting was:

"The Board shall instruct the Editor-in-Chief of the *Journal of Cryobiology* to not publish abstracts numbered 48 and 49 submitted for presentation at the 1985 Annual Meeting of the Society for Cryobiology on the grounds that publication would be detrimental to the Society for Cryobiology.

"The motion was seconded and after considerable discussion the motion passed with ten votes in favor and one abstention."

This incident caused intense anger and resentment amongst cryonicists. However, it was by no means the first example of grossly unfair and prejudicial treatment of cryonicists by cryobiologists. In 1981, an internationally renowned organ cryopreservation researcher was called into his supervisor's office (the supervisor was also an Officer and Director of the Society) and threatened with dismissal if he continued not only his low profile association with cryonicists, but also his suspension membership. It was also pointed out to this researcher that if his association with or belief in cryonics in any way became public he would never again get grants from the NIH or other routine sources. This individual, who was already wearing his suspension bracelet on his ankle to avoid public comment, was thus faced with a terrible dilemma: a choice between his chance at continued life via cryonics, or his career.

(It is ironic to note that bracelets worn around the ankle are commonly called "slave bracelets.")

A little less than a year after the meeting in Madison, the Society felt sufficiently threatened by cryonics that director Peter Mazur sent a letter to the Society's legal counsel, Mr. Joel Carr of the law firm Patterson, Belknap, Webb, and Tyler, which is quoted below:

"Some body-freezers are attempting to become members of the Society, and, whether members or not, are attempting to present papers at our Society annual meeting (abstracts of which are ordinarily published) and to publish papers in our Journal. A few have succeeded in doing so despite our efforts to prevent them.

"Our reasons for wishing to prevent them are that we feel that their association with our Society and publishing under the Society's name will have a highly detrimental effect on a legitimate field of science and consequently will have a detrimental effect on the careers of those of us in the field of cryobiology. Secondly, the association may well cause bona fide members to leave the Society or result in potential valuable members deciding not to join the Society. At our last annual meeting there were strong rumblings from some younger members about the former. Our concern is based partly on our feeling that their basic approach has no scientific validity, partly on the repercussions of media attention to their thesis and practice, and partly on the fact that they charge their clients money for the practice.

"But the other face of the coin is whether we open ourselves to legal action by preventing them from gaining association with the Society. The basic problem then is what should the Board do to protect the Society from being damaged from their association while at the same time minimizing the probability of being sued? . . . .

"The problem that we have faced is that one can conceive of three main categories of body-freezers (with many possible intergrades):

"Category 1: Individuals who are publicly known members of body-freezing organizations who wish to present or publish papers clearly relevant to body-freezing or become members of the Society.

"Category 2: Individuals like (1) except that the work they wish to present in our Society is adequate scientifically and obviously related to body freezing.

"This category gives us the most problem because they also publish pseudoscience body freezing articles and are publicly associated with body-freezing organizations.

"Category 3: Individuals privately known to espouse the aims of the body-freezers but who otherwise act as bona fide cryobiologists as we define bona fide. This category does not cause us much concern. . ." [Nor should it have, since they had already succeeded in thoroughly terrorizing them into silence.—M.D.]

". . . Two events the past month are transforming the problem from an academic exercise to reality. One is that our director's and officer's insurance is to go up five-fold next summer. The other is that we have heard that two individuals whose abstracts the Board refused to publish last fall are angry enough to possibly initiate legal action."

Cryonicists began to react to these very unfair actions on the part of the Society for Cryobiology. It was one thing to publicly criticize cryonics and to question its workability. It was quite another to accuse innocent people of fraud, suppress free exchange of scientific information, interfere with free trade, and terrorize cryonicists (who also had the misfortune of being professional cryobiologists) with destruction of their careers and loss of livelihood, and give out misinformation about basic cryobiology in the bargain.

By the mid-1980s this reaction had crystallized into a new and aggressive stance by cryonicists in dealing with cryobiologists. Cryobiologists who appeared on talk shows or in public forums opposite cryonicists no longer found them meek and amiable. Instead, they found cryonicists who were increasingly organized, capable, and willing to debate cryobiologists on the technical and scientific assertions which cryobiologists formerly made unchallenged and without supporting evidence. And above all, the cryobiologists found themselves confronting people who were bitterly angry and feeling, with plenty of justification, that through their actions cryobiologists might kill them.

Cryonicists' Growing Militance

The cryobiologists were also unaware that the passage of years had seen a number of radical changes in cryonics. Cryonics was no longer the undertaking of a few amateurs with little scientific background and inadequate debating skills. Cryonics had begun to grow up. The typical active cryonicist was now highly educated, articulate, and scientifically knowledgeable. Indeed, many cryonicists had a broader and deeper understanding of the basic principles of cryobiology and the mechanisms and extent of cryoinjury than many of the over-specialized cryobiologists they confronted in public debates.

And just as important, the technology of cryonic suspension had been vastly improved over the decade between 1970 and 1980. No longer was cryonics a back-room operation carried out by morticians and unskilled helpers. Rather, cryonic suspension was being carried out using state-of-the-art surgical and medical technology by trained professionals—including physicians, registered nurses, and, yes, professional cryobiologists (who also happened to be members of the Society for Cryobiology).

Thus, the cryobiologists who chose to debate cryonicists both publicly and privately found themselves confronting an enemy that was affluent (compared to the past!), skilled at debating, presentable, personable, professional in appearance, and fully capable of aggressively, yet rationally, challenging each and every one of the cryobiologists' unproved assertions about the evidence against cryonics.

Cryonicists also became intolerant of any public assertion on the part of cryobiologists that cryonics or its practitioners were engaged in fraud. Communications were sent apprising the Society that assertions that cryonics was fraud constituted both a serious criminal and civil allegation and that appropriate legal action would be taken if such allegations continued (cf. Series of letters from Robert Ettinger and Michael Darwin sent to the Society in the mid 1980s: specifically Letter from M.G. Darwin to H.T. Meryman dated 21 April, 1982). As a result, by and large, allegations of fraud ceased.

Yet another problem cryobiologists confront as a result of the existence of cryonics is the problem of envy. Shortly after the start of the cryonics program, cryobiologists began to suffer not only from the confusion in the public mind between cryobiology and cryonics, but from a singular lack of media attention as a result of cryonics "stealing their thunder." David Pegg, a leading organ cryopreservation researcher, has complained bitterly to the media and to cryonicists that his "valuable, serious work is virtually ignored by the media and the public in favor of the macabre lunacy of the cadaver freezers. . ." (conversation between David Pegg and Judith Hann, Presenter of BBC's "Tomorrow's World" following Pegg's appearance opposite the Author on the "Kilroy-Silk Show," aired 3 March, 1989).

Media attention on cryonics is constant and unremitting, and while often not favorable, it nevertheless remains that cryonicists have the ear of, and access to, the international public; an entrée denied even the most successful and hardworking cryobiologist. Because cryobiologists consider cryonics unworkable at best, and fraud at worst, this situation of perceived unfair media attention infuriates them and perhaps makes them feel justified in using the questionable tactics they have in attacking cryonics as a whole and individual cryonicists within their ranks.

Errors of Fact?

A more subtle problem is that cryobiologists are experts in two closely related areas: the nature of cryoinjury, and possible strategies for preventing it. As is usually the case in any scientific discipline, initial progress was made almost exclusively on the basis of empirics: a trial-and-error approach to achieving successful cryopreservation. Additionally, as is also usually the case, understanding of the mechanisms of injury (reasons why it won't work) has proceeded faster than the innovation of techniques to prevent injury from occurring.

An added problem is that until very recently there has been no unifying theory of cryoinjury which was capable of pointing the way towards a common technical method for preventing such injury in most living systems. Thus, cryobiology is a science rich in researchers whose careers have focused on the idiosyncrasies of preserving (and understanding injury in) individual systems such as red blood cells, tissue culture cells, embryos, and so on. An investigator may spend years working out the mechanics of a preservation protocol and understanding the nature of injury to a single class of cells or tissues. Thus, a red blood cell cryobiologist will employ techniques and use research approaches which are liable to differ greatly from those used by an investigator interested in cryopreserving embryos. Entire careers or significant fractions thereof may be spent on mastering the preservation of a single cell type.

Furthermore, moving from cells to organs presents a whole new series of problems to overcome. Until the work of Mazur (Mazur, P., "Causes of injury in frozen and thawed cells." *Fed Proc.* (Suppl. 15) S175-S182, 1965.), Pegg (Pegg, D.E. and Diaper, M.P. "The mechanism of cryoinjury in glycerol-treated rabbit kidneys." in *Organ Preservation: Basic and Applied Aspects* edited by D.E. Pegg, et al., MTP Press, Ltd., Lancaster, 1982.) and Fahy (Fahy, G.M., "The relevance of cryoprotectant 'toxicity' to cryobiology." *Cryobiology*, 23:1, 1986.), there was no clear, unifying understanding of cryoinjury on both the cell and tissue/organ level. With the work of Fahy in particular, a common pathway to achieving cryopreservation was laid out (vitrification, wherein no ice is formed upon cooling) which should in theory work for virtually all mammalian tissues (Fahy, G.M., and Hirsch, A., "Prospects for organ preservation by vitrification." In *Organ Preservation, Present and Future* (D.E. Pegg, I.A. Jacobsen, and N.A. Halaz, Eds.) MIT Press, Lancaster, 1981.)

As a consequence, cryobiologists tend to be "microspecialists," often with a sad lack of awareness of progress in other areas even within their own discipline. Recently, the internationally renowned in vitro fertilization expert and human embryo cryopreservationist Alan Trounsen appeared opposite the author and Alcor member Thomas Donaldson on Australian TV (the Peter Couchman program in Melbourne, Australia, 3 October 1990). Trounson vigorously asserted on that program, in front of an estimated audience of 500,000 people, that all mammalian cells freeze intracellularly (that is, the interiors of the cells freeze), even at slow cooling rates and with cryoprotectants present, and that cryonics patients are reduced to chewed-up debris by this intracellular ice.

Intracellular freezing is somewhat more of a problem with early embryos because of the tightly packed arrangement of the cells which slows water loss during freezing. This can be easily overcome by using slow enough cooling rates. It is not a problem for other mammalian cells (with the exception of egg cells; due to their large size and resulting poor surface to volume ratio, mammalian eggs must also be cooled very slowly). There can be little doubt that other cryobiologists with expertise in cell and organ cryopreservation would be aghast at the assertion that mammalian cells freeze intracellularly at slow or even moderate cooling rates! Consider the following exchange between myself and Dr. Trounson on the Couchman Programme:

Trounson: "Now what would be happening with these tissues [in a cryonic suspension patient] that have been frozen in this way, if you watch under a microscope you get a flash, which is the formation of intracellular ice, that is ice forming inside the cell. Now, in some ways if you looked at that in histology, yes, some of the structures would be pushed out of the way. But the ice also encapsulates many, or all of the small intracellular components of that cell, disrupting them. So that when the cell is thawed out even though it still has a structure, which has been pushed around, all of those minute and essential parts of the cell are destroyed. They won't function. You can look at them in histology and they are still there, but they won't function.

Couchman: "I gather that you are not prepared to accept, even letting your scientific imagination run free here that —

Trounson: "Well the problem is, Peter, that that most of those cells will in fact be destroyed [by the freezing process]. Mike's using a lot of license here in the way he is portraying this. Because he's saying "OK in 600 years we'll have great whoopee science," and that may be so; we may be able to freeze whole bodies in 100 years time because we might have worked out a totally different system.

Couchman: "That's right, because your science now would now have been great whoopee science for people in the middle ages.

Trounson: "But if you freeze a complicated group of cells, and if you take a brain that you freeze in this way—I'll tell you one possible scenario is that all the tumor cells might survive and none of the other brain cells, so that what you get back is a tumor and not the brain —

Couchman: "[Mike,] without getting involved in a really complex scientific argument that none of us can understand —

Darwin: "I'll try very hard, but he has raised scientific issues that he is simply wrong on. I must say I'm appalled. For a professional cryobiologist to sit there and say the things you did about flashover of ice inside cells.... That only occurs with intracellular freezing! You couldn't intracellularly freeze this man's brain (gesturing at Thomas Donaldson) or mine if you tried because you couldn't get a high enough freezing rate for that if you tried. When you cool at moderate rates cells are dehydrated by freezing. . ."

Trounson: "You're wrong because we freeze embryos at the slowest possible rate, 0.1°C per minute, and they form intracellular ice."

Donaldson: How many brains have you frozen?. . . . We're not discussing freezing embryos."

Trounson: "You're just wrong!"

Darwin: "We have done freeze-substitution studies on human and animal neuronal tissue and we know they do not freeze intracellularly."

Trounson: "You're wrong! You must not mislead these people. These cells are damaged beyond repair."

Darwin: "How can you say that? You're an expert on injury and you don't even seem to know about injury in tissues that are frozen slowly. You cannot sit there and say that it's never going to be possible to repair that [damage]. How can you say that?"

Fate Of Intracellular Water During Freezing

As the above illustrates, Trounson, a respected scientist and so-called cryobiologist, was (and presumably still is) unaware that cells cooled at a slow or moderate rate, indeed even cells cooled at 1°C per minute do not freeze intracellularly. Nor is this knowledge very arcane; most competent cell, tissue, or organ cryobiologists would be aware of this. I quote from cryobiologist Peter Mazur's excellent review paper "Freezing of living cells: mechanisms and implications." (*Amer. J. Physiol., (Cell Physiol.* 16), C125 (1984)):

"The chief physical events occurring in cells during freezing are depicted schematically in Fig. 1. Down to ~-5°C, the cells and their surrounding medium remain unfrozen both because of super-cooling and because of depression of the freezing point by the protective solutes that are frequently present. Between -5 and ~-15°C, ice forms in the external medium (either spontaneously or as result of seeding of the solution with an ice crystal), but the cell contents remain unfrozen and supercooled, presumably because the plasma membrane blocks the growth of ice crystals into the cytoplasm (see below). The supercooled water in the cells has, by definition, a higher chemical potential than that of water in the partially frozen solution outside the cell, and in response to this difference in potential, water flows out of the cell and freezes externally.

"The subsequent physical events in the cell depend upon the cooling velocity. If cooling is sufficiently slow (Fig 1, upper right), the cell is able to lose water rapidly enough by exosmosis to concentrate the intracellular solutes sufficiently to eliminate supercooling and maintain the chemical potential of the intracellular water in equilibrium with that of extracellular water. The result is that the cell dehydrates and does not freeze intracellularly. But if the cell is cooled too rapidly (Fig. 1, bottom and center right) it is not able to lose water fast enough to maintain equilibrium; it becomes increasingly supercooled and eventually attains equilibrium by freezing intracellularly."

As Mazur then goes on to note, for cells such as red blood cells the critical cooling rate for intracellular freezing to occur would be in excess of 1000°C per minute! For

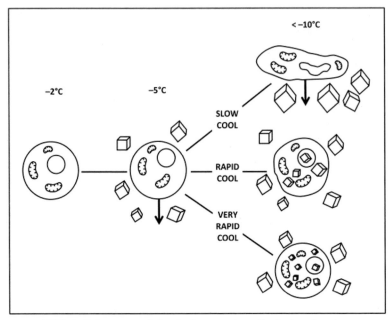

FIG. 1. Schematic of physical events in cells during freezing,
ice crystals shown as cubes.
By Perry, R. M. after Mazur, P. Freezing of living cells: mechanisms and
implications. Am. J. Physiolog. (Cell Physiol. *16): C125-C142, 1984,*
http://ajpcell.physiology.org/content/ajpcell/247/3/C125.full.pdf
(accessed 9 Feb. 2015); cited from Mazur, P. The role of supraoptimal
freezing in the death of cells cooled at supraoptimal rates. Cryobiology
14: 251-272, 1977.

human lymphocytes 40°C/min, and for mouse or human embryos frozen in 1M DMSO, 3°C/min (Trounson's assertions to the contrary notwithstanding). Please remember that the typical cooling rate for a human cryonic suspension patient is on the order of 3° to 4°C per hour, or 0.06°C/min!

A few other references documenting the absence of intracellular ice in cells and organs frozen at moderate or slow rates are presented below (there are many, many others):

Lovelock, J.E., "The mechanism of the protective action of glycerol against hemolysis by freezing and thawing," *Biochim. Biophys. Acta.* 11:28, 1953.

Meryman, H.T., "Modified model for the mechanism of freezing injury in erythrocytes," *Nature* 218:333, 1968.

Fahy, G.M., "Analysis of 'Solution Effects' Injury: Cooling Rate Dependence of the Functional and Morphological Sequelae of Freezing in Rabbit Renal Cortex

Protected with Dimethyl Sulfoxide," *Cryobiology* 18, 550-570 (1981).

Pegg, D. E., "Ice crystals in tissues and organs," in *The Biophysics of Organ Cryopreservation*, pp. 117-136, Plenum Press, New York and London, 1987.

Trounson's remarks are a telling example of the effects of over-specialization and fragmentation of knowledge about cryobiology. As Thomas Donaldson correctly asked Dr. Trounson during this exchange: "How many brains have you frozen?" This was a question Trounson never answered.

A consequence of this fragmentation and over-specialization within the cryobiological community has been a failure to see the big picture. Few cryobiologists know anything about the true nature of freezing damage to organs or whole organisms. If called upon to describe the damage on an ultrastructural, tissue, and gross level, probably not three cryobiologists in 100 could do so (and keep in mind that the Society only has approximately 300 members). This ignorance, coupled with the arrogant and mistaken certainty that the injury they have observed in their area of specialization applies to cryonic suspension patients, has resulted in heated verbal exchanges between cryonicists and cryobiologists. Rarely, if ever, have cryobiologists taken the time to educate themselves about the issues they declaim on as experts.

It is also worth noting that when errors, such as the one highlighted above, are subsequently brought to the attention of such talk-show cryobiologists (with appropriate documentation, as has been provided here) there has never been a retraction, apology, or admission of error, either public or private. Indeed, the most common response is no response at all.

Another example of the public deceit engaged in by cryobiologists is the public denial by the Society of their policies and procedures toward cryonicists. The following dialogue occurred between Society Vice-President James Southard (a highly respected hypothermic organ preservationist from the University of Wisconsin) and the Author on the "Larry King Show" (aired live, 11 July, 1989):

Darwin: The Society for Cryobiology has so harassed its members who are also cryonicists that several prominent cryobiologists who are also cryonicists are afraid to come forward because of fear for their jobs, for their very livelihoods. In fact, the Society has a regulation which prevents cryonicists from being members.

King: Is that true?

Southard: Not true. . . The Society for Cryobiology will not eliminate anybody who is doing bona fide science and who will submit their scientific papers for review. . .

Given Southard's position in the Society and the fact that it was he who accepted the abstracts for presentation at Madison it must be said that his statements above reflect either profound ignorance, an incredible lapse of memory, or an outright lie. (A letter sent to Dr. Southard following the King program documenting these errors (and others) was never answered (Letter from M.G. Darwin to J.M. Southard dated 11 July, 1989).)

Southard then went on to comment in response to remarks from Alcor Member Brenda Peters that Alcor's hypothermic dog perfusion/recovery studies were not accepted for publication because they were found as a result of peer review to "not constitute bona fide science." This is hardly the picture painted in the communications from Fahy previously cited or what the 20 June minutes reflect as the real reason the work was rejected.

Beyond an often appalling degree of ignorance about the nature and extent of cryoinjury, the first half of the cryonics problem, there is a total lack of any knowledge or understanding of the second half of the problem: the problem of repair. Cryobiologists often refer to cryonicists' discussion of speculative strategies for repairing cryoinjury as "science fiction." Further, they are often opposed on ethical grounds. Consider the following dialogue between James Southard, Alcor Member Brenda Peters, host Larry King, and me, again from the "Larry King Show" cited above which nicely illustrates both these points:

King: James, Do you want this [cryonics] to work?

Southard: No. I don't see any reason why one isn't satisfied with the one life that they have on earth. I mean from a personal standpoint.

Darwin: That's a monstrous statement to make.

Peters: Dr. Southard, what is the advantage of a normal lifespan, quote unquote?

Southard: Look at it this way, there are so many medical problems we have to solve nowadays, that's where the priorities should be. That's where the problems are and that's where the resources and that's where the money should go. I don't think we should hold out false promises to people. I mean these are false promises; it cannot be done.

King: But, and correct me if I'm wrong, all medical research, Doctor, help if I'm wrong here, all medical research is designed to extend life.

Southard: Medical research is designed to extend the quality of life.

King: Or extend it. . .

Southard: I don't believe it is necessarily to extend life itself.

King: 95% of all health care dollars are spent on extending life.

Southard: No, extending the quality of the life you're going to live on earth.

King: If you could make a good healthy person live a hundred years wouldn't you buy it?

Southard: (pause) I suppose.

Peters: That's exactly what we are talking about. . . we're talking about bringing people back healthy and strong.

Darwin: Dr. Southard is all in favor of medical research as long as it's his medical research or medical research that he gets to make the decisions about. I am sure that Pasteur and Semmelweis and other people who were responsible for vast extensions of the mean lifespan that we experience right now had exactly the same kinds of criticisms leveled at them.

Southard: Mike, I have no complaints about the fact that you want to freeze people and promise them you're gonna bring 'em back. . . There is no scientific evidence that you can freeze a body or freeze a multicellular organism and thaw it out [successfully] at this point in time. . . What you're talking about is science fiction.

Cryobiologists like Southard vigorously attack any effort on the part of cryonicists to speculate within the framework of the current understanding of physical law on possible approaches to repair, stating in effect that until such approaches can be shown to work (i.e., proven by actual experiment) they are meaningless and not worthy of considering as the basis for taking any current action (i.e., placing people into suspension now). Often they will categorically state that no repair process could ever result in recovery of patients frozen with today's techniques.

This attitude of taking no action in an otherwise hopeless situation until the action is PROVEN to work is incredible, and characterizes few, if any other human undertakings (with the possible exception of the United States drug approval process). It is essential to human survival that people take action and accept risks on the basis of reasoned speculation based on limited insight. When we invest, do an experiment, or venture into any other area of activity where we have no prior "proven" examples, we are pursuing a course of action identical to that being pursued by people choosing to enter cryonic suspension. Indeed, it can be argued that the typical day-to-day risk-taker has a far larger number of options and considerably more to lose than the typical patient entering cryonic suspension, who has no other viable options, nothing left to lose and who has after all been pronounced dead.

Summing Up The Situation

Cryobiologists are opposed to cryonics for a host of complex reasons. First and foremost, they, like many others in society, do not see cryonics as a potentially workable enterprise for several technical, social, and moral reasons. However, in and of itself, this is not sufficient to have caused the enmity that exists between the two groups. Other factors, such as the need to differentiate themselves from cryonicists due to confusion in the public eye, envy of the attention given to cryonicists, misinformation about how cryonics actually works, and ignorance about both the magnitude of cryoinjury and the possibilities of repair, all combine to create a very adverse situation suffused with intense hostility.

But beyond these fairly "objective" reasons there is another, which is perhaps the most powerful reason of all: most cryobiologists don't want cryonics to work.

I have talked with many cryobiologists about cryonics over the years. Whether young or old it has been my experience that almost universally cryobiologists consider the goal of human suspended animation and/or vastly extended lifespans anathema. I think the attitude of cryobiologists can best be summed up by the following quote from Harold Meryman taken from a letter to Charles Tandy dated 4 April, 1978:

> "I am quite unsympathetic with the goal of preserving human beings through freezing. I find the proposition mischievous in the extreme and fear that, like some other scientific 'breakthroughs' one might mention, the end result would be impossible to control and far more damaging than beneficial to society.

> "In short, I think that a national institute of low temperature biology is unjustified and the goal of freezing humans is deeply disturbing."

The above quote from Meryman was in response to a proposal by Mr. Tandy to create a National Institute of Low Temperature Biology with the express goal of achieving human suspended animation. The above quote and the previously cited one from Southard demonstrate that a major factor in the unwillingness of cryobiologists to take cryonics seriously—or even give it a fair hearing—is their deeply held desire that cryonics and human suspended animation not be realized. Not now, not ever.

Assessing The Damage

The price of the continuing enmity between cryobiologists and cryonicists has been high. The unremitting pronouncements by many cryobiologists for over two decades to the effect that cryonics cannot ever work and what's more, should not ever work have no doubt contributed to the slow growth of the program and resulted in many lost lives. Leaving aside the direct impact these pronouncements have had on individuals contemplating suspension arrangements for themselves and others, there is the broader issue of how these remarks have affected support for cryobiological research. It is an irony, no doubt totally unappreciated by the cryobiological community, that the highest price for the war between cryobiologists and cryonicists may have been paid by the cryobiologists themselves.

Progress in any human undertaking is dependent upon several factors: the competence of the individuals involved, their level of motivation, and of course, the resources available to them. Cryobiology—and in particular the discipline of organ cryopreservation—does not lack several high quality talents. And no doubt if the motivation and resources were available it would attract many more. And therein lies the problem. Individuals, investors, venture capitalists, and governments are all attracted to big ideas, to powerful ideas. Major progress within disciplines as diverse as cosmology and genetics has been driven by the strong personal motivation of the investigators as well as a sense of "mission." A quick once-through of James Watson's *The Double Helix* will clear up any doubts about the importance of personal motivation and, above all, a sense of mission.

To get good results in any undertaking it is necessary that people have genuine enthusiasm and excitement about it. People like Albert Einstein and James Watson were motivated by big ideas and extraordinary goals: to understand the universe and to understand the fundamental biological basis of life. Their undertakings had "sizzle" and offered excitement and a sense of power. In short, they had glamour, and glamour counts for a lot.

These elements are sorely lacking in nearly all organ cryopreservationists today. I believe it is also fair to say that the movers and shakers of the Society for Cryobiology even question the desirability of pursuing solid state organ cryopreservation. In fact, one of the first sessions on the first day of the upcoming annual Society meeting in Brussels will be an "assault" on the utility of the work of the last remaining serious organ cryopreservationist, Dr. Greg Fahy.

England's David Pegg, the other leading organ cryopreservationist, closed up shop earlier this year when the British Medical Research Council (MRC) declined to continue financial support for the MRC cryobiology unit. The reason this happened is simple: in nearly 15 years Pegg had failed to show any significant progress toward organ cryopreservation. He didn't seem motivated to accomplish the job he was being paid for, and, just as importantly, he was no longer motivating others to continue his support.

The Society for Cryobiology has long lamented the lack of "new blood" and "first class talent" in its ranks. They have never paused to ask the all important question "Why is this the case?" The answer is simple: cryobiology, as it is currently practiced, is a drab, overspecialized discipline which offers little prospect for changing peoples' lives or changing the world in a dramatic way; it doesn't affect the big picture. Organ preservation was the last hope to turn this around. However, within the Society there has been considerable hostility and skepticism about the prospects for achieving near-term organ cryopreservation and there has been no effort on the part of the Society to promote organ cryopreservation, lobby for its funding, or even educate the public about its short-term benefits for transplant patients. In the absence of an organized and motivated approach, nothing gets done. (Indeed, the first organ cryopreservationists were transplant surgeons; people whose motivation often exceeded their competence—but at least they DID something and what's more, believed passionately in the importance of what they were doing.)

Had cryobiologists and cryonicists achieved a rapport early on, even a modest rapport, things might have been very different. Funding for cryobiological research would likely have been broader and the labor pool of people available for lobbying and support of organ preservation would have been many times what it is now. A number of very bright young people deeply interested in cryonics and desirous of a career in cryobiology would have chosen that career path, instead of the ones they chose (rather than face the hurdles they knew would stand in their way). What's more, these people would have been highly motivated.

It is interesting to note that by far the greater part of the practical progress made in organ cryopreservation has been made by cryonicist cryobiologists "in the closet." This is no accident. There can also be no doubt that many, many times more research dollars would have been pumped into cryobiology had competent credentialed investigators been willing to undertake brain cryopreservation research; this is particularly true of recent years with the attraction of individuals of major wealth (Forbes 400 caliber) to the cryonics community.

The price has been very high. For cryonicists it has meant greatly increased resistance/hostility from the media and reduced/delayed public acceptance of the program. For cryobiologists it has meant atrophy of the entire discipline, due to their having robbed themselves of cryobiology's most dramatic and proper central goal: human suspended animation.

The Future

What of the future? What does the coming decade or two hold for the relationship between cryobiologists and cryonicists? This is, of course, an impossible question to answer. Much depends upon whether you are a pessimist or an optimist. Since I am a short-term pessimist and a long-term optimist, I shall cover the pessimistic scenario first since I think it the most likely—at least for the near and intermediate future.

Cryobiologists are unlikely to be persuaded of the "rationality" or "reasonableness" of cryonics any time soon. Indeed, many of the most polarized and vituperative opponents of cryonics are the younger members of the Society. While there has been some diminution of the criticism leveled against cryonics by cryobiologists in recent months, I believe that this has been largely as a result of the aggressive stance cryonicists have taken regarding prior comments. It's been shown we can "win" and that we can embarrass them publicly by challenging their unsupported, dogmatic, and often scientifically ridiculous statements. This aggressive response has tempered their commentary and made them a little more thoughtful and much less confrontational.

I believe, though, that they will re-group. It is certainly clear that they remain full of hate and unconvinced of any possible good to our undertaking. In my opinion no technical advances in the field of organ cryopreservation—or even successful cryopreservation of the kidney, liver, or heart—will change their position. In fact, I believe it will make them even more aggressive in trying to destroy cryonics.

I predict that if a workable method of cryopreserving organs is developed, there will be efforts to prevent its application to suspension patients. I also predict that this effort on the part of cryobiologists will have broad government support. Under new FDA guidelines an organ cryopreservation method and the equipment used to apply it would be classified as a medical procedure and a medical device, respectively. It is now very clear that the FDA intends to expand the scope of its power to controlling the application of medical devices and procedures as well as their unapproved use. I believe the evidence is clear that the Society for Cryobiology will both demand and support a ban on the use of organ cryopreservation techniques for any unapproved use.

I realize that this is quite a startling and radical position. I base it not on personal enmity or "gut feel" but rather on the remarks made by cryobiologists, both public and private, to the effect that they consider cryonics immoral and that people have, in effect, a duty to die.

It is unlikely that any successful organ cryopreservation technique developed in the foreseeable future will be applicable to the whole organism. It is much more likely that such technology will only be reliably applicable to a single organ such as the kidney, heart, liver, or brain. Viable cryopreservation of the brain with or without an accompanying less-successfully cryopreserved body will greatly increase the credibility of cryonics without proving its workability, and as a consequence greatly polarize and motivate our opponents. It may be small consolation that—at that time—

the least of our worries may be the opposition of the Society for Cryobiology. It might be argued that this is already the case; the California Department of Health Services, the California Medical Board, and their Counsel, the California Attorney General, are formidable opponents enough.

The lesson here is a harsh and sobering one: things are likely to get much worse before they get better and we would do well not to count on a thaw in relations between cryobiologists and cryonicists any time soon.

Of course, a variety of more optimistic scenarios can also be offered for consideration. It is possible that successful cryopreservation of a solid organ such as a kidney or liver would soften cryobiological hostility. Certainly it can be argued that successful cryopreservation of the mammalian brain would go a long way towards achieving this end and some both inside and outside the cryobiological community have argued that it will.

My problem with this scenario is that a successfully cryopreserved brain isn't the same as a successfully cryopreserved person in the eyes of many (including some cryonicists). There will no doubt be many who would argue against cryonics even MORE strenuously if they actually thought cryonicists capable of rendering patients' brains into a state of suspended animation while still damaging their bodies in ways medicine cannot at that time repair. Certainly the ability to suspend the brain in a non damaged state would elevate consideration of cryonics to a par with medicine, and perhaps cause it to be reclassified as such.

In the long run there can be little doubt that cryobiologists and cryonicists will have a meeting of the minds, if cryonics persists and if suspended animation is developed. However, the utility of any such union will be greatly attenuated by the time it occurs. The intervening years to decades will probably be played out on the field of battle, much as the past two decades have.

It took the efforts of one General Walter Dornberger to convince Nazi establishment scientists of the utility of Robert Goddard's dream and silence the laughter of so-called serious planetary astronomers at his "childish" notions of doing astronomy from space. When Dornberger's bombs began dropping on their heads near the end of World War II, they finally had no choice but to take notice.

It is my confident and unhappy prediction that equally dramatic events will have to occur before cryobiologists and cryonicists find peaceful co-existence and even cooperation a possibility. ■

HISTORY OF ALCOR

A BRIEF HISTORY OF ALCOR

FROM ALCOR'S WEBSITE

In 1964, a physics teacher named Robert Ettinger published *The Prospect of Immortality*, a book which promoted the concept of cryonics to a wide audience. Ettinger subsequently founded his own cryonics organization.

In 1972, Alcor was incorporated as the Alcor Society for Solid State Hypothermia in the State of California by Fred and Linda Chamberlain. (The name was changed to Alcor Life Extension Foundation in 1977.) The nonprofit organization was conceived as a rational, technology-oriented cryonics organization that would be managed on a fiscally conservative basis by a self perpetuating Board. Alcor advertised in direct mailings and offered seminars in order to attract members and bring attention to the cryonics movement. The first of these seminars attracted 30 people.

On July 16, 1976, Alcor performed its first human cryopreservation. That same year, research in cryonics began with initial funding provided by the Manrise Corporation. At this time, Alcor's office consisted of a mobile surgical unit in a large van. Trans Time, Inc., a cryonics organization in the San Francisco Bay Area, provided long-term patient storage until Alcor began doing its own storage in 1982.

In 1977, articles of incorporation were filed in Indianapolis by the Institute for Advanced Biological Studies (IABS) and Soma, Inc. IABS was a nonprofit research startup led by a young cryonics enthusiast named Steve Bridge, while Soma was intended as a for-profit organization to provide cryopreservation and human storage services. Its president, Mike Darwin, subsequently became a president of Alcor. Bridge filled the same position many years later. IABS and Soma relocated to California in 1981. (Soma was disbanded while IABS merged with Alcor in 1982.)

In 1978, Cryovita Laboratories was founded by Jerry Leaf, who had been teaching surgery at UCLA. Cryovita was a for-profit organization which provided cryopreservation services for Alcor in the 1980s. During this time Leaf also collaborated with Michael Darwin in a series of hypothermia experiments in which dogs were resuscitated with no measurable neurological deficit after hours in deep hypothermia, just a few degrees above zero Celsius. The blood substitute which was developed for these experiments became the basis for the washout solution used at Alcor. Together, Leaf and Darwin developed a standby-transport model for human cryonics cases with the goal of intervening immediately after cardiac arrest and minimizing ischemic injury. (Leaf was cryopreserved by Alcor in 1991; since 1992 Alcor has provided its own cryopreservation as well as patient-storage services.) Today, Alcor is the only full-service cryonics organization that performs remote standbys.

Alcor grew slowly in its early years, before the concept of nanotechnology helped to legitimize the possibility that future science could repair cell damage caused by freezing. The organization counted only 50 members in 1985, which was the year it cryopreserved its third patient.[1]

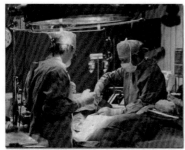

In 1986 some of Alcor's members formed Symbex, a small investment company which funded a building in Riverside, California, for lease by Alcor. That same year, Eric Drexler introduced the concept of nanotechnology in his landmark book, *Engines of Creation.* Alcor moved from Fullerton, California, to the new building in Riverside in 1987.

Alcor personnel prepare patient A-1068 for cryopreservation in Fullerton, California, 1985

Alcor cryopreserved a member's companion animal in 1986, and two people in 1987. Three human cases were handled in 1988, and one in 1989.

By 1990 Alcor had grown to 300 members. In response to concerns that the California facility was too small and vulnerable to earthquake risk, the organization purchased a building in Scottsdale, Arizona, in 1993 and moved its patients to it in 1994.

In 1997, after a substantial effort led by then-president Steve Bridge, Alcor formed the Patient Care Trust as an entirely separate entity to manage and protect the funding for cryopatients. Alcor remains the only cryonics organization to segregate and protect patient funding in this way.

In 2001 Alcor adapted cryoprotectant formulas from published scientific literature into a more concentrated formula capable of achieving ice-free preservation (vitrification) of the human brain ("neurovitrification").

Near the end of 2002 Alcor embarked on an ambitious expansion project, taking over another unit in its Scottsdale building (where remaining units currently are rented

---

1   Alcor then had two additional patients, inherited from another organization, plus Dr. Bedford, who was technically then in custody of his son and stored on premises also occupied by Alcor.

to other tenants). The first issue of an online newsletter, *Alcor News*, was distributed late in 2002. During 2003, new staff members joined the organization and work continued to create a new patient care bay, operating room, and laboratory area. A truck was purchased for conversion as an ambulance that would be large enough to permit surgical procedures. Alcor made radical changes to its medications to conform with results of resuscitation research, and purchased the prototype of an intermediate temperature storage device that promises to reduce or eliminate the risk of fracturing in cryopatients. ∎

Where did the name Alcor come from and what does it mean?

By Fred Chamberlain III and Linda Chamberlain
Cryonics, August, 1994

In September of 1970, we were asked to come up with a name for a rescue team for the Cryonics Society of California (CSC). In view of our logical destiny (the stars), we searched through star catalogs and other books on the subject, hoping to find a star with a name that could serve as a cryonics acronym. "Alcor", 80 Ursae Majoris, was just what we had been looking for. It not only had some acronymal "fit" for cryonics but was symbolic for its historic use as a test for eyesight and was located in a very well known constellation.

Alcor, a companion star of Mizar in the "Big Dipper's" handle, is approximately fifth magnitude, barely within the threshold of human vision. Additionally, it is quite close to Mizar from an angular standpoint, and dimmer. Only with excellent eyesight can one tell there are two stars rather than just one. For thousands of years, people in 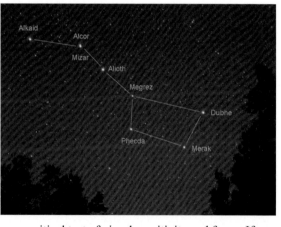 the Middle East have used Alcor as a critical test of visual sensitivity and focus. If you could see Alcor, you had excellent vision indeed. In the early days of cryonics itself, few people could see the need for a rescue team, or even the need for cryonics itself. Symbolically, then, Alcor would be a "test" of vision as regards life extension.

As an acronym, ALCOR is a close if not perfect fit with "Allopathic Cryogenic Rescue." We could have forced a five word string, but these three seemed sufficient. Allopathy (as opposed to Homeopathy) is a medical perspective wherein "any treatment which improves the prognosis is valid." Cryogenic preservation is the most powerful method known in halting the rapid, entropic disorganization of living matter following clinical death. Rescue differentiates a cryonics approach from (yet to be developed) proven suspended animation. The acronymal interpretation of ALCOR is therefore "use of a cryogenic procedure, though unproven, to preserve structure and potential viability, since failing to do so allows further disorganization to occur and reduces the probability (prognosis) of reversal and reanimation at any future time".

Some of these thoughts were presented at a CSC dinner meeting in the autumn of 1970. A number of people who have subsequently become members of the ALCOR Life Extension Foundation were present at that gathering. Over the months that followed, it became increasingly evident that the leadership of CSC did not truly desire and would not support or even tolerate a rescue team concept. Less than one year after the 1970 dinner meeting, we severed all ties with CSC and incorporated the "Rocky Mountain Cryonics Society" in the State of Washington. The articles and by-laws of this organization specifically provided for "Alcor Members," who were to be the rescue team core of activity. Difficulties in securing non-profit status in Washington then led to reincorporation in California, this time under the name "Alcor Society for Solid State Hypothermia." In the late seventies, to further broaden the organization's objectives, the present name (ALCOR Life Extension Foundation) was adopted.

Despite many transitions, the symbolism of the name remains. How long will it take for more people to see that "Ashes to ashes and dust to dust" is a meaningless destiny... to see that it is possible to reach for a distant tomorrow... perhaps to attain it... to see ALCOR for what it really is... a vehicle with which to attempt that fascinating voyage?! ■

NEW HOME, NEW LIFE: ALCOR MOVES TO ARIZONA

BY STEPHEN W. BRIDGE
Cryonics, 2nd Quarter, 1994

When last we saw our intrepid band of cryonics explorers, they had formed a company to purchase a building in Scottsdale, Arizona. The building was bought, plans were made... and then everyone sat and watched while the brave scouts (Dave Pizer and I) worked on getting the Arizona Department of Health Services to approve the permits necessary to bring our suspended patients into Arizona.

Now it's April. The DHS approved our permits, and the pioneer wagons rolled east across the desert. The patients have been in Scottsdale since February 21st, and the staff have been here since March 3rd. All of the problems aren't yet solved (are they ever?), but our direction is positive and we're delighted to be here.

Let's recap some past history before getting into new details. (I will caution readers new to these discussions that legal issues dealing with cryonic suspension patients use terms like "human remains," "interment," and "anatomical gifts." While we refer to members in suspension as "patients"—and fully consider them as such—we cannot yet make a legal case for them being "alive." Therefore we are constricted to the use of laws dealing with anatomical gifts and dead human beings in order to acquire legal custody. We have no choice but to work within this framework and attempt to use it to the advantage of ourselves and our patients.)

Alcor's Board of Directors had been looking to move Alcor out of the Riverside facility for several years. We had outgrown the building not long after moving into it in 1987 with two full-time staff and with six patients. By early 1993, we had seven full-time staff and 27 patients. Additionally, in late 1992, as part of the Conditional Use Permit issued by the City of Riverside, we were forced to swallow a "poison pill" of a ban on animal research. In the beginning of 1993, we discovered that building code-mandated changes to the building and grounds might cost us as much as $50,000 to perform.

Combine this with the growing awareness of the earthquake damage risk in Riverside, which is in an especially vulnerable position near the San Andreas Fault, and the answer was clear: get out of town. Over the past couple of years, one of the places we had looked at most closely was Scottsdale, Arizona, near Phoenix. The central valley in Arizona has very low seismic risk, and animal research is permitted in the Scottsdale Airpark, a high-tech development in one of the most desirable areas of Maricopa County. Further discussion with Scottsdale's Planning and Development Department resulted in a statement from the city that cryonics was also compatible with the Airpark's I-1 zoning.

In June of 1993, Alcor Director and Treasurer David Pizer (a resident of Phoenix) brought to the Board's attention a building for sale in the Airpark. The building was 19,800 sq. ft. and about 12 years old. It was divided into 11 units, some of which were leased; but some space was available which could be used by Alcor. The building was for sale for $770,000 (a price which later turned out to be almost $10.00 a square foot less than most other comparable buildings in the area). Alcor's Directors voted to make an offer on the building and to put down a $30,000 deposit.

At that point the amount of work suddenly quadrupled. We had 90 days to form a company to purchase the building, raise funds, and investigate the legalities and practicalities of moving a cryonics company into Arizona.

Dave Pizer and I formed *Cryonics Property, LLC,* a Limited Liability Company (LLC). An LLC is a new kind of Arizona company which combines the advantages of a corporation and a limited partnership. Several Alcor members and Alcor itself bought Interests (shares) in the LLC. Many other Alcor members sent in donations from $10.00 to $10,000 to cover Alcor's moving and remodeling expenses. This fund-raising was more difficult than we had anticipated, because it was begun during a period of intense disagreement among many active Alcor members over a wide variety of issues. The purchase of this building and the possible move to Arizona became yet two more footballs kicked onto the political field of the time.

To address the potential governmental/regulatory problems in Arizona, Dave and I (often with Dr. Mark Voelker, another Alcor Director living in Arizona at that time) engaged in a series of meetings with the Mayor of Scottsdale, Scottsdale Planning and Development, the Maricopa County Medical Examiner, and the Arizona Department of Health Services. The most complicated meetings were with the DHS, since it was likely that most of our work with patients (especially as Anatomical Donations) would fall under the jurisdiction of that Department.

There were several questions which needed to be answered by the DHS. How do we fill out the Death Certificate and Disposition Permits for anatomical donation and cryonic suspension? Do we have to register as a storage facility? Are neuropatients considered "bodies" or (as in California) "tissue samples"? The DHS staff, while a bit startled that a cryonics group was planning on moving to Arizona, was friendly and helpful and tried very hard to deal with our questions open-mindedly. The first two questions were easily answered; but the third created some sincere head-scratching. Apparently the Arizona DHS staff (unlike the California version) doesn't ordinarily sit around debating frozen heads over coffee breaks.

These issues were finally solved, but one administrative regulation dealing with dead bodies was brought to our attention by Gregg Jacquin, Associate Director for the DHS: "A body kept in a private or public vault, including a receiving vault, longer than 15 days shall be placed in an airtight casket or other container." This was potentially a big problem, since liquid nitrogen is constantly evaporating and CANNOT be kept sealed up. Of course, we pointed out that we did not use a "vault" under the meaning of this regulation and that such a regulation did not appear to be applied to other anatomical donations in the state. For instance, the medical students at the University of Arizona College of Medicine were certainly not performing cadaver dissections while locked inside an "airtight container." We also explained to Mr. Jacquin that tissue kept in liquid nitrogen did not pose a public health threat.

We thought the problem had been taken care of, so we proceeded on with plans. In September, 1993, Cryonics Property, LLC, closed on the building. Three days later we received a letter from Mr. Jacquin stating that this issue had NOT been resolved. Hastily, we hired Phoenix attorney Ron Carmichael (a fortuitous find for us, since he knew a lot of the "right" people, had the right attitude, and liked us, to boot) and arranged an early November meeting with Mr. Jacquin and his staff, plus Terri Skladany of the Attorney General's Office.

The meeting did not go particularly well. Mr. Jacquin insisted that this regulation applied to ALL bodies in Arizona, whether anatomical donations or not, and stated he was still concerned (in the face of all scientific evidence) that human tissue stored in liquid nitrogen posed a potential public health hazard. Ms. Skladany also expressed her concerns that the regulations be properly followed. We invited Mr. Jacquin and any other staff or experts he wished to bring to visit us in Riverside and see our operation first hand; but he declined.

This put us in a bit of a quandary. We didn't know what the next step was; Mr. Jacquin shortly let us know that he was asking the Arizona State Board of Funeral Directors and Embalmers to investigate the situation for possible regulation. We took a deep breath and gave out a long collective sigh—another agency to meet with and explain cryonics to. Was there no end to this?

Fortunately, about this time it dawned on us (literally dawned on me while taking my morning shower) that if this regulation were applied to anatomical donations, it would make it impossible for anyone in Arizona to donate their entire bodies for medical or scientific research. Little research could be performed in 15 days, and none could be performed in a sealed container. However, Arizona law was quite explicit (in two separate laws) that residents of Arizona do have the right to donate their remains to science and otherwise have the right to dictate the disposition of their "human remains." Enforcing the "sealed container" regulation would mean that an administrative regulation was taking precedent over a legislative statute. Clearly that is not the way laws operate.

We made this case in letters to the Funeral Board and the DHS. The Funeral Board was concerned primarily with our relationships with morticians and did not have any interest in regulating us. However, we had some good fortune when Julie Tolleson, another Assistant Attorney General at the Funeral Board meeting, became interested in our case. In conversations with Ron Carmichael and me, she agreed with our position on regulation vs. statute and agreed to look into it further.

From then on, cooperation grew steadily better on this issue. We don't know the entire story of what discussions went on in private; but we do know our attorney spent a lot of hours on the phone explaining our position to as many government officials as would listen. As the pressure on me from Alcor's Directors began to mount ("Come on, Steve. Haven't you gotten them to answer you yet?"), it still appeared to me that our point was finally getting across.

At some point in January, the DHS conceded that the sealed container regulation was no longer an issue, and the last remaining problems lay in properly handling the transit permits from California to Arizona. One end of that had been solved in California with an immense amount of sudden cooperation from... the California Department of Health Services? Yes, that's right. Now that we were *leaving*, they wanted those Disinterment and Transit forms to be processed as rapidly as possible. It took Alcor more than five years to get a registered death certificate and disposition permit on Richard Clair Jones, yet I got the disinterment/transit permit in about five minutes. Admittedly, part of this was due to a new attorney at the State DHS, who actually appeared to be a "public servant," and to new, friendly (even interested) staff at the Riverside County Health Department.

Once that end was solved, our attorney was able to point out the various legal reasons why the State of Arizona should then issue the transit permits from their end. Since the outcome was looking pretty sure now, we sent Tanya Jones and Scott Herman over to Scottsdale to begin painting and remodeling so the building would be ready for our arrival. After another couple of weeks of holding our breath (complicated by some sudden unrelated legislative problems in the DHS that side-tracked them), the transit forms were in our hand. A few days later, on February 21, 1994, the patients made their trip to Scottsdale. (See Ralph Whelan's article "Determined Not to Lose Our Patients" on p. 16-17 of the 2nd Quarter 1994 (April, 1994) issue of *Cryonics* for details on the physical aspects of the move.)

We then spent two frantic weeks packing for the move of the operating room, offices, and personal items of Mike Perry, Joe Hovey and Hugh Hixon. It is amazing how much stuff (that is the only word to describe the variety) can be crowded into one building and two mini-warehouses. It is also amazing how much of it should have been thrown away years ago. (Anyone inclined to sneer should first examine their own possessions next time they move.) Of course, Ralph, Tanya, Derek Ryan, and myself also had to find a few dozen hours at our homes to pack up our household items. (Scott had already brought most of his personal items to Scottsdale while helping to prepare our new space for occupancy.)

The two truck loads of administrative items and one truck load of our personal possessions finally arrived in Scottsdale the last week in March, along with several pretty exhausted Alcor employees and volunteers. Even at that we hadn't quite gotten everything, and we had been one person short for driving vehicles. Hugh drove the ambulance to Arizona and left his own vehicle at the airport. So a few days later we sent Hugh and Scott back to Riverside one last time to get Hugh's vehicle, empty Hugh's mini-warehouse, and finish cleaning up the old building.

Setting up the operating room had been first priority, of course, and we were only down for less than 48 hours. Even then we had the capability to perform a patient stabilization, transport, and beginning stages of a suspension with our ambulance and remote transport kit.

We were extremely fortunate in finding a solution to one huge problem we had completely failed to see: what do you do with three truckloads of equipment, desks, boxes, refrigerators, etc. while you're deciding where to place everything? The truckers have to have the truck unpacked as rapidly as possible, and it would have been chaotic to simply fill all available space in the new units with boxes and equipment. Leaving everything out in the parking lot for two weeks didn't look like much of an option.

Happily for us, the imported beer distributor next door was at the low point of their cycle for stock (and probably had too much space leased to begin with), and they had the unit closest to us (#108) entirely empty. Alcor leased unit 108 for a staging area and the crisis was averted. It appears likely that for the time being Alcor will lease a small room in that unit for continued storage, and Hugh Hixon and Joe Hovey will lease another small area for personal storage instead of getting mini-warehouses.

The other major problem that occurred early in the move was a "problem" that we have begged for in the past and could rarely get: immense media interest. In the weeks before we moved from Riverside, the *San Diego Union* and the *Los Angeles Times* had been preparing major articles on Alcor and cryonics. They added material about the move and sent reports out over the Associated Press wire. As a matter of fact, I read the *LA Times* article at breakfast on my way out of Riverside on March 3rd. And of course the Phoenix-Scottsdale media had been primed for the move for months.

Since we arrived, the phone hasn't stopped ringing. Television, radio, newspapers, magazines: everyone wanted the scoop on "Frozen Patients on Wheels."

Fairly rapidly I arranged for print interviews with the *Scottsdale Progress Tribune*, the *Arizona Republic*, and the *Phoenix Business Journal*. Since the building's interior didn't exactly look snappy and professional yet, I put off the television stations as long as I could. Finally, I allowed two local television stations in for stories, both of which were prominently featured on the evening news and which were completely positive. I made one station, whose crew just showed up at the door our first day here, go to the bottom of the list; but when they finally did our story, it was even more upbeat than that of the other stations. Other prominent print media included *Tempo* magazine of Germany, *Yes* magazine from England, the *New York Times*, the *Chicago Tribune,* the *Indianapolis Star* (my residence for 18 years), and... (trumpets blare, please) *U.S.A. Today.*

Ralph, Derek, and I did about 28 interviews the first month we were here, and just as things started to ease off a bit, on April 6th the *U.S.A. Today* article came out. They call themselves the nation's newspaper, and they must be so, for radio stations at least. All of a sudden the phones went crazy again with requests for live radio interviews and talk shows. We did interviews in Chicago, Florida, San Antonio, Palm Springs, St. Louis, Indianapolis, Pittsburgh, Las Vegas, Atlanta, Connecticut, Seattle, Detroit, and a bunch of others I've forgotten. Most prominently, we were on "Canadian World Tonight" with Phillip Till and Mutual Network's "Jim Bohannon Show."

Amazingly, with the exception of some insensitive sarcasm on the part of the *LA Times* and one couple of idiot morning "comedians" in San Bernadino (who didn't even bother to talk to us), the press coverage was *completely positive and friendly*. This was exceptionally true here in Arizona, but was scarcely diminished elsewhere. I have been involved in cryonics since 1977, when most press coverage (if you could get a writer or editor to write some space filler) and most audience reaction at talks (if anyone came at all) was "Look at these weirdos!" Beginning in 1986 with the publication of *Engines of Creation* (K. Eric Drexler, Anchor-Doubleday), we noticed a significant change in the seriousness with which people took this idea. The initial bad press surrounding the Dora Kent case in early 1988 slowly changed to positive stories about the brave individualists battling the government, a change that became more marked in the reporting of Thomas Donaldson's court battle to preserve his brain in 1990.

But it seems that even more has changed today. The attitude of most of the reporters and interviewers this year seems to be: "There are lot of amazing developments in science and medicine today. Here are some people banking on those developments to change the way we look at death." Yes, a lot of the writers actually get the point of cryonics! Those of you who are newcomers to the field or who have not dealt with the press over the years may not fully appreciate what a massive change this represents. I'm not saying this means thousands of people will rush to sign up next month. But positive reporting from a large number of writers provides a start for more positive reporting from the next wave. An increasing number of people out of there will be getting the unconscious message that cryonics is "interesting" (instead of "weird"), "future-oriented" (instead of "sci-fi"), and "a positive choice" (instead of "desperate" or "a scam").

Our reactions from Arizona businesses and government have also been positive. When my new auto insurance agent came by to set up my policy, she was very friendly and excited to meet us. She said that she would "really have some status with my kids now." This attitude seems to prevail with most visitors, even the ones that don't know they are coming to a cryonics facility. Quite a number of students have already been in for tours, and we have spoken to two "Death and Dying" classes and a retired adults club at a local community center.

This week we also had a tour for representatives of the Department of Health Services, the Attorney General's Office, and the head of the Committee on Health Care of the Arizona House of Representatives. It is clear we will continue to deal with these agencies and individuals in the future, and I think we are off to a very positive start. It is likely that some kind of cryonics regulations may be put in place here in the next year or two; but we look on this as potentially positive. We are getting the opportunity to influence those regulations in an active manner, and regulation in itself can provide a type of acceptance or legitimization. These are perhaps scary words to our more libertarian members and readers; but states WILL eventually regulate cryonics. That's what states DO. It could be to our advantage to have the first regulations here where we are building comparatively friendly relations.

Most of you will want to know how the money worked out. We raised just about enough money for our initial moving and remodeling plans. Unfortunately part of that money is still in donated shares of Symbex Property Group (the company which owns the Riverside Building), which can't become liquid until the building is sold. Our cash flow for finishing some tasks has become tight, and we would still welcome donations toward making this building the best we can.

In future issues of the magazine we will begin listing plans we are developing and enacting for improvements in suspension patient security, laboratory and operating room equipment, and transport capability. This week we have also begun taking the first steps toward developing a new research plan and plans for suspension team training. Please let us know if any of these areas interest you. We will be needing advice, volunteers, and funding for each of them.

Now we've parked our wagons, put up the new home, and settled in. We're proud of our new home and would love to show it off to you. Hope to see you soon. ■

THE ALCOR PATIENT CARE TRUST

BY STEPHEN W. BRIDGE AND BRIAN WOWK, PH.D.

Cryonics, 3rd Quarter, 1997
(Updated version published online 9-20-13, edited for this publication 8-10-2014)

In the early days of cryonics, patient long-term care was paid for by periodic payments from still-living relatives. This system simply did not work, and resulted in the loss of a number of patients – but never at Alcor.

At Alcor, patient long-term care costs are paid from the Patient Care Trust. This conservative funding arrangement is designed to cover the cost of patient long-term care solely from the income from the Trust, thereby assuring that such funding will continue indefinitely into the future. The irrevocable Patient Care Trust is included under Alcor's tax-exempt status, but nevertheless is a separate legal entity that provides liability protection for these assets. This arrangement is one of the reasons our members have confidence in Alcor.

It doesn't do any good to use the most advanced techniques to get our members into cryopreservation unless we can *keep them there*, as well as build capital to eventually fund revival and reintegration. Ongoing care for cryopreservation patients is the number one element of our purpose in being cryonicists, and *financial protection* for the patients is a critical component of this. There is no use in starting this possibly centuries-long project, if we don't do centuries-long financial planning. Providing this kind of protection through a conservative, long-term view of long-term care costs is one of the main reasons why cryopreservation costs so much.

When an Alcor member is cryopreserved, a significant portion of the member's funding is placed into the Patient Care Trust. The investment income from this money is then used for the ongoing long-term care costs. Alcor accepts only secure funding arrangements where the entire funding amount is available within a few days after the legal death of the patient. Most people arrange this through a simple life insurance policy, with Alcor as the beneficiary, although other arrangements are possible. Because of our non-profit 501(c)(3) charitable status, Alcor does not keep separate funding accounts by patient. All patient care funding is grouped together in the Patient Care Trust so that all patients are treated equally (with the exception of the inherent differences between whole-body patients and neuro patients).

Creating the Alcor Patient Care Trust

The Patient Care Fund (before it was a separate Trust) was originally part of Alcor's regular internal fund accounting system. By late 1991, this fund approached one million dollars and was by far the largest segment of Alcor's assets. The Alcor Board realized that a better way was needed to protect this money. For one thing, it was a possible "deep pocket" in any potential lawsuit against any part of Alcor's operation. For another thing, there was the potential temptation to raid the fund for other purposes during tight financial times. So the idea was born to create a legally separate Trust to shield the fund from either of these possibilities.

> A trust is a legal device by which property is held by one person (the *trustee*) for the benefit of another (the *beneficiary*). The person who sets up the trust is called the *settlor*. The property that is held in trust is known as the *corpus* or *trust fund.*
> — Brown, Byers, Lawler, *Business Law* (Macmillan/McGraw-Hill, Seventh Edition, 1989).

Creating the Trust turned out to be much easier said than done, and the process ended up taking almost eight years. The unique business Alcor was in necessitated the breaking of new legal ground in creating this Trust. For one thing, although the patients are supposed to be the true beneficiaries of the Trust, the patients have no legal existence and hence could not be the beneficiaries (instead, Alcor was made the beneficiary).

Over a period of nearly four years, Alcor consulted with several expert trust attorneys who did nothing more than educate Alcor on the difficulty of creating this Trust. Finally, in 1995, Alcor found an Arizona trust attorney, Larry Stevens, who was willing to take on the task. "Yes, this can be done" he said, "but it will require some unique legal thought." Alcor needed to write much of the Trust itself because only Alcor could understand what it wanted to accomplish, and there was a lot of internal debate on exactly how to do that. Within the next three years, the final draft of the Trust was written by attorney Larry Stevens and former Alcor President Steve Bridge, with input from Alcor Board members, various attorneys, and other thoughtful reviewers.

In May 1997, the original Trust document was approved unanimously by the Alcor Board of Directors and the five original Trustees. The final amendments made in 1999 were also approved unanimously by both the Alcor Directors and the Trustees.

The Trust Document

You can read the entire Alcor Patient Care Trust document in the Library section of Alcor's website. (http://www.alcor.org/Library/html/patientcaretrust.htm) Below are a few highlights of how the Trust operates in practice.

• As of May 1999, the Trust is irrevocable. This means that the Alcor Board cannot ever cancel the Trust until the purposes of the Trust are fulfilled. Since the purposes of the Trust can be summarized as "keep all the patients in cryopreservation until they can all be repaired and revived," this Trust is going to be in existence for a long time.

- The Trust Board consists of five persons, all of whom must be cryopreservation members of Alcor. One and only one Trustee must be a member of Alcor's Board of Directors. Three of the Trustees must have a relative or significant other currently in cryopreservation.

- The members of the Trust Board are appointed by the Alcor Board of Directors. They have five year terms, staggered so that one term expires each year. If a suitable person who has a relative in cryopreservation cannot be found, a Temporary Trustee with a term of up to one year can be appointed who is not a relative (so far this has not occurred).

- No Trust Board member may be an employee or officer of Alcor, or receive any compensation from Alcor or the Trust other than expenses incurred by carrying out duties involved in managing the Trust.

- If the income from the Trust in any given year exceeds by 30% the actual patient care expenses for that year, the additional income above that 30% can be placed in a separate account to fund research in procedures to revive the patients. If the repair and revival of patients ever becomes feasible, the Trust may expend whatever amount is necessary to accomplish this, provided it is done in such a manner as not to jeopardize the care of any patients remaining in biostasis.

- Each month, Alcor bills the Patient Care Trust for Alcor's expenses related to patient care. The specific costs related to patient care are itemized according to a formula mutually agreed upon by Alcor and the Patient Care Trust. According to the current formula, the Trust pays for all direct liquid nitrogen costs plus an allocated percentage of staff cost applied to general overhead (currently set at 9.4%). In addition, the Trust pays for direct capital expenditures related to patient care, such as dewars (the specialized containers for long-term care of the patients) and construction work on the Patient Care Bay.

Trust Assets

As of December 31, 2013, the Alcor Patient Care Trust Fund had total assets of $9,464,543, invested as follows:

- 84% of the shares in Cryonics Property, LLC, the limited liability company that owns the Alcor building (all other shares being owned by Alcor members). These shares (representing the Trust's equity in the Alcor building) are valued at $474,400 based on the original purchase price of the building (they would be higher at current market value). Alcor pays rent to Cryonics Property, LLC. Since Alcor does not occupy the entire building, there are additional tenants who also pay rent, which provides some additional value for the Patient Care Trust.

- 100% of the mortgage on the Alcor building, valued at $100,297.

- Capital equipment (primarily dewars) and leasehold improvements (capital improvements to the Patient Care Bay) valued at $426,357. These are carried on the books and subject to depreciation, but are not assets that would be liquidated.

- A Research Account with a book value of $190,000.

- A cash account in which income (other than investment account income) is placed, expenses are disbursed, and money is transferred to the investment account. On the above date it contained $359,626.

- An Accounts Receivable on the above date of $119,893.

- Miscellaneous assets of $12,340.

- An investment account held at the firm of Morgan Stanley, containing $8,256,030. Thus far, no withdrawals from this account have ever been made.

The balance for the Patient Care Trust Morgan Stanley Investment Account and other investment details are posted on Alcor's website monthly: http://www.alcor.org/AboutAlcor/patientcaretrustfund.html

A Testimonial by Attorney Gary Meade

As an attorney as well as an Alcor member and someone who has a loved one in cryopreservation, I am pleased to give my wholehearted professional and personal endorsement of the Alcor Patient Care Trust. I believe the Trust will provide the best means of legally protecting the patient care fund assets, thereby helping to ensure the long-term care of the patients in cryopreservation. That is the reason I enthusiastically agreed to serve as a Trustee and Chairperson of the Trust [Gary served from 1997 to 2002].

Conceptually, the Trust is an excellent idea. The assets in the patient care fund have been placed in trust, to be held by the Patient Care Trust as a separate legal entity. This will provide the maximum legal protection for these assets, both against claims by others as well as possible misuse for purposes other than patient care. The

Trust Agreement requires the Trustees to act in accordance with the Trust's legal purpose, which is "providing care" for the patients in cryopreservation. The Alcor Life Extension Foundation is the legal beneficiary of the Trust, and as such has the absolute legal right to enforce the Trust Agreement and ensure that the Trustees act in such a manner.

The Trust itself is well-planned and skillfully crafted. This is the first trust ever established to care for those who are legally dead and who therefore have no rights under the law. This presented some novel legal challenges. The drafters of the Trust overcame these and I believe the completed Trust successfully accomplishes everything it was intended to do.

Everyone with an interest in cryonics owes a tremendous debt of gratitude to those who worked so hard to set up the Trust, including the outside trust counsel, the Alcor Board, and especially Steve Bridge. Of course, those having the greatest such debt are the patients themselves. It may be presumptuous of me to do so, but I would like to extend on their behalf a most sincere "Thank you" to all for a job very well done.

The Patient Care Trust Board

When the Alcor Patient Care Trust was originally formed, the five Trustees were Gary Meade (attorney), Warren Robertson (CPA), Thomas Donaldson (mathematician), Robert A. Schwarz (HVAC mechanic), and Carlos Mondragon (banker and Alcor Director).

Current members of the Alcor Patient Care Trust Board are: Robert A. Schwarz (retired), David Brandt-Erichsen (genetics research technician and web designer), Michael Riskin (Psychotherapist, CPA, and Alcor Director), David A. Kekich (Insurance executive and venture capitalist), and Michael F. Korns (computer and financial researcher).

For more information on the current Trustees, see Alcor's web site: http://www.alcor.org/AboutAlcor/patientcaretrustfund.html ■

RESEARCH IN CRYONICS

EVALUATION OF THE CONDITION OF DR. JAMES H. BEDFORD AFTER 24 YEARS OF CRYONIC SUSPENSION

BY MICHAEL DARWIN
Cryonics, August, 1991

Introduction

On 12 January, 1967, Dr. James H. Bedford became the first man to enter cryonic suspension. The story of his suspension and his care over the intervening years is covered elsewhere.[1,2,3] The purpose of this article is to document Dr. Bedford's condition as assessed by a brief external exam conducted on 25 May, 1991. At this time, Dr. Bedford was transferred from the horizontal sealed-in-the-field (Galiso, Inc.) cryogenic dewar—into which he had been welded in April, 1970—to a state-of-the-art multipatient dewar.

Removal From The Dewar

At approximately 09:30 on 25 May the foot end of the dewar containing the patient was elevated on concrete blocks, effectively submerging the patient's head and torso. Beginning at about 10:00 AM, an abrasive cutting wheel was used to open the outer shell of the dewar, in the process breaking the vacuum (at 10:15). The outer head was then removed and the reflective barrier in the annulus between the inner and outer cans, consisting of multiple layers of dimpled aluminized mylar (Dimplar), was torn away. The inner head was then opened by an abrasive cutting wheel; this process was completed at 10:55.

Mike Darwin and Jerry Leaf transfer Dr. Bedford from his original "cryocapsule."

The metal framework (bed) supporting the patient was then slid out of the unit. The patient, contained in a sleeping bag, was freed from the bed by cutting the nylon rope securing him to it. The patient was then transferred to an insulated, open-topped

---

1   Nelson, R.F. and Stanley, S., *We Froze The First Man,* Dell Publishing Co., Inc., New York, 1968.
2   Nelson, R.F., Personal communication, 23 September, 1982.
3   Darwin, M.G., "Dear Dr. Bedford", *Cryonics,* 12(7), 15-22 (1991).

bath of liquid nitrogen for examination and evaluation.

In order to avoid any possibility of rewarming, the patient was evaluated while submerged in liquid nitrogen. The necessity of conducting the examination under these conditions limited its scope.

Evaluation

External visual examination discloses a well-developed, well nourished male who appears younger than his 73 years. The skin on the upper thorax and neck appears discolored and erythematous from the mandible to approximately two cm. above the areolas. The area of discoloration is fairly sharply demarcated on the thorax. The head is turned to the left and two puncture marks are noted approximately 1 cm apart over the anteriomedial aspect of the sternocleidomastoid muscle (approximately paralleling the internal carotid artery). These puncture marks are clot-free and present a fresh, "cored" appearance (suggesting a large-bore needle).

The skin on the left side of the neck is distended with what appears to be a fluid bolus(es) injected into the subcutaneous space. The position of the patient's head precludes careful examination of the skin for puncture marks on the left side. There is frozen blood issuing from the mouth and nose. A smear of bright-red blood covers the skin around the nose and mouth in a pattern which appears to have been defined by a respirator mask. A larger quantity of darker red blood appears to have flowed out of the mouth during freezing to dry ice temperature, as it retains the folds and contours of the wrapping material which presumably covered the patient's face during freezing.

The eyes are partially open and the corneas are chalk-white from ice. The nares are flattened out against the face, apparently as a result of being compressed by a slab of dry ice during initial freezing. The head is fringed with short-cropped, uniformly gray hair. Several small pieces of adherent aluminized mylar are present on the occiput.

The skin on the ventral thorax, abdomen, and limbs appears free of lesions and of normal color with the following exception: the right forearm and hand appear discolored and erythematous and appear to be the site of an intravenous line or subcutaneous injection of a hemolytic or irritating product. Most of the abdomen and thorax were covered with a thin, transparent, polyethylene sheet which was reflected back to facilitate examination. The chest is covered with sparse gray hair.

Close examination of the skin on the chest over the pectoral area disclosed sinuous features that appeared to be fractures. When these were probed under the liquid with a spinal needle it was noted that the skin was discontinuous over these areas. Subsequently, two small samples of skin were secured from the edges of one of these "fractures" with the gentle use of a wood chisel. The samples are currently being maintained in liquid nitrogen vapor for subsequent ultrastructural evaluation.

It is noted that in addition to the presence of unmelted water ice obscuring the genitals, there was another mass of unmelted water ice between the right arm and abdomen, just above the pelvis. A part of this ice mass was lifted free with a spinal needle and was observed to still retain some of the original small cube structure, attesting to the fact that it had not been warmed above 0°C.

The genitals are not visible due to the presence of unmelted water ice which anchors the plastic film.

The lower legs are crossed with the right foot over the left. There is aluminized mylar tape, of the kind used to secure superinsulation inside cryogenic dewars, wrapped around the toes of both feet. This tape was removed for examination; upon rewarming the tape retained its adhesive properties. It is presumed this tape was placed after cooling to -79°C for the purpose of anchoring thermocouple probes used to monitor temperature descent in the Cryo-Care storage unit.[4]

Owing to the need to maintain the patient submerged in liquid nitrogen, and the logistic aspects attendant to his transfer from one dewar to another, the dorsal aspect of the body was not examined.

Conclusions

Overall this examination indicates that the patient has at least not been warmed above 0°C. Further, the presence of undenatured hemoglobin as evidenced by the presence of bright red blood, and the appearance of the water ice remaining on the patient, including what appeared to be loose (i.e., unrecrystalized) condensed "frost" from his cooling to -79°C suggests that rewarming was not to any high subzero temperature (i.e., it seems likely that his external temperature has remained at relatively low subzero temperatures throughout the storage interval).

Given the patient's thermal history, which consists of nearly a decade and a half of cycling between liquid nitrogen vapor temperature at 80°K and liquid nitrogen temperature at 77°K, and at least two previous instances of removal from cryogenic storage and transient exposure to ambient temperature while being transferred from storage dewar to storage dewar, it is not surprising that he should show evidence of surface fracturing.

In 1983, during examination of another patient converted from whole body to neurosuspension who had been previously rewarmed to -79°C and then cooled to -196°C a second time, external fractures were also noted.[5] However, one marked dissimilarity between the fractures present in that patient and those present in this one was that the skin in the former patient had separated from the underlying tissues in spots, sometimes presenting a "peeling paint" appearance. This phenomenon was not

---

4   Kraver, T., Personal communication, 3 June, 1991.
5   Federowicz, M., Hixon, H., and Leaf J., "Post-mortem examination of three cryonic suspension patients." *Cryonics*, (September, 1984).

observed to have occurred with this patient.

It is assumed that the erythematous discoloration observed in the skin of the jaw, neck, upper thorax, and right arm were as a result of the hypodermic injection of highly concentrated cryoprotectant solution or perhaps pure dimethylsulfoxide as has been reported by Nelson[6] and Prehoda.[7] It is the author's opinion that the nature of the discoloration is due to hemolysis from this agent(s).*

Bloody fluid issuing from the mouth and nose was a not completely unanticipated finding; photos made during the patient's transfer from the Cryo-Care storage vessel to the Galiso unit in 1970 suggest this. The character of this fluid appears to be whole blood, ruling out purging of gastric contents (an early post-mortem sign of decomposition) as a cause. The source of this blood is presumed to be pulmonary hemorrhage secondary to prolonged cardiopulmonary resuscitation and friable lungs as a result of the extensive pulmonary metastases which were the proximate cause of deanimation. It is well-established that pulmonary edema is a common consequence of prolonged closed chest cardiopulmonary resuscitation clinically[8] as well as in prolonged cardiopulmonary support of cryonic suspension patients using closed chest cardiac compression.[9] ∎

6   Nelson, R.F., Personal communication, 23 September, 1982.

7   Prehoda, R., Unpublished interview conducted in May, 1983.

8   Ornato, J.P., et al., "Measurement of ventilation during cardiopulmonary resuscitation." *Crit. Care Med.*, 11(2), 79-82 (1983).

9   Unpublished case histories of Alcor patients A-1103 and A-1036.

*   Mike Perry notes: "Robert Prehoda and B. Renault Able both indicate in published sources that the perfusate compositon was 15% DMSO with 85% Ringer's solution. The 15% concentration of DMSO is confirmed by Prehoda in a taped interview Oct. 24, 1991. Robert Nelson stated in an unpublished communcation 9 Sep. 2009 (original spelling): 'While I did not see with my own eyes the actual mixing of the 15% DMSO to 85% Ringers solution perfusate, I have every reason to believe that is exactly what was used for the perfusion of Dr. Bedford. Robert Prehoda, Dante Brunoll, Robert Ettinger and I had discussed this prior to Bedford's freezing on several occasions, and this is what Prehoda and Brunoll reported to me afterwards.' Some additional details on these sources will be found in my article on the Bedford freezing included in this volume, and an alternative explanation to hemolysis for the discoloration ('bruised' area) observed here."

A BRIEF HISTORY OF ALCOR RESEARCH

BY R. MICHAEL PERRY, PH.D.
Cryonics, 4th Quarter, 1994

Alcor's research was inaugurated Sept. 24, 1977, with the freezing of a dog. There was a brief notice in that month's *Alcor News,* a predecessor of *Cryonics,* and a more ample report by then-president Laurence Gale in *Long Life Magazine,* the following year.[1] At this time Alcor did not have its own suspension team but suspension services were performed by the Trans Time team, headed by Jerry Leaf and a few Alcor personnel. They met at a facility provided by Benjamin Schloss, Ph.D., an antiaging proponent and cryonics sympathizer (14 months later, at 65, he died of leukemia but was not frozen).[2] The anesthetized dog, a shepherd mix (as many later Alcor animals would be), was perfused with a solution formula used in the suspension, the previous year, of Alcor's first patient, Fred Chamberlain Jr. (Mr. Chamberlain was the father of Alcor cofounder Fred III.) The objectives of the experiment were to: (1) to duplicate procedures used in the preceding suspension, (2) increase skills of the suspension and rescue team, and (3) establish a baseline for future work. Like Fred Jr.'s, the dog's suspension was head-only. One of the notable results was to recover some functioning brain cells after cooling to liquid nitrogen temperature and thawing (with cell viability verified by dye uptake).

This experiment was to be the "first of a series" but in fact several years would pass before any further substantial research was done at Alcor. The next mention I find of such work is in the Oct. 1981 *Cryonics,* which reports on a gathering of cryonicists at Lake Tahoe, Sept. 11-14.[3] (This was hosted by Alcor's cofounders, Fred and Linda Chamberlain, who would stage further similar gatherings, the now well-remembered Lake Tahoe Festivals, over the next several years.) At the conference, Alcor staff member Hugh Hixon gave a brief presentation of his findings on the problem of oxygen contamination in liquid nitrogen storage vessels. Oxygen content in such a vessel that had been in use for 3 years registered 2% by volume (oxygen being also liquid at LN2 temperature), enough to cause worry in view of the corrosive properties of this highly reactive element. About a fifth of the atmospheric mass is oxygen. It thus has ample opportunity, over time, to condense inside storage vessels which in turn must have outside ventilation to accommodate the boiloff of liquid nitrogen. Some oxidation,

---

1   Laurence Gale, "Alcor Experiment: Surviving the Cold," *Long Life Magazine*, July-Aug 1978, 59.
2   Carl Carlyle, "Passing the Torch: Project 1989 Lives!" *Long Life Magazine*, Jan-Feb 1979, 2.
3   Mike Darwin, "A Cryonics Weekend," *Cryonics*, Oct 1981, 5.

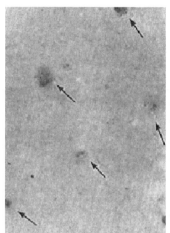

Alcor's first dog experiment, 1977: Light micrograph at 1260x magnification shows live nerve cells in dog brain (cerebral cortex) which were previously at liquid nitrogen temperature.

which could affect both organic matter and the steel vessels used to contain it, is still possible at low temperatures, though in view of a later study (again by Hugh) the problem does not appear serious, reaction rates being very greatly slowed. (For example, to get the amount of the fastest known biological reaction that happens in one second at body temperature, we would have to wait 25 million years at liquid nitrogen temperature!)[4]

Alcor's First Golden Age of research began sometime in 1983 and extended into 1987. By this time Alcor had acquired the services of two of the best research talents cryonics has seen to date, Jerry Leaf and Mike Darwin. Jerry, an instructor in thoracic surgery at UCLA, had set up his own company, Cryovita, to provide cryonics-related services, such as suspensions. (During the '80s Cryovita would work so closely with Alcor the two would virtually become one organization.) Mike was a hemodialysis technician who had been involved in cryonics-related work since grade school. Assisting them was another person with substantial skills, biochemist Hugh Hixon, who also possessed an engineering talent. Together they were able to accomplish things worthy of much better-funded institutions enjoying the support of the scientific mainstream. There are some two dozen writeups on the dog work and other projects Alcor carried out at this time, occupying many pages of *Cryonics*, so my coverage here is highly abridged. I'll report what I judge to be of greatest significance.

There's a little bit of magic (black or white, depending on your orientation) in the idea of rendering an organism clinically dead—no heartbeat or respiration, cold as a winter's day—then restoring it to life. It's an important precursor of what we are trying to accomplish through cryonics and it is disturbing to many people. It suggests, for example, such irreverent thoughts as that death is a process, not an event; an organism is a machine that can be restarted after the "vital" processes have ceased; when you're "dead" you may not really be dead; etc. It is especially inspiring, gratifying, and/or disturbing to bring back a large, warm-blooded creature from a state of lifeless cold. Alcor was the first cryonics organization to accomplish such a resuscitation, July 21, 1984. (It had been done earlier by non-cryonics researcher Gerald Klebanoff, who had

---

4   Hugh Hixon, "How Cold is Cold Enough?" Cryonics, Jan 1985, 19 (see also G. Feinberg, "Physics and Life Prolongation," *Physics Today*, Nov 1966, 45).

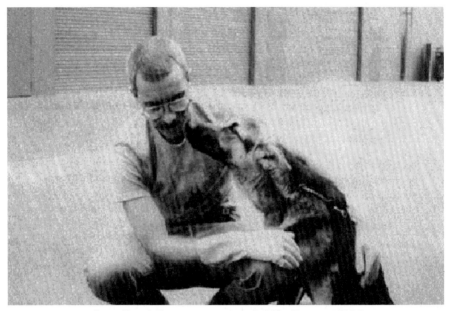

Star, Alcor's first resuscitee, with Mike Darwin, 1984

extended his results to the human clinical level by 1972.)[5] A shepherd dog, "Star," was subjected to a total body washout (replacement of blood with a chemical solution) and an hour of bloodless perfusion at 4°C, then rewarmed, transfused with blood, and resuscitated.[6] The animal made a perfect recovery, and eventually became a much-valued pet. A crucial part of the recovery process was dialysis during rewarming, with an artificial kidney machine, which allowed for normalization of blood glucose and electrolyte levels.

Aside from its suggestiveness for the much more difficult feat that cryonic resuscitation is going to be, the work was important for the procedures used in the early stages of cryonic suspension. This is when the patient is cooled from body to near-ice temperature and the blood is replaced with base perfusate, a preliminary step for the later perfusion with cryoprotectant. The success with a dog did not happen on the first try, though it did happen sooner than expected. Some changes in previous procedures were necessary (notably, use of a new base perfusate).[7] It could then be seen that the initial stages of suspension were not injurious to life, and it strengthened the case for the ultimate revivability of cryonics patients.

The success with Star was followed, within two months, by resuscitation of an

---

5   Mike Darwin, "The Dog and Phony Show," *Cryonics*, May 1987, 3, http://www.alcor.org/Library/html/DogAndPhonyShow.html, accessed 16 Feb 2015.

6   Alcor Staff, "A Brief Overview of Recent Alcor Research," *Cryonics*, Sep 1984, 13.

7   Alcor Staff, "New Perfusate Formulation," *Cryonics*, Jul 1984, 2.

animal after 4 hours of bloodless perfusion at 4°C, with full recovery, including (as far as could be ascertained) full memory and personality.[8] After this, recovery of animals after 4 hours became routine. Improvements in procedures made recovery faster and easier on the staff consisting of Alcor members, several of whom put in long volunteer hours each time to ensure success. Sometimes problems would appear. Manual ventilation of animals had to be used, for example, because of a freakish interaction between a new electrocautery tool and an electrically powered respirator that prevented recovery of several animals before it was detected.[9] Another time, an animal nearly died when, upon rewarming, it was transfused with blood that turned out to be contaminated—but the dog was saved with an artificial blood substitute.[10] In all, the experiments helped refine suspension protocols and provided invaluable training for a wide variety of emergency conditions.

Experiments with animals raise ethical issues: mainly, how it can be proper to subject innocent creatures to procedures that may cause them to suffer and die. These issues are addressed in an article that accompanies a recounting of one of the early experiments.[11] Nobody wants to see an intelligent, sensitive, friendly creature like a dog sacrificed or subjected to discomfort—that much is acknowledged. On the other hand, we are playing for very high stakes here: ultimately, nothing less than the elimination of death itself, and the hideous suffering and indignity that is often unavoidable in our journey through life. (People who think this suffering extraordinary should visit a nursing home and witness dying under the various forms of torture provided by the normal aging process.) People are worth more than animals. In trying to continue life and make it worthwhile, one is sometimes faced with choices that require a sacrifice of what is less important. We don't like to have to make those choices, but when the alternatives are worse, we justifiably make them. As has generally been the policy with animal work in cryonics, every reasonable effort was made to carry out experiments as humanely as possible, all surgical work, for example, being done under general anesthesia. Moreover, it was always an Alcor policy (and still is) never to use an animal more than once in a total body washout. If it survived and was not sacrificed (painlessly) as part of the experiment, it would then become a pet.

In addition to the dog work, there were other experiments that added knowledge or helped develop new technology. One unusual opportunity presented itself. Due to a shortage of funding, three whole-body suspension patients that had been stored at Trans Time were converted to neuropreservation; their bodies were then thawed and

8   Alcor Staff, "Two More Total Body Washouts Completed," *Cryonics*, Nov 1984, 3.
9   Alcor Staff, "TBW Success," *Cryonics*, Aug 1986, 10.
10   Alcor Staff, "Total Body Washout #7—Wrapping Up," *Cryonics*, May 1985, 11.
11   Alcor Staff, "Total Body Washouts—More Progress," *Cryonics*, Dec 1984, 3.

autopsied at Alcor.[12] In this way it was found that substantial cracking had occurred in the prior cooldown to liquid nitrogen temperature. Presumably this problem also existed with other suspensions; efforts then were made to minimize it, for example, by use of slow, controlled cooling and higher concentrations of cryoprotectant.

Another project was a study of cat brains. These were perfused and frozen under a variety of conditions, in an effort to assess problems that would occur in human suspensions. Examinations were made at the macroscopic, histological (cellular), and ultrastructural levels.[13] Results showed that, while fine structure clearly was being preserved, the preservation was not perfect. Basic questions remained unanswered, such as whether identity-critical information would be adequately retained in frozen brain tissue. (These questions are still unanswered and await better understanding of how memories are stored.)

Some important innovations affecting suspensions resulted from Alcor's research during this period. The change in perfusate was mentioned (not the last). Another achievement was the Mobile Advanced Life Support System (MALSS—now renamed Mobile Advanced Rescue Cart or MARC)—a specially equipped gurney for maintaining circulation and oxygenation while transporting a patient."[14] "Silcool," a silicone oil, replaced isopropyl alcohol as a heat exchange medium for cooling patients to dry ice temperature. (Unlike silcool, the alcohol is volatile, flammable and damaging on contact with tissue.)[15] Other innovations were made in patient storage, for example, a fire protection system (for vaults used to store neuropatients) based on water-filled pipe sections,[16] and an alarm system.

With the Dora Kent crisis that erupted at the end of 1987, and the subsequent legal battles and other problems, Alcor's research effort was slowed, though not halted entirely. Some significant accomplishments over the next few years included a computer program for modeling perfusions,[17] and more recently, an automated cooldown system.[18] Another serious blow to the research program, however, was the suspension of Jerry Leaf in 1991 followed by the departure of Mike Darwin from Alcor in 1992, to head his own research team. Early in 1993 Alcor's animal work was finally halted by local regulatory restrictions. (For the last project, that January, there was an

12   Mike Federowicz, Hugh Hixon, and Jerry Leaf, "Postmortem Examination of Three Cryonic Suspension Patients," *Cryonics*, Sep 1984, 16; Nov 1984, 13.

13   Alcor Staff, "Where We've Been and Where We're Going," *Cryonics*, Jul 1985, 1.

14   Alcor Staff, "Review of the 1986 Lake Tahoe Life Extension Festival," *Cryonics*, Nov 1986, 30 (article starts 28).

15   Alcor Staff, "Silicone Cooling Fluid," *Cryonics*, Oct 1985, 8; "Silcool," Nov 1985, 4.

16   Alcor Staff, "Cephalarium Vault," *Cryonics*, Oct 1984, 1.

17   R. Michael Perry, "Mathematical Analysis of Recirculating Perfusion Systems, with Application to Cryonic Suspension," *Cryonics*, Oct 1988, 24.

18   H. Keith Henson, "Cool Heads," *Cryonics*, Jan 1993, 6; Hugh Hixon, "Cooling Down," 3rd Quarter 1994, 33.

attempt to recover a hypothermic dog without subsequent hemodialysis; this objective was not achieved but there were tantalizing indications that it should be possible.)[19] The move from California to Arizona in February 1994 removed the prohibitions on animal work, and with other favorable conditions, including some new talent, doors again were opened for a major research effort. This will take time to acquire full momentum, but there is optimism that major discoveries and developments are in the offing.

[More recent Alcor research has focused on (1) adapting vitrification procedures, which were developed for conventional organ preservation, to the human central nervous system, and (2) developing storage at temperatures somewhat above that of liquid nitrogen to prevent cracking.]

Much thanks to Hugh Hixon for consultations during the writing of this article. ∎

---

19   Tanya L. Jones, "Research and Training Update," *Cryonics*, Feb 1993, 10.

THE 21ST CENTURY MEDICINE SEMINAR: AMAZING BREAKTHROUGHS IN CRYOBIOLOGY AND RESUSCITATION

Cryonics, 1st Quarter, 1999

After 13 years of unsuccessful attempts to improve his own best cryoprotectant formula, cryobiologist Gregory Fahy has discovered a way to develop a whole new family of compounds that should enable human organs to be vitrified in the very near future. "Vitrification" means changing a liquid to a glass-like solid as temperature falls, *without* forming ice crystals that damage cells. For twenty years, cryobiologists have questioned whether vitrification of human organs will ever be practical. The fundamental problem now seems to have been solved.

21CM's November 8, 1998 conference; a view from the audience.

Concurrently, biophysicist Brian Wowk, a former President of CryoCare Foundation, has discovered a different family of cryoprotectant compounds which enable vitrification at lower concentrations and higher temperatures. Wowk has also developed synthetic "ice blockers" that enhance many other cryoprotectants and eliminate problems associated with rewarming vitrified organs.

Finally, Mike Darwin, a former President of Alcor, has led a highly successful initiative to minimize ischemic injury—the damage that is caused by insufficient blood flow, typically when the heart stops beating. Darwin's team now holds the unofficial world record for resuscitating dogs after up to 17 minutes of "death" at normal body temperature. (Since his research has been conducted separately from the work in cryobiology, it is summarized at the end of this article.)

These multiple breakthroughs should enable preservation of human brains with minimal or even zero ice damage, and may lead to *reversible* brain cryopreservation within ten years. If this goal is achieved, cryonics will not have to rely on future technology to repair damage caused by freezing or toxicity, and will take a major step toward credibility in conventional science.

Long before that, however, the research has applications outside cryonics that should be highly profitable for 21st Century Medicine and its stockholders. Biologist Christopher Rasch and surgeon Yasumitsu Okouchi collaborated with Gregory Fahy and Brian Wowk on their work, while Steven B. Harris, MD, Sandra Russell, Joan O'Farrell, and Carlotta Pengelley participated with Mike Darwin.

21st Century Medicine was founded in 1993 by Saul Kent and Bill Faloon, long-time cryonics activists who run a lucrative vitamin mail-order business and offer information on dietary supplements via their Life Extension Foundation. In 1997, after Kent and Faloon won a long legal battle with the FDA, they purchased a second building for 21st Century Medicine, hired additional personnel, and are spending currently almost $2 million a year on research.

At a seminar on November 8th,1998 in Ontario, California, the principal researchers from 21st Century Medicine described some amazing payoffs that have resulted from the investment by Kent and Faloon, far sooner than anyone expected. The presentations were tantalizing, because key information is being withheld while patents are being filed. Still, a huge amount of information was communicated, and I can provide only a partial summary here. 21st Century Medicine is selling videotapes to

Dr. Gregory Fahy anyone who wants the complete version.

New Cryoprotectants

Brian Wowk began the presentations by describing his search for cryoprotectant molecules that would bind less readily with each other, and more readily with water molecules, thus reducing viscosity and enabling faster perfusion. "The idea that we came up with was to replace hydroxyl groups on cryoprotectant molecules with methoxyl groups," he said.

For example, propylene glycol consists of a chain of carbon atoms, with two OH (hydroxyl) atomic groups attached to the first two atoms in the chain. Wowk proposed replacing one of the hydroxyl groups with an OCH_3 (methoxyl) group, creating a methoxylated version of propylene glycol. "We can make similar modifications to a variety of other standard cryoprotectants," he said. "If you do this, you get some rather dramatic results."

In the case of propylene glycol, the methoxylated version is almost 100 times less viscous than the regular version. Ethylene glycol and glycerol can be modified in the same way, though the improvements are less extreme.

The modified compounds penetrate cells much faster than conventional cryoprotectants. Ethylene glycol is probably the most penetrating cryoprotectant known, but the methoxylated version gets into red blood cells about four times faster.

Better still, the methoxylated compounds inhibit ice formation and enable vitrification far more effectively. Wowk showed a cooling curve for a 45 percent glycerol solution, and another curve for the same concentration of methoxylated glycerol. The former indicated significant ice formation; the latter showed virtually none.

Moreover, methoxylated compounds vitrify at higher temperatures. Wowk predicted that in the future, we won't need to use liquid nitrogen for long-term storage because a suitable cocktail of methoxylated compounds should vitrify above –79 degrees Celsius (dry-ice temperature), which will reduce storage costs and the risk of structural cracking.

One problem with the new compounds is that they are more toxic to cells. However, Wowk has found that toxicity can be mitigated by mixing appropriate compounds. In the lab, viability of cells has been measured in terms of their ability to pump potassium and sodium ions across their membranes, while they are exposed to cryoprotective agents. Ultimately Wowk found that if he replaced propylene glycol with methoxylated glycerol in VS4-1A (the previous state-of-the-art cryoprotectant developed more than ten years ago by Gregory Fahy), it enhanced the ability of cells to survive. Since VS4-1A formerly was the least toxic vitrifying agent known, Wowk felt that this was "a pretty impressive result." However, he went on, "Dr. Fahy completely destroyed these results with new results that surpassed them by almost an order of magnitude."

Another Cryoprotectant Family

At this point during the presentations, Gregory Fahy took the microphone from Brian Wowk to describe his own discovery. He began by noting the mysterious behavior of cryoprotectants. "We don't understand their toxicity, and we can't predict their toxicity," he said. He added that "there is no consensus, no common denominator, no basic grasp of what it is we are seeking and how to get to a less toxic solution."

Initially he suspected that solutions which are more liable to denature proteins would be more toxic—but found that just the opposite is true, which "makes no sense." He also thought that a less-concentrated solution would be less likely to disrupt biological systems, but found no correlation between cryoprotectant concentration needed for vitrification and viability of cells.

In 1998, Fahy came up with a novel idea to make sense

Dr. Brian Wowk

of the data. This led him to a new way to measure concentration of cryoprotectants, which does correlate properly with viability of cells. "Suddenly all the data points fall on a straight line," Fahy told his audience at the 21st Century Medicine seminar.

He would not reveal the exact nature of his insight, but claimed it enabled him to understand how to reduce toxicity in cryoprotectants more effectively than has ever been achieved before. He came up with a solution which he calls VX. For thirteen years he had been trying to find something less toxic than his previous achievement, VS4-1A, a 55 percent solution of DMSO, formamide, and propylene glycol. VX turned out to be the answer.

Using it as a starting point he developed four new vitrification solutions, "each of which is statistically significantly superior to the previous world champion solution, VS4-1A." One of the new VX mixes should enable 100-percent survival of perfused rabbit kidneys, according to Fahy.

Still, this did not solve the problem posed by larger organs that cannot be cooled as rapidly as rabbit kidneys, and tend to suffer from increased ice damage as a result. Fahy said he considered using "some tricks from nature" to inhibit the ice crystal growth.

The trick he tried was an antifreeze protein found in arctic fish. When he added it to conventional cryoprotectants, it achieved barely measurable results. However, when he used a new "vehicle" to deliver the cryoprotectant, and then added the antifreeze protein, he reduced the amount of ice formed in a solution of VS4-1A by a factor of 1,000.

He also tried a different vehicle designed to enhance a different antifreeze protein found in a species of beetles. This reduced ice formation even more effectively, by an additional factor of 10. The practical bottom-line result was that he could achieve vitrification with a slow cooling rate of 1 degree Celsius per minute—which is practical for human kidneys.

Also he found that the beetle protein would eliminate another intractable problem: ice crystals forming when a vitrified sample is rewarmed. Typically, a sample has to be rewarmed extremely fast to get it from its deep subzero temperature to above freezing point without ice crystals causing catastrophic damage along the way. Since raising the temperature of large organs rapidly is quite difficult, zero-damage rewarming has always been a formidable challenge. But with Fahy's new vehicle and 1 per-cent beetle protein, he found he could avoid ice formation at a warming rate of just 1 degree per minute.

"This is wonderful," he told the audience at his presentation, "but beetle protein is hard to come by and is expensive. We wanted to come up with our own solution, our own ice-blocking agent, which is dirt cheap. Why not? Let's ask for the moon, maybe we'll get it. And luckily Brian found the moon for us, and now Brian will deliver it."

Ice Blockers

Brian Wowk took over from Gregory Fahy at this point and described his search for "synthetic ice blockers, hoping they could be made more inexpensively than natural antifreeze proteins." He mentioned that the beetle protein used in Fahy's experiments costs about $1,000 per milligram. Some researchers are working to synthesize a substitute, but Wowk believes even this will be relatively expensive, plus its ice-blocking action will be most effective near freezing point. He wanted a substitute that would work at the much lower temperatures required for organ storage.

"We were successful in this, almost completely successful," he said. "We were able to devise a family of synthetic ice-blocking molecules that are very inexpensive, a small fraction of the cost of even fish antifreeze proteins."

He showed a graph of vitrification enhancement that occurred when he added an ice blocker that he referred to as 21CM-X1 to a solution of dimethyl sulfoxide (DMSO). Without the ice blocker, a 50 percent concentration of DMSO is needed to avoid ice formation when cooling at 7 degrees per minute. Adding 1 percent of the ice blocker enabled the same results with 47 percent DMSO. "That doesn't sound like a lot," said Wowk, "but in terms of toxicity, it is."

Also, X1 turned out to work like beetle protein in preventing ice damage during rewarming. "Even if you have a perfectly vitrified system, generally when you rewarm it, ice forms in it like crazy," Wowk said. "However, we found that by adding very small amounts of X1, we may, in fact, have got the devitrification problem under control at even very modest rewarming rates." He showed a videotape of a lab experiment in which a beaker of DMSO solution formed ice crystals when it was rewarmed, while the same solution with a tiny amount of ice blocker showed virtually no ice at all. Another video demonstrated that a vitrified solution of ethylene glycol could be rewarmed relatively slowly, without any ice forming, if the X1 ice blocker was added.

Real-World Applications

Having described his discoveries, Fahy listed some immediate, potentially lucrative applications. First, there's the transplant field. "Most kidneys are not matched to the recipient," Fahy said. "This causes rejection.... 95 percent of the time we have a bad match between the recipient and the donor in terms of tissue type. Livers and hearts are an even worse problem."

Obviously if organs can be kept "on ice," this would allow time for better matching. About 15,000 organs are transplanted each year in the United States; if a banking system enabled more efficient use of these organs by solving the problem of rejection, this would justify the expense of setting up the system and paying a royalty to 21st Century Medicine for its preservation techniques.

But according to Fahy, "The really big market is in artificial tissues and organs, because there's no limitation on supply." He estimated that the total market is for at least 100,000 implants a year.

Initially he hopes to cryopreserve kidneys, since this is the organ that has been used most extensively in experiments and is best understood. "I've had clinicians tell me that as soon as I think I'm ready, they'll go ahead and transplant a human kidney at the drop of a hat," Fahy said.

At the same time, he noted that 21st Century Medicine is "negotiating a contract with a major university which is skilled in cardiac preservation, and we will test out our new vitrification solutions in that laboratory." 21st Century Medicine will retain the commercial rights to results of the research.

"We also have some possibilities for going into liver cryopreservation," Fahy went on. "We're now negotiating a contract with a liver transplant laboratory that is interested in developing short-term liver cryopreservation at relatively high subzero temperatures, and we will move forward at their expense on that, but 21st Century Medicine again will own the commercial rights."

Summing up, Fahy said, "We are now building a perfusion machine to actually do the experiments in house. The surgical facilities are ready to go. And we're already engaged in friendly negotiations with a number of organ preservation labs, to go further."

Other Markets

Fahy said he had never paid much attention to freezing small organisms such as sperm, because the problem seemed "too trivial" compared with freezing a large, complexly structured organ such as a kidney. Still, 21st Century Medicine can acquire revenue and credibility if its research improves existing procedures such as cryopreservation of sperm or corneas.

Fahy valued the market for human sperm at $20 million, while bovine sperm is a $200 million market, and human corneas are a $400 million market. He said, however, that when he investigated these areas, he found that between 90 and 95 percent of donors are rejected because their sperm cannot survive the primitive preservation procedures, while vitrifying corneas has been considered so difficult, no one is even trying to do it anymore. "Currently there are about 50,000 cornea transplants a year," Fahy said, "but I'm told by the top people in the field that if you could bank corneas without limit, this market would expand by a minimum of 5-fold, so the corneas alone would be worth $2 billion a year, and we'd get whatever royalty we could charge on that."

He showed a video tape in which sperm died in a 1 molar glycerol solution, but survived in his new VX cryoprotectant. "We're new at this," he admitted. But, "Our result, preliminary though it may be, is better than what's out there, so it is possible we can help the sperm bankers with their problem of expanding the donor pool and saving money. That means a market for 21st Century Medicine."

He predicted similar success in vitrifying corneas, though he has not tried this yet using VX. "We're currently collaborating with a major-name medical clinic to have a venture to demonstrate that we can cryopreserve corneas by vitrification, using the new technology."

Brain Cryopreservation

For cryonicists, the most exciting aspect of the conference came at the end, where Brian Wowk and Gregory Fahy revealed results of their first two experiments applying new cryoprotectant formulas to rabbit brains. "In general," Fahy commented, "we think we have achieved complete vitrification of the brain."

A year ago, no one had any idea that this might be achieved so quickly. Moreover, the procedure does not require extremely rapid cooling, high atmospheric pressures, or other exotic techniques, and a sample brain has been not only cryopreserved but rewarmed with virtually no damage. There is some chemical damage from toxicity, which would prevent restoration of function. Additional research will be needed to address this.

Currently, under ideal circumstances (which are often unavailable), a cryonics patient is perfused with a solution of glycerol reaching a final concentration of 7 to 7.5 molar, after which the patient is cooled at approximately one-tenth of a degree per minute. This is the best we can hope for. But as Brian Wowk demonstrated at the conference, the results are extremely unsatisfactory. He showed a slide (reproduced in Photo 5) of a two-liter solution of 7.3 molar glycerol that was cooled at 0.1 to 0.3 degrees per minute, to a temperature of –100 degrees. The chalky white appearance is caused by millions of tiny ice crystals in the solution. In a human brain, each crystal is likely to cause significant damage.

Photo 4 illustrates this damage. The picture is a reproduction of an electron micrograph of a canine brain that was perfused with 7.5 molar glycerol, cooled using optimal cryonics protocol, and then rewarmed. The white, "empty" areas almost certainly were caused by ice forming and displacing or destroying tissue. After

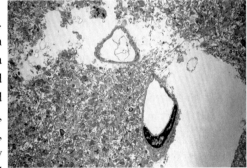

Photo 4

Photo 5   *Photo 6*   *Photo 7*

rewarming, the ice melts and debris remains. Remember, this is the best we can hope for, using current procedures.

Photo 6 shows an obvious improvement. This flask contains a 7.2 molar glycerol solution to which 1 percent of Wowk's "X1" ice blocker was added before freezing. The solution is now partially vitrified, meaning that it has turned into a uniform glass-like substance interspersed with hundreds of ice balls a few millimeters across, as opposed to millions of tiny ice crystals. The large pale object at the bottom of the flask is not ice; it is a stir bar. Wowk estimates that ice now constitutes only 10 percent of the mixture, by volume.

This is still less than ideal, but it can be achieved right now just by adding the X1 ice blocker that Wowk has discovered. No special cooling technology is required.

What if we use a 7.5 molar glycerol solution with 2 percent X1? Photo 7 shows the result. There is now virtually no ice, and almost 100 percent vitrification has occurred.

The 7.5 molar solution is so viscous it can be used on human patients only with difficulty. Also, there's no guarantee that the insides of cells will be completely protected, because the X1 ice blocker does not penetrate cell membranes. If cooling can be done more rapidly, however, internal cell damage should be minimized, because (in very simple terms) ice has less time to form.

Until relatively recently, no one knew how to cool a human patient faster than .1 degree Celsius per minute. The new technique of perfluorocarbon perfusion, however, offers a radical improvement. First, the patient would be perfused normally with cryoprotectant. Then the vascular system would be flushed with a perfluorocarbon, which is nontoxic and remains free-flowing at temperatures as low as -130 degrees. Potentially this can produce a cooling rate of almost 10 degrees per minute—100 times the best rate for a cryonics patient using conventional methods. Because the temperature differential diminishes as cooling takes place, the cooling rate will diminish also; but 1 degree per minute is still possible at -110 degrees. This has actually been verified in dog experiments.

The procedure will require a specially insulated room where perfluorocarbon can be sprayed onto the patient and perfused through the patient under remote control. A prototype cold room has been built at 21st Century Medicine.

Perfluorocarbon cooling is such a powerful technique, it enables vitrification with lower concentrations of cryoprotectant. A 7 molar solution of glycerol, with X1 ice blocker added, should be sufficient.

Unfortunately, even a 7 molar glycerol solution is biochemically toxic to cells. Perhaps chemical damage will be much easier to undo in the future than structural damage, but still we would prefer, obviously, to do no damage at all.

Wowk and Fahy have taken a step in that direction. Shortly before the conference, assisted by biologist Christopher Rasch and surgeon Yasumitsu Okouchi, Fahy perfused two rabbits (the first consisting of the upper body, the second consisting of the head only) using two different perfusates. The composition of the perfusates is not public information at this time, but one of them relied more on concepts developed by Brian Wowk in his research into methoxylated compounds, while the other

incorporated ideas relating to the VX series of cryoprotectants formulated by Fahy.

Photo 8 shows the perfusion in progress, using an open circuit in which concentration was gradually ramped up, as shown in Graph 1. This procedure is roughly similar to that used in rabbit-kidney cryopreservation.

After perfusion, Photo 9 shows one of the specimens being cooled in the plastic bucket just in front of the stainless-steel dewar. Note the electric drill clamped

Photo 8

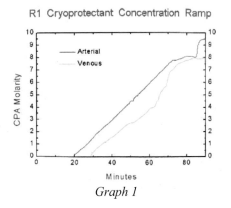

Graph 1

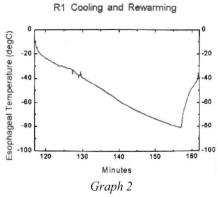

Graph 2

Photo 9

over the bucket, which provided rapid stirring, promoting heat exchange.

Graph 2 shows the rate of cooling. Note the small bumps around 130 minutes and -40 degrees C. These irregularities suggest that a small amount of water froze, briefly liberating latent heat as it turned to ice.

Photo 10 is an electron micrograph showing the condition of the brain after rewarming. An intact synapse and pre-synaptic neurotransmitter vesicles are visible, with good postsynaptic density. Some shrinkage has occurred because of the high concentration of cryoprotectant, creating the small white spaces around cells. Fahy feels that this shrinkage is not very significant because the structure seems intact.

Photo 11 is at a smaller scale (the original electron micrographs range from 10,000 to 40,000 magnification) showing an intact axon with clearly defined cell membrane. "We do see some cavities on the local level,"

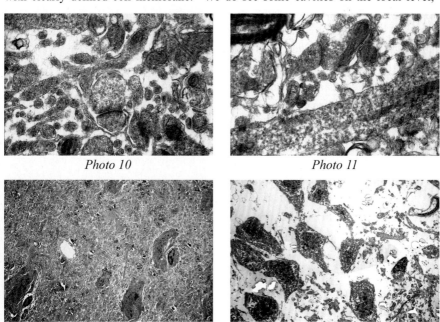

Photo 10

Photo 11

Photo 12

Photo 13

R2 Cryoprotectant Concentration Ramp

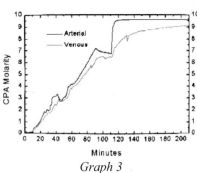

Minutes

Graph 3

R2 Cooling and Rewarming

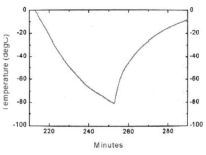

Minutes

Graph 4

Fahy commented when he showed this picture at the conference. But these cavities are minimal compared with the damage in brain tissue perfused conventionally with glycerol.

Photo 12 provides a broader overview showing no apparent ice holes. There are some slightly shrunken neurons, but again the membranes are intact and structure is clearly visible.

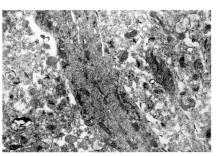

Photo 14

Not all areas of the brain were preserved so successfully. Photo 13 shows cells that have been damaged by ice, toxicity, or inadequate osmotic pressure allowing tissue edema. "Nevertheless, this seems a substantial advance over glycerol," Fahy commented.

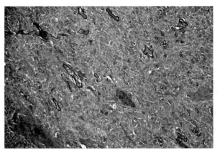

Photo 15

In their second rabbit experiment, Fahy's team attempted total vitrification of the brain. "We did various things to optimize the perfusion," he told his audience at the conference, though he would not reveal specific details. Graph 3 shows the increase in concentration of perfusate over time, while Graph 4 is a remarkably smooth cooling curve, showing no kinks or bumps that would indicate ice formation as the temperature fell, and no ice forming either

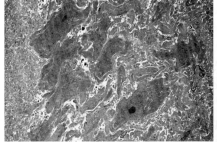

Photo 16

during the rewarming phase.

Electron micrographs of this brain revealed truly exceptional results. Photo 14 shows an axon containing neural filaments—individual conglomerations of molecules. These are clearly discernible in the original picture but may be harder to see here because of the limits of half-tone printing. "We have never seen those [filaments] in any cryopreserved brain, ever," Mike Darwin commented, as the slide was shown at the conference.

"This is a level of preservation that's really unprecedented," Fahy agreed.

A lower-magnification overview of the second brain, in Photo 15, shows no pockets of cell damage of the kind seen in the first brain. There are moderately dehydrated but basically intact cells amid shrinkage spaces that are moderate and probably not a source for concern. Intact myelin sheaths are visible around axonal processes.

All the electron micrographs mentioned so far were of the cerebral cortex. Photo 16 is of the hippocampus,which is the area most sensitive to ischemic insults. Although the cells seem dehydrated and shrunken, they remain well connected to the neuropil surrounding them.

Fahy was quick to warn his audience that these two experiments are just the first that have been done using the new processes developed this year at 21st Century Medicine. "We expect that we can go farther than this fairly rapidly," he said, "now that we have a better feel for the kind of cooling and warming rates that we're dealing with."

Sitting next to Fahy, Mike Darwin added that "I've spent twenty years doing cryoprotective perfusions and subsequent evaluations of brains. My opinion is a very dismal one about the utility of current procedures, particularly in preserving the fine connections of the cells to the neuropil, which is probably where you're at, where your identity is really encoded." But he went on: "I just cannot emphasize the difference between this [new work] and the previous work that has been done. We've eliminated virtually all of these terrible tears, massive tears that occur at 10 and 30 micron intervals, and the ultrastructure is remarkably better. I think that within very short order, we're going to have significant viability, 50 percent viability, in brains that are treated with techniques that yield the same kind of ultrastructural results."

Of course, we don't know how easily the work will translate and scale to human brains. Also, the researchers at 21st Century Medicine have been exploring several different approaches, in parallel, to the same basic problems of reducing damage. "We have not completely and fully combined [these ideas] to get the most powerful possible approach to cryopreservation," Fahy said, adding that the next step will involve "fine tuning all the parameters in order to get the best possible result. But it's just a straightforward process, there's nothing magical about it."

"The magic is the money and the time," Darwin commented.

Questions and Answers

After the formal presentations, Mike Darwin, Steve Harris, MD, Gregory Fahy, and Brian Wowk received questions from the audience.

Linda Chamberlain of Alcor asked about the price and availability of perfluorocarbon compounds. Mike Darwin replied that it had been difficult to obtain them, but recently he located a new supplier with a large stock. The compounds may cost between $20 and $35 per pound, but in a perfluorocarbon perfusion circuit, most of the chemicals can be retained and reused.

Another questioner asked exactly how antifreeze proteins prevent ice from forming. Brian Wowk explained that they "form a kind of antibody-antigen match onto the a-axis face of ice. They coat it and prevent growth in that direction."

Fred Chamberlain of Alcor wondered what happens if you increase the concentration of ice blockers or methoxylated compounds, and whether they will be prohibitively expensive.

Brian Wowk answered that a higher concentration of methoxylated compounds will tend to dissolve cell membranes. "We're cruising on the edge of that," he said. A problem with X1 is that it tends to increase viscosity of cryoprotectants. Overall, Wowk said he expects that the optimum concentration of X1 will be "a few percent."

Saul Kent said it was premature to talk about pricing, but Brian Wowk pointed out that anyone with a chemical catalogue could find methoxylated compounds available off-the-shelf. "Technically the only thing to stop you from using them is infringement on our pending patent," he said.

As for ice blockers, "We could probably supply as much as you want at a reasonable price. Chemical synthesis houses making this compound for us are not giving us anywhere near the kind of sticker shock that antifreeze protein synthesis gives us."

Another questioner asked how long we have to wait for viable suspended animation. Brian Wowk said it should be possible within ten years for the brain, but much sooner for kidneys, because this is the major focus of research. "If sufficient funds become available from people who are interested in the [brain] problem," he went on, "we could tackle the brain just like any other organ."

Mike Darwin agreed that "somebody has to fund the work on brains, and it isn't going to be the people funding the work on hearts or kidneys or livers," because that research has an obvious financial payoff, while brain preservation interests only cryonicists. Consequently, according to Darwin, "this audience and the people they represent are going to be the ones who pay for it, else it just isn't going to get done."

"To get to the point where a brain is successfully cryopreserved in every sense of the word is an enormously complicated and resource-intensive process," Gregory

Fahy commented. "We don't have the manpower to divert a lot of extra attention into those areas unless they are funded." He said he expects to discover "all kinds of adverse things that we have no clue exist right now, all kinds of things we haven't thought of, and we'll have to solve those problems. This will take a dedicated team working week in, week out, year in, year out, relentlessly, until the problem is solved. We just don't have the assets for that now."

Another questioner asked how much it might cost.

"$10 million has been speculated," Brian Wowk answered, adding that this is a reasonable guess. He didn't think it would cost as much $100 million, but he was sure it would cost more than $5 million.

The panel discussion broke up shortly after this, and many of the attendees visited the two laboratories where the research has been done. Some people complained that the presentations had been overly technical, while others wondered whether the owners of the new technology will make it available on an affordable basis. Saul Kent said subsequently that he intends to offer results of the research at a reasonable price to all cryonics organizations. Obviously 21st Century Medicine hopes to reap profits from applications outside cryonics, which is a minuscule market by comparison.

Question & Answer Panel: Mike Darwin, Dr. Gregory Fahy, Dr. Steven Harris

Conclusion

The prospects for human cryopreservation have never looked better. Prospects, however, don't turn into realities without an infusion of money and labor.

The new brain studies at 21st Century Medicine are immensely promising, but the company must pursue research that will generate revenue, and brain research is unlikely to fulfill this need in the immediate future. Therefore, if we want zero-damage, reversible brain cryopreservation, we can't count on outside investors to pay for it. We, as cryonicists, will have to pay for it ourselves.

Six years ago, I bought $10,000 of stock in 21st Century Medicine. This represented about one-quarter of my savings at that time. Some others also purchased stock, but the wealthiest people in cryonics showed only a token interest—or no interest at all. Consequently, Bill Faloon and Saul Kent shouldered the primary burden. By my estimate, they have spent about $10 million so far.

I am constantly amazed by the reluctance of wealthy cryonicists to put money into research that could increase their own chances of survival. It seems grossly irresponsible to assume that others in the future will fix freezing damage for us, when we could address the issue ourselves.

In the past, there was some doubt that investment in research would pay off. This doubt should be dispelled, now, by the evidence presented at the 21st Century Medicine seminar. Kent and Faloon have demonstrated that money really can buy remarkable progress within a short space of time, and almost certainly reversible cryopreservation can be ours if we really want it.

Within the next year we will see whether cryonicists are willing to acknowledge this fact—or whether "Let someone else deal with the problem" will continue as the dominant motto in cryonics, as it has for the past thirty years. ∎

Treating and Minimizing Ischemic Injury

For several years, Mike Darwin has been looking for new techniques to inhibit or treat brain damage that occurs after blood circulation stops suddenly, as in a heart attack. In his presentation at the 21st Century Medicine seminar, Darwin noted that sudden cardiac arrest is the leading cause of death in the United States, afflicting 540,000 people annually. He said that despite the advent of CPR and widespread deployment of paramedic teams, fewer than 1 percent of cardiac patients survive without any brain damage if they suffer four to six minutes of cardiac arrest.

Any treatment that can improve these dismal statistics obviously would be extremely valuable in emergency medicine, and Darwin told his audience that the methods he has developed with his primary team, Steven B. Harris, MD, Sandra Russell, Joan O'Farrell, and Carlotta Pengelley, could save 300,000 lives each year.

The research is important also to cryonicists, since we are concerned with preserving the brain with minimal damage in all phases of our procedures, including the first crucial minutes after legal death is pronounced.

Darwin and his team have been remarkably successful, routinely reviving dogs after 15 to 17 minutes of cardiac arrest near normal body temperature, under anesthesia. (These results should not be confused with those of previous dog experiments where much longer survival times were achieved with deep hypothermia.)

A major factor in the success of recent resuscitation research was Steve Harris's suggestion that ischemic injury can be viewed and treated as an inflammatory response, similar in some ways to the swelling and inflammation that occur after any localized injury.

Darwin reported that in eight separate experiments with dogs, three achieved excellent recovery after six weeks (showing no neurological deficit at all), three showed good results, and two did not survive. He claimed that these results have not been matched by any other laboratory.

Unfortunately the protocol is complicated. After blood flow is restored, multiple drugs must be delivered within 5 to 15 seconds, while body temperature must be lowered by about 4 degrees Celsius within 3 to 5 minutes. How can this be achieved by paramedics working out in the field?

Darwin said that a computer-controlled system will be needed to deliver the drugs. The FDA has been reluctant to approve biomedical software, and also is generally opposed to multidrug cocktails. Consequently, the approach developed by Darwin and his team may be applied only outside of the United States, initially at least.

The challenge of rapid cooling seems severe. Darwin told the audience at the seminar that external cooling via a stirred ice-water bath typically requires about 80 minutes to lower body temperature by 5 degrees Celsius. This is far too slow, and requires about 300 pounds of ice and 200 pounds of water, making it impractical for use in the field.

However, Darwin said that the lungs can be used as a heat exchanger. Since all cardiac output flows through the lungs, which have a huge surface area of 70 square meters, they provide an excellent opportunity to draw heat out of the blood, which then cools the brain.

Cold air cannot remove heat rapidly enough, but a breathable liquid is effective and can be applied by intubating the patient, which is a standard emergency procedure. According to Darwin, experiments with dogs have proved that mixed-mode liquid ventilation using a perfluorocarbon at about 2 degrees Celsius can provide more than enough breathable oxygen while lowering body temperature by about four degrees in the first five minutes. An average cooling rate of .36 degrees Celsius per minute has been achieved, and dogs have recovered fully after their temperature has been reduced by as much as 10 degrees.

Since liquid ventilation is not only effective but could be deployed relatively easily in the field, it has a clear advantage over any other method of reducing temperature. It could be used to treat head injuries as well as ischemic injury caused by cardiac arrest, according to Darwin.

He said that inspection of lungs after liquid ventilation showed "some isolated areas of injury," particularly at the bottom part of the lungs, probably from contact with the very cold perfluorocarbon liquid. Still, the animals showed no sign of distress, and light and electron microscopy revealed no sign of structural damage in other areas of the lungs.

"If you can automate this process, any paramedic can do it," Darwin told his audience. He predicted that it could be "a potential profit center" that could save a lot of lives, and said he hopes to see clinical trials 2 to 3 years from now.

Although Darwin didn't mention the use of liquid ventilation in cryonics cases, obviously it would be extremely valuable and could be applied in the very near future. ■

Systems for Intermediate Temperature Storage for Fracture Reduction and Avoidance

By Brian Wowk, Ph.D.

Cryonics, 3rd Quarter, 2011

Introduction

Cryopreservation by vitrification partially replaces water inside cells and tissue with chemicals called cryoprotectants that prevent ice formation. At high enough concentrations, cryoprotectants can prevent freezing. Instead of freezing, the mixture of water and cryoprotectants becomes more and more viscous like syrup during cooling. At a temperature near -120°C the viscous solution solidifies, an event called the "glass transition." This solidification without freezing is the physical basis of cryopreservation by vitrification.

Liquid nitrogen provides an inexpensive, stable, and highly reliable storage environment for cryopreserved tissue at a temperature of -196°C. Unfortunately the process of cooling to this very cold temperature tends to cause cryopreserved tissues to fracture. Such fractures probably do not compromise the neuroanatomical information preservation goals of cryonics as long as tissue remains cold and solid. However fractures prevent future recovery of cryopreserved tissue by any simple means. They are also alarming by contemporary biomedical standards.

Fracturing can be reduced, and sometimes avoided, by cooling through the glass transition temperature slowly and stopping cooling at temperatures warmer than liquid nitrogen. Much progress has been made within the past decade at developing systems able to safely store tissue at temperatures warmer than liquid nitrogen. Such systems have come to be called "intermediate temperature storage" (ITS) systems because they store at temperatures intermediate between liquid nitrogen and the glass transition temperature. ITS technologies are more complex and expensive than simple immersion in liquid nitrogen. Although ITS technologies for cooling and storing tissue in relative safety at adjustable temperatures now exist, the basic science knowledge of how to control temperature to avoid fracturing in tissues as large as a whole human body still does not exist. Only fracture reduction is presently possible.

Physical Causes of Fracturing

The vibration of molecules gives rise to a characteristic volume, or density, of a liquid or solid material at a given temperature. As temperature decreases, the volume of an object slightly decreases. This is called thermal contraction. Figure 1 shows thermal contraction of a cryoprotectant solution cooled in a test tube. Warmer solution in the center of the test tube continues cooling and contracting after solution near the walls has solidified, creating a dimple.

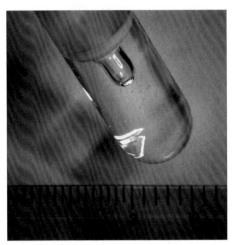

Fig. 1. Differential thermal contraction of vitrification solution cooled in a test tube causes a dimple to form. The warmer inside of the solution continues contracting after the colder outside has solidified and begun cooling at a slower rate.

Thermal contraction can cause cryoprotectant glasses (solidified vitrification solution) to fracture by several different mechanisms.[1] Figure 2 shows a cryoprotectant solution in a borosilicate glass flask fracturing after vitrification and cooling. This fracturing occurred because the cryoprotectant solution adhered to the glass wall when it solidified. Cryoprotectant glasses have thermal expansion coefficients ten times greater than the flask container walls. Therefore cryoprotectant glasses will shrink ten times as much during cooling as glass containers that hold them. The cryoprotectant glass in Fig. 2 broke due to accumulated stress as it tried to retract away from the flask wall during cooling. Vitrified cryoprotectant solutions or tissues are less likely to fracture if held

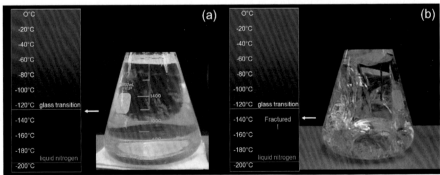

Fig. 2. A two liter volume of solidified M22 vitrification solution shown (a) just below the glass transition temperature and (b) after further cooling. The solidified solution fractured during further cooling below the glass transition temperature.

1   B. Wowk, "Thermodynamic aspects of vitrification," *Cryobiology* 60 (2010) 11-22.

in containers made of hydrophobic materials that solutions don't adhere to, such as polyethylene plastic.

Cryoprotectant glasses or vitrified tissue can also fracture due to internal stress during temperature change regardless of container material. If different parts of tissue have different thermal expansion properties, the different parts will seek to contract by different amounts during cooling, causing stress that can result in fractures.

Even completely homogeneous tissue or pure cryoprotectant solutions can fracture during cooling. If different parts of a material cool at different rates, the rates of thermal volume contraction will be different. For example, near the end of cooling, the outside of an object may only contract at 0.1% per minute as its temperature nears that of the surroundings. However the inside of the object may be trying to contract at 0.2% per minute because it is warmer and still cooling faster. The core of the object therefore tends to pull away from the periphery, causing mechanical stress, which causes fracturing if the mechanical strength of the solid is exceeded. This phenomenon is illustrated schematically in Fig. 3.

Fig. 3. As cooling slows at the cold exterior of a vitrified object, the warmer interior will cool faster until a uniform temperature is reached throughout the object. Faster interior cooling causes faster thermal contraction of the interior, causing the interior to pull away from the exterior along the dotted line. These forces can cause the vitrified object to fracture.

In practice, it's difficult to cool volumes of more than a few milliliters of vitrification solution to the temperature of liquid nitrogen without fracturing. This is because the thermomechanical properties of cryoprotectant glasses (thermal expansion coefficient 40×10^{-6} per °C, fracture strain 0.3%, fracture stress 3 MPa[2,3]) make them much weaker than other glasses we are accustomed to. For example, window glass has a fracture stress of approximately 100 MPa due to its strong covalent chemical bonds.

Fibrous material present in a vitrification solution will increase the vitrified solution's fracture strength and reduce the likelihood and extent of fracturing. Tissue itself is fibrous, so tissues and organs generally do not fracture as easily or extensively as bare cryoprotectant solutions

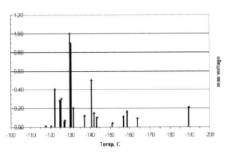

Fig. 4. Acoustic events believed to be fractures detected in the brain of Alcor patient A-2063 during cooling after perfusion with B2C vitrification solution. Such events are detected in all patients during cooling between the glass transition temperature (-123°C) and liquid nitrogen (-196°C).

like the solution in Fig. 2(b). However organs are still capable of fracturing during cooling.

Prevalence of Fracturing in Cryonics

In late 1983 Alcor performed postmortem examinations of three whole body cryonics patients who had been transferred from another cryonics facility for conversion to neuropreservation and continued storage at Alcor. In every patient, several full thickness fractures of the skin were observed as well as multiple fractures of most internal organs. The spinal cord of one patient was cleanly fractured every 6 cm over a 20 cm length examined. These patients were frozen with low concentrations of cryoprotectant rather than vitrified, so fracturing is a phenomenon that can occur in either frozen or vitrified tissue during cooling to liquid nitrogen temperature. It is not unique to vitrification. These findings were documented in a report in the September 1984 issue of *Cryonics* magazine.[4] There was further discussion of these findings on page 28 of the 1st Quarter 1995 issue of *Cryonics*.[5]

In 1994 Alcor performed a postmortem examination of the brain of Alcor patient A-1242 who had been ordered removed from cryopreservation after a court overturned the 1990 cryopreservation arrangements made by her husband. It was discovered that the brain had fractured into five major pieces. Details were reported on page 29 of the 1st Quarter 1995 issue of *Cryonics*.[5]

In 1997 Alcor brought into regular use an acoustic fracture detection system called the "crackphone." The crackphone is a custom designed system that performs digital data processing of sound signals recorded by microphones placed in contact with the brain during deep cooling of cryonics patients. It detects and records acoustic events believed to correlate with fracturing.

Acoustic events consistent with fracturing were found to be universal during cooling through the cryogenic temperature range. They occurred whether patients

4   M. Federowicz, H. Hixon, J. Leaf, "Postmortem Examination of Three Cryonic Suspension Patients," *Cryonics* September (1984) 16-28. M. Federowicz, H. Hixon, J. Leaf, "Postmortem Examination of Three Cryonic Suspension Patients," *Cryonics* September (1984) 16-28.

5   H. Hixon, "Exploring Cracking Phenomena," *Cryonics* 1st Quarter (1995) 27-32.

were frozen or vitrified. If cryoprotection is good, they typically begin below the glass transition temperature (-123°C for M22 vitrification solution). If cryoprotective perfusion does not go well, then fracturing events begin at temperatures as warm as -90°C. Higher fracturing temperatures are believed to occur when tissue freezes instead of vitrifies because freezing increases the glass transition temperature of solution between ice crystals. The temperature at which fractures begin is therefore believed to be a surrogate measure of goodness of cryoprotection, with lower temperatures being better.

The crackphone is believed to be highly sensitive to fractures, but its specificity is not clear. Cracking sounds can often be heard during cooling of vitification solutions or vitrified tissue with no fractures later being found (unpublished observations of the author). So it is not clear whether every acoustic event detected during cooling is necessarily a fracture. Studies correlating acoustic events with physical fracturing have not been done. Still, it is believed that the brain and other major organs of every cryonics patient cooled to the temperature of liquid nitrogen to date have some fractures.

Significance of Fracturing

Fracturing does not cause tissue to break into widely separated pieces at the time of fracture. As shown in Fig. 5, fractures are not macroscopically obvious at cryogenic temperature. The actual physical displacements associated with fracturing are small, and are believed to remain small as long as tissue remains solid. Future repair strategies for fracturing are therefore anticipated to begin at low temperature with the tissue still in the solid state.[6,7]

Fractures in bare cryoprotectant solutions such as those in Fig. 2 are observed to be optically smooth. In other words, the fracture surfaces are smooth on a scale smaller than a wavelength of light, which is less than one millionth of a meter. Although the fracture faces of vitrified tissue have not been specifically studied, it is assumed that they are also relatively smooth. When frozen tissue is fractured for microscopy in a procedure called "freeze fracture," the resulting faces are smooth enough for electron micrographic study of cell membranes. From an information theoretic standpoint, it seems likely that fracturing does not cause loss of neural connectivity information provided that tissue remains vitrified, and provided that some future means exists to match and restore structure across fracture faces. However further study is needed.

---

6   R.C. Merkle, R.A. Freitas, "A Cryopreservation Revival Scenario Using Molecular Nanotechnology," *Cryonics* 4th Quarter (2008) 6-8.

7   "Appendix B. A 'Realistic' Scenario for Nanotechnological Repair of the Frozen Human Brain," in Brian Wowk, Michael Darwin, eds., *Cryonics: Reaching for Tomorrow,* Alcor Life Extension Foundation, 1991.

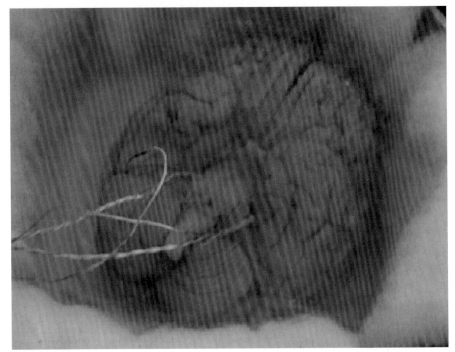

Fig. 5. Vitrified brain of Alcor patient A-2077 under liquid nitrogen. This brain is almost certainly fractured, yet it remains an integrated whole. Movements between fracture planes appear to remain microscopic provided that tissue stays cold and solid.

Unfortunately fracturing excludes any future repair strategy that might begin by simple warming and reperfusion. It's therefore a barrier to the development of reversible suspended animation of large organs or humans no matter how good cryoprotectant technology becomes. Fracturing underscores that cryonics as currently practiced is an information archiving technology that will require very arcane technology to reverse. It is not anything close to suspended animation.

Reduction and Elimination of Fracturing

To prevent fracturing, stresses such as those shown in Fig. 3 need to be minimized. This can be achieved by slowing cooling as the glass transition is approached so that the temperature is as uniform as possible within tissue during descent through the glass transition. Holding for a period of time near or just below the glass transition to allow stress relaxation before further cooling is especially helpful. Figure 6 shows a cooling protocol that permitted storage of a rabbit kidney under liquid nitrogen with no

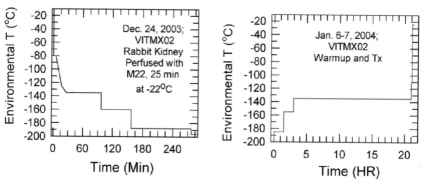

Fig. 6. Slow cooling and warming protocol followed for a vitrified rabbit kidney that was successfully stored under liquid nitrogen for two weeks prior to transplantation without fractures. (Data courtesy 21st Century Medicine, Inc.)

evidence of fracturing during later transplantation.[8] Faster cooling has been observed to result in fracturing.

Another strategy has allowed even bare vitrification solutions, which are highly susceptible to fracturing, to reach liquid nitrogen temperature without fracturing. That strategy is to cool slightly below the glass transition temperature, then rewarm above it, and then finally resume cooling as shown schematically in Fig. 7. This allows interior temperatures to catch up to the cooler exterior temperature so that the whole object passes through the glass transition at a more uniform temperature and cooling rate. This avoids "locking in" stresses that would otherwise result from non-uniform passage through the glass transition.

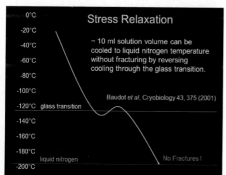

Fig. 7. Warming above the glass transition temperature after descending slightly below it can reduce temperature gradients and associated stress, allowing 10 mL solution volumes to reach liquid nitrogen temperature without fracturing.

Molten silicate glass (window glass) that is cooled too quickly will also fracture for the same reasons that cryoprotectant glasses do. To prevent this, silicate glasses are held during manufacturing for a period of time near their glass transition temperature to reduce stress. This process is called annealing. After annealing and slow cooling to a lower temperature, called

---

G. Fahy, "Vitrification as an approach to cryopreservation: General perspectives," *Cryobiology* 51 (2005) 348-414.

the strain temperature, silicate glass can be quickly cooled to room temperature without fracturing. A similar annealing process allowing cooling of large volumes of cryoprotectant glasses to liquid nitrogen temperature without fracturing is theoretically possible. Unfortunately, due to the physical weakness of cryoprotectant glasses compared to silicate glass, very long annealing times may be necessary.

Whether for long periods of annealing or permanent storage, systems for storing cryopreserved tissue at temperatures between the glass transition temperature and liquid nitrogen temperature are necessary if fracturing is to be avoided. In cryonics, such systems have come to be called Intermediate Temperature Storage (ITS) systems.

Progress in Development of Intermediate Temperature Storage (ITS) Systems

For decades mechanical laboratory freezers have been available that are capable of maintaining temperatures as low as -140°C. They've been sold under names such as Queue and CryoStar. In the year 2000 a 10 cubic foot CryoStar freezer was acquired for testing by Alcor for possible use storing neuropatients. It included a liquid nitrogen backup system able to maintain temperature in the event of a power failure, and was also filled

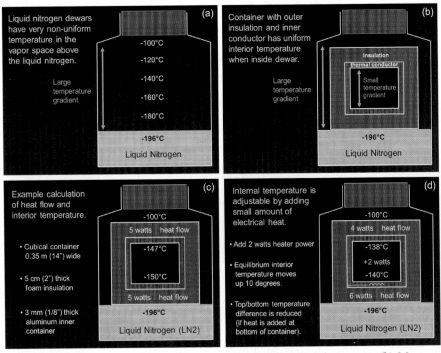

Fig. 8. (a) The temperature in the vapor space above liquid nitrogen. (b) More uniform temperature inside an insulated storage container with a thermally-conductive inner liner. (c) Calculated heat flows inside container. (d) Adjustment of container temperature with electrical heat.

Fig. 9. Prototype neuropod suitable for maintaining single neuropatients at a stable and adjustable intermediate storage temperature, (a) showing neurocan inside, (b) with top insulation in place, (c) and (d) inside a small dewar with 8 liters of liquid nitrogen at the bottom able to maintain -140°C inside the neuropod for 90 hours between refills. Longer times between refills are possible with larger dewars. The dark cable connects to a small temperature controller that supplies electrical heat to the inside of the neuropod to maintain the desired interior temperature. The neuropod requires 0.15 watts heating for each °C temperature difference between the interior and mean exterior temperature.

with dry ice as thermal ballast. Alcor used it for two patients between 2002 and 2006 before advancing to newer liquid nitrogen ITS systems. The newer systems had much lower power consumption, no temperature cycling, and other advantages described below.

"Vapor phase" storage systems that store at temperatures warmer than liquid nitrogen in the vapor space above liquid nitrogen have long been available. However as shown in Fig. 8(a), they suffer from large uncontrolled temperature differences in the vapor space. They are used in cryobiology not because of their warmer temperature, but because they prevent transfer of pathogens between samples stored under a common pool of liquid nitrogen.

Figures 8(b) and 8(c) show that if an insulated container with a conductive inner liner is placed above liquid nitrogen, the non-uniform temperature outside the container becomes converted into a more uniform temperature inside the container. The addition of a small thermostat-controlled electric heater inside the container as shown in Fig. 8(d) allows the uniform interior temperature to be adjustable. 21st Century Medicine, Inc., obtained US Patent 7,278,278 for this and related types of intermediate temperature storage systems in 2007.

In 2003, Alcor acquired the prototype "neuropod" storage device shown in Fig. 9 for testing. Using the principles explained in Fig. 8, the neuropod was designed to hold a single neuropatient at an adjustable, uniform, and stable intermediate temperature. The neuropod itself could be placed into any uncontrolled cryogenic environment, such as the vapor space above liquid nitrogen in a conventional storage dewar. An electric heater supplied by a temperature controller added small amounts of heat as necessary to maintain the desired temperature inside the neuropod. The heat automatically adjusts to maintain a stable internal temperature even when the outside temperature fluctuates, such as during dewar refilling (temperature drop) or transfer through ambient air between dewars (temperature rise). The power requirements of the controller are so low (<10 watts) that they can easily be met by small battery backup systems.

The advantages of this type of ITS system are numerous.

- No moving parts
- Low power requirements
- Individual temperature control
- Power failure results in cooling rather than warming
- Temperature stability in presence of external instability or non-uniformity
- Storage flexibility (containers will function in any cryogenic environment that is on average colder than the target interior temperature)

In 2004 Alcor acquired and began testing another neuropod that was designed to be "patient rated." It incorporated dual redundant temperature controllers and heaters, and other safety features.

The advantage of individual storage pod temperature control is a disadvantage in terms of complexity and cost. An alternative approach is to construct an intermediate temperature storage system that maintains a large common volume at the same temperature. In 2003 21st Century Medicine, Inc., developed and constructed an ITS storage dewar for cryobiology applications capable of maintaining adjustable and uniform storage temperatures in the -120°C to -150°C range using liquid

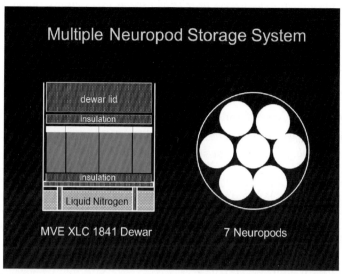

Fig. 10. Collections of neuropods could be stored in the vapor space of conventional liquid nitrogen dewars. The temperature inside each one could be individually controlled to manage complex cooling plans for annealing protocols lasting years if necessary.

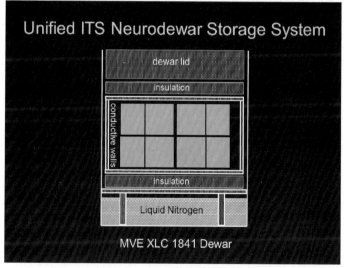

Fig. 11. Instead of containers with individual environment control, the ITS Neurodewar system stores 14 smaller uninsulated neurocontainers in a common temperature environment inside a liquid nitrogen dewar. One large storage chamber with thermally-conductive walls ensures a uniform shared storage temperature. Like the neuropod system, small amounts of electrical heat under active control maintain the desired storage temperature in the shared environment.

nitrogen. Since then, such dewars have been used at 21st Century Medicine instead of laboratory freezers. Unlike mechanical freezers, ITS dewars have very low power consumption, no heat output, no moving parts, no noise, and limited temperature excursion if they fail.

In 2005 Alcor placed an order with 21st Century Medicine for an ITS dewar large enough to hold 14 neuropatients. After tedious development efforts, the ITS Neurodewar shown schematically in Fig. 11 and photographically in Figs. 12 and 13 was delivered to Alcor in 2008. The unit has been in uneventful operation and evaluation at Alcor since then. The specifications are:

Storage Volume:	15.5 cubic feet
Temperature Uniformity (top-to-bottom):	3°C
Temperature Stability (empty chamber):	2°C during 2" liquid nitrogen fill
Operating Temperature Limits:	-159°C to -124°C
Lower Failsafe Temperature:	-159°C (0 watts heater power)
Upper Failsafe Temperature:	-124°C (48 watts heater power)
Maximum Liquid Nitrogen Capacity:	6.0" or 118 liters
Liquid Nitrogen Consumption at -159°C:	0.6" or 12 liters per day
Liquid Nitrogen Consumption at -145°C:	1.0" or 20 liters per day
Liquid Nitrogen Consumption at -140°C:	1.2" or 24 liters per day
Rate of Warming Following LN$_2$ Depletion:	1°C per hour

Comparision of ITS vs. Liquid Nitrogen Immersion Storage

The storage method traditionally used in cryonics is immersion in liquid nitrogen at a temperature of -196°C. Storage vessels that hold liquid nitrogen are kept almost full to the top. ITS systems use dewars that are only partially filled with liquid nitrogen. For example, the ITS dewar of Fig. 13 contains only about 120 liters of liquid nitrogen in a pool at the bottom. This is sufficient to last only 5 days when operating at a temperature of -140°C. In contrast, the tall "Bigfoot" dewars used by Alcor for liquid nitrogen immersion storage contain more than 1,000 liters of liquid nitrogen that can last weeks between refills without catastrophic warming. As shown in Fig. 13, ITS dewars can automatically refill themselves from external liquid nitrogen tanks (or be manually refilled if electric power is unavailable), but this is intrinsically less reliable than having the liquid nitrogen already in the dewar.

The ITS Neurodewar of Fig. 13 costs as much as a Bigfoot dewar, but has only one third the neuropatient holding capacity. When operated at -140°C it consumes

Fig. 12. (Left) ITS Neurodewar under construction, showing storage chamber with seven storage compartments. (Right) Neurodewar in operation with main lid open, showing closed storage compartment lids.

Fig. 13. (Left) ITS Neurodewar with dual redundant temperature controllers and displays on the right side of the unit. (Right) Neurodewar in operation at Alcor, maintaining an internal temperature of -140°C. The unit automatically refills itself from the connected liquid nitrogen tank.

liquid nitrogen at twice the rate of a Bigfoot dewar. (Liquid nitrogen consumption can be reduced in future units if the operating temperature range is made smaller.) Transfer losses are also expected to be larger due to more frequent filling. Therefore the cost of ITS storage is at least three times that of conventional liquid nitrogen immersion storage.

Whole Body ITS Systems

The same concepts of individual temperature-controlled storage pods, and common temperature storage dewars, can be applied to the design of whole body ITS storage systems. Cryogenic engineer Michael Iarocci and architect Stephen Valentine of the Timeship Project have designed several different whole body ITS systems. Some systems even consume less liquid nitrogen per patient than Bigfoot dewars, but at greater capital cost.

Unresolved Issues

The most important unresolved issue of intermediate temperature storage is how to use it to avoid fracturing. Despite some attempts to avoid fracturing over the last decade, some including months of annealing, acoustic data indicated that fracturing was still occurring during descent to target intermediate storage temperatures. Therefore ITS is presently a means to reduce fracturing, not avoid fracturing. Perhaps ITS is best characterized as a necessary tool to develop future protocols to avoid fracturing. However presently it is not even possible to say whether pod-type storage systems permitting individual temperature control are cost-justified over common temperature environments because it is not known how to use either system to avoid fracturing. There is only a general presumption that a future fracturing avoidance protocol may require lengthy individual temperature conditioning.

A related question is what storage temperature is appropriate for ITS. The lower the temperature the more stable the storage, but the more difficult it is to avoid fracturing. Viscosity at and below the glass transition is so high that chemical reactions can probably be neglected over less than geologic timescales. However a phenomenon called ice nucleation happens at high a rate near the glass transition temperature, and in some studies doesn't become undetectable until 20 degrees below it. Ice nucleation—the local reorientation of water molecules into nanoscale ice crystals—doesn't cause immediate structural damage. However it can make avoiding ice growth and associated structural damage during future rewarming more difficult. The extent and significance of ice nucleation in highly concentrated cryoprotectant solutions is still poorly understood.[1]

More research is required on fracturing avoidance for large cryopreserved organs and tissues. Valuable research may continue to come from mainstream cryobiology, but some research will need to be specific to cryonics. In the meantime, cryonics organizations face difficult decisions in whether to make an expensive and complex technology that is still unsuccessful in its final objective clinically available. ITS is not unlike cryonics itself. ■

CHRONOLOGY OF DEVELOPMENTS RELATED TO FRACTURING AND INTERMEDIATE TEMPERATURE STORAGE

1966

Kroener and Luyet observed fracturing in vitrified glycerol solutions. (C. Kroener, B. Luyet, "Formation of cracks during the vitrification of glycerol solutions and disappearance of the cracks during rewarming," *Biodynamica* 10, (1966) 47-52.)

1984

Alcor noted fractures in human cryopreservation patients. (Federowicz, M., Hixon, H., and Leaf, J. "Postmortem Examination of Three Cryonic Suspension Patients." *Cryonics*, September, 16-28 (1984))

1990

Fahy published a detailed study of fracturing in large volumes of vitrification solution. (Fahy, G., Saur, J., and Williams, R. "Physical Problems with the Vitrification of Large Biological Systems." *Cryobiology* 27, 492-510 (1990))

1993 March

A detailed discussion and design exercise for a -130°C "Cold Room" of 100-person capacity took place on the CryoNet email list.

1994

Alcor noted fractures in the brain of a patient following removal from cryopreservation. Various other aspects of the fracturing problem were discussed in the same article, including possible intermediate temperature storage systems, and the development of a new acoustic fracturing monitoring device, the "crackphone." (Hixon, H. "Exploring Cracking Phenomena," *Cryonics* 1st Qtr., 27-32 (1995))

Architect Stephen Valentine began studying Cold Room intermediate temperature storage design concepts as part of a large cryonics facility design that would eventually be called Timeship.

1997

The crackphone acoustic fracturing monitoring device was brought into clinical use by Alcor.

2000

Alcor acquired a -130°C Harris CryoStar laboratory freezer from GS Laboratory Equipment and began testing its utility for possible storage of neuropatients. ("BioTransport Purchases CryoStar Freezer," *Cryonics* 3rd Qtr. 11 (2000))

2002

Physicist Brian Wowk and Brookhaven National Laboratory cryogenic engineer Mike Iarocci began an intensive collaboration with architect Stephen Valentine to design intermediate temperature storage systems suitable for cryonics in connection with the Timeship Project.

In summer 2002, an Alcor neuropatient reached the lowest temperature ever recorded without fracturing prior to that time, -128°C. This was attributed to a uniformly low glass transition temperature resulting from excellent cryoprotective perfusion. Professional cryobiologist consultants expressed the opinion that the case may have been the best cryopreservation of any cryonics patient to date, and recommended transfer to the CryoStar freezer for continued slow cooling and annealing for fracture avoidance. In December another patient, A-1034, was also placed into the CryoStar to accommodate wishes of the family for this type of storage.

2003 June

In Ontario, California, presentations were made to the Alcor board of directors by Brian Wowk, Mike Iarocci, and Stephen Valentine on new designs for intermediate temperature storage systems. Alcor purchased and took delivery of an experimental single-patient "neuropod" intermediate temperature storage system developed by Brian Wowk at 21CM. (*Alcor News* #13, July 1st, 2003 and *Alcor News* #14, August 1st, 2003)

2003 July

The first patient transferred to the CryoStar freezer was transitioned to liquid nitrogen storage because fracture avoidance during slow cooling to -140°C was not successful.

2003 August

Alcor Research Fellow Hugh Hixon began photoelasticity studies of fracturing using a polariscope and polarized light to image stress in cryoprotectant glasses.

Carnegie Mellon University received a $1.3 million grant from the U.S. government to study fracturing during vitrification of tissue for medical applications, resulting in many new and valuable papers in the scientific literature about this subject. ("Carnegie Mellon Researchers Developing New Ways to Store Tissue, Organs," *Science Daily*, August 13, 2003)

2003 October

21st Century Medicine, Inc., constructed a prototype laboratory ITS dewar in which most of the volume of the dewar was converted into a uniform-temperature storage space kept cold by liquid nitrogen.

2004 March

Alcor purchased and took delivery of a "patient rated" neuropod intermediate temperature storage unit for individual neuropatients.

2005 November

Alcor placed an order with 21st Century Medicine, Inc., for a custom ITS dewar large enough to hold 14 neuropatients at a stable intermediate temperature ("ITS Neurodewar").

2006 January

US Patent 6,988,370, Cryogenic storage system with improved temperature control, was awarded to Mike Iarocci, Stephen Valentine, and Brian Wowk.

An Alcor neuropatient cryopreserved with M22 vitrification solution set a new record for lowest temperature reached without fracturing of -134°C.

2006 April

Alcor transferred patient A-1034 from the CryoStar freezer to the validated neuropod purchased in 2004.

2007 October

US Patent 7,278,278, Cryogenic storage system, was awarded to Brian Wowk and Mike Iarocci.

2008 December

Alcor took delivery of the ITS neurodewar ordered in 2005. Patient A-1034 was transferred into the new storage unit, and three cryopreserved brains that had been stored by private individuals were accepted into ITS storage.

ALCOR PROCEDURES
AND TECHNOLOGIES

HOW COLD IS COLD ENOUGH?

BY HUGH HIXON, M.S.

Cryonics, January, 1985

Why don't you store people: (pick one)

- In your freezer at home?
- In a low temperature laboratory freezer?
- In the permafrost in Alaska?
- On the Greenland icecap?
- On the Antarctic icecap?
- In Siberia?
- Packed in dry ice?
- Other?

After all, it's really cold there, and all this fooling around with liquid nitrogen seems like a lot of unnecessary hassle. And besides, it's (free/costs less)(circle appropriate words).

—various people, some of them ostensibly with scientific educations.

Misapprehensions concerning why we use liquid nitrogen for cryonic storage fall into roughly three classes: 1) Economic considerations; 2) Legitimate bafflement caused by the use of a simple arithmetic temperature scale where a more complex scale is much more appropriate; 3) Disnumeria, or disability to deal with numbers. This may range from reluctance to use a calculator to inability to count above five, because you need the other hand for counting. The temperature scale for people so afflicted goes something like: very hot-hot-warm-comfortable-cool-cold-very cold-freezing. I will attempt to answer 2) and 3) together, with an explanation and examples, and then treat the economic aspect in a short afterword.

For a suspension patient, the object of cryonics is to arrest time. It is never possible to do this completely, but as we will see, our best is remarkably good. We cannot affect nuclear processes, such as radioactive decay, but for the period of time we are concerned with, radioactivity and its attendant problems are largely irrelevant. Our primary focus is on chemical processes. The human body is a dynamic structure, with creation and destruction of the chemical compounds essential to life going on in it simultaneously and continually. A good analogy would be a powered airplane, lifted by the efforts of its engines and pulled down by gravity. When the engine quits, sooner or later you're going to get to the bottom. When we die, only the destructive functions remain. Fortunately, these are all chemical processes, and proceed in such a fashion that they are well described by the Arrhenius equation.

STOP!!! DO NOT GO INTO SHOCK OR ADVANCE THE PAGE!!! The elements of the Arrhenius equation have familiar counterparts that you see every day, and while it cranks out numbers beyond the comprehension of even your Congressperson, beyond a certain point they are either so large or so small that we can safely ignore them.

To continue. The Arrhenius equation takes the form:

$$k = A \exp(-E/RT)$$

where

- k is the rate of a given chemical reaction
- A is a fudge factor to make the numbers come out right
- exp is the symbol for a particular arithmetic operation, like +, -, X, or /
- E is the Energy of Activation of the reaction, like the push it takes to start a car when the battery is dead (small for VW's, large for Cadillacs)
- R is the Ideal Gas Constant. Another fudge factor, but a well defined one, like a dollar bill. Here, its value is 1.9872 calories/degree-mole.
- T is the Absolute Temperature in degrees Kelvin (K). Which is just the Celsius (centigrade) temperature + 273.16. I should remark that the Absolute Temperature Scale is a rather arbitrary definition of a real property, and that R is used to make things come out right.

By itself, k isn't very useful so I will relate it to itself at some other temperature. For the purposes of this article, I will pick two temperatures, 77.36°K and 37°C. These are, of course, liquid nitrogen temperature and normal body temperature, respectively.

Dividing the rate at some given temperature by the rate at liquid nitrogen temperature will give ratios which will have some meaning. At the given temperature, chemical reactions will occur so many times faster or slower than they would at liquid nitrogen temperature. I will then invert the process and divide the rate ratio at 37°C by the rate ratio at the other temperatures, and say that if the reaction proceeds so far in one second at 37°C, then it will take so many seconds, minutes, days, or years to proceed as far at some lower temperature.

Now, if you'll just close your eyes while I use this page to perform a simple algebraic manipulation:

$$k[T]/k[77.36°K] = \frac{A \exp(-E/RT)}{A \exp(-E/R(77.36°K))}$$

A is the same in both cases and cancels itself out. The rest of the right side of the equation also contains several identical terms (E and R), and I will simplify it by rearranging,

$$k[T]/k[77.36°K] = \exp(-E/R(1/T - 1/(77.36°K)))$$

Now, R is a constant and we will not worry ourselves more about it. E we will select later, and give reasons for doing so. The rest of the equation, we will examine to understand its properties better.

"exp" is the operation for an exponential function. A familiar example of this is to take a number and add zeros to it, thus:

5 50 500 5,000 50,000 500,000 5,000,000 50,000,000 etc.

This is called exponentiating 10. With the "exp" operation a similar thing occurs, but the number is not 10, but 2.71828..., a number with useful mathematical properties, but not of interest to us otherwise.

The other important part of the equation is:

$1/T - 1/77.36°K$

where

$1/77.36 = 0.0129265...$

$1/T$ is called a reciprocal function, and its particular property is that when T is larger than 1, $1/T$ is less than 1, and the larger T gets, the more slowly $1/T$ gets small. It does not, however, ever become zero.

Thus, the behavior for

1/T - 0.0129265...

is that at high temperatures, it approaches the value -0.0129265... closely, but at temperatures much below 77.36°K, it gets larger fairly rapidly, and then extremely rapidly.

Putting the equation back together again, we can predict that far above 77.36°K, say at 37°C, the rate ratio will change relatively slowly, but that as the temperature drops, the rate ratio will change increasingly rapidly. That is, we will see that the change from 0°C to 20°C is about 2.4, the change from -100°C to -80°C is about 8.6, and the change from -200°C to -180°C (around liquid nitrogen temperature) is about 31,000. From -240°C to -220°C, the change is a factor of 227,434,000,000,000,000. As I mentioned at the beginning of this explanation, the temperature scale that we normally use can be very misleading.

Now. Somewhere in the distant past, I was actually taught to do this kind of calculation with pencil, paper, a slide rule, and a book of tables. But I have a computer now, and I'm going to give it a break from word processing and let it go chase numbers. Some of them were bigger than it was.

One last question remains before I turn the computer loose. What should my value for E, the *Energy of Activation* of the reaction be, or rather, since each chemical reaction has its own E, what reaction should I choose?

I am going to be pessimistic, and choose the fastest known biological reaction, catalase. I'm not going to get into detail, but the function of the enzyme catalase is protective. Some of the chemical reactions that your body must use have extraordinarily poisonous by-products, and the function of catalase is to destroy one of the worst of them. The value for its E is 7,000 calories per mole-degree Kelvin. It is sufficiently fast that when it is studied, the work is often done at about dry ice temperature. My friend Mike Darwin remarks that he once did this in a crude fashion and that even at dry ice temperature things get rather busy. Another reason to use it is that it's one of the few I happen to have. E's are not normally tabulated.

I had never specifically done this calculation before, and I confess that I was a bit startled by the size of some of the numbers. Enough to check my procedure fairly carefully. I am reasonably confident of the picture that they show.

The first thing to notice about the table is that somewhere slightly below -240°C, the computer gave up. I *did* say that the equation goes rather fast at low temperatures. The last three numbers in the "Rate relative... " column I did by hand. You can see what the computer was attempting to do in the "exponent" column, trying to perform the "exp" operation. As noted, the relative rate at liquid helium temperature would be

Degrees Celsius	Degrees Kelvin	1/T	Exponent	Rate relative to LN2 (77.36°K)	Time to equal 1 sec. at 37°C
37	310.16 (Body temperature)	0.0322	34.1173	776,682,000,000,000	1 second
20	293.16	0.003411	33.5817	360,555,000,000,000	2.154 sec
0	273.16 (Water freezes)	0.003660	32.6389	149,588,000,000,000	5.192 sec
-20	253.16	0.003950	31.6201	54,007,200,000,000	14.381 sec
-40	233.16	0.004289	30.4266	16,371,100,000,000	47.439 sec
-60	213.16	0.004468	29.0091	3,967,220,000,000	3.263 min
-65	208.16 (Limit of simple mechanical freezers)	0.004804	28.6122	2,667,460,000,000	4.853 min
-79.5	193.66 (Dry ice)	0.005164	27.3451	751,335,000,000	17.229 min
-100	173.16	0.005775	25.1917	87,222,100,000	2.474 hrs
-120	153.16	0.006529	22.5353	6,123,060,000	1.468 days
-128	145.16 (CF4, lowest boiling Freon)	0.006889	21.2678	1,723,820,000	5.213 days
-140	133.16	0.007510	19.0810	193,534,000	46.448 days
-160	113.16	0.008837	14.4056	1,804,070	13.652 years
-164	109.16 (Methane boils)	0.009169	13.2649	576,591	42.714 years
-180	93.16	0.010734	7.7227	2,259	10.9 thousand years
-185.7	87.46 (Argon boils)	0.011434	5.2584	192	128.16 thousand years
-195.8	77.36 (Liquid nitrogen)	0.012926	0.0	1	24.628 million years
-200	73.16	0.013669	-2.6141	0.07324	336.285 million years
-220	53.16	0.018811	-20.728	0.00000000099	24760.5 trillion years
-240	33.16	0.030157	-60.694	0.[26 zeros]44	5,390,000,000, 000,000,000 trillion yrs
-252.8	20.36 (Liquid hydrogen)	0.049116	-127.48	0.[54 zeros]22	Long enough
-260	13.16	0.075988	-222.14	0.[95 zeros]29	Even longer
-268.9	4.26 (Liquid helium)	0.234741	-781.35	0.[338 zeros]19	Don't worry about it

about 0.0.... (eight and a quarter lines of zeros)....19. The next thing to notice is that a reaction that would take one second at body temperature takes 24,000,000 years at liquid nitrogen temperature. This is clearly a case of extreme overkill, and seems to support advocates of storage at higher temperatures.

However, note how fast things *change* as the temperature drops closer to 77°K. At dry ice temperature, "only" 115 degrees higher, 100 years is about equal to 40 days dead on the floor. Clearly unacceptable.

So what is acceptable? Here is my opinion. People have fully recovered after being dead on the floor for one hour, when the proper medical procedure was followed. [Note: This was based on some work by Dr. Blaine White, of Detroit, that was reported in the January 18, 1982 issue of *Medical World News*. It was not subsequently reproduced. However, the current record for drowning in ice water with subsequent resuscitation is now over one hour. -HH (1992)] There are reasonable arguments to support the idea that brain deterioration is not significant until somewhere in the range of 12 to 24 hours, although changes in other organs of the body probably make revival impossible. Say 12 hours at 37°C is a limit. How long can we have to expect to store suspension patients before they can be revived? Again I guess. Biochemistry is advancing very fast now, but I do not see reanimation as possible in less than 25 years, with 40-50 years being very likely. If we cannot be reanimated in 100 years, then our civilization has somehow died, by bang or whimper, and probably neither liquid nitrogen, nor dry ice, nor even refrigeration may be available, and our plans and these calculations become irrelevant. Let us set a maximum storage period of 100 years.

Thus: In 100 years there are about 876,600 hours. In 12 hours, there are 43,200 seconds. The temperature must be low enough that each 20 hours is equal to one second at 37°C. (The ratio is about 73,000 to 1). From the table, the storage temperature should be no higher than -115°C. Add to this additional burdens, all eating into your 12 hours: time between deanimation and discovery; time to get the transport team on location; transport time; time for perfusion; time to cool to the storage temperature. -115°C is for when things go *right*.

There is one bright spot. Below -100°C, the water in biological systems is finally all frozen, and molecules can't move to react. We use cryoprotectants that have the effect of preventing freezing, but somewhere around -135°C they all have glass transition points, becoming so viscous that molecules can't move and undergo chemical change. While the table indicates that staying below -150°C is safe from a rate of reaction standpoint, in fact any temperature below -130°C to -135°C is probably safe due to elimination of translational molecular movement as a result of vitrification.

Okay, you say, why not use a mechanical system to hold a temperature of -135°C? First problem: They don't *hold* a temperature. They cycle between a switch-on temperature and a switch-off temperature. This causes expansion and contraction, and mechanical stresses. Cracking. We don't know what is acceptable yet. This problem can probably be eliminated by the application of sufficient money. Second problem: If the power goes, you start to warm up. Immediately. Emergency generator? Sure, but you'll need at least 8 kilowatts, and it has to reliably self-start within minutes, unattended. Expensive. Third problem: Have you priced a mechanical system? $20,000 up front, and then you start paying the electric bill. Small units like this are rather inefficient so the electric bill is not a minor consideration. Fourth problem: Eventually, the system is going to die on you. Next year. Next month. Next week. Tomorrow. Read the warranty. It doesn't say a thing about a loaner within five minutes. Buy another one for backup. You may get a deal for buying two at once.

How about using some other compound with a boiling point above that of nitrogen? With careful examination of the *Handbook of Chemistry and Physics*, I came up with 30 compounds with boiling points below -80°C. When you eliminate the ones that boil above -115°C, the mildly poisonous ones, the very poisonous ones, the corrosive ones, the oxidizers, the explosively flammable ones and the very expensive ones, you're left with nitrogen and the rather expensive ones. To retain the rather expensive ones, you either need a mechanical system, with all the problems mentioned before except that you are much more tolerant to power-outs and breakdowns, or you use a liquid nitrogen condenser. If you use a condenser, you may as well use liquid nitrogen directly and save the cost of the special gas and the condenser system.

How about moving to the arctic, and using the low temperatures there to assist the refrigeration? This is a potentially good idea, but there are severe problems of cost and logistics. It's nice of you to volunteer to go up there, though.

THAT'S why we use liquid nitrogen.

As a footnote to all the above arguments, it is worth noting that Alcor (in Riverside, CA) is in an unusually favorable position with respect to liquid nitrogen. Los Angeles is a major industrial center, and liquid nitrogen is a major industrial chemical, particularly in the aerospace industry. As a result, there are at least two major liquid nitrogen plants in the LA area; one out at Fontana, about 30 miles northeast of us, and one on the Long Beach Harbor area, about 30 miles to the southwest. Each plant is several acres in size, and as efficient as only a plant that size can be. Our delivered cost for liquid nitrogen is about $0.31/liter. A short calculation will show that at that price, you can get a lot of years of liquid nitrogen for just the buy-in price of the schemes mentioned above. This does not mean that we will always use LN2, however. If our further studies on the cracking problems we have reported here previously (CRYONICS, September 1984) confirm what we have seen so far, we will certainly have to consider storage temperatures above 77°K. As I have indicated though, the economic penalties may be severe. ■

HISTORY OF DMSO AND GLYCEROL IN CRYONICS

BY MICHAEL DARWIN
Cryonics, 3rd Quarter, 2007

In The Beginning: Vitrification or Freezing?

In *The Prospect of Immortality*, the book which launched cryonics, Robert C.W. Ettinger suggests that glycerol might be used as the cryoprotectant for human cryopreservation[1] based largely on the fact that it was the dominant cryoprotective agent (CPA) at that time (1962-64) and most of the positive results with sperm and tissues had been achieved with glycerol. Due largely to the flare and flamboyance of "the Father of Dimethyl Sulfoxide (DMSO*)," Dr. Stanley W. Jacob, who was Assistant Professor of Surgery at the University of Oregon Health Sciences Center Medical School, DMSO entered the public consciousness in a big way in the mid-to-late 1960s.[2,3,4] DMSO's anti-inflammatory, and seemingly incredible skin-penetrating properties, were much talked about.

Robert Ettinger (foreground) demonstrates use of the Iron Heart, a mechanical chest compressor

Sometime between 1966 and 1967, Ettinger asked Dr. Dante Brunol, an Italian national living in the US, to produce a formal, written protocol for cryopreserving cryonics patients. Brunol was a biophysicist (Ph.D.), M.D., and surgeon with experience in cardiopulmonary bypass. Brunol, writing under the nom de plume of Mario Satini, M.D., produced a complicated protocol which, while it has a number of deficiencies, is really quite remarkable, and even visionary in several respects.[5] Brunol opens his protocol with the following remarks:

"The writer has always favored supercooling rather than the freezing of humans. Supercooling does not lead to the formation of ice crystals. It should be possible to find

1   Robert C.W Ettinger: *The Prospect of Immortality,* Doubleday, New York, 1964.

2   Laudahn G. & Jacob S.: *Symposium on DMSO Berlin,* Germany, 1965.

3   Laudahn G. & Jacob S.: *Symposium on DMSO Berlin,* Germany, 1966.

4   Jacob SW, Rosenbaum E.E., Wood, D.C.: *Dimethyl Sulfoxide (Basic Concepts),* Marcel Dekker, Inc., New York, 1971.

5   Robert F. Nelson & Sandra Stanley: *We Froze The First Man,* Dell Publishing Company, New York, 1968, pp. 136-56.

Dr. Dante Brunol, 1967

methods to store humans at temperatures warmer than -30 degrees C, for four or five years, the time necessary to perfect methods of freezing.

"When Professor Ettinger, author of *The Prospect of Immortality,* asked me to devise a method to freeze humans, at first I declined the offer. In my opinion, only a chemical inducing vitrification could save the cells from damage due to (ice) crystallization."

The First Human Cryopreservation Protocol

Brunol then goes on to explain how vitrification is achieved through ultra-rapid cooling and, without naming it, introduces the idea of the glass transition point of water (T_g), a temperature below which water has become a glass and cannot organize into crystals. He further explains why such ultra-rapid cooling cannot be applied, even to tissues, let alone whole humans. Brunol details his protocol which consists of the following core elements:

1) Immediate commencement of CPR at the time medico-legal death is pronounced, preferably augmented with an artificial airway and high FiO2 (fraction of inspired oxygen in a gas) oxygen administration (15 liters per minute). He recommends at least 30 compressions per minute, with one ventilation every four minutes.

2) Placement of a thermistor in the rectum to monitor body core temperature. The thermistor is affixed to a 10" wooden dowel with straps to hold it deeply in the rectum.

3) Immersion of the patient in a special tub filled with ice and 10% DMSO in water while mechanical CPR continues. The tub supports the patient so that his head remains above the water level allowing manual ventilation to continue.

4) Use of the Westinghouse Iron Heart (a mechanical chest compressor) as soon as possible to continue CPR during cooling. CPR with the Iron Heart is to continue until the patient reaches a core temperature of 15 degrees C, or until extracorporeal cooling using closed-circuit cardiopulmonary bypass (CPB) can be commenced via femoral-femoral bypass using a heat exchanger.

5) Inject 2 liters of ice-cold 5% Dextran in an isotonic solution via both internal carotid arteries to hemodilute and cool the brain.

6) Femoral-femoral cannulation followed by open circuit perfusion (blood washout) of ~20 gallons (80 liters) of heparinized 20% DMSO, 20% glycerol in saline or other isotonic solution at a pressure of 120 mm Hg, and a temperature of between 1 degree and 4 degrees C.

7) Using a fairly complex circuit Brunol demonstrates a good knowledge of physiology, and proposes perfusing the pulmonary circulation by turning on the Iron Heart and pressurizing the venous circulation (via retrograde flow through the femoral venous cannulae) to 20 mmHg at very low flow, while opening the arterial cannulae to allow effluent to exhaust retrograde into a discard-reservoir. Perfusion of the pulmonary circuit is to commence when the patient's temperature reaches 10 degrees C and is to continue for 15 minutes.

8) Preferably, perfusion with the CPA mixture should terminate when the patient's core temperature is -4 degrees C.

9) Brunol was very concerned about interstitial and intracellular ice crystal damage and he proposed vitrifying the cells by initiating ice crystal formation in the vasculature. He proposed doing this by following CPA perfusion with the perfusion of a quantity of 10% Dextran at near 1 degree C in saline into both the arterial and the pulmonary circulation. The idea was that this solution would start to freeze immediately, before the CPA could equilibrate from the intracellular and interstitial spaces. Ice would thus form first in the vessels and dehydrate the cells to ~30% of their normal volume.

10) The GI tract, pleural space, and peritoneum were to be filled with a solution (apparently) chilled to below freezing consisting of 20% DMSO, 20% glycerol, and 10% ethanol to facilitate core heat exchange. Each pleural space and the peritoneal cavity are to be filled with 1 liter of this fluid. The balance (of up to ~4 gallons as necessary) was to be used to fill the GI tract (upper and lower).

11) Transfer the patient to a container with a perforated bottom to allow the escape of water from melting ice, and pack the body in ice and granular salt: one layer of salt, one layer of ice, etc., to achieve a temperature of -20 degrees C for 24 hours (to allow for maximal extracellular ice growth and intracellular CPA concentration).

12) Transfer the patient to an insulated container and pack in dry ice followed by cooling to -196 degrees C as soon as possible.

Minus the post CPA perfusion of 10% dextran-saline, this protocol would have been vastly better than anything that would be used in cryonics until at least 1979. Brunol was incorrect in assuming that ice formation would start and subsequently outpace diffusion of CPA into the 10% dextran-saline solution. However, his idea of initiating and largely confining ice formation to the large vessels of the vasculature and the body cavities is an intriguing one. Interestingly, the ability to control the location where ice nucleation begins may today be possible by adding the potent ice-nucleation protein produced by the common soil bacterium, *Pseudomonas syringae,*[6] to the perfusate in the circulatory system. If this was done *in addition* to ice-blocking polymers, it might allow for considerable ice formation, but only in the form of very small, non-damaging ice crystals.[7] Being able to tolerate significant ice formation would decrease the concentration of cryoprotective agents needed for successful preservation, and thus decrease the injury due to cryoprotective agent toxicity.

When James H. Bedford, the first man cryopreserved, died on 12 January, 1967, Robert F. Nelson of the Cryonics Society of California (CSC) had made virtually none of the preparations Brunol recommended. Some DMSO had been acquired, but no carrier solution was available, such as Lactated Ringer's (LR). Similarly, Robert Ettinger had sent Nelson an Iron Heart, but Nelson had not bothered to get oxygen to power it. Thus, Bedford was pin-cushioned with injections of pure DMSO via syringe, with attempts made to inject the DMSO directly into the right internal carotid artery.[8]

Glycerol and the Cryonics Society of New York

Largely because of DMSO's almost mythical property of being able to penetrate cells, it seems to have become the CPA of choice amongst cryonicists on the West Coast from 1967 until 1979. By contrast, the people at the Cryonics Society of New York (CSNY), including Paul Segall, Harold Waitz and Curtis Henderson, read Brunol's protocol and decided to try to implement those parts of it that they thought reasonable and practical. Brunol recommended that an Amtec 209 industrial roller pump, with a Zero-Max speed controller, be used to deliver perfusate. Curtis Henderson, CSNY's President, purchased one of these circa 1968 (I still have it to this day).

Zero-Max (mechanical) controllers were the primary way motor speeds were regulated before solid-state electronic controls came into wide use in the 1970s.

6   Graether SP, Jia Z: Modeling Pseudomonas syringae ice-nucleation protein as a beta-helical protein. *Biophys J. Mar;* 80 (3): 1169-73; 2001.

7   Fahy GM. The role of nucleation in cryopreservation. In: *Biological Ice Nucleation and Its Applications* (R.E. Lee, Jr., G.J. Warren, and L.V. Gusta (Eds.), APS Press, 1995, 315-336.

8   Darwin M: "Dear Dr. Bedford (And those who will care for you after I do), A thank you note to a pioneer." *Cryonics* Volume 12(7) Issue 132 JULY, 1991. [Editors' note: This article is also reprinted elsewhere in this book. There is some significant disagreement on what really happened at the Bedford cryopreservation. See Michael Perry's added comments at the end of the reprint of "Dear Dr. Bedford…" in this book.]

The Zero-Max is an oil-immersed adjustable speed drive with four or more one-way clutches that move back and forth, each rotating the output shaft a partial turn for each stroke transmission. Zero-Max controls were used extensively to control speed before the widespread application of solid state motor controllers in the 1970s. The bubble trap was designed by a physician associated with CSNY at that time, Dr. Jane Enzman, daughter of the maverick physicist and engineer Dr. Robert Duncan Enzman.

Unfortunately, this set-up was never used on a patient. CSNY used a Porti-Boy embalming machine. Paul Segall modified the Brunol protocol in a number of unfortunate ways. Segall eliminated any attempt at maintaining post-arrest circulation writing, *"No attempt is made to maintain circulation of the blood for the following reason. It has been observed that if the blood flow falls under 70 mm Hg for more than 5 minutes there is irreversible damage (by today's standards) to the cerebral brain centers. Evidence has shown that perhaps this [is] due to the blockage of the microcirculation of the brain (the capillaries become clogged because of the formation of blood clots). In all likelihood, artificial circulation after death could not be started fast enough to reach the cerebral centers."* [9]

Segall, in contrast to Brunol, apparently never understood the importance of achieving an adequate intracellular concentration of cryoprotectant. Brunol actually does the math and concludes, based on dilution calculations, that the terminal intracellular concentration of CPA will be 22%.[10] Segall's protocol called for an initial flush with 6 liters of ice-chilled heparinized Ringer's Lactate solution for each 30 pounds of body weight (thus, a 150 pound man would be flushed with 30 liters of Ringer's). This was to be followed by a flush of 8 liters of ice-chilled 20% glycerol in Ringer's for a 150 pound man. An additional liter of 20% glycerol-Ringer's was to be used to fill the GI tract. Following this, the patient was to be transferred to a body bag and packed in ice and salt for 12 hours and then transferred to an insulated box and packed in dry ice.

This protocol, which was used on CSNY patients Steven Mandell and Ann Deblasio, would have resulted in negligible concentrations of glycerol in the patient's tissues—levels not even cryoprotective for cells in culture. Failure to use CPR and anticoagulation as soon after cardiac arrest as possible resulted not only in massive systemic clotting, but greatly delayed cooling as well. Segall's rationale for using glycerol as the sole CPA was based on Suda's work with cat brains.[11] CSNY had acquired DMSO, but did not use it.

---

9   Segall P: "The body is now ready for storage." *Cryonics Reports.* 4 (3);1969.
10   Robert F. Nelson & Sandra Stanley: *We Froze The First Man*, Dell Publishing Company, New York, 1968, pp. 156-9.
11   Suda I, Kito K, Adachi C: "Viability of long-term frozen cat brain in vitro." *Nature.* Oct 15;212(5059):268-70;1966.

Learning the Hard Way

By contrast, CSC continued to use DMSO, mostly as a 20% solution in Ringer's. There is no documentation of the temperature, pressure, or volume of solution used. In the early to mid-1970s there was an extensive round of correspondence and a second attempt to formulate an optimum perfusion protocol. This time it was Dr. Peter Gouras who was chosen for this task. Gouras proposed using DMSO's "extraordinary" permeation qualities to infiltrate the patient with 65% DMSO after Elford and Walter[12] by soaking him in progressively higher concentrations of DMSO as the temperature was concurrently reduced.[13] This led Art Quaife, who was both a gifted mathematician and President of Trans Time, to produce a highly sophisticated mathematical analysis of the diffusion kinetics showing that equilibration by soaking the patient in DMSO would take many months even at 0 degrees C.[14]

During this extensive collaborative correspondence a consensus was reached to use 20% DMSO in a modified Collin's solution base perfusate, following blood washout with heparinized Ringer's Lactate. This was the beginning of the end of using DMSO in cryonics. In February of 1974, two patients were perfused on the same day on opposite coasts of the US using DMSO-Collins by Trans Time (San Francisco, CA) and the author (operating as Cryo-Span Midwest) using DMSO-Ringer's (Cumberland, MD).[15] Both patients experienced long periods of warm and cold ischemia before perfusion was possible. Almost immediate and massive edema occurred in both patients with rapid deterioration of venous return, and ultimately, failure of perfusion. Five-percent of DMSO, followed by 20% DMSO in modified Collins solution, was used to perfuse Frederick Chamberlain, Jr., (the first neuropatient), in 1976. Fred, Jr. had been given immediate and continuous cardiopulmonary support, as well as good external cooling. While edema was slower to develop, it nevertheless occurred, and again resulted in failure of venous return.[16]

When Jerry Leaf (Cryovita Laboratories) did his first human case for Trans Time, Samuel Berkowitz, in June of 1978,[17] DMSO was again used, but the quantity of perfusate was small, as was the case when K.V.M. (initials used for privacy) was

---

12　Elford BC & Walter, CA: "Preservation of structure and function of smooth muscle cooled to –79 degrees C in unfrozen aqueous media." *Nat New Biol.* 15;236(63):58-60;1972.

13　Communication from the Bay Area Cryonics Society, 1739 Oxford St., #6, Berkeley, CA 94709. "Arthur Quaife, Chairman Jerome B. White, and others have been working with Dr. Peter Gouras and other scientists to formalize an updated freezing protocol." in *Man Into Superman* by Robert C.W. Ettinger, Doubleday, New York, 1971.

14　Quaife A: "Mathematical Models of Perfusion Processes," Manrise Technical Review. 2:28-75; 1972.

15　Unpublished Case Data, Alcor Life Extension Foundation, Patient A-1056, 09 February, 1973.

16　Unpublished Case Data, Alcor Life Extension Foundation, Patient A-1001, 16 July, 1976.

17　Leaf JD: "Cryonic Suspension of Sam Berkowitz: Technical Report," *Long Life Magazine.* 3: (2), March/April, 1979.

perfused in December of 1978.[18] In both of these cases, despite the low volume of perfusate, edema was a serious problem. The last case done with DMSO was L.R., a Trans Time neuropatient who was perfused (again with a very small volume of 20% DMSO: ~6 liters) in March of 1979.[19] This patient did not experience noticeable edema, probably owing to the small volume of solution used, prompt post-arrest CPR, and minimal warm or cold ischemic injury since she was transported directly from home by ambulance to the Trans Time facility in Emeryville, CA, where perfusion was carried out.

In the summer of 1979, Jerry Leaf and I began intense discussions, both in writing and by phone, about improving the protocol for human cryopreservation. It was during these discussions that the issue of both the CPA to use and the proper volume of perfusate required to reach an adequate tissue concentration arose. I pointed out that the volumes of perfusate being used by Cryovita-Trans Time were only achieving "homeopathic" levels of CPA in the patients' tissues. Jerry was in complete agreement and explained that the CPA protocol he was using had been determined by Paul Segall, of Trans Time.

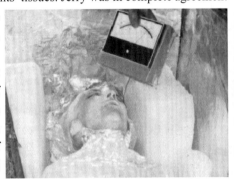

Clara Dostal, 1972
(Note the lack of edema.)

As of 1977, I had decided that DMSO was unacceptable, because of the consistent problems with edema observed, and its documented destructive effects on the vascular endothelium of kidneys being perfused for attempted organ cryopreservation.[20] On 10 December, 1972 Clara Dostal, a CSNY member, was perfused with multiple passes of increasing concentrations of glycerol in Lactated Ringer's (LR) solution in an attempt to achieve multi-molar equilibration of glycerol in the brain.[21] Perfusion was via the right internal carotid artery using standard mortuary technique. This meant that only one cannula was available so perfusion had to be alternated between the head and trunk with the arterial cannula being removed and repositioned after each pass of perfusate. The patient's head was flushed with 6.5 liters of LR before commencing

18   Leaf JD: "Case Study: K.V.M. Suspension." *Cryonics*, August, 1981, pp8-18.
19   Leaf JD & Quaife AD: "Case Study of Neuropreservation: Cryonics suspension of L.R." *Cryonics*, November, 1981 pp. 21-28.
20   Jeske AH, Fonteles, MC, Karow AM. Functional preservation of the mammalian kidney. III. Ultrastructural effects of perfusion with dimethylsulfoxide (DMSO). *Cryobiology.* Apr;11(2):170-81;1974.
21   Corey F. Noble and Michael D. Federowicz, "The Perfusion and Freezing of a 60-Year-Old Woman," *Manrise Technical Review* 3(1) 7-32 (Mar. 1973).

cryoprotective perfusion. Three passes of glycerol in LR were used: 2.26 M, 4.34 M, and 5.78 M with concentration on perfusing the brain due to the limited volume of perfusate available. Twenty-seven point two (27.2) liters of perfusate was used with a perfusion time (combined head and trunk) of 157 minutes. The final cranial (right internal jugular) effluent glycerol concentration was ~4.0 M glycerol.

Despite the comparatively large volumes of perfusate used, this patient did not develop edema. (Note: until 1981 this volume of cryoprotective perfusate would have been considered large.) In the winter of 1977, under the auspices of the Institute for Advanced Biological Studies in Indianapolis, IN, I began research on brain ultrastructure following perfusion and freezing of rabbit heads using 2 M glycerol. In November of 1978, I perfused my terminally ill dog, (a ~16 kg mongrel), with 10 liters of 7% v/v glycerol and 30 liters of 20% v/v glycerol.[22] None of these animals experienced edema. Indeed, the problem was systemic osmotic dehydration. On the basis of these experiences it was decided that glycerol would be used in future human cases, with a target terminal tissue glycerol concentration of 3M.

In January of 1980 two consecutive cryopreservation cases (see Graphs A & B) were carried out at Cryovita Laboratories for Trans Time by Jerry Leaf and myself.[23] A total of 80 liters of perfusate was used, with the following quantities and compositions:

5% glycerol perfusate, 25 liters
10% glycerol perfusate, 10 liters
15% glycerol perfusate, 10 liters
20% glycerol perfusate, 10 liters
25% glycerol perfusate, 10 liters
50% glycerol perfusate, 15 liters

A combination of open and closed circuit perfusion was used. Incredibly, perfusion was possible in one case for 500 minutes before cerebral edema became the limiting factor. In this patient a terminal venous concentration of 2.32 M glycerol was achieved. In the second patient, a terminal venous concentration of 2.87 M glycerol was achieved after only 133 minutes of perfusion, without either systemic or cerebral edema terminating perfusion.

From that time forward it was clear that glycerol was vastly superior in terms of perfusability. For the first time it was possible to achieve desired levels of cryoprotection, using extended perfusion if necessary, even in patients who had suffered serious warm and cold ischemic injury. In the mid-1980s the target tissue glycerol concentration was

22   Bridge SW: Fifteen Years in Cryonics, Part III. *Alcor Indiana Newsletter*. #5 July/August 1992.
23   Case Report: Two consecutive suspensions, a comparative study in experimental suspended animation. *Cryonics* 6:11;1985.

increased from 3.0M to 4.5M on the basis of the "Smith Criterion,"[24] and, on the basis of dog brain ultrastructural research conducted by BioPreservation in 1995,[25] terminal tissue glycerol concentration was increased to 7.5 M (the maximum concentration possible to perfuse due to viscosity constraints).

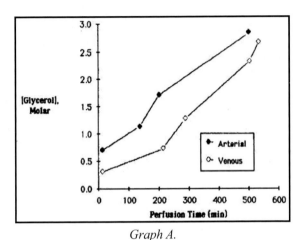

Graph A.
SP1 Glycerol Concentration vs. Perfusion Time

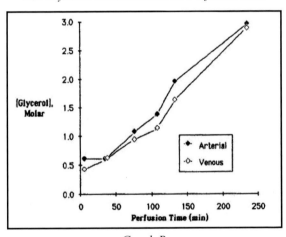

Graph B.
SP2 Glycerol Concentration vs. Perfusion Time.

24   Wowk B & Darwin M: *Alcor Reaching for Tomorrow*, Appendix A: The cryobiological case for cryonics. Alcor Life Extension Foundation, Riverside, CA; 1988. pp. A-1 to A-9.

25   Darwin, M: "BPI Tech Brief 16: Canine Cryopreservation," CryoNet #4468, #4474 (31 May 1995), http://www.cryonet.org/000144.html. Also, summarized, excerpted, and illustrated by Charles Platt, "New Brain Study Shows Reduced Tissue Damage," *CryoCare Report* 4: 1, 7-12 (July 1995).

An attempt was made by the Cryonics Institute to switch to a perfusate containing propylene glycol in November of 1987.[26] This resulted in severe edema which terminated perfusion well before target CPA concentration was reached. Until the introduction of 21CM vitrification solutions in the summer of 2001,[27] all patients were perfused with glycerol as a mono-agent. ■

---

26   Ettinger, RCW: Personal Communication, May, 1991.
27   Lemler, JB, et al. Alcor cryotransport case report: patient A-1505, 22 March, 2001.

Mathematical Analysis of Recirculating Perfusion Systems, with Application to Cryonic Suspension

By R. Michael Perry, Ph.D.

Edited and abridged by the author, Sep. 2013. Original containing additional mathematical details appeared in Cryonics, *Oct. 1988, 24-38.*

Introduction

The objective of cryopreservation is to place today's terminally ill patients into a state of arrested metabolism via cryopreservation with as little injury from ischemia (interrupted circulation) and the cryopreservation process as possible. The principal method of reducing cryopreservation associated injury is the replacement of a substantial portion of the cell and tissue water content of the patient with a "cryoprotective agent(s)" (CPA), which acts both to minimize the amount of ice formed during deep cooling and to stabilize cell membranes against freeze-induced disruption.

Replacement of 30% to 40% of a patient's body water with CPA can only be achieved by the circulation of a solution containing high concentrations of the CPA throughout the patient's vascular system. The circulation of a fluid through the vascular system of a patient, organ, or tissue is called "perfusion." In a normally functioning living organism, perfusion serves as a vehicle for mass exchange: delivering needed nutrients and dissolved gases to tissues and carrying away waste products. Similarly, cryoprotective perfusion carried out in preparation for cryopreservation also involves mass exchange: in this case the introduction of cryoprotective agents and the removal of unwanted tissue water.

Unfortunately, the introduction and removal of cryoprotective agents is not a completely benign process. CPAs used in human cryopreservations and in solid state organ preservation studies present a number of challenges to tissue viability. These challenges fall into three broad classes: osmotic injury, toxic injury, and mechanical stress (e.g., excessive shear or excessive pressure) caused by injection of fluids during perfusion.

Osmotic injury can occur during introduction of cryoprotectant when the rate of introduction of the agent results in excessive cellular dehydration and/or vascular overexpansion. Injury from osmotic effects can be minimized or eliminated by carefully controlling the rate of introduction of CPA in a manner which prevents buildup of large concentration gradients and allows sufficient time for the agent to equilibrate across the cell membranes, assuming the permeation rate across the membrane is not negligible.

Injury from toxicity occurs due to the direct and indirect effects of the CPA on macromolecules which compose cell structures. CPA may dissolve out key components, precipitate inorganic ions, remove excessive amounts of water needed for structural integrity, or directly bind to macromolecules, rendering them nonfunctional. Generally speaking, injury from toxicity is a function of both the temperature and the time of exposure. Another source of injury, which can be viewed as a form of toxicity, is cellular deterioration caused by prolonged ischemic exposure.

The considerable osmotic activity of CPAs and the need to reach high concentrations of these agents in the tissues of the patient dictate that introduction be gradual. This allows time for the agent to diffuse across capillary and cell membranes and slowly exchange with water present both within and between the cells. Too rapid a rate of introduction of CPA will result in dehydration (shrinkage) of the cells and injury due to osmotic stress. Additionally, excessive flow rates will result in elevated perfusion pressure leading to excessive fluid accumulation in the extracellular space, causing edema (swelling).

On the other hand, CPA toxicity can best be minimized by reducing the amount of time the tissue is exposed to CPA at the relatively high (above-freezing) temperatures required to carry out perfusion. The more rapidly CPA is introduced the shorter will be the time of exposure at such temperatures, and the less the injury from toxicity and other temperature/time dependent deterioration.

Clearly, a balance must be struck between the optimal CPA perfusion protocol designed to minimize osmotic injury and edema and the optimum protocol to minimize toxicity. Such a protocol requires careful control over the rate of introduction of CPA.

The most straightforward way to achieve such control would be to continuously

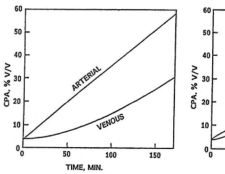

Figure 1. Single-pass perfusion.

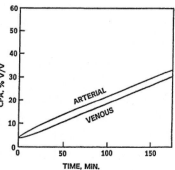

Figure 2. Recirculating perfusion.

deliver a constant flow of perfusate to the arterial system of the patient while continuously increasing the perfusate CPA concentration and discarding the effluent draining from the venous circulation. In this case (assuming a patient neither dehydrating nor retaining fluid) the incoming (arterial) and outgoing (venous) flow rates are equal, and all the outflow (effluent) is discarded. The more rapidly the perfusate is pumped through and carried out with reasonable speed assuming a moderate rate of withdrawal, the shorter will be the time of perfusion. It has a serious drawback, however, in that it is likely to induce large gradients in the concentration of CPA, hence large osmotic stresses.

A powerful way of reducing the osmotic stresses is to recirculate some of the perfusate through the patient while maintaining a constant rate of withdrawal. Perfusate that is withdrawn is replaced by perfusate at higher CPA concentration than before. The superiority of this recirculating system is illustrated in figs. 1 and 2, which show simulations of a whole-body cryopreservation giving the increase of CPA concentration with time in volumetric units under different flow rates (further details in section 6). Fig. 1 shows a single pass system with an arterial flow rate and effluent withdrawal rate of 0.4 liters/min. (This, it should be pointed out, is shown to illustrate one advantage of a recirculating system over a single pass system; in practice the single-pass system would also be impractical for other reasons noted below.) In fig. 2 the arterial flow rate is 2.4 liters/min. while the withdrawal rate is 0.4 liters/ min. as before, so that a net flow of 2.0 liters/min. is recirculated. It will be seen that the time to reach the desired CPA concentration of 30% is about the same for the two perfusions and in fact, perfusate and CPA requirements are also nearly the same. However, the osmotic stresses, as indicated by the difference in arterial and venous CPA concentrations, are unacceptably large for the single pass system, but much smaller and well within acceptable limits for the recirculating system.

The single pass system would offer another serious difficulty too. With such a low flow rate into the patient there would be insufficient pressure to drive the CPA into the entire vascular bed, resulting in inadequate perfusion of tissues. A much higher flow rate, on the other hand, would require a much larger amount of perfusate to overcome non-instantaneous absorption of CPA.

Use of a recirculating perfusion system introduces a number of complications, however. What effluent withdrawal and CPA concentrate addition profiles will yield the desired profile of increase in CPA concentrations? How many liters of a given concentration of CPA concentrate will be required for a patient of any given mass? Given a specified per minute rate of CPA concentration increase how long will perfusion last and how much CPA toxicity will the patient experience as a consequence?

When a patient presents for cryopreservation these questions must be answered rapidly and with reasonable confidence. One highly useful tool for obtaining those answers is mathematical modeling, or prediction of the course of CPA perfusion from given starting or boundary conditions. Such prediction, of course, is always imperfect due to the enormous complexity of the system, but it can still furnish valuable insights.

In this paper consideration is given to a perfusion system consisting of n reservoirs with arbitrary, pairwise interconnections and flow rates that are constant with time. A binary solvent-solute mixture is circulated through the reservoirs, each of which is assumed to instantaneously mix all incoming fluids. We wish to know the concentration of solute in each reservoir as a function of time. This in turn depends on a linear, ordinary differential equation involving flow rates into and out of the reservoir. The equation is solved numerically (details summarized here, given more fully in original version), using a Taylor's series approximation, and is then generalized to the case in which the flow rates vary with time.

Application of this technique to the problem of CPA perfusion during a cryopreservation is then considered. A computer program was written to predict the concentration of CPA in a cryonics patient as a function of time, assuming constant flow rates into and out of the patient and the reservoirs involved in perfusion.

This program was used during a whole-body cryopreservation at the Alcor Life Extension Foundation [1]. Rough estimates were obtained, in advance, of time and perfusate requirements under different assumed flow rates, and actual flow rates were adjusted accordingly to reduce anticipated osmotic stress. A more careful study was done after the preservation to try to reconstruct the course of CPA perfusion. Comparison of predicted and observed CPA concentrations sheds light on certain physical changes, such as reduction of patient circulating volume, believed to have been caused by vascular occlusion secondary to ischemic clotting. Other programs have since been written that allow for variable flow rates, to allow optimal perfusion profiles under certain models of cell stress. Calculations from one of these programs are shown. Work is continuing, and possible future applications are discussed, including a computer-driven system for cryopreservations.

Background

The pioneering analysis of perfusion systems for cryopreservation was carried out by Quaife in 1972 [10]. All three phases of preservation (blood washout and cooling, CPA perfusion, and freezing) were considered, with modeling of the patient more advanced than that described here. Solutions were obtained for (among other things) concentrations of CPA in a recirculating perfusion circuit as a function of time. Simplifying assumptions, such as fixed or highly controlled fluid volumes in the reservoirs, allowed expression of these concentrations in terms of elementary mathematical functions (mainly exponentials). In addition to the buildup of CPA, the problem of cooling the patient through perfusion was considered, and it was noted that the two problems are mathematically equivalent under reasonable approximating assumptions. Results pertaining to heat flow during cryopreservation were extended in a later study [9].

Meanwhile Fahy and Harris obtained solutions for a simple though new, variable-volumes perfusion circuit that has no recirculation [4,7]. Fahy has also considered, though not analyzed in full generality, a variable-volumes circuit that does provide for recirculation, with CPA introduced by gravity feed from a concentrate reservoir, which is a close approximation to the circuit used at Alcor during the present study [5,6]. The problem for this latter circuit is solved as a special case of the more general reservoir problem.

The Mathematical Problem (Summary)

For the general case we assume n reservoirs, numbered 1,2,..., n. Each reservoir contains a time-varying quantity $V_i(t)$ of a binary solution of "perfusate" consisting of a volume of "cryoprotective agent" (CPA) dissolved in a solvent. The concentration of CPA in the ith reservoir is also a time-varying quantity and is denoted by $C_i(t)$, given in units of volume for volume (v/v). (A concentration of 0.5 thus denotes an equal volume of CPA and solvent; we assume that volumes add linearly on mixing.) The substances used as CPA and as solvent are assumed to be the same for each reservoir; only the concentration of CPA and the volume of perfusate can vary from one reservoir to another. In a typical cryopreservation, for instance, the solvent will be water and the CPA glycerol.

Next, for each ordered pair (i,j) of reservoirs we assume a nonnegative, possibly zero flow rate f_{ij} from i to j (see fig. 3). This will allow us to model a perfusion system of great generality; in particular, we can achieve the case of arbitrary connections or barriers between reservoirs accordingly as the flow rates are set to positive or zero values. (One possible advantage of this level of generality is that it could help in modeling an organ or a body itself, both being complicated interconnected systems of reservoirs, although we will assume a one-reservoir model of the body in the application considered later.) It is perfectly possible, for instance, to have two reservoirs i, j interconnected by a pair of flow tubes, with perfusate flowing back and forth between i and j (that is, both f_{ij} and $f_{ji}>0$). In the present analysis, however, flow from a reservoir immediately

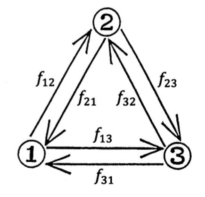

Figure 3. **Recirculating system for $n=3$, showing all interconnections for the three reservoirs.**

into itself is not physically meaningful; thus we set $f_{ii}=0$ for all i. Mathematically, the system of reservoirs forms a complete, directed graph on n nodes with nonnegative-weighted edges. As noted above we assume the flow rates are constant with time.

Finally we assume that the volumes V_i and CPA concentrations C_i are given at a starting time t_0. The basic problem then is to calculate these volumes and concentrations for $t > t_0$. Since the flow rates are assumed constant, the volumes are a simple linear function of time. Concentrations, however, will vary nonlinearly. The basic relation governing the behavior of the concentrations $C_i(t)$ can be conveniently determined by considering the total quantity of CPA in reservoir i at time t, $C_i(t)V_i(t)$. Over a short interval of time, the net inflow of CPA into reservoir i will be proportional to the sum of the flow rates into i, times the associated concentrations from the other reservoirs, minus the sum of the flow rates out of i times the concentration in reservoir i. In this way we obtain an expression for the time derivative of $C_i(t)$ that is linear in the concentrations $C_j(t)$ and flow rates f_{ij}, f_{ji}, and reciprocal in the volume $V_i(t)$. Similarly, an expression for the *mth* time derivative of $C_i(t)$ can be constructed that is linear in the $(m-1)st$ derivatives of $C_j(t)$ and flow rates f_{ij}, f_{ji}, and reciprocal in the volume $V_i(t)$. From this a Taylor's series is obtained for $C_i(t)$ in terms of a starting time t_0.

In the application considered here, values of the concentrations $C_i(t)$ and its derivatives are computed at 1-minute intervals, from the previously computed concentrations $C_j(t_0)$ and their derivatives. Since in this case $t - t_0$ is only 1 min., rapid convergence of the series is usually assured, the only exception being when one of the reservoirs is nearly empty. Although we have considered only the case of constant flow rates f_{ij}, it is nearly as easy to deal with nonconstant flow rates, provided these do not change too much over the 1-minute interval; one merely substitutes the new flow rates at each 1-minute step. (Updating more frequent than every minute could be used to improve the accuracy for the nonconstant flow rates, but this has not proved necessary.) In fact it is possible to adjust the flow rates to achieve some desired "perfusion profile" or increase in concentration as a function of time (considered in the original article).

Application to Cryopreservation: General Principles

During a cryopreservation it is necessary to recirculate cryoprotective agent through the patient prior to freezing. The circulation of CPA is a second perfusion operation that occurs after "total body washout" or replacement of the blood with initial or base perfusate, which contains little or no CPA. (The reason for removal of blood before CPA introduction is that red blood cells undergo changes which affect their rheology during CPA and low temperature exposure, seriously impeding perfusion of the capillary bed.) The circuit that was used at Alcor for this second perfusion is shown schematically in fig. 4. The perfusate, an aqueous solution containing CPA, is

Preserving Minds, Saving Lives

introduced into the patient's arterial circulation through the capillary bed. The solution is delivered to the patient from the recirculating reservoir and venous effluent from the patient is partly discarded and partly returned to the recirculating reservoir, where it will again be cycled through the patient. Since the flow rates into and out of the patient are nearly equal, the flow discarded results in a net loss of fluid from the recirculating reservoir. This in turn causes a flow by gravity from the concentrate reservoir, increasing the CPA concentration in the recirculating reservoir. A consequence of this is the delivery of an increasing amount of CPA to the patient. A greater flow discarded will thus result in a greater flow of concentrate, hence a more rapid increase of CPA in the patient.

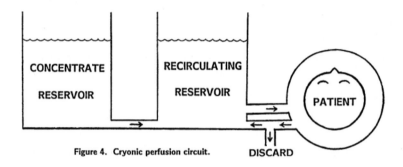

Figure 4. Cryonic perfusion circuit.

In order for CPA perfusion to be biologically safe and effective we need to know in advance what levels of CPA in the patient can be expected from a given set of starting conditions, how much difference in arterial and venous concentrations of CPA there is likely to be, and finally, how much perfusate will be required. We thus are interested in a time development for a simulated perfusion circuit.

To obtain a first-order approximation for such a simulation, we assume constant flow rates into and out of the patient and out the discard, and treat the patient as another reservoir with instantaneous mixing (rapid mixing already occurs in the recirculating reservoir). With a further simplifying assumption about the flow rate of CPA from the concentrate reservoir, all flow rates will be constant. This assumption is that the densities of perfusate in the concentrate and recirculating reservoirs are equal, which would cause liquid levels in both reservoirs to be equal throughout the perfusion. In fact, glycerol has a density (1.26) significantly greater than that of water, but the gravity-feed flow from the concentrate reservoir is restricted by the viscosity of the glycerol concentrate in such a way as to largely counteract the expected effect of the greater density. (The level of concentrate is generally slightly greater than that of recirculating perfusate, not less as would be expected from the greater density.)

With these assumptions the theory of section 3 can be applied so that volumes and concentrations in the different reservoirs can be computed as a function of time. In effect we have 4 reservoirs ($n = 4$): (1) the concentrate reservoir, (2) the recirculating reservoir, (3) the patient, and (4) the discard. Note that for reservoir 1 there is no inflow and for reservoir 4 there is no outflow (f_{j1} and $f_{4j} = 0$ for $j = 1, 2, 3, 4$). In fact the only nonzero flow rates are f_{12}, f_{23}, f_{32} and f_{34}. The two reservoirs which are of primary interest are the recirculating reservoir (2) and the patient (3) which, as suggested earlier, model respectively the arterial and venous CPA concentration in the patient. Knowing these two concentrations allows us to calculate their difference (the "a-v difference") and thus to estimate the osmotic stress. It is found in particular that the a-v difference varies dramatically with the choice of values of starting parameters, thereby shedding light on the problem of selecting an "optimal" perfusion profile that will minimize injury or "cost" to the tissues being perfused.

Modeling the Cryonic Perfusion Circuit

In modeling the cryonic perfusion circuit it is convenient to introduce certain notation as follows.

C_0 = CPA concentration in concentrate reservoir, assumed constant.

$V_{REC}(t)$ = volume of recirculating reservoir as a function of time t.

$a(t)$ = CPA concentration in recirculating reservoir, the "arterial" concentration.

f_{IN} = flow rate into patient from recirculating reservoir.

V_{PT} = volume of patient, assumed constant.

$v(t)$ = CPA concentration in patient, the "venous" concentration.

f_D = flow rate from patient discard.

f_{REC} = flow rate from patient back to recirculating reservoir.

In comparing this circuit with the generalization of section 3, certain simplifications are evident. Volumes in the concentrate and recirculating reservoirs are equal at all times, due to the gravity-induced flow between them. Due to the assumption of constant patient volume we have $f_{IN} = f_D + f_{REC}$, so that the flow of perfusate into the patient results in a net loss from the recirculating reservoir at the rate f_D. Gravity feed from the concentrate reservoir will replenish half of this loss, or enough to equalize the liquid levels in the concentrate and recirculating reservoirs, which will require a flow rate of $f_D/2$. The quantities relevant to modeling the circuit, previously expressed in the generalized notation of section 3, are then given by

$$V_1(t) = V_{REC}(t),$$
$$C_1(t) = C_0,$$

$$f_{12} = f_D/2,$$

$$V_2(t) = V_{REC}(t),$$

$$C_2(t) = a(t),$$

$$f_{23} = f_{IN},$$

$$V_3(t) = V_{PT},$$

$$C_3(t) = v(t),$$

$$f_{34} = f_D,$$

$$f_{32} = f_{REC} = f_{IN} - f_D.$$

The programs that have been written to model this circuit are given starting values of a, v, C_0, reservoir volumes and flow rates (or some of these quantities are computed from other initial conditions). Values of a and v and their derivatives are then computed at 1-minute intervals from values determined on the previous time step. The 1-minute updating is convenient for monitoring the course of perfusion and also insures convergence of the series defining the computation under conditions which normally hold in practice.

Computational Results

This section deals with computations of the predicted course of cryonic perfusions, assuming the circuit of the previous section. The most important quantities are the arterial and venous CPA concentrations calculated as a function of time. Comparisons between the calculated values and those observed during a representative cryopreservation show that the method is able to account reasonably well for the actual values observed, despite the uncertainties of modeling a whole-body preservation patient. Another useful feature is that perfusate requirements can be forecast with reasonable confidence. A further advantage of mathematical modeling is that whole-body perfusion can be compared in details with the neuro (head-only) variety. It is found that, when flow rates are adjusted to equalize perfusion times for the two procedures, a reduction in osmotic and other stresses is achieved through neuropreservation, the improvement resulting from the decrease in effective patient volume. A third area of interest is use of nonconstant flow rates to achieve an "optimal" perfusion profile, as briefly addressed in the original paper.

Some computational results were considered briefly in section 1, in which a single-pass and a recirculating system were compared. Further particulars for these stimulated perfusions, which will serve as an introduction to the cases considered later, are given below.

Starting volumes, recirc., and conc. reservoirs .... 40 liters

Patient fluid volume .... 45 liters

Flow rate into patient (f_{IN}) single-pass system .... 0.4 liters/min.

f_{IN}, recirculating system .... 2.4 liters/min.

Discard flow rate f_D .... 0.4 liters/min.

Concentration of CPA in conc. reservoir C_0 .... 67%

Starting concentration of CPA, recirc. reservoir 4%

Starting concentration of CPA, patient 4%

Time requirement, single-pass system .... 176 min.

Time requirement, recirculating system .... 179 min.

Perfusate requirement, single-pass system .... 70.2 liters

Perfusate requirement, recirculating system .... 71.4 liters

Thus in both cases about 3 hr. was required to reach a final venous CPA concentration of 30%. (This percentage of glycerol is needed to achieve "Smith's criterion" under which it is believed that tissues can be frozen without mechanical damage from ice.) About 75% of the available perfusate was required, leaving 9-10 liters each in the concentrate and recirculating reservoirs.

These statistics can be compared with data from an Alcor whole body preservation, as follows [11].

Starting volumes, recirc. and conc. Reservoirs .... 41 liters

Patient fluid volume, estimated .... 45.7 liters

Flow rate into patient f_{IN} .... 0.8-1.4 liters/min.

Discard flow rate f_D .... 0.1-0.3 liters/min.

Concentration of CPA in conc. reservoir C_0 .... 67%

Starting CPA concentration of CPA, recirc. reservoir 4%

Starting CPA concentration of CPA, patient 0%

Time requirement .... 252 min.

Perfusate requirement .... 66.6 liters

This, it should be noted, was nearly a worst case scenario due to the inability to provide a normal transport protocol and the long period the patient was ischemic (about 24 hours) before the preservation protocol could be started. Flow rates were reduced and perfusion time increased. It will be noted that otherwise most of the statistics of the simulated perfusions agree fairly closely with the actual counterpart.

Very likely the true circulating patient fluid volume was also less than the estimated value of 70% of the body weight of water, due to vascular obstruction from ischemia and other problems [1]. (The flow rate into the patient was adjusted periodically to maintain an approximately constant pressure of 50 mm Hg, considered a safe value for perfusion.) A more accurate simulation of the actual perfusion was obtained by (1) using the actual flow rates shown in fig. 5, and (2) assuming an effective patient volume of 29 liters (63% of the estimated fluid volume); fig. 6 shows a and v concentrations for this perfusion (solid curves) versus values measured experimentally (dots). The time of the simulated perfusion (terminated at $v=30\%$), 252 min., agreed precisely with the actual value. A still better fit to the clinical data has been obtained by modeling patient edema and leakage of perfusate from the body, both of which were significant though not overwhelming influences. A larger effective patient volume, 38 liters, or 83% of the estimated total, was found to give the best fit, suggesting that circulation was not so restricted as it otherwise appeared to be. In general it is expected that a more elaborate theoretical model will provide a better fit to the empirical evidence, and if the extra fitting power is well-coupled to observable complications, more insight as well. (It is also worth mentioning that to model edema requires a departure from the simplified theory of section 5 since flow out of the patient, $f_{REC} + f_D$, is now less than the flow in, f_{IN}. But the more general theory of section 3 still applies.)

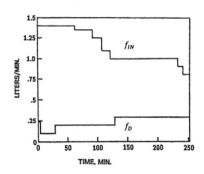

Figure 5. Flow rates for actual perfusion.

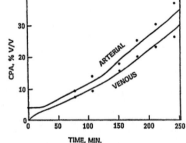

Figure 6. CPA concentrations for actual perfusion (dots) and values calculated from model (solid curves).

The above, then, will serve to illustrate how the perfusion circuit theory can be applied to model an actual cryopreservation, leading to a better understanding of the course of events. The results are preliminary and suggestive, not conclusive; more elaborate studies of this and other preservations are planned.

Whole Body versus Head-Only Preservation

One significant issue that perfusion modeling sheds light on is whole-body versus neuro- or head only preservation. Typically the latter is performed by tying off vasculature thus directing circulation to the head and neck only. Effective patient volume is thus reduced to approximately 10% of the whole-body value or less. After perfusion the head is surgically removed from the body and frozen.

Neuropreservation may be justified on grounds that care of the brain, the seat of the patient's personality, can be optimized if the bulk of the body is not also involved. (It is anticipated, of course, that eventually the technology will exist to regrow a new body and repair and reintegrate the brain.) A full discussion of the rationale for neuropreservation is beyond the scope of this paper and is treated elsewhere [2].

By opting for neuro- as opposed to whole body preservation it is possible to greatly reduce both perfusion time and osmotic stress, though it is not known how significant this reduction will prove in terms of ultimate patient recoverability. Fig. 7 illustrates the potential for osmotic stress reduction. The difference between arterial and venous concentration is plotted as a function of time for (1) the simulated whole body perfusion of fig. 6, in which the effective patient volume is 29 liters, and (2) a simulated neuroperfusion in which the effective patient volume is 5 liters. Flow rates for the whole body perfusion are those shown in fig. 5.

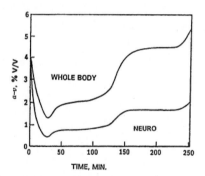

Figure 7. a-v differences for simulated neuro vs. whole body perfusion.

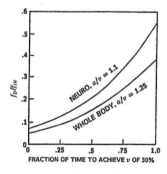

Figure 8. Flow rate ratios for constant a-v ratio during perfusion.

The neuroperfusion flow rates are obtained by multiplying the whole-body rates by a proportionality constant, 0.426, to normalize the perfusion time for comparison purposes. (This in fact results in flow rates in the neighborhood of 0.5 and 0.1 liters/min. for f_{IN} and f_D respectively, which are within the expected range for a neuropreservation; for example, see [3].) Starting volumes of 25 liters in the recirculating and concentrate reservoirs of the neuro are assumed, consistent with contemporary practice at Alcor. The generally smaller values of the a-v difference for the neuro case is striking, though it should be pointed out that the larger differences for the whole body case are considered well within safe limits. (The starting values of 4% for the a-v differences resulted from a minor oversight on the original perfusion; the patient was to have been flushed with 4% v/v glycerol solution but the glycerol was omitted.) It should be noted that the a-v differences plotted are for an idealized system with instantaneous mixing; in practice these differences could well be larger as shown in fig. 6. The time of the neuroperfusion could also be significantly reduced by increasing the flow rates; generally a neuropreservation can be more quickly done at the same level of mechanical stress or pressure [3].

Conclusions

Cryonic perfusion, undertaken to protect tissues from damage during the freezing process, is nonetheless not a completely benign process. Cells and tissues can suffer damage during perfusion from (1) toxicity of cryoprotective agent(s), (2) osmotic stress, and (3) stress resulting from mechanical forces under excessive fluid pressure. For this reason the perfusion process must be carefully controlled so that CPA is introduced rapidly but without extreme concentration gradients or excessive pressure. Perfusion circuits in use by Alcor allow careful control of CPA buildup through control of the flow rates into and out of the patient and other fluid reservoirs involved in the perfusion. How to control the fluid flow rates to achieve an effective perfusion is a complex problem, but one that can be addressed through mathematical modeling of perfusion circuitry. It thus becomes feasible to predict with reasonable accuracy the rate of increase in CPA concentration for cryonic perfusion circuits in use. The method shows promise in elucidating what is happening to a patient during perfusion, in comparing different perfusion protocols on the basis of quantities related to cell and tissue stress, and in selecting protocols to achieve optimal perfusion under given models of stress.

References and Notes

[1] Darwin, M. G., "Long-time Alcor member enters biostasis," *Cryonics*, 9(5), 2 (1988).

[2] Darwin, M. G., "But what will the neighbors think?! A discourse on the history and rationale of neurosuspension," *Cryonics*, 9(10), 40 (1988).

[3] Darwin, M. G., J. Leaf and H. Hixon, "Case report: neuropreservation of Alcor patient A-1068," reprinted from *Cryonics*, 7(2-3), 17 (Feb 1986). Reprinted by the Alcor Life Extension Foundation, Riverside, Calif., 1986.

[4] Fahy, G. M., "Activation of alpha adrenergic vasoconstrictor response in kidneys stored at 30°C for up to 8 days;" appendix. *Cryo-Letters*, 1, 317 (1980).

[5] Fahy, G. M., T. Takahashi and A. M. Crane, "Histological cryoprotection of rat and rabbit brains." *Cryo-Letters*, 5, 33-46 (1984).

[6] Fahy, G. M. unpublished manuscript.

[7] Harris, S. B. unpublished manuscript.

[8] Johnson, L. and R. D. Riess, *Numerical Analysis*, Addison-Wesley, 1977, pp. 284-333.

[9] Quaife, A., "Heat flow in the cryonic suspension of humans," *Cryonics* 6(9), 9 (1985).

[10] Quaife, A., "Mathematical models of perfusion processes." *Manrise Technical Review*, 2, 28 (1972).

[11] Based on preliminary, unpublished figures. Minor corrections may be made before a final report is published.

The author thanks Michael Darwin, Jerry Leaf, and Greg Fahy for technical assistance in preparing this paper, and Thomas Donaldson and Art Quaife for additional useful suggestions. ∎

Getting to 8M Glycerol and Other Perfusion Problems

By Hugh Hixon, M.S.
Cryonics, November, 1993

Last year we got an opinion from one of our expert consultants that, rather than limiting ourselves to a final glycerol concentration of 4.5M, we should take the cryoprotectant concentration as high as possible. The previous limit of 4.5M (about 41%, weight/ volume, or 36% volume/volume) we imposed on ourselves many years ago because we knew that 50% glycerol solution was used to dissolve cell walls for a preparation of muscle protein. Subsequent research by our consultant indicates that this does not appear to be the problem we thought it was, and that the more water was replaced by cryoprotectant, the better.

Accordingly, when I gave the instructions for mixing of perfusate for the April suspension, I set the system up for the maximum final cryoprotectant combination convenient under the circumstances (time, filtration difficulty, cost, etc.). The key consideration was, given that we used two of our standard 20 liter perfusate component prepackages, how to split that 40 liters between initial circulating volume and concentrate volume. I settled on 5 liters to circulation and 35 liters to concentrate.

We contacted our consultant during the suspension to reverify that we could do this and he confirmed his recommendation, but got a little conservative when he understood we were really going try to go as high as possible. His final recommendation was to stop at 8M (9.3M is his figure for complete vitrification); and that was about where we ran out of concentrate.

When we stopped the cryoprotective ramp generator, the arterial (input) concentration was 8.23M and the venous (output) concentration was 7.83M. Circulating for another 45 minutes produced the final glycerol concentration of 7.85M in both the arterial and venous sides of the perfusion loop.

Since part of the protocol for maximizing the concentration was to minimize that part of the circulating volume in the mixing reservoir, Perfusionist Ralph Whelan had to keep constant watch on the mixing reservoir to avoid pumping air or bubbles (he didn't let any through, but he still gets a little terse when he speaks to me about it). I have since constructed several very small mixing reservoirs to deal better in the future with this aspect of the problem.

The minimization of the circulating volume also exacerbated a problem which we have seen before: the slow reduction of the circulating volume, observed as an abnormal decrease in the level of perfusate in the mixing reservoir. Up to this time we had speculated that this loss of volume was due to leakage from the patient and off the table. I am now sure that this is only part of the explanation.

Jerry Leaf's two-loop perfusion circuit contains a cryoprotective ramp generator with two mechanically equivalent tubing pumps ganged together. However, it seems that they are not hydraulically equivalent. I have manufacturer's literature for tubing pumps that makes it quite clear that the pumping efficiency is dependent on the viscosity of the liquid. Viscous liquids are pumped less efficiently, and as the speed of the pump is increased during perfusion, the efficiency may drop quite dramatically. The Leaf ramp generator attempts to add cryoprotective concentrate at the same rate at which it removes an equal amount of the perfusate that is being returned from the patient. Hence, any difference in efficiency between the ganged pumps will quickly become apparent in the circulating volume of the perfusion circuit. Since the cryoprotective concentrate is always more viscous than the circulating perfusate, the inevitable result is loss of volume in the circuit; the removal pump is always working more efficiently than the less viscous circulating perfusate.

Other considerations, such as osmotic extraction of water from the patient by the hyperosmotic perfusate, may increase the amount of perfusate in the mixing reservoir, but the mechanism given above always applies to the total circulating volume. Leakage from the patient onto the table will, of course, also decrease the total circulating volume.

Correction of this problem during a suspension remains as it has always been: the perfusionist clamps the inlet line to the removal pump side of the ramp generator to increase the circulating volume, accepting a temporary decrease in the rate of the cryoprotective ramp.

But it's nice to finally have an explanation for a problem that has baffled us for years.

Finally, I have added tubing to our standard perfusion tubing pack to attempt to eliminate an irritating little problem that we have had for years.

When the burr hole is made in the patient's skull to observe the size of the brain and estimate brain ischemia, a side effect is that perfusate leaks out the hole, either from exudation by the brain or from bleeding from the dura (the thin, tough membrane between the brain and the skull). The rate of this leakage is often a substantial proportion of the flow rate of perfusate through the patient.

The fix for coping with this loss has been a "bucket brigade," with one of the perfusion team members holding a container under the burr hole to catch the leakage, and then dumping it into the chest cavity of the patient, to be returned to the perfusion circuit through the cardiotomy sucker that deals with the leakage from the surgery there.

This has been a silly inefficiency in the use of team members' time, and a point with high potential for a break in sterile technique. It has a simple solution: add a second sucker line in parallel with the cardiotomy sucker to return the burr hole leakage to the circuit through the cardiotomy reservoir. ■

HOW CRYOPROTECTANTS WORK

BY BRIAN WOWK, PH.D.

Cryonics, 3rd Quarter, 2007

Life is a complex chemical process that happens in water. Without liquid water, there is no life, or at least no life process. Cryoprotectants are chemicals that protect living things from being injured by water freezing during exposure to cold. How cryoprotectants work is a mystery to most people. In fact, how they work was even a mystery to science until just a few decades ago. This article will explain in basic terms how cryoprotectants protect cells from damage caused by ice crystals, and some of the advances that have been made in the design of cryoprotectant solutions.

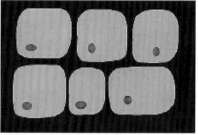

Figure 1A. Cells before freezing.

How Freezing Injures Cells

Water expands when it freezes, but contrary to popular belief it is not expansion of water that causes injury. It is the purification of water during freezing that causes injury. Water freezes as a pure substance that excludes all else. It is this exclusion process that causes injury. Instead of remaining a solvent that allows the molecules of life to freely mix within it, water that freezes gathers itself up into crystals pushing everything else out. This is illustrated in Figure 1.

Freezing causes damage by two distinct mechanisms. The first is mechanical damage as the shape of cells is distorted by ice crystals. The second is damage caused by chemical and osmotic effects of concentrated solutes in the residual unfrozen water between ice crystals. This is so-called "solution effects" injury.

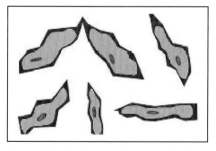

Figure 1B. Cells after freezing. Cells are squashed between ice crystals and exposed to lethal concentrations of salt. Contrary to popular belief, slow cooling causes water to freeze outside cells, not inside cells. Cells are dehydrated by the growing concentration of salt in the unfrozen liquid around them.

How Cryoprotectants Protect Cells

Cryoprotectants are chemicals that dissolve in water and lower the melting point of water. For applications outside cryobiology, such chemicals are sometimes called "antifreeze." Common examples are glycerol, ethylene glycol, propylene glycol, and dimethylsulfoxide (DMSO).

A cryoprotectant concentration of about 5% to 15% is usually all that is required to permit survival of a substantial fraction of isolated cells after freezing and thawing from liquid nitrogen temperature. Figure 2 shows the essential concept of cryoprotection during cell freezing. Growing ice compacts cells into smaller and smaller pockets of unfrozen liquid as the temperature is lowered. The presence of cryoprotectants makes these pockets larger at any given temperature than they would be if no cryoprotectant were present. Larger unfrozen pockets for cells reduces damage from both forms of freezing injury, mechanical damage from ice and excessive concentration of salt.

Properties of Cryoprotectants

Not all chemicals that dissolve in water are cryoprotectants. In addition to being water soluble, good cryoprotectants are effective at depressing the melting point of water, do not precipitate or form eutectics or hydrates, and are relatively non-toxic to cells at high concentration. All cryoprotectants form hydrogen bonds with water. Since the discovery of glycerol as the first cryoprotectant more than 50 years ago[1], approximately 100 compounds have been explicitly identified and studied as cryoprotectants, although only a handful are used routinely in cryobiology.[2]

The best and most commonly used cryoprotectants are a class called penetrating cryoprotectants. Penetrating cryoprotectants are small molecules that easily penetrate cell membranes. The molecular mass of penetrating cryoprotectants is typically less than 100 daltons. By entering and remaining inside cells, penetrating cryoprotectants prevent excessive dehydration of cells during the freezing process.

Vitrification as an Alternative to Freezing

Organized tissue is more damaged by freezing than isolated cells. Unlike suspensions of disconnected cells, tissue doesn't have room for ice to grow, and cannot easily sequester itself into unfrozen pockets between ice crystals. Organs are especially vulnerable to freezing injury. For an organ to resume function after freezing, all the diverse cell types of the organ, from parenchymal cells to cells of the smallest blood vessels, have to survive in large numbers. The 25% survival rates often seen in cell

1   C. Polge, A.U. Smith, A.S. Parks, Revival of spermatozoa after vitrification and dehydration at low temperature, *Nature* 164 (1949) 666.

2   A.M. Karow, Cryoprotectants—a new class of drugs, J. *Pharm. Pharmac* 21 (1969) 209-223.

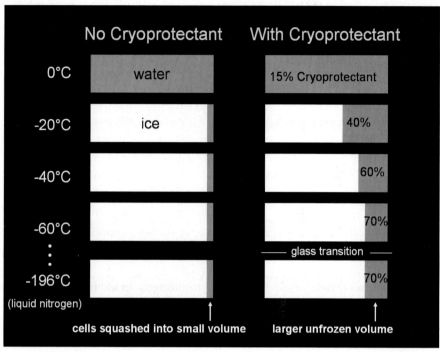

Figure 2. Water when frozen without and with added cryoprotectant. Without cryoprotectant, almost the entire water volume freezes during cooling. Only salts and other dissolved molecules prevent water from freezing completely. With cryoprotectant, the percentage of cryoprotectant present in solution increases as ice grows. At any given temperature, ice growth stops when the cryoprotectant becomes concentrated enough to make the melting point equal to the surrounding temperature. Eventually the cryoprotectant reaches a concentration that cannot be frozen. No more ice can grow as the temperature is lowered, and there is more room for cells to survive between ice crystals. Below approximately -100°C, the remaining unfrozen liquid pocket solidifies into a glass, permitting storage for practically unlimited periods of time. Cells survive freezing by existing inside the glassy solid between ice crystals. The larger the starting cryoprotectant concentration, the larger the unfrozen volume will be at the end of freezing.

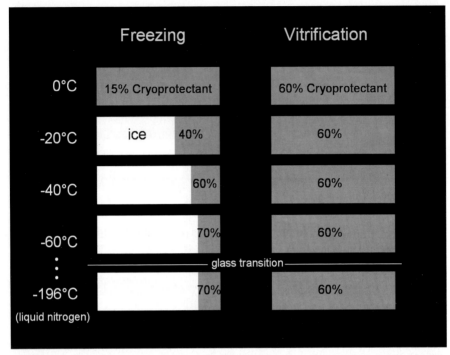

Figure 3. Freezing vs. vitrification. Vitrification loads cells and tissue with a high concentration of cryoprotectant at the very beginning. Cooling quickly then allows the entire volume of tissue to become a glassy solid, or "vitrify", without any freezing at all.

freezing are not good enough. For cryopreservation of organs, a different approach is required.

In 1984 cryobiologist Gregory Fahy proposed vitrification as an approach to cryopreservation.[3] Vitrification, which means "turn into a glass," was previously known in cryobiology as a process that occurred when water was cooled too fast to form ice crystals. It was also believed to be the process by which cells survived in unfrozen pockets of concentrated cryoprotectant between ice crystals at very low temperatures. Fahy proposed a way to turn the entire volume of a tissue or organ into the equivalent of an unfrozen glassy pocket of concentrated cryoprotectant.

To achieve vitrification, it was proposed that the tissue or organ be loaded with so much cryoprotectant before cooling that it could avoid ice formation during the entire cooling process. If cooling is fast, this could be done with actually less cryoprotectant

---

3   G.M. Fahy, D.R. MacFarlane, C.A. Angell, H.T. Meryman, Vitrification as an approach to cryopreservation, *Cryobiology* 21 (1984) 407-426.

concentration than cells are exposed to during the final stages of conventional freezing. The concept is illustrated in Figure 3.

By avoiding mechanical distortion caused by ice, and by allowing salts and other molecules to remain undisturbed in their natural locations, vitrification avoids the major damage mechanisms of freezing. The price paid is damage from cryoprotectant toxicity.

Cryoprotectant Toxicity

In cryopreservation by freezing or vitrification, more than half of the water inside cells is ultimately replaced by cryoprotectant molecules. Cryoprotection can be regarded as a process of replacing water molecules with other molecules that cannot freeze. When one considers the crucial role that water plays in maintaining the proper shape and form of proteins and other molecules of life, it is astonishing that this can be survived.

The toxicity of cryoprotectants administered at near-freezing temperatures is a different kind of toxicity than the toxicity experienced by living things at warm temperature. For example, to a person under ordinary conditions, propylene glycol is non-toxic, while ethylene glycol is metabolized into a poison. However at high concentrations near 0°C, ethylene glycol is less toxic to cells than propylene glycol. Usual rules don't apply. New rules relating to how life responds when large amounts of water are substituted at low temperature remain to be discovered.

Mechanisms of cryoprotectant toxicity are still poorly understood,[4,5] but a few empirical generalizations can be made. Lipophilicity (affinity for fats and oils) strongly correlates with toxicity. Molecules with an affinity for fat can partition into cell membranes, destabilizing them. It has also been recently discovered that strong hydrogen bonding correlates with toxicity, possibly by disrupting the hydration shell around macromolecules. This led to the unexpected result that cryoprotectants with polar groups that interact weakly with water are best for vitrification, even if a higher concentration is required to achieve vitrification.[6] The electrical properties of cryoprotectant solutions have also been related to membrane toxicity.[7] Certain cryoprotectants, such as glycerol and possibly DMSO, are also known to have adverse reactions with specific biochemical targets. Finally, mutual toxicity reduction, especially as seen in the DMSO/formamide combination, has been very useful in vitrification solution development, although the mechanism of this toxicity reduction

---

4   G.M. Fahy, The Relevance of Cryoprotectant "Toxicity" to Cryobiology, *Cryobiology* 23 (1986) 1-13.

5   G.M. Fahy, Cryoprotectant Toxicity and Cryoprotectant Toxicity Reduction: In Search of Molecular Mechanisms, *Cryobiology* 27 (1990) 247-268.

6   G.M. Fahy, B. Wowk, J. Wu, S. Paynter, Improved vitrification solutions based on the predictability of vitrification solution toxicity, *Cryobiology* 48 (2004) 22-35.

7   I.B. Bakaltcheva, C.O. Odeyale, B.J. Spargo, Effects of alkanols, alkanediols and glycerol on red blood cell shape and hemolysis, *Biochem Biophys Acta* 1280 (1996) 73-80.

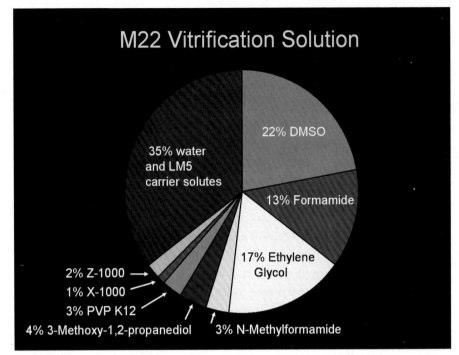

Figure 4. Composition of M22 vitrification solution. All ingredients are penetrating cryoprotectants, except for LM5 carrier solutes, Z-1000 and X-1000 ice blockers, and PVP K12 polymer. M22 is a "sixth generation" vitrification solution, incorporating two decades of progress in the development of vitrification solutions for mainstream medical tissue and organ banking.

is still unknown.[5]

Components of Cryopreservation Solutions

More than just cryoprotectants must be added to cells and tissues to protect against freezing injury. A cryopreservation solution, which may be either a freezing solution or vitrification solution, consists of:

Carrier Solution

Carrier solution consists of solution ingredients that are not explicit cryoprotectants. The role of the carrier solution is to provide basic support for cells at temperatures near freezing. It contains salts, osmotic agents, pH buffers, and sometimes nutritive ingredients or apoptosis inhibitors. The ingredients are usually present at near isotonic concentration (300 milliosmoles) so that cells neither shrink nor swell when held in carrier solution. Carrier solution is sometimes called "base perfusate." The carrier solution typically used with M22 cryoprotectant solution is called LM5.

Different concentrations of cryoprotectant may be required at various stages of cryoprotectant introduction and removal, but the concentration of carrier solution ingredients always remains constant. This constant-composition requirement can be regarded as the definition of a carrier solution. As a practical matter, this means that cryopreservation solutions must be made by means other than adding cryoprotectants to a pre-made carrier solution because naïve addition would dilute the carrier ingredients.

Penetrating Cryoprotectants

Penetrating cryoprotectants are small molecules able to cross cell membranes. The role of penetrating cryoprotectants is to reduce ice growth and reduce cell dehydration during freezing. In vitrification, the role of penetrating cryoprotectants is to completely prevent ice formation. As is shown in Figure 4, penetrating cryoprotectants are the majority ingredients of vitrification solutions.

Non-penetrating Cryoprotectants (optional ingredient)

Non-penetrating cryoprotectants are large molecules, usually polymers, added to cryoprotectant solutions. They inhibit ice growth by the same mechanisms as penetrating cryoprotectants, but do not enter cells. Polyethylene glycol (PEG) and polyvinylpyrrolidone (PVP) are examples. Non-penetrating cryoprotectants are usually less toxic than penetrating cryoprotectants at the same concentration. They reduce the amount of penetrating cryoprotectants needed by mimicking outside the cell the cryoprotective effects of proteins inside the cell. It has also been recently discovered that using non-penetrating cryoprotectants to increase the tonicity (osmotically active concentration) of vitrification solutions can prevent a type of injury called chilling injury.

Ice Blockers (optional ingredient)

Ice blockers are compounds that directly block ice growth by selective binding with ice or binding to contaminants that trigger ice formation (ice nucleators). Conventional cryoprotectants act by interacting with water. Ice blockers complement conventional cryoprotectants by interacting with ice or surfaces that resemble ice. Ice blockers are like drugs in that only a small amount is required to find and bind their target. Low molecular weight polyvinyl alcohol and polyglycerol, called X-1000 and Z-1000, and

Figure 5. Effect of ice blockers on ice formation. The flask on the left contains 55% w/w ethylene glycol solution that was cooled to -130°C. The flask on the right contains the same solution, except with 1% of the ethylene glycol replaced by 0.9% X-1000 and 0.1% Z-1000 ice blockers. It is almost completely vitrified, with the majority of the solution being a transparent glass rather than white crystalline ice.

biological antifreeze proteins are examples of ice blockers.[8,9] Ice blockers are only used in vitrification solutions, not freezing solutions (See Figure 5).

How Cryoprotectants are Used

Freezing solutions containing relatively low cryoprotectant concentrations near 10% are typically added in a single step. This causes the classic shrink-swell response of cryobiology in which cells first shrink by osmosis in response to the high solute concentration outside the cell, and then swell as penetrating cryoprotectants enter the cell. Within several minutes, or tens of minutes for thin tissue pieces, the cryoprotectant concentration inside and outside cells equalizes, and cells return to a volume defined by the tonicity of the carrier solution. The cells or tissue are now ready for freezing. For cryopreservation by freezing, cooling is done slowly, typically less than 1°C per minute. This allows time for water to leave cells as freezing progresses so that the

---

8   B. Wowk, E. Leitl, C.M. Rasch, N. Mesbah-Karimi, S.B. Harris, G.M. Fahy, Vitrification enhancement by synthetic ice blocking agents, *Cryobiology* 40 (2000) 228-236.

9   B. Wowk, G.M. Fahy, Inhibition of bacterial ice nucleation by polyglycerol polymers, *Cryobiology* 44 (2002) 14-23.

cryoprotectant concentration inside cells rises together with the concentration outside cells. This prevents cell interiors from freezing. Freezing can also sometimes succeed even though cryoprotectant concentration remains low if freezing and thawing are done extremely rapidly so that there is not enough time for ice to grow inside cells.

Vitrification solutions containing cryoprotectant concentrations near or exceeding 50% cannot be added in a single step because the initial osmotic shrink response would be too extreme. Instead, material to be vitrified is successively exposed to several solutions containing exponentially increasing concentrations of cryoprotectant, such as 1/8 x, 1/4 x, 1/2 x, 1 x full concentration vitrification solution, typically for 20 minutes each step. The addition is done at a temperature near 0°C to minimize toxicity. The material is then ready for vitrification. For cryopreservation by vitrification, cooling and rewarming are done as quickly as possible.

Unlike cell suspensions or small tissue pieces, organs are too large to absorb cryoprotectant by just soaking in an external solution. For organ cryopreservation, cryoprotectants are added by perfusion, a process in which the cryoprotectant solution is circulated through blood vessels just as blood would flow through the organ. This ensures that no cell is more than a few cells away from contact with the circulating solution. Rather than adding cryoprotectant in discrete steps, it is more convenient during perfusion to increase the cryoprotectant concentration continuously.

Cryprotectants are removed by reversing the steps described above, except that all removal solutions except for the very last contain several hundred millimoles of an osmotic buffer, such as mannitol. The role of the osmotic buffer is to reduce the extent of the initial swell response of cells as they are exposed to decreased external cryoprotectant concentration.

Special Considerations for Organs

The time required to introduce and remove cryoprotectants from organs is longer than for cells. For vitrification solutions, perfusion times of hours are typical. This is because cryoprotectants must move through small spaces between cells that line the inside of blood vessels, the capillary endothelium. This makes cells of the capillary endothelium among those most vulnerable to cryoprotectant toxicity because they are exposed to the highest concentrations of cryoprotectant for the longest time while waiting for other cells in the organ to catch up.

The brain has an additional difficulty in that the spaces between capillary endothelial cells are especially small. This is the so-called blood brain barrier, or BBB. The BBB causes penetrating cryoprotectants to leave blood vessels even more slowly than other in organs, and doesn't permit water-soluble molecules bigger than 500 daltons to leave at all. Therefore non-penetrating cryoprotectants do not pass through an intact BBB.

However this doesn't mean that non-penetrating agents have no effect on brain tissue. The osmotic movement of water across the BBB is determined by the entire cryoprotectant solution composition. Water moves to equalize the solution melting point, or "water activity," on either side of the BBB. This means that any ingredient that lowers the melting point of the cryoprotectant solution also increases the resistance of tissue outside the BBB to ice formation by drawing out water and increasing the concentration of solutes naturally present in the brain. The brain is an organ in which penetrating cryprotectants and dehydration seem to act in tandem to provide cryoprotection.

Six Generations of Vitrification Solutions

Vitrification solutions have progressed greatly since the initial proposal of modern vitrification by Fahy in the early 1980s. This progress may be viewed as occurring in six generational leaps.[10] Generations three through six were developed at 21st Century Medicine, Inc.

Generation 1

The simplest vitrification solutions are single cryoprotectants in carrier solution.

Generation 2

It was discovered that higher total cryoprotectant concentrations with acceptable toxicity could be achieved by combining DMSO with amides such as acetamide or formamide, and then adding propylene glycol. The combination of DMSO, formamide, and propylene glycol was the basis of the VS41A (also called VS55) vitrification solution, the most advanced vitrification solution of the mid 1990s.

Generation 3

A breakthrough occurred with Fahy's discovery that cryoprotectant toxicity correlated with the number of water molecules per cryoprotectant polar group at the critical concentration needed for vitrification, so-called $qv*6$. This led to the replacement of the propylene glycol in VS41A with ethylene glycol, generating the VEG vitrification solution.

Generation 4

The use of polymers in vitrification solutions permitted further reductions in toxicity by reducing the concentration of penetrating cryoprotectants necessary to achieve vitrification.

---

10   G.M. Fahy, unpublished.

Generation 5

The use of ice blocking polymers permitted still further reductions in toxicity by reducing the concentration of all cryoprotectants necessary to achieve vitrification. VM3 is a fifth generation vitrification solution.[6]

Generation 6

It was discovered that chilling injury, a poorly-understood injury caused by just passing through certain sub-zero temperature ranges, could be overcome by increasing the tonicity of non-penetrating components of vitrification solutions.[11] M22, the cryoprotectant currently used by Alcor, is a sixth generation solution.

Successful vitrification has now been demonstrated for heart valves,[12] vascular tissue,[13] cartilage,[14] cornea,[15] and mouse ovaries.[16,17] Progress continues for the rabbit kidney, with recovery of the organ demonstrated after cooling to below -40°C while cryoprotected with a vitrification solution,[11] and one reported instance of long-term survival after vitrification.[18] Vitrification has also shown utility for viable preservation of diverse tissue slices, including brain slices,[19] and histological preservation of larger systems.[20]

Future generations of cryoprotectant solutions will have to address many problems that are still outstanding, including molecular mechanisms of cryopreservation failure,[21] and especially cryoprotectant toxicity. Cryoprotectant toxicity is emerging as a final frontier of cryobiology. The greatest future breakthroughs in cryobiology may come from better understanding and mitigation of cryoprotectant toxicity. ∎

11   G.M. Fahy, B. Wowk, J. Wu, J. Phan, C. Rasch, A. Chang, E. Zendejas, Cryopreservation of organs by vitrification: perspectives and recent advances, *Cryobiology* 48 (2004) 157-178.

12   K.G. Brockbank, Y.C. Song, Morphological analyses of ice-free and frozen cryopreserved heart valve explants, *J. Heart Valve Dis.* 13 (2004) 297-301.

13   Y.S. Song, B.S. Khirabadi, F.G. Lightfoot, K.G.M. Brockbank, M.J. Taylor, Vitreous cryopreservation maintains the function of vascular grafts, *Nature Biotechnology* 18 (2000) 296-299.

14   Y.C. Song, Y.H. An, Q.K. Kang, C. Li, J.M. Boggs, Z. Chen, M.J. Taylor, Vitreous preservation of articular cartilage grafts, *J. Invest. Surg.* 17 (2004) 65-70.

15   W.J. Armitage, S.C. Hall, C. Routledge, Recovery of endothelial function after vitrification of cornea at -110?C, *Invest. Opthalmol. Vis. Sci.* 43 (2002) 2160-2164.

16   F. Migishima, R. Suzuki-Migishima, S.Y. Song, T. Kuramochi, S. Azuma, M. Nishijima, M. Yokoyama, Successful cryopreservation of mouse ovaries by vitrification, *Biol. Reprod.* 68 (2003) 881-887.

17   M. Salehnia, Autograft of vitrified mouse ovaries using ethylene glycol as cryoprotectant, *Exp. Anim.* 51 (2002) 509-512.

18   G.M. Fahy, Vitrification as an approach to cryopreservation: General perspectives, *Cryobiology* 51 (2005) 348. [Abstract]

19   Y. Pichugin, G.M. Fahy, R. Morin, Cryopreservation of rat hippocampal slices by vitrification, *Cryobiology* 52 (2006) 228-240.

20   J. Lemler, S.B. Harris, C. Platt, T.M. Huffman, The Arrest of Biological Time as a Bridge to Engineered Negligible Senescence, *Ann. N.Y. Acad. Sci.* 1019 (2004) 559-563.

21   J.M. Baust, M.J. Vogel, B.R. Van Buskirk, J.G. Baust, A molecular basis of cryopreservation failure and its modulation to improve cell survival, *Cell Transplant* 10 (2001) 561-571.

VITRIFICATION ARRIVES: NEW TECHNOLOGY PRESERVES PATIENTS WITHOUT ICE DAMAGE

BY FRED CHAMBERLAIN III
Cryonics, 4th Quarter, 2000

The below discussions of vitrification and its possible implications for Alcor's membership services and funding are controversial. They do not as yet reflect positions, resolutions, or other decisions by the Alcor Life Extension Foundation Board of Directors. When such decisions are reached, Alcor's members will receive them promptly. Details of the technical aspects, to the point of specific phraseology, are largely supplied by researchers involved, yet their names do not appear here. This is not a report of scientific findings; rather, it is a statement of steps being taken toward applications of new technologies by Alcor and BioTransport, Inc. With those reservations, read on. For years, we have been waiting for the day when ideas such as these could appear in Alcor's publications. That day is here!

Effective immediately, neuropatients will no longer be frozen by the Alcor Life Extension Foundation. This does not mean that Alcor is closing down! Rather, Alcor will now use a method of preservation that has never before been used in cryonics. Specifically, Alcor will now vitrify neuropatients instead of freezing them. There are limits, of course. Any delays in starting the procedure or other compromise may mean damage that is not easily reversible.

Vitrification is a method of stopping biological time that does not involve freezing. It is a method of converting biological tissue into a low-temperature glass that does not contain any damaging ice crystals. Vitrification was first proposed two decades ago by cryobiologist Dr. Gregory Fahy as a method for cryopreserving complex tissues such as whole organs. The motivation for vitrification was that conventional freeze preservation invariably destroyed organs by disrupting sensitive tissue structures with ice crystals. Reversible vitrification has since been demonstrated on embryos, ova, ovaries, skin, pancreatic islets, and, most recently, intact blood vessels for transplant. Recent breakthroughs in the field suggest that reversible vitrification of whole mammalian organs may also be achieved in the near future.

Freezing vs. Vitrification

When water is mixed with antifreeze chemicals (cryoprotectants) and is frozen, it becomes filled with millions of tiny ice crystals. If a biological tissue is being frozen, these ice crystals tear cells apart from each other (Fig. 1a), destroying the normal, organized structure of the tissue. Adding a high concentration of cryoprotectants can

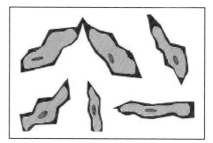

Figure 1a.

limit the amount of ice that forms during freezing so that less disruption occurs (Fig. 1b). This has been the approach used by Alcor for the past decade.

Unfortunately, even freezing with high cryoprotectant concentrations still causes serious structural damage. Figure 2a shows a transmission electron micrograph of a canine brain treated with 7.5 Molar glycerol, frozen, and then thawed. Numerous voids are present on a cellular scale where ice crystals formed and then melted. Furthermore, glycerol becomes freeze concentrated in the areas between ice crystals, resulting in fatal

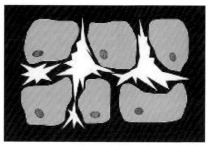

Figure 1b.

cellular toxicity. This combination of structural damage and toxicity makes recovery of frozen neural tissue impossible with current technology.

Vitrification offers a solution to these problems. If a very high concentration of cryoprotectant is rapidly cooled, the mixture can cool to any temperature without forming ice. Water molecules simply don't have time to find enough of one another among the cryoprotectant molecules to form ice. The water/cryoprotectant mixture just becomes more and more viscous, like cold syrup. Finally, at temperatures below the

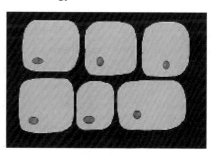

Figure 1c.

"glass transition" temperature (typically near -120°C), the mixture solidifies into a hard glass. This is vitrification. If cells and tissues are saturated with the mixture, they are incorporated into this glass like an insect in amber and can remain stable indefinitely. Unlike an insect in amber, even the cytoplasm inside cells turns to glass so that biological time is truly stopped.

The biological difference between freezing and vitrification is striking.

Vitrification essentially stops biology "in place" (Figure 1c) without any structural damage. Figure 3 shows rabbit kidneys that have been frozen (left) vs. vitrified (right). Both kidneys are at a temperature of -130°C, and are rigid solids. Yet the vitrified kidney looks essentially normal. The electron micrographs of Fig. 2 show the difference between brain tissue that has been cooled to -80°C and then rewarmed after treatment with a freezing solution (2a) vs. vitrification solution (2b). The brain treated with the vitrification solution shows essentially no structural disruption except for mild, reversible dehydration. Published "freeze substitution" electron micrographs of vitrified blood vessels confirm that cooling all the way to -130°C results in no structural damage to tissues treated with vitrification solutions.

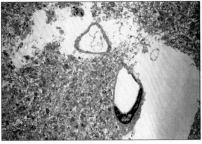

Figure 2a.

Figure 2b.

Recent Breakthroughs

The primary problem with vitrification that has prevented widespread application is cryoprotectant toxicity. Small systems such as embryos and heart valves can be cooled and rewarmed rapidly, which reduces the concentration (and toxicity) of cryoprotectants required to achieve vitrification. Large systems with slow heat transfer, such as organs, require toxic concentrations of cryoprotectants to achieve

Figure 3.

vitrification. For objects as large as cryopatients, heat transfer is so slow, and the necessary cryoprotectant concentrations so large, that a vitrifiable concentration of glycerol cannot even be perfused into cryopatients due to viscosity limitations.

Three breakthroughs have occurred within the past two years that dramatically change the prospects of successfully vitrifying large systems. First, scientists conducting conventional organ preservation research at 21st Century Medicine, Inc. (21CM), have discovered new cryoprotectant mixtures with drastically reduced toxicity compared to previously known solutions. Second, 21CM has also discovered chemical additives ("ice blockers") that significantly reduce the concentration of cryoprotectants required for vitrification. Third, Alcor itself has developed a new method for external cooling of cryopatients that cools neuropatients approximately ten times faster than previous methods. These developments now appear to make possible what was previously only dreamed of: *complete ice-free preservation of cryopatients.*

21CM has licensed a variant of their new low-toxicity vitrification formulas to BioTransport, Inc., for use with Alcor cryopatients. The Hippocampal Slice Cryopreservation Project, conducted by the Institute for Neural Cryobiology (INC) in cooperation with 21CM, recently showed that a similar cryoprotectant formula permitted the vitrification and rewarming of rat hippocampal brain slices with a viability equal to 53% of untreated controls. While the formula that will be used on cryopatients is more concentrated than the one used in these experiments, there is still good reason to believe that partial viability of brain tissue will be retained during cryopatient vitrification. There is no question that the viability will be higher than what is now being achieved with glycerol. The new vitrification procedure to be used on cryopatients will therefore eliminate structural injury and increase cellular viability at the same time.

Optimum Storage Temperature

Vitrified systems will fracture (break into pieces) if cooled to liquid nitrogen temperature (-196°C). Fracturing is also known to occur in conventionally frozen patients during descent to liquid nitrogen temperature. With frozen patients this has not been a concern because the damage caused by ice crystals is much more severe than the damage caused by fracturing (both will require advanced nanotechnology to fix). However, vitrified patients do not have ice crystal damage, so fracturing becomes the sole structural damage mechanism. If fracturing can be avoided, vitrification provides a means of achieving perfect structural preservation of cryopatients.

Fracturing of vitrified systems can be avoided by not cooling far below the glass transition temperature. This implies a long-term storage temperature somewhere between -130°C to -150°C. Holding temperatures too close to the glass transition causes nucleation of ice to slowly proceed on the molecular level, which will cause problems with ice growth when it is time to rewarm the system. Storing too cold increases the risk of fracturing. The risk of fracturing can be reduced by "annealing" (holding for long periods at temperatures slightly above the target temperature). Protracted annealing might even permit fracture-free storage at liquid nitrogen temperature, but much research remains to be done. In the meantime it will be safest to hold patients ten to twenty degrees below the glass transition temperature.

Concern has sometimes been expressed about the safety of intermediate temperature storage systems. Freezers that operate at temperatures down to -140°C are off-the-shelf commercial items routinely used for storage of cryobiological material. But what happens if there is a mechanical breakdown or power failure? Units are available (such as the Harris CryoStar freezer recently purchased by BioTransport for use by Alcor) with a liquid nitrogen backup capability so that a pressurized liquid nitrogen source can maintain temperature. A standard 230-liter liquid nitrogen cylinder should provide at least 24 hours of backup. Alternatively, the large, pressurized liquid nitrogen reservoir recently installed at Alcor could provide days of backup. In any case, it is clear that sufficient freezer capacity must exist to take individual freezers offline for maintenance when necessary. The same is true for cryogenic dewars holding liquid nitrogen. Cryogenic dewars can also fail catastrophically (with loss of vacuum) and exhaust their nitrogen load within hours. Robust backup systems and procedures must be in place regardless of the specific storage temperature or technology used to produce it.

It's also possible to contemplate hybrid systems that use dewar technology to hold a reservoir of liquid nitrogen at the bottom of a dewar to maintain an intermediate temperature in the vapor space above the liquid. These systems will have to be custom-built and require significant research and development. Unfortunately, the need for custom development appears unavoidable because existing commercial freezers are not large enough to accommodate whole-body patients, or to store neuropatients with good economies of scale.

For the immediate future, Alcor plans to store vitrified neuropatients at liquid nitrogen temperature. Options for fracture-free storage will be made available as soon as appropriate costing and backup plans are developed. We do not want to delay introduction of this technology. Even with storage in liquid nitrogen, vitrification is still far superior to freezing.

No More Nanotechnology?

For three decades the practice of cryonics has been based on the need for almost unimaginably advanced repair technologies. These technologies came into clearer focus in the 1980s with the proposition of molecular nanotechnology by Eric Drexler. Ralph Merkle, Robert Freitas, and others built on Drexler's foundation to examine specific technical questions concerning the reversibility of cryoinjury by nanotechnology and concluded that mature nanotechnology implies very broad (almost arbitrary) capabilities for reversing freezing injury in the future. Whether extensive repair of freezing injury would result in full recovery of a cryopatient is a more uncertain question given current limited knowledge of the neurological effects of freezing injury. Even if freezing injury is completely repaired, conceivable outcomes range anywhere from full recovery to restoration of an amnesiac clone. The same limitations apply, of course, to patients who are vitrified after ischemic episodes with biological damage that is presently irreversible.

In cases where vitrification can be applied to high viability patients, these questions are moot. Vitrification removes all damage mechanisms of cryopreservation and leaves only one: cryoprotectant toxicity. No more nanoscale excavation of ice. No more "inferring the original structure" from debris. No more nanocomputers and nanomachines operating at deep subzero temperatures. In fact, no more nanomachines at all. The molecular mechanisms of cryoprotectant toxicity are still unknown, but there are good reasons to believe that a limited number of targets are involved. With no structural damage to contend with, treating toxicity in cells that are already partially viable is a problem of advanced pharmacology, not advanced nanotechnology. Vitrified tissue (without fractures) simply needs to be rewarmed, cryoprotectants removed, and treatment initiated under physiological conditions.

Even restoration of neuropatients to wholeness is not intrinsically a problem for nanotechnology. Recent developments in neural tissue regeneration and nuclear transfer technology (therapeutic cloning) show that tasks previously thought impossible without nanotechnology can often fall into the realm of simple biotechnology. In vitro growth of replacement tissues and organs around an isolated central nervous system is certainly conceptually feasible without molecular nanotechnology. Nature has been producing new tissues and organs from single cells for eons without nanotechnology.

Some cryonics advocates assert that nanotechnology is "necessary and sufficient" for revival of cryopatients and on this basis argue that preservation technology isn't very important. Yet as preservation technology continues to improve, certainly a day will come when better preservation will make a clear difference in time-to-revival and probability of success. Under favorable conditions, that day may well be today. Nanotechnology provides a powerful view of the limits of the possible and a persuasive argument for why cryonics must, to some extent, ultimately succeed. But it should not encourage complacency about preservation technology. The repair requirements of vitrification are so drastically different from freezing that the two procedures cannot be considered equivalent, even with access to nanotechnology.

Costs and Benefits

Alcor will initially perform vitrification of neuropatients ("neurovitrification"), without increasing funding minimums, for those presently having arrangements. If the increases to cost are modest, we hope to continue performing neurovitrification and storage in liquid nitrogen without requiring any modifications in existing member funding. However, an increase to funding for new members with neuro arrangements may be required, under which existing members would be "grandfathered" as in the past. No decisions have as yet been reached about the increases that may be made or the dates for the changes.

It is important to realize that due to the widely varying conditions under which members come into Alcor's care, it may not always be possible to perfuse sufficient cryoprotectant to achieve vitrification. In cases where vitrification is not possible, members will be conventionally frozen. However, with new surgical techniques recently pioneered at Alcor for avoiding clots in large vessels and other complications, we are hopeful that vitrification will be possible even after substantial post-mortem delays.

Alcor will make an option for fracture-free vitrification storage available in the near future, pending finalization of costing and backup contingency issues. This storage will be performed in modified BigFoot units (large cryogenic dewars now in service at Alcor, holding four whole-body patients and five neuropatients, which are expected to accommodate 40 neuropatients after modification for fracture-free storage). Considerable development work will be required on an urgent basis and is expected to be carried out under a grant proposal now in preparation. The complexity of monitoring and operating this system will be greater than for liquid nitrogen immersion of neuropatients, but this may be offset by lower heat flow at the somewhat higher cryogenic temperatures. Increases to the funding requirements for new neuropatient members might make this upgrade available to existing members without changes to their funding requirements. We anticipate more definite answers to be announced by January 2001.

Whole-Body Vitrification

Alcor regrets that vitrification is not yet available for whole-body patients. The present container system used for whole-body patients is not compatible with the rapid cooling rates necessary for vitrification. A new closed container system with accommodations for circulating coolant will have to be developed. Development of the total system will require months of work and tens of thousands of dollars. Funding for this work is being sought on an urgent basis, through a grant proposal, along with funding for development of fracture-free storage systems for vitrified whole-body patients. Only neuropatients will be able to benefit immediately from this quantum leap in technology, and then they are likely to be the first to benefit from a fracture-free storage system. With this in mind, members who are signed up for whole-body preservation might consider switching to neuro until whole-body vitrification becomes available. Members wishing to financially support the construction of new vitrification, or fracture-free whole-body vitrification, should contact Alcor. Progress will definitely be more rapid if any grant funding obtained is supplemented by additional donations.

A New Era

The advent of vitrification might well mark a new era in the public perception of human cryopreservation. A successfully vitrified patient is not a frozen patient. All the tired clichés about "freezer burn," "bursting cells," and revival being equivalent to recovering "cows from hamburger" fall into irrelevance. Scientific critics will now be forced to examine what vitrification is rather than resorting to pat analogies concerning frozen tissue or even frozen food (!) Offhand disparagement must become discussion on the merits. The scientific debate of cryonics will be elevated to a new level. For under ideal conditions, vitrification is so qualitatively distinct from past practice that perhaps it shouldn't even be called "cryonics" anymore. ■

Selected References

"Freezing of living cells: mechanisms and implications," P. Mazur, *Am J Physiol.* **247**, C125—142 (1984).

"Vitrification as an approach to cryopreservation," G. M. Fahy, D. R. MacFarlane, C. A. Angell, H. T. Meryman, *Cryobiology* **21**, 407—426 (1984).

"Ice-free cryopreservation of mouse embryos at -196 degrees C by vitrification," W. F. Rall, G. M. Fahy, *Nature* **313**, 573—575 (1985)

"Physical problems with the vitrification of large biological systems," G. M. Fahy, J. Saur, R. J. Williams, *Cryobiology* **27**, 492—510 (1990).

"Vitreous cryopreservation maintains the function of vascular grafts," Y. C. Song, B. S. Khirabadi, F. Lightfoot, K. G. Brockbank, M. J. Taylor, *Nat Biotechnol.* **18**, 296—299 (2000).

"Vitrification enhancement by synthetic ice blocking agents," B. Wowk, E. Leitl, C. M. Rasch, N. Mesbah-Karimi, S. B. Harris, and G. M. Fahy, *Cryobiology* **40**, 228—236 (2000).

"Vitrification solutions of reduced toxicity," G. M. Fahy, B. Wowk, C. Rasch, K. Kersh, and J. Phan, Abstract presented at 37th Annual Meeting of The Society for Cryobiology (2000).

"Molecular engineering: an approach to the development of general capabilities for molecular manipulation," K. E. Drexler, *PNAS (USA)* **78**, 5275—5278 (1981).

Nanosystems: Molecular Machinery, Manufacturing, and Computation, K. E. Drexler, John Wiley & Sons, 1992.

"The technical feasibility of cryonics," R. C. Merkle, *Med Hypotheses.* **39**, 6—16 (1992).

Nanomedicine, Volume 1: Basic Capabilities, R. A. Freitas, Landes Bioscience, 1999.

Figure 1 Caption

A schematic representation of tissue that is (a) frozen with a low concentration of cryoprotectant, (b) frozen with a high concentration of cryoprotectant, and (c) vitrified. The vitrified tissue is indistinguishable from the unfrozen state, except that all translational molecular motion is stopped.

Figure 2 Caption

Transmission electron micrographs of brain tissue cooled to –80°C and rewarmed. Micrograph (a) is a canine brain treated with 7.5 Molar glycerol cryoprotectant, the highest concentration of glycerol that can be perfused into a cryonics patient. Large voids are present where frozen/thawed ice crystals have disrupted cell structure. Micrograph (b) is a rabbit brain treated with a vitrification solution. This brain has completely escaped damage from ice crystals.

Figure 3 Caption

Frozen (left) and vitrified (right) rabbit kidneys cooled to –130°C. Both kidneys are embedded in a vitrification solution. Only the vitrified kidney, having itself turned into a glass, remains undamaged inside the surrounding glassy solution.

New Cryopreservation Technology

By Alcor Staff

Originally published in October, 2005 online at:
http://www.alcor.org/Library/html/newtechnology.html

Overview

Reversible suspended animation requires successful preservation and recovery of structure and function of an organism, especially the brain. Historically cryonics has focused on preservation of cell structure as revealed by electron microscopy. It was reasoned that if at least structure was well preserved, nanotechnology could reverse chemical changes that caused loss of function. This led Alcor to increase the concentration of glycerol used for freezing during the 1990s, and ultimately to switch to cryoprotectant mixtures capable of vitrification (ice-free preservation) after the turn of the century.

Alcor first implemented vitrification for neuropreservation cases using B2C cryoprotectant solution. It was not possible to immediately extend this technology to whole bodies because B2C could not be perfused into whole bodies without causing tissue swelling, and because the physical apparatus for cooling whole bodies quickly to the required temperature of -120°C did not exist. Whole body cases therefore continued to be treated with either conventional glycerol cryoprotection and freezing, or by separation of the head for better brain preservation by neurovitrification, and separate freezing of the body. This combination procedure caused much media misunderstanding.

In 2005, Alcor completed construction of a cold nitrogen gas cooling system for attempting vitrification of whole bodies. Also, another cryoprotectant solution suitable for large system vitrification had been validated in brain and whole animal studies. This solution, called M22, did not permit vitrification of all parts of the body because some tissues absorb cryoprotectant too slowly. However it seemed adequate for vitrification of tissues with a rich supply of blood vessels, such as the brain. Therefore it should be possible to vitrify the brain during cryopreservation of the entire body, not just the head. The rest of the body would experience varying degrees of vitrification and freezing during the process, with freezing injury reduced by presence of M22 solution.

This "M22 procedure" is Alcor's new cryopreservation technology. M22 solution will now be used for both whole body and neuropreservation cases, making B2C obsolete. It also marks an important technology transition as Alcor begins to move beyond just structure preservation toward better preservation of biochemistry and functional capacity. The advantages of M22 over B2C are discussed below.

Solution Comparison

In 2001 Alcor switched from high concentration glycerol to B2C vitrification solution for cryoprotection of neuropatients. B2C is a more concentrated variant of the VM3 vitrification solution used in mainstream cryobiology for vitrification of mouse ova and kidney slices[1]. B2C was designed as a "hyperstable" vitrification solution, meaning that it's so concentrated that it's virtually impossible to freeze. This was done to help ensure that Alcor's first attempts at brain vitrification would be successful, with the understanding the cellular viability by conventional spontaneous recovery criteria would be low to non-existent. Thus the purpose of B2C was to eliminate structural damage from ice under good conditions, not preserve viability by conventional measures.

The composition of B2C is:

Dimethyl sulfoxide	24.765% w/v
Formamide	17.836%
Ethylene glycol	17.401%
Polyvinyl pyrrolidone K12	2%
Polyvinyl pyrrolidone K30	2%
X-1000 ice blocker	1%
Z-1000 ice blocker	1%

The solution was prepared in a carrier solution of non-penetrating solutes called B1, similar in composition to the published vitrification carrier solution LM5[2].

Figures 1 and 2 show electron micrographs prepared from rabbit brains after perfusion with B2C solution in a manner that replicates Alcor's neurovitrification protocol prior to deep cooling. The micrographs therefore represent the state of the brain immediately prior to deep cooling for vitrification. The second figure is more representative of human cases since the peak concentration phase of perfusions are more likely to last two or more hours rather than the one hour of Fig. 1. Both figures show disturbing structural alterations.

More recent developments in cryobiology offer a better alternative. A new vitrification solution called M22 has been developed by mainstream tissue banking researchers [2]. The published composition is as follows:

---

1   G.M. Fahy, B. Wowk, J. Wu, S. Paynter, Improved vitrification solutions based on the predictability of vitrification solution toxicity, *Cryobiology* 48 (2004) 22-35.

2   G.M. Fahy, B. Wowk, J. Wu, J. Phan, C. Rasch, A. Chang, E. Zendejas, Cryopreservation of organs by vitrification: perspectives and recent advances, *Cryobiology* 48 (2004) 157-178.

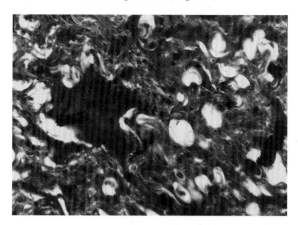

Figure 1. B2C perfusion for one hour at -4°C (no further cooling). Rabbit *hippocampus at 6700x magnification. White holes appear to be shrinkage spaces caused by extreme cellular dehydration. While less damaging than ice, such artifacts are still undesirable. Two opaque black particles on the micrograph are preparation artifacts.*

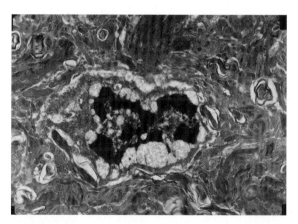

Figure 2. B2C perfusion for two hours at -4°C (no further cooling). Rabbit *cerebral cortex at 8000x magnification. There is less dehydration space than in Fig. 1, but unusually pale cytoplasm and dark chromatin clumping in the central cell. With the exception of the unusual appearance of this cell, other structures appear intact. This type of cell was seen infrequently.*

Dimethyl sulfoxide	22.305% w/v
Formamide	12.858%
Ethylene glycol	16.837%
N-methylformamide	3%
3-methoxy-1,2-propanediol	4%
Polyvinyl pyrrolidone K12	2.8%
X-1000 ice blocker	1%
Z-1000 ice blocker	2%

The solution must also contain non-penetrating solutes of a suitable carrier solution, such as LM5[3], at isotonic concentration brought to a final pH of 8.

M22 has a critical cooling rate of approximately 0.1°C per minute, and a critical warming rate of 0.4°C per minute after rapid cooling. The critical warming rate is approximately 1°C per minute after slow cooling. This is more than sufficient for structural vitrification of an object the size of the human brain, which can be cooled at 0.4°C per minute with no near-term need for warming. Figure 3 shows a two liter volume of M22 vitrified by standing in unstirred cold nitrogen for 18 hours.

Figure 3. Two liters (5 pounds) of M22 solution cooled at 0.14°C/minute (18 hours) until vitrified at a temperature of -124°C.

Alcor has previously published the results of rabbit brain vitrification with M22.[4] These results have now been extended to confirm that vitrification still occurs even when cooling at human neuropatient rates. Figures 4 and 5 show electron micrographs

3   G.M. Fahy, B. Wowk, J. Wu, J. Phan, C. Rasch, A. Chang, E. Zendejas, Cryopreservation of organs by vitrification: perspectives and recent advances, *Cryobiology* 48 (2004) 157-178.

4   J. Lemler, S.B. Harris, C. Platt, T.M. Huffman, The arrest of biological time as a bridge to engineered negligible senescence, *Annals of the New York Academy of Sciences* 1019 (2004) 559-563.

of M22-perfused rabbit brains that were cooled at the same rate as the core of an Alcor neuropatient, and subsequently rewarmed as rapidly as possible by forced convection. Both brains successfully vitrified, showing no signs of ice formation. This is very remarkable in the case of Fig 5, for which only 81% of normal M22 solute concentration was used. That concentration of M22 would not remain vitrified if tested as a bare solution, indicating that brain tissue can be more stable against ice formation than the solution it is perfused with (perhaps because of dehydration effects). This is consistent with other studies that show large ice-free areas in brains treated with high concentration glycerol, even though such concentrations of glycerol would not vitrify under ordinary circumstances.

Figure 4. M22 perfusion for one hour at -3ºC followed by vitrification at -125ºC and rewarming. Rabbit hippocampus at 1400x magnification. Structural preservation is good, with greatly reduced dehydration artifacts compared to B2C. The hole at the bottom right is a capillary. Circular mottling is a film processing artifact.

The results of Figs. 4 and 5 are also notable because these studies included a proprietary additive to the carrier solution that reduces edema (tissue swelling) in whole body patients. The results of Figs. 4 and 5 can therefore be obtained in both neuro and whole body patients, permitting in-situ brain vitrification of whole body patients without neuroseparation. This was impossible with B2C, which could not be used for whole body perfusions.

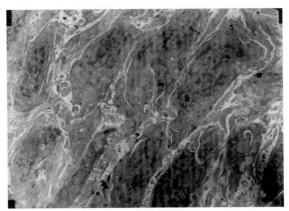

Figure 5. M22 at only 81% full concentration perfused for one hour at -3ºC followed by vitrification at -125ºC and rewarming. Rabbit hippocampus at 1400x magnification. Remarkably, no ice damage was seen anywhere in the brain despite the reduced cryoprotectant concentration. Mottling is chromatin clumping.

Figure 6 shows that perfusion with M22 is compatible with preservation of brain cells even on the synapse level. Similar results were previously obtained with glycerol and cooling in Fig. 3 of this study, but unlike M22, glycerol could not be perfused at concentrations sufficient to prevent ice formation through the entire brain volume.

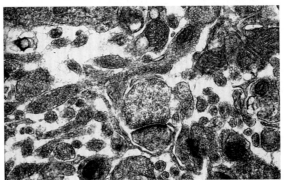

Figure 6. M22 perfusion for one hour at -3°C (no further cooling). Rabbit brain synapse at high magnification. The synapse and neurotransmitter vesicles remain intact. White spaces are due to dehydration induced by the cryoprotectant.

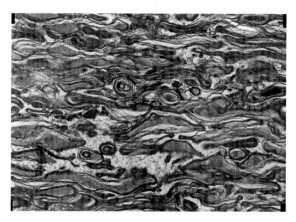

Figure 7. Suprahippocampal white matter after perfusion with M22 for 60 min at -3°C, cooling to below the glass transition temperature, rewarming, and perfusion fixation. The myelinated fibers are shrunken but intact; lighter spaces are believed to be benign shrinkage spaces. No debris resulting from lysed structures is present. Magnification approximately 5000X on original film.

M22 will be the first solution used in cryonics that preserves both structure and tissue viability under certain circumstances in published studies. In particular, M22 has been used to successfully recover and then transplant whole kidneys after cooling to a temperature of -45°C.[5] This success required perfusing M22 at a temperature of -22°C for only 25 minutes, which is colder and shorter than currently required to prepare a brain for vitrification. So while the same tissue viability seen in published kidney studies cannot be expected in cryonics patients, the use of a solution with such favorable toxicity properties will be less damaging to cell biochemistry than previous solutions used in cryonics.

M22 is less viscous than B2C. Shortened perfusion times will be another advantage of using the solution.

In summary, M22 offers the following advantages:

- Solution of published composition.
- Published success recovering kidneys from -45°C.
- Published success at structural brain vitrification.
- Low toxicity per published studies.
- Low viscosity for faster perfusions.
- Compatible with additives permitting whole body perfusion. ■

5   G.M. Fahy, B. Wowk, J. Wu, J. Phan, C. Rasch, A. Chang, E. Zendejas, Cryopreservation of organs by vitrification: perspectives and recent advances, *Cryobiology* 48 (2004) 157-178.

Cooling Down

By Hugh Hixon, M.S.
Cryonics, 3rd Quarter, 1994

Everyone says cooling a patient from 5°C to –196°C should be easy to automate. I know I said it back in the late '70s when I was part of the Cryovita suspension team. Given a reasonable budget, I suppose it is, but cryonics organizations don't have reasonable budgets. They have survival budgets. And major projects that aren't absolutely essential get put off indefinitely. In any event, this is history. In April of this year, Alcor did a suspension, and the cooldown protocol was entirely controlled by computer. As far as I am aware, this is the first time that this has been done in the history of cryonics.

The object of the suspension procedure is to arrest deterioration of the patient after the pronouncement of legal death. There are two fundamental ways to achieve this: chemical, and physical. In general, the chemical methods are forms of embalming. There is only one physical method: extreme cold. There have been a number of proposals to preserve people at ambient temperatures chemically; there are some very impressive chemical preservation methods available, primarily for pathology work, and not having to maintain cryogenic temperatures for a long period would be a real advantage. These have uniformly been rejected for this reason: Organisms have been demonstrated to survive cryogenic storage; no chemical method can claim this. Chemical preservation methods are not at this time reversible. Ultimately, it may turn out that cryogenic storage was not the right method to use, but we do not now know enough to do any more than place our bet.

There are a number of ways to cool a suspension patient, and they have all been used. First, of course, there is simply dropping them into LN_2, and this was done often in the early days of cryonics. This gives the fastest rate of heat transfer, and has the virtues of speed and simplicity but is likely to result in mechanical cracking, as the outside of the patient contracts faster than the inside. For sufficiently small specimens, such as bacteria or individual cells, it can work quite well; but for large objects such as human patients, problems of scale make it totally unacceptable.

All other cooldown systems attempt to regulate the heat flow between the object and the cold sink (refrigeration, dry ice, or liquid nitrogen). The most basic of these couple the object directly to the sink with an intermediate liquid or gas. Because of their high heat capacity, liquids can remove heat at a high rate with a small temperature difference. For a gas to do so at the same rate requires a much larger temperature difference, which results in undesirable surface contraction. The fundamental law here is that the rate of heat transfer is proportional to the temperature difference. The accompanying proportionality factor is somewhat more involved, depending on such things as the boundary layer, circulation, heat capacity, molecular weight, diffusion constant, insulation, etc. In any passive system, the upshot of this relationship is that the initial cooling rate is faster than the final cooling rate. Since we have 200°C to traverse, the ratio of initial to final cooling rate exceeds 20-to-1. In practical terms, the initial rate is so great as to create unnecessary and undesirable mechanical stresses, and if the proportionality constant is reduced (say, by insulation) to produce a reasonable initial cooling rate, the heat transfer rate near the final temperature is impractically slow.

The next innovation in regulation is to perform the cooldown as a series of steps. This is usually done by adding refrigerant at intervals and waiting for the system to approach equilibrium. Make the temperature intervals small enough, and we will get a reasonably smooth cooldown curve (the heat capacity—or "thermal inertia"—of the patient and the rest of the system help to smooth the curve). Perform enough of these cycles, and we get to the end. And here is the problem: To do this properly requires checking at an interval of 15 minutes or less for over a week. Done manually, the effect on the people in this feedback loop is not good. It takes two to four people for the necessary continuous coverage, they can't do much of anything else, and turning them temporarily into control automatons is not easy and not pleasant. Some do well at the job, some do poorly, but no one has ever liked it.

For several years, we had a system for LN_2 cooldown that was partially automated. An industrial control relay injected LN_2 at regular intervals. The results were erratic. It was necessary to hunt for a balance in the system, or it ran away from us. And the balance was very narrow; small differences accumulated very rapidly. There was a little control and a lot of illusion of control.

That was for whole-body suspensions. For neuropreservation cooldowns from dry ice to LN_2, I devised a different and less temperamental system. In LN_2 dewars, with cold liquid in the bottom and ambient temperature at the top, the natural tendency is for the system to stratify, so that there is a natural and stable temperature gradient in the gas. In practice, the temperature goes from –197°C at the liquid to about –140°C under the dewar lid. The gradient changes most rapidly near the liquid. By progressively lowering the patient in the dewar, we achieved a stepwise temperature descent. The interval from –78°C to –140°C I dealt with by creating a heated convection zone under the lid. Cold gas rising up the dewar was heated by a resistor bank powered by a variable autotransformer. The result was a stable temperature zone in the top of the dewar. Before adding the patient to the system, the power to the resistor bank was increased until the zone was at dry ice temperature. Then the patient was suspended in the zone, and the power was slowly reduced. Results were good, but slow. When the power to the resistors was zero, we lowered the patient slowly stepwise down through the temperature gradient. Near the liquid, the gradient got steeper, and control got tricky.

About 1990, Mike Darwin was Easter-egging a new Cole-Parmer Instrument Company catalog and came across a new instrument; a microprocessor-controlled scanning thermocouple. It had 12 thermocouple inputs, an internal elapsed-time clock, thermocouple compensation, alarms, limited external programming, and a serial printer port. There was also a program available for a computer to read the serial port. The price was under $700. Jerry Leaf bought the first one for Cryovita Labs, to monitor and print out temperatures during a suspension. Alcor got one to monitor patient storage. Alcor now has three.

About 1992, Keith Henson took on the cooldown problem. He modified the computer program that came with the scanning thermocouple to provide a simple control loop, and he built a breadboard neuropreservation cooldown system in a box for the descent to dry ice temperature. The box was the interesting part. Without getting into a lot of detail, it had some neat prototyping tricks, an ingenious refrigeration system, and it worked. It did however, bear watching, because it was an extraordinary bug trap. Just about everything in it did go wrong at some point. Later, I built another neuro cooldown unit, and I am convinced that I avoided a lot of problems by carefully evaluating Keith's box. Which is, of course, exactly what a prototype is for!

Due to business commitments, Keith's involvement in the cooldown project was subsequently reduced, but there was now something to work with, and Scott Herman and Mike Perry undertook to complete the programming part of the project. Scott also built the relay box that interfaces between the computer and the physical part of the system. Since they have a lot of things to do at Alcor, their progress has been off-again, on-again. Of particular note, Mike Perry wrote an adaptive subroutine to determine the switch-on interval.

In the suspension of April of 1993, they made their first live run, as the computer controlled the descent to dry ice temperature. Further work before and after Alcor's move to the Phoenix area positioned them for a mad sprint to a functional system at the suspension that Alcor performed in April of this year. Someone was always awake to watch it (first time, you better believe it!), but except for minor tweaks, all they had to do was load dry ice and swap out LN_2 supply dewars. Mike and Scott are now engaged in the final step, from functional to easy-to-use.

Our current cooldown scheme is done in two steps. Between 5°C and about −50°C, deteriorative chemical reactions can still take place. Thus there is a premium on rapid cooling. To avoid a large temperature difference while moving a lot of heat quickly, a liquid heat-transfer medium is used. There are a number of compounds that are liquid in the interval from room to dry ice temperature. A few of these are not particularly volatile at room temperature. Other properties to be avoided include high flammability, forming solutions with water condensed from the air (which tends to make the liquid more viscous), ability to extract water from the patient's tissues, toxicity, etc. No inexpensive compound meets all these criteria. In the early '80s, Mike Darwin examined a number of more exotic chemicals, and Alcor adopted a silicone oil, a polydimethyl-siloxane, as the first-stage heat transfer fluid. Its viscosity is relatively constant over the required temperature range, condensed water simply freezes out as ice, it is about as flammable as kerosene (that is, not very flammable, on a scale that includes ether, acetone, neopentane, propyl alcohol, etc), and it is sufficiently nontoxic that we kept mice in it for a week without observing any ill-effects. Its commercial use is as a food and cosmetic additive. Its biggest disadvantage is its cost—about $50 per gallon—which leads to our purifying it after each use. We lose several pints to various places in each suspension. We currently have about 80 gallons on hand. We refer to it as Silcool. Its commercial name is Dow-Corning DC200, 5 centistoke.

In practice, the patient, protected by plastic bags, is immersed in circulating Silcool. From time to time Silcool at dry ice temperature is added to the circulation. For the neurocooler, this is from a reservoir tank with dry ice in it, the liquid being replaced in the reservoir by overflow from the cooling tank. For the whole-body cooling tank, Silcool is pumped into a tray filled with dry ice, which drains into the tank that the patient is in. The circulating pump in the neurocooler is a swamp cooler water pump. In the whole-body tank, it is a long-shaft bilge pump. The primary criteria for the selection of these pumps were toughness and low cost. In both units, the computer controls a gear pump that circulates Silcool over the dry ice. Direct contact with the Silcool (instead of an intermediate circulating loop) was picked because of its simplicity and efficiency of heat transfer. The gear pump, driven by a 1/3 hp motor, was selected because I believe that it is a great deal more robust than a solenoid valve and does not have to be primed with liquid to pump (that is, it can suck liquid up). An open system such as this accumulates ice that can be expected to jam a solenoid valve. All the pumps can be removed instantly for maintenance. I have taken the design philosophy here that the cooldown units are a hostile, almost impossible to work in, environment, and gone for simplicity, robustness, and ease of maintenance. The best way to avoid repair work below the surface of a very cold liquid is to design the problem out of the system.

Unfortunately, Silcool is not a liquid much below about $-100°C$, so the second cooling step from dry ice temperature to liquid nitrogen temperature is done with cold gas. The patient is transferred to the permanent LN_2 storage container, appropriately insulated, and the container placed in a cooldown dewar. A cooldown lid with a stirring fan, LN_2 injector solenoid valve, and gas vents is placed in the dewar mouth and the cooling sequence started. The fan is to circulate the cold gas around the patient container and prevent stratification. The solenoid is controlled by the cooldown computer, and from time-to-time releases a shot of LN_2 into the circulating gas, cooling it as required by the cooling profile. The circulating fan is driven by a long-shaft motor mounted on the top of the cooldown lid. There are motors made that will work at LN_2 temperature, but they are expensive. The problem that normal motors have at low temperatures is that the oil in the bearings freezes and stalls the motor. A long shaft through the insulation of the lid gets away from the problem.

I have been involved in the problem of regulating cooldown since 1978. There has never been any question that the system that we have now nearly completed is necessary. Good control, data collection, and a better use for people than to bind them to a grueling, necessary job. We've finally done it!

To all the people who have stayed up day and night after the intense and grueling effort of a suspension to do the cooldown. Laurence Gale, Jerry Leaf, Steve Bridge, Mike Darwin, Arthur McCombs, Fred and Linda Chamberlain, Carlos Mondragon, Paul Garfield, Scott Herman, Dave Christiansen, Max More, Tanya Jones, ESPECIALLY Mike Perry, and a lot of others whose names I've forgotten, THANKS! And .... *Never again.*

REGRETS

There is one simple feedback control scheme. Two thermocouples can be wired back-to-back (so that their potentials oppose each other). If one thermocouple is inside the patient, and the other outside, and refrigerant added as necessary to maintain a constant readout temperature (which means a constant temperature difference), the result will be a smooth and gradual descent. This scheme is used in old Linde cooldown refrigerators (would you believe vacuum tubes). For some reason, however, we never adapted the Linde units we had to our use, and the only time we attempted to implement the scheme with new equipment, it got sidetracked and dumped. Looking backward, I believe we just never mustered the will to carry the project through, until this last time.

Cooldown Technology at Alcor Since 1994 (by Mike Perry in consultation with Hugh Hixon)

Since Hugh Hixon's article was written there have been a number of innovations in cooldown technology at Alcor. We have made improvements in automation so that now (2014) the system we use is very reliable and highly crash-resistant. The cooldown program in use in 1994, written in GW-Basic by Scott Herman and Mike Perry, was upgraded by Mike to a program in Q-Basic with a detailed manual in 1998. With some modifications this was used for many years. It was replaced in 2010 by a system in LabVIEW written by Joel Anderson with superior graphics showing temperature descent and other useful features. At the physical end we abandoned the use of silicone oil and dry ice around 2003 and now do all cooling with cold nitrogen gas. Neuro cooldowns are done in one container throughout (a small dewar standing about 3' tall); the patient does not need to be moved until transferred to long-term storage. Whole body cooldowns are done in two stages as before (started in a horizontal, formerly "dry ice," box, finished in an upright container after the temperature drops to -80°C or thereabouts) but again cold nitrogen gas is used throughout. The two-stage cooldown is used for a whole body due to its larger size: to expedite a rapid cooling initially and a slower cooldown later to minimize thermal stresses. For the second stage the patient is insulated—in a sleeping bag inside a pod—and is cooled at a slower rate inside an upright container. ■

Elements of a Transport

By Tanya Jones
Cryonics, 2nd Quarter, 1995

People are usually surprised when I tell them that when handling the suspension of an Alcor patient, my biggest sense of accomplishment and relief usually occurs before the actual suspension procedures even begin. I've participated in about a dozen suspensions and almost that number of transports. With some suspensions, I've felt joy. With others, terror. But either way, from the moment I walk in the door with a patient, a huge weight begins to lift from my shoulders. While the job is far from over, the hard part is done.

Why is it that most of the major obstacles to a favorable cryonic suspension occur before the patient arrives at the Alcor facility? What makes transporting a "legally dead" person so complicated? Presenting and explaining the many aspects of a "successful" transport is difficult, but it's important that Alcor Suspension Members and potential Members understand the complexity involved, since each of you is in a position to dramatically improve your chances of a successful transport by taking some action now.

The major components of a cryonics patient transport are Infrastructure, Mobilization, Patient Acquisition, Stabilization, and Transport. Let's look at each of these separately.

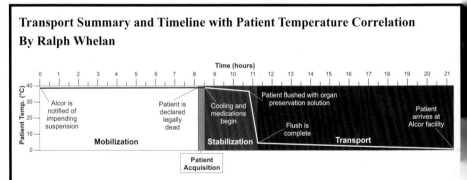

Transport Summary and Timeline with Patient Temperature Correlation
By Ralph Whelan

The transport of a cryonic suspension patient can be broken down into five basic categories. Four of those categories are graphically displayed in the illustration at the top of this page, along with patient temperatures for a hypothetical transport beginning in New York and ending in Arizona. The fifth category, *Infrastructure*, is not depicted because it refers to transport readiness, rather than an aspect of the actual transport.

Mobilization

When Alcor is notified that a cryonic suspension is imminent, we immediately put our representatives in touch with the hospital personnel caring for the patient, while other Alcor personnel notify transport team members local to the patient, begin negotiations with local morticians, and begin air transport arrangements for team members and for the patient. In this example, the patient is distant from the Alcor facility, but is expected to live for several hours.

Patient Acquisition

About eight hours after Alcor's notification, and shortly after the arrival of the transport team, the patient is pronounced legally dead. The hospital allows the team to begin immediate surface cooling, so his temperature slowly begins to drop. Meanwhile, various legal requirements for his release are being fulfilled by Alcor personnel and a local mortician. Twenty minutes pass before the hospital is prepared to release the patient.

Stabilization

Once in Alcor's care, the patient receives medications that will prevent clotting, reduce metabolic demand, protect his cells and prepare them for the low temperatures ahead. The team relocates to a local mortuary, where a field Operating Theatre is already assembled. A "femoral cutdown" is performed and the patient's blood is replaced with an organ preservation solution, while his core temperature is quickly reduced to near (but above) freezing.

Transport

The patient is packed in ice in a specially designed transport container and taken to a local airport; the airport personnel are expecting him. He is placed on the very next available flight, though most of the transport team must take a later flight. Waiting in Phoenix are more Alcor personnel, who've negotiated with the local airline representatives for a prompt transfer to the waiting Alcor ambulance. The patient is driven to Alcor's main facility.

Infrastructure

A patient stabilization generally involves cooling the patient in a portable ice bath, administering medications to protect cellular integrity, replacing the patient's blood with an organ preservation solution, and preparing the patient for shipment to Alcor. For local emergency response, Alcor has an ambulance. This ambulance is well equipped to allow a transport team to carry out each of these steps internally, but naturally ambulance travel is usually limited to the Phoenix area. (Air travel is much faster for distant regions.) With several days' notice of a member's decline, however, the ambulance has traveled to northern and southern California, and may be used in other nearby states.

Remote emergency response (where "remote" means beyond ambulance range) requires Alcor's remote stabilization kit. This kit consists of eight sturdy boxes which accompany transport team members on a commercial airline. Together, these boxes replicate the capability of the ambulance in a relatively compact, if less convenient, package. Because shipment of the remote kit could cause serious delays in the patient's stabilization if pronouncement is unexpected, some local groups of Alcor members have been issued smaller versions of this kit. These kits generally contain medications and a portable ice bath. Some also contain a mechanical cardiopulmonary support device and oxygen. With this equipment and the cooperation of a local mortician or funeral director and/or trained local Alcor volunteers, a patient may be stabilized for shipment to Alcor.

Simply having equipment available is not enough to carry out a transport, nor is it enough to ensure that a patient will receive a good stabilization or transport. There are many things that people may do to prepare for their eventual suspension.

First and foremost, of course, a person must be a member, i.e. sign up. Generally, a cryonics organization will not suspend an individual who has not chosen to be frozen. Legal documents establish this intent, and some states have laws which require that a person's wishes for the disposition of their human remains must be followed as long as they don't impose a financial hardship on the family. A signed *Cryonic Suspension Agreement and Authorization for Anatomical Donation* will go a long way toward demonstrating the desire to be frozen. For those who haven't decided which organization to sign up with, but who know that they do wish to be frozen, the *Declaration of Intent to be Cryonically Suspended* is a form which establishes intent without obligating the individual to a specific organization, and without empowering or obligating a suspension organization to freeze him/her. (These forms are available from Alcor upon request.)

Another legal document which is useful to a cryonic suspension patient is the *Durable Power of Attorney for Health Care*. With this form, an individual chooses a medical surrogate (an agent to make medical decisions when the individual is unable to communicate his intentions) and states the degree of medical intervention in an emergency. For example, I have no desire to be connected to life support equipment if there is no hope of my waking from a coma with my identity intact, and this is specifically detailed in my DPAHC.

A transport may be impeded by relatives of the patient, especially if they haven't been informed of the patient's desire to be suspended before Alcor's services are required. In one of Alcor's cases, the patient's relatives had only heard cryonics mentioned by the patient once, and that had been years before he became ill. They had no idea that any paperwork had been signed and were initially defensive and unhappy. For this patient, things ultimately worked out well, because he came from an understanding and supportive family. The desire for confidentiality will always be respected by Alcor; however, a person who informs his family of his cryonics arrangements before decisions must be made during a crisis will probably receive a stabilization superior to one who does not. Family members will often be the ones to call Alcor when a member becomes ill, and having their cooperation is crucial. We are always willing to have discussions with family, medical staff, and morticians in advance of a suspension.

Having some familiarity with Alcor's cryonic suspension protocol will also help an individual explain cryonics to others. Alcor's introductory handbook, *Cryonics: Reaching For Tomorrow,* and *Cryonics* magazine carry information about Alcor's procedures, in the form of suspension or research reports and explanatory articles. Detailed information is available to those who attend Alcor's transport certification course. (To date, Alcor has offered this course at no charge.) During this week-long course and subsequent refresher weekends, Alcor members are introduced to the specific cryonic suspension protocol, to the equipment used during a transport, and to the multitude of technical and medical references used to formulate the procedures. They are shown how every hand can be of assistance during a transport. Many go home and share this information with other Alcor members, their family, and friends, thus expanding the resources upon which Alcor may call during an emergency.

Knowing about the protocol is great, but there's much more than that to optimizing your own chances for a favorable transport. Each Alcor member should consider preparing a list and map of local suppliers for transport supplies and consumables and sending copies of these to Alcor. As an example, oxygen cylinders may not be transported on commercial airlines, and oxygen is needed both to power the mechanical cardiopulmonary support (CPS) device and to oxygenate the patient during stabilization. Alcor's central remote kit carries an air compressor (which has never been tested in a field situation) as an alternative for the CPS device and a bagging device which will respirate the patient with room air as an alternative to pure oxygen. However, these alternatives are less effective and more labor intensive and will only be used in cases where compressed oxygen is unavailable. Ice (hundreds of pounds) must be available 24 hours a day. Generally, local grocery markets carry ice in this quantity and increasing numbers are perpetually open as well. Having a central list with this and similar information will aid the transport team in their attempt to do the best that they can for you.

For legal reasons, in most states no transport can be performed without a local funeral director or mortician's involvement. We expect this to change as cryonics continues to become more commonplace. Adding the names, addresses, and phone numbers of local funeral homes and mortuaries can save a lot of time during an emergency. Contacting some in advance is even better. Morticians are generally quite interested in cryonics and sympathetic to an individual's desire to be cryonically suspended instead of buried or cremated. Morticians are usually needed to secure the release of a patient from a hospital; they have space, equipment, and supplies which can be useful—especially in an emergency; they are frequently willing to assist with femoral surgery or perfusion and are experienced in carrying them out quickly; and they have a comprehensive knowledge of the legal and practical requirements for transporting a patient across state lines and are frequently willing to prepare the paperwork.

A member who chooses to assist Alcor in negotiating a contract with a local mortician has many things to discuss, and should have some familiarity with Alcor's protocol. (However, if a member simply finds a cooperating funeral director, Alcor personnel are available to conduct the contract negotiation.)

Mortuary contracts should at least address the 24-hour availability of an individual who is capable of signing for the release of a patient from the hospital. Some morticians have had sufficient personnel available to stand by with the transport team members to enable the fastest possible release of the patient from the hospital. If a mortuary transport vehicle is to be used to take the patient to the funeral home and the patient will be in the portable ice bath, the mortician will generally have to remove his gurney from the back of his vehicle before taking it to the hospital, so that the patient may be loaded.

Alcor will usually supply the personnel needed to stabilize the patient for transport, and in these cases, will need the uninterrupted use of a "prep" room table for at least two hours. If suction is available, it might be useful during the washout procedure.

Because of the volume of equipment needed during a stabilization, storage space is also required for the duration of the standby. If the equipment is placed in a prep room that will not be needed by the mortician during the time frame of the standby and transport, it may be possible to string the perfusion circuit in advance of pronouncement (and save up to thirty minutes later).

In cases where insufficient trained personnel or equipment are available, morticians have been used to perform femoral surgery, and their embalming pumps have been used (only when those pumps have variable pressures which may be set to meet our needs). The conservative approach to cryonics requires that the conditions of a hospital operating room be duplicated throughout a stabilization. As a result, any mortuary equipment which is used must be thoroughly cleaned and rinsed with sterile water (and sterilized, whenever possible) before being used on a patient.

It's important to note that, while morticians and their equipment are sometimes relied on heavily in an emergency, members can usually avoid the risks inherent in this option by (when feasible) keeping Alcor well-informed of all serious surgeries and life-threatening conditions. Note as well that, while mortuary contracts have been negotiated at the last minute, they have occasionally turned out to be with unprincipled persons who charge Alcor unreasonable amounts because of a misconception that cryonics is a profit-making venture. Emergency contracting should be avoided whenever possible.

When an emergency response begins, a transport team must have access to everything listed above (and more). Having things done in advance means that the team members may concentrate on other, equally critical aspects of preparedness.

Mobilization

Transport team members are deployed by Alcor Headquarters upon notification of an Alcor member's distress. There are three basic categories of emergency mobilization and each is dependent upon the condition of the patient when Alcor is called: the patient has a known terminal illness and will suffer a predictable course of deterioration; the patient has been admitted to the hospital after the sudden onset of illness or accident and is unlikely to survive for more than 12-24 hours; and the patient has died suddenly and is at risk of autopsy.

Advance Notice of Death

With advance notice, a remote standby may be deployed. In a standby, a transport team is deployed before the member has been pronounced legally dead. Advance deployment generally means that the team can prepare for the impending transport, take the time to negotiate service contracts, facilitate a smooth and speedy release of the patient, and procure all of the necessary equipment and personnel before the patient is pronounced. This significantly improves the chances of a smooth stabilization. Standby contracts are optional but highly recommended.

A transport team may consist of one or more Alcor staff members, one or more experienced transport team members flown in from around the country, and one or more local volunteers. These team members will invariably interact with members of the conventional medical community. Every interaction between the physician, hospital administrators, charge nurses, or hospice nurses and Alcor personnel will affect how well the patient is treated prior to and immediately following the pronouncement of legal death.

The climate is changing. In the past, when transport team members discussed cryonics with conventional medical personnel they were often met with hostility and fear. Today, I can't remember when I last encountered this attitude during an emergency. This doesn't mean that there is uniform acceptance of cryonics in the medical community, but there certainly is more curiosity than ever before. An interested physician or nurse can do a lot to see that the patient is given a head start toward a good stabilization. (But this is a hospital—the shifts change every eight hours or so, and the cryonics arrangements must be discussed anew with each staff member.)

What would we ask for? We'd like access to the patient. (After all, it's something we ought to know if the rosy-cheeked patient who laughed heartily with you that morning is lethargic and pale by evening.) We'd like to wait nearby. Is the floor lounge comfortable? The transport protocol demands that cooling begin immediately after pronouncement. Ideally, we should have our equipment in place at the moment of pronouncement, and that can only be accomplished if it is stored nearby. How about the next room or the storage room down the hall?

Cryonic suspension procedures may only be implemented after legal death has been pronounced. Because of the known dangers of ischemia, we'd like to have a physician available at all times to pronounce. If we have to wait, may we pack the patient's head in ice? Can the hospital provide the ice? Many patients will receive intravenous (IV) therapy during their hospitalization. If any IV lines are in place, leaving them in means that once the patient is released, Alcor personnel can begin injecting cell-stabilizing medications immediately without placing a new line. (This also applies to airways.) Will they leave all lines secure? And if there are no IV lines, may one be placed before pronouncement? Lastly, we'd like to begin our transport procedures immediately after pronouncement, as we are running for the door.

Most doctors encountering a transport team have called in the hospital administrators when faced with these questions. The transport team leader will present cryonics to an administrator (and sometimes, to an accompanying attorney) who is primarily concerned about hospital liability. A *Hold-Harmless Agreement* may be offered to the hospital which states that Alcor will not hold the hospital responsible for any charges or damages arising from a civil lawsuit over the cryonic suspension of the patient.

Alcor literature and other cryonics information is carried with the remote kit, and may be handed out freely to doctors and administrators. Transport team members have occasionally found themselves performing impromptu talks when many hospital workers express an interest in Alcor. Taking the time to inform these individuals about cryonics and the unusual way they can help their patient is rarely a waste of time, and it can be quite invigorating to present a neat idea to a receptive group of people.

Some terminal patients are discharged from the hospital and placed into home hospice care. Home care is generally limited to patients with a terminal illness who wish to die at home. Performing a transport from an Alcor member's home can be challenging.

All of the above considerations apply in these cases as well. The question of prompt pronouncement becomes more critical, as in some states hospice nurses may pronounce legal death. In others, the patient's physician must pronounce. Whoever declares legal death, the patient's physician must sign the death certificate. Without a signed death certificate, no patient may be transported anywhere. (Certified copies are obtained later.)

Emergency Notification

In cases where little advance notice is available, there will be little time to negotiate contracts or cooperation. The quality of these transports is often determined by the caliber of people the team encounters, and the speed with which the team members and equipment arrive. Depending on how long it takes to obtain custody of the patient, the stabilization protocol may be modified.

If there is significant delay before the team can begin, oxygen may not be used at all. Reintroducing oxygen to a physiology which has used all of its oxygen supplies and is consuming alternative forms of energy causes additional damage. Some of this "reperfusion injury" may be avoided if the patient is not oxygenated during stabilization. This is generally only for patients who have experienced more than an hour without heartbeat or breathing before stabilization procedures are started.

If the delays are extreme (several hours), it may not be possible to replace the patient's blood with an organ preservation solution before shipment. Decisions of this nature are made by the transport team leader in consultation with Alcor Headquarters.

Sudden Death

Sudden deaths are rare, but they do occur. When they do, members of the transport team often will interface with a coroner or medical examiner, and the patient risks autopsy. Currently, five states (New York, California, Rhode Island, New Jersey, and Ohio) allow an individual to state his objection to being autopsied by signing a Religious Objection to Autopsy, and there is no requirement to state the specific objection. Maryland also has a weaker, but still useful, version of these statutes.

There are some cases where an autopsy is required by law, and the religious objection form will not prevent the dissection. The Centers for Disease Control (headquartered in Atlanta, Georgia) have the authority to require an autopsy for all patients dying from specific contagious illnesses. This has never happened to a cryonic suspension patient (to the best of my knowledge) and if it ever does, the patient will probably be fortunate if any portion of their brain is suspended. Local coroners have also been known to conduct independent investigations into disease. In one Florida county, the coroner stated his intention to autopsy every person dying of AIDS in his county. (He later softened his position on this somewhat, after local Alcor members met with him to discuss the matter.)

Autopsies may sometimes be unavoidable, but there are things which may be done to minimize the damage to the patient. Transport team members should try to have the scope of an autopsy limited to the minimum dissection necessary to determine the cause of death. The pathologist may be able to avoid damaging the brain and still fulfill the requirements of the investigation. An attempt should be made to have the autopsy performed right away. If the patient dies late in the afternoon, and no autopsies are scheduled until the next morning, the transport team leader may offer to compensate the county for any overtime involved, if the autopsy is performed immediately. If there will be a delay, the patient should be kept in a morgue cooler at temperatures above 0°C to prevent the tissues from freezing. Patients who are autopsied almost never receive a washout or cryoprotective perfusion.

Once the autopsy is complete, the transport team leader must verify that all of the organs are intact or have been placed with the patient. Then the patient is shipped to Alcor.

Patient Acquisition

The legal status of cryonics is somewhat ambiguous. Because our patients have been declared legally dead, the custody of their human remains may be transferred to Alcor via the Uniform Anatomical Gift Act; but little legislation exists in this country which deals specifically with cryonics (see "The Legal Status of Cryonics" by Steve Bridge, *Cryonics*, 1st Qtr, 1995).

Personnel in the field will work with Alcor Headquarters to secure the release of the patient. Alcor will deliver copies of the patient's paperwork to the hospital and mortuary, as the situation merits. These legal documents consist of the *Cryonic Suspension Agreement, the Authorization for Anatomical Donation, the Consent for Cryonic Suspension,* and powers of attorney for health care or *Relative's Affidavits.*

The staff at Alcor Headquarters is available to provide documentation of the patient's intent, to discuss cryonics procedures with hospital personnel (over the phone), and to provide general support for the team members in the field. Copies of relevant court decisions are available, if the circumstances merit a firmer approach during negotiations. Additional letters have been generated for hospital administrators who are unfamiliar with cryonics, and these letters are sent from Alcor Headquarters after they've been modified for the situation. They may also be sent out in advance of a patient's admission to the hospital.

In some suspensions, little documentation has been needed except for the patient's legal paperwork. If a physician and hospital choose to cooperate with Alcor personnel, they may improve the patient's chances for a quality transport.

A physician has the opportunity to prescribe medications for a patient who is legally alive, and there are a few which have been shown to improve later cryoprotective perfusion if administered before pronouncement. Some of them are also in Alcor's stabilization protocol. If these items will not interfere or react with the medications currently being taken, a physician might prescribe vitamins C and E, selenium, magnesium, and beta carotene. These are powerful anti-oxidants which help to reduce the damage caused by inadequate tissue oxygenation. Dilantin is also recommended as a calcium channel blocker. Cimetadine hydrochloride (Tagamet) will reduce the accumulation of stomach acid. Many patients have experienced gastric bleeding during stabilization, and have lost large volumes of fluid through holes in the stomach lining. This damage may be mitigated by the administration of Tagamet within the hours before pronouncement. Prior to pronouncement, these medications may be administered only by conventional medical personnel acting under a physician's orders. Premedicating a patient requires a cooperating physician and a patient willing to request the assistance, and generally, is one of the last topics broached by transport team members when discussing the prompt release of the patient.

Once the patient is released to Alcor personnel after pronouncement, the stabilization may begin.

Stabilization

At the earliest possible moment after pronouncement, transport team members will initiate the stabilization protocol. First, the patient is transferred to the portable ice bath and surrounded on all sides with crushed or cubed ice. Some water may be added to the bath if the team has access to a circulating pump and tubing. This device is called a "squid" and makes it possible to cool the patient using circulating ice-water, which cools much faster than simply surrounding the patient in ice.

Once the patient has been transferred to the portable ice bath, a mechanical CPS device (such as the Michigan Instruments Heart-Lung Resuscitator) is placed and started. This will restore circulation. An airway is placed to restore respiration, and IV medications are administered to combat the damage of oxygen deprivation and hypothermia. Ideally, all of this is done and documented in the transport notes before the patient leaves the hospital premises. As a minimum, the patient should be packed in ice and administered heparin (an anticoagulant), which should be circulated for 5-10 minutes using conventional manual cardiopulmonary resuscitation.

A local patient may be brought directly to the Alcor facility, with all of the stabilization procedures (except the washout) being performed in the ambulance. Whether the organ preservation solution will then be administered before cryoprotective perfusion begins depends upon the readiness of the perfusate. This perfusate takes many hours to prepare in sufficient quantity for a cryonic suspension (although we are working on shortening this procedure), and if mixing the perfusate is expected to take longer than the open-heart surgery, the washout may be performed while the perfusion preparations are completed.

Once released from the hospital, a remote patient will be transported to the cooperating funeral home. There, the blood replacement surgery will begin, and the patient's blood will be replaced with an organ preservation solution through the femoral artery and vein. During the blood replacement, a heat-exchanger will cool the fluids being introduced, and the patient's core temperature will drop to about 5°C.

After the washout is complete, the patient must be packed for shipment to Alcor. This usually involves Alcor's custom-engineered water-tight container. This is sent out as part of the central remote kit, and its arrival might delay the shipment of a patient to Alcor if there was little or no advance notice of the suspension. A conventional mortuary shipping container also may be modified to hold the patient and ice. The patient should be placed inside a body bag and completely surrounded by sealed bags of ice. (Ziploc bags work well.) Containers carrying human remains must not leak, or they will be removed from the commercial carrier and quarantined until the coroner has an opportunity to inspect them.

Once the patient is packed for shipment, the necessary transit paperwork has been prepared, the operating theater has been cleaned, and the mortician paid, the patient may be taken to the airport for transport. A cooperative mortician will be able to recommend commercial carriers and will have a familiarity with the shipping requirements; he may even be willing to make all of the necessary arrangements and should also provide transportation for the patient to the airport. Alcor should be kept apprised of progress, since we have often been able to speed arrangements through the local airline offices.

Transport

Shipping a patient should be the easiest aspect of the operation, but there are still occasional snags. The patient should be placed onto a direct flight to Phoenix, if possible, and care should be taken when selecting an airline and flight path. Some airlines advertise their flights as direct, when in fact, the plane will make additional stops before it reaches its ultimate destination. Avoid these flights if possible (choose nonstop) to minimize delays in transport time.

Delays can be expected before the patient is loaded onto the aircraft. Most commercial airlines require that cargo be taken to the loading dock at least four hours before flight time. In the past, we have found a few airlines (like America West) to be especially cooperative, and they have waived this requirement for our suspension patient. Such cooperation has been unusual, though, and should not be expected or planned for during a transport.

At least one transport team member should be on the same flight as the patient and should have copies of all relevant transport permits and the death certificate. All of the transport equipment should also be shipped. Medication kits and other consumables are inventoried and replaced at Alcor Headquarters before the remote kits may be redeployed.

Conclusion

Of course, even after all of this has been accomplished, the actual suspension has still not begun. But it may be clearer to you now why my overwhelming emotion is relief when I finally arrive at the Alcor facility with each new patient. There are many, many variables affecting the quality of a stabilization and transport, several of which are completely out of the hands of Alcor personnel. Once those variables can no longer prevent a successful cryonic suspension, the patient's future is a little more secure.

Please remember that much of the groundwork for a successful transport can be done in advance by local cryonicists. Many of you live in areas which Alcor has not had the time or opportunity to include in its transport preparedness infrastructure. You can help us change this, and though it will certainly save Alcor personnel a major headache if you do, the primary beneficiary is you.

Anyone wishing to discuss local preparedness should contact me at Alcor for more information.

My thanks to Ralph Whelan for his invaluable assistance in the preparation of this article. ■

Cardiopulmonary Support in Cryonics: The Significance of Legal Death in Cryonics

By Brian Wowk, Ph.D.

Published on Alcor's website, October, 2003

"Cardiac death isn't a diagnosis of death, it is a prognosis of death."

David Crippen, MD, FCCM
Department of Critical Care Medicine
University of Pittsburgh Medical Center
(private correspondence with the author)

The common belief that life and death are simple binary states misleads people into thinking that cryonics practiced after legal death is a hopeless enterprise, almost by definition. It is not realized that legal death is a statement of prognosis more than a statement of condition. The biological state of a patient declared legally dead can be highly variable. It can range from fully alive (but brain dead) when an organ donor is maintained on life support, to alive (but dying) when the heart of a terminally-ill patient stops beating, to completely dead when a decomposed body is found. Because of this complexity, cryonics cannot be dismissed solely based on a legal pronouncement of death. The biological circumstances of the pronouncement and subsequent cryonics care must be considered.

Perhaps the most misunderstood aspect of cryonics is that cryonics procedures can, in fact, be legally done on patients that are still biologically viable. For terminal patients with DNR ("Do Not Resuscitate") orders on their chart, legal death is determined when a qualified medical authority pronounces death based on cardiopulmonary arrest. In other words, the patient is legally dead when their heart stops beating. However, CPR (cardiopulmonary resuscitation) can maintain life when the heart is stopped if done promptly. "Do Not Resuscitate" orders are necessary precisely because such heroics would inappropriately extend the dying process if implemented in a conventional medical setting. In the context of cryonics, though, DNR status allows a cryonics team to use resuscitation techniques to keep the brain viable despite occurrence of legal death.

The objective of initial stabilization in cryonics is resuscitation of the patient in all respects except cardiac resuscitation. Within the first couple of minutes after cardiac arrest, vigorous CPR is begun on the patient using a device called a heart-lung-resuscitator (HLR). This is essentially a mechanical CPR machine that compresses the chest more effectively than human hands, and ventilates the patient with 100% oxygen. Despite continued cardiac arrest, breathing and circulation can be partially restored. Anesthetic drugs are used to reduce brain oxygen requirements and ensure that the patient remains unconscious. Rapid cooling also further reduces brain oxygen requirements.

Best Case Scenario

How viable is a cryonics patient during stabilization? Perhaps the most successful cryonics stabilization documented to date was that of CryoCare patient James Gallagher in 1995. Mr. Gallagher was a cancer patient who suffered cardiac arrest in his home under supervision of his family and personal physician after voluntary discontinuation of oxygen therapy. When his heart stopped beating, his physician pronounced legal death, and the cryonics transport team waiting in an ambulance outside began their work. The BioPreservation, Inc., team used a custom-modified Michigan Instruments HLR that was capable of delivering simultaneous Active-Compression-Decompression-High-Impulse CPR (ACDC-HICPR). HLR support was begun three minutes after cardiac arrest, and an arterial oxygen saturation over 90% was maintained for the next two hours until external life support with a blood pump and oxygenator was begun. This level of blood oxygenation is the same as that experienced by passengers in commercial airliners at cabin altitudes near 8000 feet, and it is certainly sufficient to maintain life. The blood gases, electrolytes, enzymes, and other clinical laboratory parameters of this patient have been published,[1] and establish that this legally deceased patient was biologically viable during the initial cooling phase of his cryopreservation.

The Value of Cooling

Cryopatients must be cooled during stabilization before blood substitution and perfusion with cryoprotectants (anti-freeze compounds) can begin. Fortunately, prompt cooling following cardiac arrest is known to be profoundly protective of the brain. First Aid courses teach that the brain begins to die four minutes after the heart stops. However, research has shown that resuscitation without brain injury is possible after up to ten minutes of cardiac arrest (plus another ten minutes of low flow CPR) if

---

1   *CryoCare Report,* January, 1996, "Cryopreservation of James Gallagher." See also *BPI Tech Brief* #18 Part II.

cooling is started at the same time as CPR.[2]

The neuroprotective effects of cooling mean that not only can cryopatients be kept biologically viable during stabilization, but they can be kept viable with cardiopulmonary support that is started later and less efficiently than would ordinarily be the case. Even ordinary high impulse CPR (the type of CPR delivered by an off-the-shelf Michigan Instruments HLR) is probably adequate to maintain neurological viability of cryopatients during stabilization and cooling given the combined metabolism-reducing effects of cold and anesthesia. The trickle flows of manual CPR can keep a brain alive at normal temperatures for up to ten minutes.[3] The combination of cooling, drugs, and high impulse mechanical CPR no doubt extend this time even longer.

The purpose of CPR in cryonics is to act as a bridge until cardiopulmonary bypass (heart-lung machine) support can be established, in which an external blood pump and oxygenator take the place of the patient's heart and lungs. Under good conditions, the surgery to achieve this can be accomplished in less than an hour. Trained personnel and specialized equipment can initiate cardiopulmonary bypass even faster. In fact emergency cardiopulmonary bypass was recently used with good success in conjunction with CPR on out-of-hospital cardiac arrest patients in Japan.[4]

The very low temperatures (<10°C) reached by cryopatients before cryoprotectant perfusion are also consistent with new approaches being explored by mainstream medicine for stabilizing and recovering patients after cardiac arrest due to exsanguinating trauma.[5] In fact, in the 1980s Alcor president Michael Darwin and Jerry Leaf (vice-president) performed a pioneering series of experiments[6,7,8] in which dogs were blood-substituted and cooled to +4°C for four hours without heartbeat or breathing, and then recovered without neurological damage. This amazing work was conducted explicitly to verify that cryonics procedures as then conducted by Alcor were in principle reversible right up to the point of cryoprotective perfusion.

---

2   *Critical Care Medicine* 19, 1991, 379-389 "Mild hypothermic cardiopulmonary resuscitation improves outcome after prolonged cardiac arrest in dogs" Sterz F, Safar P, Tisherman S, Radovsky A, Kuboyama K, Oku K.

3   *American Journal of Emergency Medicine* 3, 1985, 114-119 "Survival of out-of-hospital cardiac arrest with early initiation of cardiopulmonary resuscitation" Cummins RO, Eisenberg MS, Hallstrom AP, Litwin PE.

4   *Journal of the American College of Cardiology* 36, 2000, 776-783 "Cardiopulmonary cerebral resuscitation using emergency cardiopulmonary bypass, coronary reperfusion therapy and mild hypothermia in patients with cardiac arrest outside the hospital." Nagao K, Hayashi N, Kanmatsuse K, Arima K, Ohtsuki J, Kikushima K, Watanabe I.

5   *Critical Care Medicine* 28, 2000, N214-N218 "Suspended animation for delayed resuscitation from prolonged cardiac arrest that is unresuscitable by standard cardiopulmonary-cerebral resuscitation." Safar P, Tisherman SA, Behringer W, Capone A, Prueckner S, Radovsky A, Stezoski WS, Woods RJ.

6   *Cryonics Magazine,* November, 1984.

7   *Cryonics Magazine,* February, 1985.

8   *Cryonics Magazine,* March, 1985.

Importance of Good CPR

The maximum benefits of post-cardiac arrest cooling are seen when cooling occurs rapidly after CPR is begun. The most rapid way to cool a body is to use circulating blood as the cooling medium. The more rapidly blood is circulated (carrying heat from inside the body to skin cooled by ice) the more rapidly the body will cool. This makes effective CPR doubly important to cryonics: It reduces brain injury caused by inadequate blood flow, and enhances the most powerful injury protection mechanism (cooling).

The effect of good CPR on cooling is most vividly illustrated by the cooling rate achieved in the case of cryopatient James Gallagher (the "best case scenario" patient already discussed). The combination of ACDC-HICPR and colonic and peritoneal lavage with ice-cold saline achieved a cooling rate of over 1°C per minute during the first ten minutes of CPR, which is three times greater than the fastest cooling rate previously observed in a cryopatient.

Recently a new technology for rapidly cooling resuscitated cardiac arrest victims has been developed by Mike Darwin and Steve Harris that involves cold fluorocarbon lung lavage.[9,10] By performing heat exchange through the lungs rather than skin, this simple and convenient technology could remove the need for patient ice baths in cryonics. However, this technology also critically depends on good blood circulation for effectiveness.

The Importance of Feedback

Because the cryogenic (below freezing) phase of cryonics is still unperfected and dependent upon future technology for reversal, there is an ever-present temptation to pass off problems to the future for solution. What has historically distinguished Alcor from other cryonics organizations, and the legacy established by Leaf and Darwin, is a resistance to this temptation. In practice, this means aggressive use of existing and emerging technologies for post-cardiac arrest life support.

Maintaining neurological viability up to the late stages of cryoprotective perfusion improves feedback, chances of success, and medical credibility of the whole enterprise. By imposing real-time feedback with parameters such as blood oxygenation, end-tidal CO2, and pH, quality control is maintained. By keeping procedures reversible for as long as possible, the least speculative and most conservative course is being pursued, thereby increasing the chance of success. And the future road to true suspended animation is left clear and paved.

---

9   *Discover Magazine,* October, 2001, "Here, Breathe This Liquid"

10   *Resuscitation* 50, 2001, 89-204 "Rapid (0.5°C/min) minimally invasive induction of hypothermia using cold perfluorochemical lung lavage in dogs" Harris SB, Darwin, MG, Russell SR, O'Farrell JM, Fletcher M, Wowk B.

Death as a Cultural Obstacle

Alcor activist Thomas Donaldson frequently points out that suspended animation and cryonics are not the same thing. There will always be patients who are so badly injured that they are irreversibly "dead" to the medicine of their time, regardless of resuscitation efforts. Donaldson and others argue that these patients should be preserved anyway because future technology may still be able to recover them. In other words, short of total destruction, you can't be sure what the future definition of "death" will be, so the conservative course of action is to preserve all "dead" patients. This moral argument is perhaps the most general meaning of the term "cryonics."

While the cryonics argument may be noble, many people are unreceptive to this argument based on cost/benefit grounds. Even more people are unreceptive on religious grounds. The vast majority of people will not take cryonics or suspended animation seriously unless it is done before death.

But does death always matter? In cases where death is expected, there need be no biological difference between cryonics implemented before legal death or immediately after if proper procedures are used. For such cases, the occurrence of legal death is a purely cultural issue. ■

Rapid Stabilization in Human Cryopreservation

By Aschwin de Wolf

Alcor website, September 04, 2007

This article was written in 2006 for the second Immortality Institute anthology on life extension, which was never completed. A revised version of the article was published on the Alcor Life Extension Foundation website.

The goal of stabilization in human cryopreservation is to keep the brain viable by contemporary medical criteria *after the patient has been pronounced legally dead. The importance of stabilization does not only reflect a desire to protect the patient from injury after pronouncement; successful stabilization may also improve the chance of successful cryoprotection. Stabilization of the patient includes cardiopulmonary support, combinational pharmacology, rapid induction of hypothermia, and substitution of the blood with an organ preservation solution. A basic introduction to the pathophysiology of cerebral ischemia is presented, and different modalities of intervention are reviewed. Conceptual issues surrounding the concept of brain viability are also discussed. The article concludes by identifying some weak links and unknowns in current stabilization procedures and proposing future research objectives.*

Introduction

The objective of human cryopreservation (or cryonics) is to use cryogenic temperatures to preserve patients that are pronounced dead by today's medical criteria with the possibility that future medical technology may be able to treat them. Technical objections to the science of human cryopreservation fall broadly into two categories: (1) that freezing humans causes ice formation that destroys cells; and (2) that patients who present for cryonics are dead.

Freezing Damage

Historically, advocates of human cryopreservation have responded to the freezing damage objection by pointing out that the argument that freezing results in massive intracellular ice formation, which causes cells to rupture, is a gross oversimplification of what currently is known about freezing damage in biological systems [1]. Cryoprotectants such as glycerol and DMSO, which are routinely used to preserve cells at cryogenic temperatures, also reduce ice formation in complex organs and cryonics patients. And even if some freezing damage remained unavoidable and irreparable by contemporary medical technology, it might be reparable with more advanced technology. As long as ice damage is not of such a nature that the structural biochemical basis of identity and memory can no longer be deduced, the only technical limitation to resuscitation is the feasibility of cellular repair by molecular machines [2].

One claim that advocates of human cryopreservation couldn't make, however, is that resuscitation of patients in human cryopreservation would not require any kind of repair at all. A fair degree of technological optimism has therefore always been a fundamental element of cryonics. The situation improved again at the dawn of the 21st century when the Alcor Life Extension Foundation started offering cryopreservation by means of vitrification. Instead of reducing ice formation by perfusing a patient with high concentrations of glycerol, new cryoprotectants (B2C and M22) were introduced that prevent ice formation altogether. For the first time good ice-free structural preservation was shown to be possible in some tissues, including the brain.

The current challenge is to achieve this degree of preservation without compromising cellular viability or causing fracturing during cryogenic cooldown. The paradigm shift from mitigating ice damage to designing vitrification agents that further reduce toxicity is of such a nature that the possibility of reversible vitrification of humans merits serious scientific debate.

Irreversible Death

The prospect of reversible vitrification would eliminate the freezing damage objection to human cryopreservation, but still would leave the second objection – that cryonics patients are dead – unaddressed. Currently all patients who present for human cryopreservation have been pronounced *legally dead*. How can legal pronouncement of death be reconciled with the prospect of future resuscitation?

The answer to this question revolves around the fact that most people who are currently pronounced dead still possess the neural biochemistry that constitutes identity and memory. Even in the case of advanced Alzheimer's disease, a person is ultimately not declared dead *because* of the loss of personhood, but as a consequence of secondary whole brain death or cardiac and respiratory arrest. In essence, today's medicine routinely prolongs life while allowing destruction of the *person* but pronounces death, using cardiac criteria, *without loss of personhood*.

Advocates of human cryopreservation argue that long term preservation of a terminally ill person is possible if the patient is maintained at cryogenic temperatures (currently at -196 degrees Celsius). This low temperature form of critical care allows a terminally ill patient to reach a time when medical technologies may be available for effective treatment. As a consequence, minimizing brain injury during this transition from terminal illness to cryogenic temperatures is of utmost importance.

Although many pathophysiological events occur within minutes of cessation of blood flow (see below), necrosis of brain cells is a much more time-consuming affair and research on global permanent ischemia indicates this process may take 9-24 hours at room temperature. The claim that the brain, or the most vulnerable parts of the brain, cannot tolerate interruptions of blood flow in excess of 5 minutes does not refer to immediate destruction of brain cells but to the clinical observation that even short interruptions of oxygen and glucose to the brain can produce irreversible death of some brain cells (such as the CA1 neurons of the hippocampus) *after resuscitation*. Because normothermic resuscitation of the patient is not the objective of cryonics procedures, this observation is largely irrelevant to typical cryonics patients. Long term care at cryogenic temperatures may even offer some patients a better chance of preserving personhood than contemporary medical technologies can offer after successful resuscitation.

The objective of stabilization in human cryopreservation, therefore, is to keep the brain viable *by contemporary medical criteria* after the patient has been pronounced legally dead [3]. Several reasons to strive for this goal have been proposed by cryonics authors.

The most fundamental reason to keep the brain viable by means of stabilization is that we do not completely understand to what extent a patient can sustain brain injury without destroying identity- and memory-relevant information, even allowing for sophisticated future molecular repair technologies. The idea of preserving viability by contemporary medical criteria is therefore perceived to reflect a prudent and *conservative* approach.

Assuming that the patient does not suffer from a serious identity- and memory-compromising disease, by preserving the brain in the state it was in immediately before cardiac arrest, the "only" obstacle to future resuscitation is a cure for the illness that interfered with the patient's ability to function as an integrated biological system. For many patients this will also depend upon significant scientific progress in halting, or even reversing, the aging process itself to ensure that a patient will not go through endless futile cycles of pronouncement of legal death, cryopreservation, and resuscitation.

Another important reason to maintain the brain in a viable state through the cryopreservation process is that, even if long periods of warm cerebral ischemia and freezing-induced cell damage are compatible with future resuscitation, resuscitation might be a more costly and time consuming effort in cases where damage is most severe. This will make the patient more vulnerable to social and political threats to his survival. All other things being equal, the expected resuscitation attempts of patients in cryostasis will likely have the character of "best in, first out; worst in, last out."

Although one might expect a strong correlation between this principle and "first in, last out; last in, first out," it should be kept in mind that the state of the art in stabilization and cryoprotection technologies is only one element that determines the quality of patient care. Indeed, though technological capability is paramount, it currently competes with more mundane issues such as rapid access to the patient, the risk of autopsy, hostile family members, and the quality of the personnel providing care.

Stabilization of the patient requires immediate intervention in order to meet the goal of brain viability. To this purpose providers of human cryopreservation deploy a standby team to ensure that knowledgeable and experienced cryonics technicians will be at the bedside of the patient at the moment of pronouncement of legal death.

To stabilize the patient, the team employs three kinds of medical interventions. First, blood circulation and oxygenation are restored to supply oxygen and nutrients to energy-deprived cells. Second, medications are administered to improve (cerebral) blood flow, prevent blood coagulation, and mitigate cerebral ischemia. Third, hypothermia is induced to reduce metabolic rate. If standby and stabilization are performed in a remote location, the patient's blood is washed out and replaced with an organ preservation solution to prevent cold-induced agglutination (clumping) of red blood cells, blood coagulation during transport, and to provide metabolic support for the cells.

The challenge of securing brain viability after pronouncement of death demands a thorough understanding of the mechanisms of cerebral ischemia. If our understanding of the biochemical cascade that follows reduced or no blood flow enables us to maintain viability, let alone significantly extend the window of opportunity to secure this aim, the objection that human cryopreservation patients are irreversibly dead can be countered.

Cerebral Ischemia

Cardiac arrest produces a state of global ischemia characterized by lack of blood flow to the brain and other vital organs. The length of time humans can withstand normothermic cardiac arrest without neurological injury after resuscitation is a complicated question; but in the absence of sophisticated resuscitation technologies, the limit is currently assumed to be around five minutes. A fundamental question in resuscitation science is whether this window of opportunity can be extended.

Although the adult human brain accounts for only 2% of total body mass it accounts for about 20-25% of total oxygen consumption. A significant amount of this energy is expended to maintain ion gradients across cell membranes. Because the amount of oxygen and glycogen that is stored in the brain is extremely limited, sudden loss of oxygen produces unconsciousness in less than 10 seconds, and a flat EEG in about 20 seconds. The first response of the brain is to switch from oxygen-based aerobic metabolism to glucose-based anaerobic metabolism, producing lactic acid in the process. Within about 4-6 minutes neurons completely run out of energy, setting in motion a complex multi-factorial biochemical cascade.

When brain cells run out of energy, membrane-bound ion pumps fail to maintain cellular homeostasis. Potassium leaves the cell and sodium and calcium enter the cell in unphysiological concentrations. Cytosolic calcium concentrations are further increased by release of calcium from intracellular calcium stores (e.g., the endoplasmic reticulum and mitochondria). This marked increase of cytosolic calcium overwhelms the ability of cells to buffer and sequester excess calcium, activating multiple biochemical pathways implicated in neuronal injury. The loss of physiological ion gradients across cell membranes also causes cytosolic edema as a result of a net influx of water.

Depolarization and calcium overload of brain cells triggers the release of massive amounts of the excitatory amino acid glutamate in the extracellular space. Without energy-dependent presynaptic glutamate reuptake, excitatory amino acid receptors are continually activated, leading to a sustained increase in cytosolic calcium. This again releases more glutamate into the extracellular space, triggering a positive feedback loop of excitotoxity-induced calcium overload. The role of calcium overload and excitotoxic amino acid neurotransmitter release in neural death is consistent with the fact that the brain cells that are most vulnerable to cerebral ischemia (such as the hippocampal CA1 neurons) have a relatively large number of excitatory amino acid receptors and calcium channels.

Intracellular calcium overload also activates calcium-dependent enzymes that break down membrane lipids and proteins, activate apoptosis (controlled cell death), and synthesize nitric oxide. Nitric oxide can be either beneficial or deleterious in ischemia, depending on its specific isoform. During ischemia and reperfusion, nitric oxide combines with superoxide to produce the harmful nitrogen radical peroxynitrite. Peroxynitrite and oxygen-derived radicals damage DNA, overactivating the nuclear DNA repair enzyme poly(ADP-Ribose) polymerase (PARP). Upon reperfusion, PARP will rapidly deplete vital energy sources for cell metabolism. Cardiac arrest-induced hypercoagulability and inflammation further contribute to neural injury by compromising microcirculation after reperfusion, resulting in the so called "no-reflow" phenomenon.

In the context of human cryopreservation it is important to understand the importance of optimum (micro) circulation. Securing brain viability is not the only reason for maintaining circulation during stabilization; long periods of warm ischemia with associated clotting and compromised cerebral circulation may frustrate subsequent attempts to adequately circulate the vitrification agent in the brain. As a consequence, cryoprotective perfusion may have to be abandoned early and parts of the brain will suffer ice formation. This relationship between mitigating cerebral ischemia and achieving optimum perfusion of the brain is another important reason for securing brain viability by contemporary medical criteria.

Although our understanding of the cellular pathophysiology of cerebral ischemia is still incomplete, it is clear that after the window of opportunity for securing brain viability by conventional resuscitation has closed, only combination treatment may achieve this goal. This conclusion can be derived from the fact that, further downstream in the ischemic cascade, just restoring adequate blood flow will not automatically reverse all the biochemical pathways that are activated by energy depletion of the cells. For this reason restoring adequate cerebral blood flow by cardiopulmonary support is only one form of treatment employed in human cryopreservation.

Cardiopulmonary Support
Unless access to the patient is significantly delayed, the first priority is to intervene in the ischemic cascade as early as possible. Because the most fundamental and upstream event is lack of blood circulation and oxygen, the importance of restoring blood circulation and oxygenation cannot be understated. In human cryopreservation this is called cardiopulmonary *support* because the goal is not to resuscitate but to *stabilize* the patient. Cardiopulmonary support is not only important to provide energy to the patient, it is also necessary to distribute medications and enhance surface cooling.

The ideal form of cardiopulmonary support would be to restart blood circulation using extracorporeal bypass to ensure adequate blood flow. Because this requires invasive surgery to obtain direct access to the circulatory system, this is not an option for *immediate* intervention. The second best option would be to perform open heart cardiac massage. This is not only an invasive procedure, but also would create a serious public relations issue in a hospital or hospice setting. Therefore, the preferred method of initial cardiopulmonary support in human cryopreservation is external cardiac massage using a mechanical device.

There are many advantages to using a mechanical device to do chest compressions and ventilations. Once set up, it frees team members to attend to other important tasks such as administering medications, drawing blood samples, and data acquisition. This is especially beneficial in situations where the number of team members is limited. It also prevents fatigue and the associated decline in performance and consistency of manual compressions. In cryonics, cardiopulmonary support for more than an hour is not uncommon. Another advantage is that if the device is used in combination with a portable ice bath, chest compressions can continue during transport of the patient from one location to another. But the most important advantage of mechanical cardiopulmonary support is that adequate cerebral perfusion may require CPS techniques that are beyond the motor skills of even the finest paramedics.

The most basic form of mechanical cardiopulmonary support is a pneumatic piston-driven device that delivers chest compressions and ventilations at a consistent depth and rate. The most popular device in human cryopreservation has been the Michigan Instruments "Thumper." The Thumper allows for a wide range of body sizes and compression depth and, in some models, has the option to do either continuous compression or compression and ventilations. The base of the Thumper slides onto a backboard under the patient and conversion from manual to mechanical CPS can be achieved within 30 seconds without interruption of chest compressions. A custom-made version of the Thumper has been produced that can be mounted on both sides of a portable ice bath, so that it can be used conveniently while the patient is partially immersed in melting ice.

In the mid 1980s a modality of delivering chest compressions was introduced that used high acceleration on the downstroke with the goal of improving forward blood flow. This technique, called high impulse CPR (HI-CPR), has received mixed reviews in peer reviewed literature to date [4]. A more widely adopted refinement of conventional CPR has been active compression-decompression CPR (ACD-CPR). During ACD-CPR a suction cup is used to actively compress and decompress the chest. Venous return to the heart (cardiac preload) is enhanced by pulling up the chest during the recoil phase. This technique can be performed either using a manual suction cup or by modifying an existing mechanical device. In the mid 1990s, a custom-designed Michigan Instruments Thumper combining high impulse and active compression and decompression was introduced to the field of human cryopreservation by cryonics researcher Michael Darwin. Like HI-CPR, ACD-CPR has received mixed reviews in peer reviewed literature [5]. To date no ACD-CPR devices have been FDA-approved in the United States for use in resuscitation. Because human cryopreservation procedures can only start after pronouncement of legal death, this is an example where cryonics patients can benefit from a technology that is not available to the general public.

Another enhancement of CPS that optimizes cardiac preload is the use of an inspiratory impedance threshold valve. The valve is placed between the airway of the patient and the oxygen source and prevents air from entering the patient during the recoil phase of chest compressions. As a result, intrathoracic pressure is reduced, improving venous return to the heart. In the late 1990s Michael Darwin recognized the potential value of this mechanism, and built the first prototype for use in human cryopreservation. In 2005, two leading human cryopreservation service providers adopted the first commercially available impedance valve as a part of their stabilization protocols. Positive findings using this airway adjunct in conventional CPR and in conjunction with ACD-CPR culminated in a recommendation of the impedance valve in the American Heart Association's 2005 guidelines for cardiopulmonary resuscitation.

The desirability and optimum rate of ventilations during CPR has been a much debated topic in emergency medicine. There is a growing consensus that frequent interruption of chest compressions for ventilations may do more harm than good. Especially in one-person CPR, interruption of chest compressions to give ventilations significantly reduces coronary perfusion pressure and reduces overall efficiency of cardiopulmonary resuscitation. Charles Babbs et al., assuming realistic parameters of lay person performance, evaluated a wide range of different compression to ventilation ratios using Monte Carlo simulations, and found that a ratio of 60:2 produces maximum oxygen delivery [6]. In 2005 the American Heart Association announced a change from 2 ventilations for 15 chest compressions to 2 ventilations for 30 chest compressions for adult CPR.

As in conventional cardiopulmonary resuscitation, the patient can be ventilated by either manual or mechanical means. Airway access can be established by conventional emergency medicine techniques ranging from endotracheal intubation, in which a tube is placed directly in the trachea, to more invasive techniques like a tracheotomy, in which a surgical incision is made to access the trachea. Some cryonics organizations prefer the use of a dual-lumen intubation device called the Combitube because it is easier to place, and the other lumen can be used to administer Maalox to neutralize gastric hydrochloric acid.

Because of pre-mortem hypoxia and post-arrest ischemia, the question whether to oxygenate the patient or not is a complicated issue. During the early stages of the ischemic insult, oxygenation of the patient provides metabolic support. However, if rapid intervention does not take place, positive pressure ventilations with 100% oxygen further downstream in the cascade may produce more harm than good by generating oxidative stress. On the other hand, human cryopreservation medications generally include a variety of antioxidants and free radical scavengers, raising the issue whether administration of these medications can offset longer durations of cerebral ischemia. At any rate, it is undesirable to ventilate more than necessary. Ventilation volumes and ratios need to be adjusted for induction of hypothermia. Circulating free radical scavengers (and anti-inflammatory medications) *prior* to initiating ventilations or just using room air may be other modalities worth investigation.

Stabilization Medications

Medications and fluids are administered in human cryopreservation to accomplish different objectives. Vasoactive medications and fluids are given to enhance cardiopulmonary support by supporting blood pressure and hydrating the patient.

Anticoagulants, fibrinolytics, and antiplatelet agents are given to dissolve existing blood clots and keep the circulatory system open. Neuroprotective agents that intervene in different parts of the ischemic-reperfusion cascade are given as well. Some of the core medications of stabilization pharmacology are reviewed here.

The first medication administered is the general anaesthetic propofol. Propofol is a rapidly acting lipid soluble intravenous anaesthetic that enhances inhibitory synaptic transmission in the brain. Propofol is given for two reasons. The main reason is to prevent the patient regaining consciousness after legal death has been pronounced. Second, propofol reduces metabolic demand in the brain. Propofol has antioxidant and free radical scavenging properties, and there is also evidence that propofol delays the onset of excitotoxic neuronal death and reduces peroxynitrite mediated apoptosis [7]. The major disadvantage of propofol, however, is a reduction in blood pressure.

Ideally, vasopressors such as epinephrine and vasopressin are immediately administered to selectively increase blood flow to the core of the body and the brain. Another vasoactive medication is *S-methylthiourea* (SMT), an inducible nitric oxide synthase (iNOS) inhibitor. *SMT* is primarily used to mitigate the production of inducible nitric oxide and associated formation of peroxynitrite. *SMT* increases mean arterial pressure (MAP).

Premortem pathology, post-ischemic inflammation, and cardiac arrest-induced blood stasis combine to produce hypercoagulability, which frustrates attempts to circulate medications and subsequent cryoprotection of the brain. A number of medications are administered to prevent and reverse this situation such as the anticoagulant *heparin*, the fibrinolytic *streptokinase*, and the antiplatelet agent *aspirin*. A volume expander like *Dextran-40* is given to improve cerebral microcirculation by hemodilution. *Dextran-40* has also been reported to mitigate cold-induced clumping of red blood cells, a problem that is more serious in human cryopreservation than conventional medicine because of the central importance of inducing deep hypothermia during stabilization procedures.

Medications to mitigate cerebral ischemia have always been a cornerstone of human cryopreservation stabilization pharmacology, ranging from interventions to support cell metabolism to molecules that inhibit specific parts of the ischemic cascade. Current stabilization protocol includes a cocktail of antioxidants and free radical scavengers including *vitamin E, melatonin,* and *alpha-phenyl-tert-butyl nitrone (PBN),* as well as chemicals that inhibit excitotoxicity, inducible nitric oxide synthase, and PARP. PARP inhibition is a relatively recent addition to the cryonics stabilization protocol and intervenes further downstream in the ischemic cascade, providing a larger window of opportunity for intervention. The oncotic agent *mannitol,* primarily given to prevent and reverse cerebral edema, is also reported to have free radical scavenging properties. Another fluid that has been a mainstay in stabilization is *tris-*

hydroxymethyl aminomethane (THAM), used to maintain pH balance. Although buffer therapy is a controversial topic in resuscitation medicine, maintaining physiological pH in a cryonics patient is important because some of the stabilization medications are pH sensitive.

Gaining access to the circulatory system of a patient to deliver these medications and fluids is not a trivial matter. Many patients have advanced arteriosclerosis and are severely dehydrated at the time of pronouncement, presenting a time-consuming challenge for achieving rapid intravenous access. Unless medical staff can be persuaded to leave an IV line in place, attempts to place an IV have often interfered with the goal of rapid stabilization. Following a renewed interest in emergency medicine to administer medications and fluids through the bone marrow, two cryonics organizations have recently adopted a technology to access the circulatory system through the sternum. Sternal intraosseous infusion is expected to reduce the time to establish vascular access (even by relatively inexperienced team members), in addition to other advantages such as the ability to infuse larger volumes.

Hypothermia

The third, and most fundamental, intervention in stabilization is induction of hypothermia. Induction of hypothermia is the most fundamental intervention because it confers potent neuroprotection and is the first step in cooling down the patient to cryogenic temperature. Unlike cardiopulmonary support or pharmacologic treatment, induction of hypothermia is implied in the concept of human cryopreservation itself. This does not necessarily mean that induction of hypothermia is the *first* priority in stabilization. If immediate access to the patient after pronouncement is possible, cardiopulmonary support in conjunction with vasoactive medications is the most time-efficient intervention to mitigate cerebral ischemia. A scenario where the cryonics team needs to choose *between* CPS, medications, or cooling generally indicates inadequate preparation, an uncooperative hospital, or sudden death. Immediately starting all three types of interventions is a core objective of stabilization procedures.

The importance of rapid induction of hypothermia in cryonics is routinely conveyed by referring to the rule that for every 10 degrees Celsius reduction in temperature metabolic rate is reduced by 50 percent. Although this $Q10 = 2$ rule is useful to communicate the effectiveness of hypothermia in reducing metabolic rate to the general public, it cannot explain the potent neuroprotective effects of hypothermia that are observed when the temperature is dropped by only a few degrees. It is possible that different parts of the ischemic cascade, such as excitatory amino acid release, are reduced by a rate vastly exceeding that expected by applying this Q10 value [8]. Although the exact mechanisms of hypothermic protection need further elucidation, this phenomenon provides strong support for rapid cooling as a means to keep the brain viable after pronouncement of legal death.

Different degrees of hypothermia have been distinguished based on the core body temperature of the patient:

Mild hypothermia: 32-36 degrees Celsius

Moderate hypothermia: 28-32 degrees Celsius

Deep hypothermia: 18-28 degrees Celsius

Profound hypothermia: 5-18 degrees Celsius

Ultraprofound hypothermia: 0-5 degrees Celsius

The objective in stabilization is to achieve ultraprofound hypothermia as fast as possible. Under no circumstance is the patient cooled below 0 degrees Celsius during stabilization procedures and transport to the facility. This will cause freezing damage *prior* to cryoprotection and eliminates the ability to perfuse the patient with a cryoprotective agent.

The reason aggressive cardiopulmonary support is more effective as an *immediate* intervention is because induction of hypothermia by external cooling is relatively inefficient. The effectiveness of external cooling of the patient is further hampered by cold- and vasopressor-induced vasoconstriction. With limited peripheral blood flow, cooling efficiency is reduced.

Three different methods of external cooling of the patient are possible: cooling by evaporation, cooling by conduction, and cooling by convection. At high body temperatures, evaporating water is generally more effective in reducing body temperature than melting ice. The major limitation of this method of cooling is that it is impractical to continuously spray water on the patient and use a fan for evaporation. Its limitations during actual transport of the patient between locations are even more serious.

Packing the whole body in ice is the minimum that should be achieved during stabilization. In case the cryonics team has a portable ice bath, the ice does not need to be bagged because this adds a layer of insulation between the patient and the ice. Emphasis is given to the areas that have large vessels close to the surface such as the anterior neck, the axilla, and the groin.

Convective cooling can be achieved by circulating ice water around the patient using a submersible pump. Circulating ice water around the patient in conjunction with cardiopulmonary support is the closest approximation to immersing a patient in streaming ice cold water that is compatible with other stabilization tasks such as cardiopulmonary support, medications administration, and monitoring.

A slight drop in temperature can also be achieved by introducing the stabilization medications and fluids at low temperatures. The advantage of this technique should be weighed against increased viscosity, and the risk that some medications and fluids that should not be chilled (such as Mannitol) will be included accidentally. Additional chilled fluids, or ice slurries, can be introduced intravenously to the patient, but care should be taken to ensure that the fluids are not hypotonic and (extreme) hypervolemia is prevented.

More effective methods to cool down the patient are generally more invasive. In gastric lavage a large bore gastric tube is used to introduce a chilled fluid by gravity and return it by suction. Because of the risk of pulmonary aspiration, this technique requires that the patient is intubated. In colonic lavage a chilled fluid is introduced through the rectum. In peritoneal lavage, a surgically placed catheter is used to introduce chilled fluids in the abdominal cavity. In a landmark cryonics case in 1995, the cryonics service provider BioPreservation used external circulating ice water cooling, together with colonic and peritoneal lavage, and achieved cooling rates over 1.0 degrees Celsius per minute, by far the fastest cooling rates ever recorded during initial stabilization [9].

In the late 1990s Michael Darwin et al. developed a minimally invasive form of cyclic lung lavage to induce hypothermia. Although the feasibility of ventilating the lungs using fluids has been demonstrated since the 1960s, this liquid ventilation-derived technology represents a significant breakthrough for inducing rapid hypothermia in cryonics and emergency medicine.

Because all circulating blood must pass through the enormous surface area of the lungs, the lungs basically work as an endogenous heat exchanger. The fluid of choice in cold lung lavage is a perfluorocarbon, a hydrocarbon in which the hydrogen atoms are replaced by fluorine atoms. Perfluorocarbons are stable, inert, and have good oxygen and carbon dioxide carrying ability. Cyclic lung lavage only requires endotracheal intubation and can be started promptly after pronouncement of death. In conjunction with other internal and external cooling methods, cooling rates approaching those achieved by cardiopulmonary bypass are possible [10].

Blood Substitution

Holding the patient close to zero degrees Celsius during (remote) transport significantly reduces metabolic rate, but long stabilization and transport times may still risk loss of viability of the brain. Induction of (ultra) profound hypothermia can also produce adverse effects such as cold-induced red cell clumping and edema. To keep the brain viable during transport, the patient's blood is washed out and replaced with an organ preservation solution similar to what is used in conventional organ transplantation.

In an ideal remote stabilization case, surgery to gain access to the circulatory system is started immediately after pronouncement of legal death. A more typical scenario is to transport the patient to a cooperating funeral home where surgical access and blood washout is performed. In *either* scenario stabilization procedures should not be halted for most parts of the surgery. Vascular access is generally secured by cannulating the femoral artery and vein using sterile technique. Following femoral cannulation, the patient's blood is substituted with the organ preservation solution using an air transportable perfusion device (ATP). The ATP also contains a heat exchanger and oxygenator to cool down and oxygenate the patient.

The organ preservation solutions that have been used for more than 20 years in cryonics are variants of a solution called *MHP*, which stands for **M**annitol **HEPES** **P**erfusate. *MHP* is designed as an "intracellular" organ preservation solution to provide metabolic support and reduce hypothermia-induced passive movement of ions across cell membranes. Ischemia- and hypothermia-induced edema is minimized by the sugar-alcohol *mannitol* and the synthetic colloid *hydroxyethyl starch*. Other components include *adenine* and *d-ribose* to support cellular metabolism, *HEPES* and *sodium bicarbonate* to stabilize pH, and *glutathione* to mitigate oxidative stress. Some versions of *MHP* also include *insulin* to improve glucose uptake in non-neural tissue.

In a series of seminal experiments, cryonics researchers Mike Darwin, Jerry Leaf, and Hugh Hixon used *MHP* to recover dogs from three hours of ultraprofound hypothermic asanguineous circulatory arrest, and five hours of low flow perfusion [11]. These experiments support the theory that continuous physiological metabolic activity is not necessary for life. The experiments also indicate that the stabilization phase in human cryopreservation is potentially reversible by *contemporary* medical technology. The increased clinical interest in asanguineous hypothermia as an intervention for sudden cardiac arrest and hemorrhagic shock provides further validation of the research that was done by these early cryonics pioneers.

Evaluating Brain Viability

If securing brain viability by contemporary medical criteria is the goal of stabilization, how can we know if this objective has been achieved when the patient is not being resuscitated? Given that the patient's brain is viable at the time of pronouncement of death, vital signs and blood chemistries during stabilization can be collected and compared to baseline values obtained prior to, or immediately after, the start of stabilization. Although this may provide a rough idea of the efficacy of stabilization, brain injury can be consistent with adequate cerebral blood flow and physiological blood chemistries. As our understanding of the pathophysiology of cerebral ischemia grows, more selective biomarkers of neural injury may be considered.

The central question of what exactly constitutes viability by contemporary medical criteria may not be as simple as it appears. It requires that we take several other related questions into consideration. What constitutes contemporary medical technology? How do we classify a patient who suffers brain injury that *can* be reversed by contemporary medical technology?

A good example of the complications surrounding the concept of cerebral viability is apoptosis of brain cells. Because the execution of apoptosis requires energy, DNA transcription, and protein synthesis, ischemia-induced apoptotic cell death is only possible by restoration of blood flow. A somewhat troubling implication of this fact is that, during typical stabilization procedures, energy is supplied to assist cell death by apoptosis. On the other hand, because apoptosis is an organized and time-consuming process, the alternative—cell death by necrosis—is likely to be worse in cryonics.

Because cells undergoing (very) early apoptosis may still be considered viable, it is an interesting question if a patient in the early stages of neural apoptosis should be considered viable by *contemporary* medical criteria. This may depend on the question whether the activation of apoptosis can be reversed by contemporary medical technology. If this is not the case, the argument that the patient's brain can be considered viable by contemporary medical criteria is problematic.

The science of human cryopreservation raises some important ethical issues. Although our understanding of the molecular mechanisms of cerebral ischemia and potential treatments is growing, irreversible neurological injury is still a common outcome in many cardiac arrest and stroke cases. The time separating onset of the insult and completion of cell death is generally sufficient to stabilize and cool down such patients to cryogenic temperatures. Human cryopreservation may not only offer a treatment option for patients that are considered dead by contemporary medical criteria, it should also be investigated as a treatment option for patients who have been resuscitated after serious cardiovascular and cerebral insults but who will lose all dignity if kept alive at normothermic temperatures after the insult.

Evidence-Based Cryonics

The science of human cryopreservation has made significant advances since the concept was first popularized by Evan Cooper and Robert Ettinger during the 1960s. To most observers, cryonics is mainly a practical cryobiology problem that needs to be solved. This perspective neglects that even in a society where suspended animation has become routine, medical emergencies requiring rapid stabilization may still exist. It should also not be assumed that the technical possibility of reversible vitrification of humans will lead to widespread acceptance of the practice of cryonics. Stabilization of cryonics patients will remain a core component of cryonics procedures in the foreseeable future.

One consequence of this "cryobiology bias," however, is that more generous resources have been allocated for research to achieve reversible vitrification than for research into stabilization technologies. This trend has been further reinforced by statements within the cryonics community questioning the value of stabilization. As a result, it should not be surprising that progress and quality of care in stabilization in cryonics has been variable.

Evidence-Based Cryonics (EBC) represents an approach to human cryopreservation in which all procedures should be supported by research and evidence-based medical practice. An important element of evidence-based cryonics is the awareness that findings in mainstream research and conventional medicine may need further investigation in a realistic cryonics context. An example of such an approach would be to validate neuroprotective agents in a model that includes cryoprotectant perfusion. Meticulous data acquisition during cases and meta-analysis of case reports should be used to generate a general clinical theory of human cryopreservation.

The concept of evidence-based cryonics is basically a restatement of the research driven approach to cryonics that was pioneered by Jerry Leaf and Michael Darwin in the late 1970s and 1980s. A comprehensive review of desirable research objectives is beyond this article, but some general directions in the area of stabilization are discussed.

Cardiopulmonary support may be further optimized by a detailed study of the physiology of forward blood flow during chest compressions. Modalities of CPS that better reflect the typical pathophysiology of cryonics patients before and during stabilization may be beneficial as well. A systematic review of reperfusion injury in cryonics should give more specific guidelines to determine when restarting circulation and/or ventilating the patient is beneficial. Progress on practical issues such as the noise and ease of use of mechanical chest compression devices is desirable as well.

Human cryopreservation stabilization pharmacology reflects the increasing understanding that the complex multifactorial nature of cerebral ischemia requires combination therapy. Current cryonics protocol may benefit from an up-to-date exposition of the pathophysiology of global cerebral ischemia, emphasizing the temporal aspects of combination treatment. The relationship between hypothermia and the pharmacodynamics and pharmacokinetics of various drugs is a topic that has not yet been addressed in much detail. Sternal intraosseous infusion is a promising technique to gain access to the circulatory system, but more remains to be discovered about its efficacy after administration of high-dose vasoactive agents and its interaction with active compression decompression CPS.

In addition, the specific mechanisms of cerebral protection by induction of hypothermia require further elucidation. Awareness of the possibility that induction of ultraprofound hypothermia may also produce detrimental effects in terms of brain viability is important. Induction of hypothermia by packing the patient in ice should be complemented by a variety of other cooling modalities, including routine use of liquid ventilation. It is possible that lung lavage and CPS techniques have to be modified to optimize the synergistic performance of both interventions. Monitoring techniques may be modified for liquid ventilation as well. In a hospice or rescue vehicle, some of the other internal cooling techniques discussed above should become routine.

Although the cold organ preservation solutions in cryonics give extended brain viability for asanguineous *low flow perfusion*, the current practice to use the solution as a static blood substitute during (air) transport of the patient to a cryonics facility means that the goal of stabilization cannot be secured for the majority of remote cases. The quality of care in cryonics may benefit from more emphasis on the element of *perfusion* during washout. A better understanding of how blood washout may contribute to reperfusion injury is desirable. New cold organ preservation solutions should be validated in models of warm and cold ischemia.

Without good scribe work and comprehensive data acquisition, rapid progress in the science of human cryopreservation will be limited. A renewed interest in physiological monitoring in cryonics is evidenced by the introduction of new technologies such as bedside blood gas analyzers (such as the i-STAT) and equipment that can produce a complete respiratory profile (such as the *CO2SMO*). This opens opportunities for real-time intervention that were not available in the earlier days of cryonics. It may also provide more specific answers to the question of how well the goal of stabilization is achieved for a particular patient.

Impressive progress in cryobiology and a growing understanding of the molecular mechanisms of cerebral ischemia have made the prospect for human cryopreservation to become a part of critical care medicine look better than ever. ∎

References

1.   Mazur Peter, in: *American Journal of Physiology* (1984, vol. 247), "Freezing of living cells: mechanisms and implications," p.125-142.

2.   Drexler Eric, in: *Engines of Creation* (1986), Anchor Press/Doubleday.

3.   Wowk Brian, "Cardiopulmonary Support in Cryonics," Alcor Life Extension Foundation.

4.   Halperin Henry, Rayburn Barry K. in: *Cardiopulmonary Resuscitation,* Humana Press, 2004, "Alternate Cardiopulmonary Resuscitation Devices and Techniques," p. 177-199.

5.   Halperin Henry, Rayburn Barry K. in: *Cardiopulmonary Resuscitation,* Humana Press, 2004, "Alternate Cardiopulmonary Resuscitation Devices and Techniques," p. 177-199.

6.   Babbs Charles F., Kern KB. in: *Resuscitation.* 2002 Aug; 54(2):147-57, "Optimum compression to ventilation ratios in CPR under realistic, practical conditions: a

physiological and mathematical analysis."

7. Deng Xin-sheng , Simpson Victoria J, Deitrich Richard A. *The Internet Journal of Pharmacology.* 2004. Volume 2 Number 2. "Nitric Oxide and Propofol."

8. Nakashima Ken and Todd Michael M. *Stroke*, May 1996; 27: 913 - 918. "Effects of Hypothermia on the Rate of Excitatory Amino Acid Release After Ischemic Depolarization."

9. Darwin Michael, in: *Biopreservation Tech Briefs* (1996, no. 18), "Cryopreservation of CryoCare Patient #C-2150."

10. Harris SB, Darwin MG, Russell SR, O'Farrell JM, Fletcher M, Wowk B. *Resuscitation.* 2001 Aug; 50(2) :189-204. "Rapid (0.5 degrees C/min) minimally invasive induction of hypothermia using cold perfluorochemical lung lavage in dogs."

11. Leaf Jerry D, Darwin Michael G, and Hixon Hugh, "A mannitol-based perfusate for reversible 5-hour asanguineous ultraprofound hypothermia in canines." Cryovita Laboratories, Inc. and Alcor Life Extension Foundation.

Securing Viability of the Brain at Alcor

By Aschwin de Wolf
Cryonics, 2nd Quarter, 2007

The main objectives of care at Alcor are to maintain viability and preserve the ultrastructure of the brain during all procedures. Because of its high metabolic demand and low capacity for energy storage, the brain is extremely vulnerable to injury caused by lack of blood flow (cerebral ischemia). The ability to secure viability and good ultrastructural preservation of the brain is therefore an excellent measure of the current state of the art in cryonics. Because identity and memory are assumed to reside primarily in the brain, both whole body and neuropreservation members would agree that this organ should be given preferential treatment.

This article will briefly describe all the steps involved in a typical cryopreservation case and discuss how far we have come in achieving this objective at Alcor.

Structure versus Viability

One distinction that is often made in cryonics is that between ultrastructure and viability. In this context viability means that the brain is able to resume function upon reversal of some, or all, of the procedures employed in cryonics. Preservation of ultrastructure refers to preservation of the detailed structure of a cell, tissue, or organ that can be observed by electron microscopy. Naturally, these two concepts are related. For example, if an organ were straight frozen (placed into liquid nitrogen without cryoprotectant perfusion) after a long period of warm ischemia, we would expect to find poor ultrastructure and, therefore, poor viability. But there can also be examples where good preservation of ultrastructure does not necessarily guarantee a good outcome in terms of viability. Examples of this would be procedures that result in good preservation of ultrastructure but which cause mitochondrial failure, denatured proteins, or massive activation of apoptosis (programmed cell death).

Terminal Patients

One aspect often neglected by cryonics writers is that many patients who present for cryonics go through a prolonged terminal period before cryonics stabilization procedures are initiated. During this period the patient may experience a number of pathological conditions such as shock, respiratory distress, dehydration, electrolyte imbalances, systemic inflammation, upregulation of coagulation factors, multiple organ failure, intracranial pressure, and activation of apoptosis. Consequently, the objective of stabilization, explained further below, is much more difficult to achieve or may even be defeated *before* the cryonics team gains access to the patient.

Because Alcor will not treat the patient before legal pronouncement of death, it is largely the patient's responsibility to execute the proper paperwork to ensure that medical treatment during the agonal phase will not be detrimental to achieving a good cryopreservation. Examples that come to mind are to have a Do Not Resuscitate (DNR) order in place to avoid multiple resuscitation attempts (with associated cycles of ischemia-reperfusion injury) and to express a desire for certain supplements during palliative care. Where the cryonics organization can make a difference during this period is in being guided by the "pre-mortem" condition of the patient when starting stabilization procedures such as promptly restoring fluid volume and vascular tone after a patient has been pronounced dead.

Mike Darwin sits with Enkidu as the canine gains strength the day following complete blood washout and cooling to ~ 5°C. Photo courtesy of Michael Darwin.

Stabilization

Stabilization procedures at Alcor consist of three different interventions: cardiopulmonary support, induction of hypothermia, multi-modal medications treatment, and in remote cases, blood washout and substitution with an organ preservation solution. Stabilization of the patient is one part of Alcor's protocol where a number of cryonics authors have explicitly stated that cerebral viability by contemporary medical criteria should be the objective.[1] In this vein, Alcor and associated research companies have done research to demonstrate that securing cerebral viability during stabilization is a realistic objective.

Two groundbreaking experiments provide evidence that securing viability during stabilization might be achieved with current technologies. In the late '80s and early '90s Darwin, Leaf et al. demonstrated that induction of ultraprofound hypothermia (temperatures lower than 5°C) in conjunction with blood washout and substitution with an organ preservation solution is reversible in a canine model. Dogs were revived from up to 5 hours of low flow perfusion with an organ preservation solution called

---

1   Wowk Brian, "Cardiopulmonary Support in Cryonics," Alcor Life Extension Foundation. http://www. alcor.org/ Library/ html/CardiopulmonarySupport.html

MHP-2.[2] In the mid '90s Darwin, Harris et al. successfully resuscitated dogs from up to 17 minutes of normothermic cardiac arrest using a large number of medications and tight post-resuscitation regulation of hemodynamics.[3]

Impressive as these results are, there are also some caveats. First, as mentioned previously, the typical patient who presents for cryonics has gone through a prolonged terminal period. How realistic is it to expect a similar outcome under such conditions? Second, current Alcor procedures are not identical to the protocol that was investigated. For example, in remote cases the organ preservation solution is used in a static (no flow) fashion, often without oxygenation, instead of constantly perfusing the patient at low flow during transport to the cryonics facility. In the case of the normothermic cerebral resuscitation experiments it is also important to note that the dogs were pre-heparinized prior to cardiac arrest (heparin is administered after cardiac arrest in cryonics cases) and that resuscitation doesn't involve a long period of external chest compressions as is the case in cryonics stabilization. Finally, some techniques that are possible during experimental work in a laboratory—such as rigorous medications administration, tight control over hemodynamics and sophisticated monitoring—are currently not available to cryonics organizations.

Cryoprotectant Perfusion
The objective of securing viability during cryoprotective perfusion can be broken down into two stages. During the initial phase, following surgery to obtain vascular access, the patient's blood (or the organ preservation solution in a remote case) is flushed out. Because this phase is not fundamentally different from remote blood washout, securing cerebral viability should be possible in principle, provided that the transition from stabilization to initiation of OR procedures is structured in such a fashion that there is (1) no major interruption in circulation or (2) no marked rise in temperature. Unlike the first condition, the latter condition is not only a practical challenge but a clinical challenge as well. Effective washout is a function of temperature and this presents a delicate trade-off between the risk of ischemic injury produced by elevated temperatures and the benefit of reduced washout times.

A related problem is encountered in the second phase of perfusion during which a cryoprotective agent is gradually introduced to the patient. Classical cryoprotective agents like glycerol do not penetrate cell membranes very well at lower temperatures (close to 0°C). To compensate for this fact, a deliberate elevation of temperature was

---

2   Leaf Jerry D, Darwin Michael G, and Hixon Hugh, "A mannitol-based perfusate for reversible 5-hour asanguineous ultraprofound hypothermia in canines." Cryovita Laboratories, Inc. and Alcor Life Extension Foundation, unpublished paper 1987. Online at: http://www. alcor.org/Library/html/ tbwcanine.html

3   This work has been done by Critical Care Research. Unpublished research results.

required during glycerol-based cryoprotection. Although this was a rational choice (considering the alternative of extremely long perfusion times), the introduction of a very concentrated cryoprotective agent at relatively high temperatures likely compromised cerebral viability as a result of increased ischemic exposure and cryoprotectant toxicity. Alcor's current cryoprotective agent is no longer based on glycerol and includes components such as DMSO, which have improved permeability at lower temperatures.

The real limiting factor for maintaining viability of the brain is that all currently-known cryoprotectants have toxic effects when whole brains are exposed to them long enough to prevent ice formation and achieve vitrification during cooling. At the time of writing, the M22 cryoprotectant mixture used by Alcor is the least toxic vitrification solution ever published for use in large organs.[4] However, it is still not sufficiently non-toxic to permit reversible cryopreservation of the whole brain. Another reason why cerebral viability might be compromised during introduction of cryoprotectants is that, under "ideal" circumstances, the cryoprotectant induces an extreme degree of brain shrinking which may compromise vascular and cellular integrity and even set the stage for apoptosis upon resuscitation. Overcoming these problems will require further advances in basic research.

Cryogenic Cooldown and Long-Term Care

Because we can deduce that cerebral viability is lost during the later stages of cryoprotective perfusion, we know that cerebral viability can no longer be maintained during cryogenic cooldown and long-term care of the patient. In general, if cerebral viability is lost at some earlier phase, it cannot be restored during any later phase of cryonics procedures. Consequently, the emphasis from that point will be on preserving ultrastructure as well as possible. During cryogenic cooldown this means cooling at least fast enough to inhibit any ice formation, which is currently 0.1°C/minute for the cryoprotectant M22. A cooling rate of ~ 0.4°C/ minute can be achieved for an organ as large as the human brain. Since an adequate cooling rate can be achieved to prevent ice formation in the brain, the remaining issues of immediate concern include cryopreservation-induced injuries independent of ice formation like chilling injury and thermal stress at lower temperatures.

Chilling injury involves injury caused by exposure to low temperatures and includes cell membrane phase transitions and protein denaturation. Although M22 was designed to prevent chilling injury in large organs, this problem has not been investigated in cryonics patients. Aside from the practical problems in identifying chilling injury during cryoprotective perfusion and cooldown, it may be hard to

---

4   "New Preservation Technology", Alcor Life Extension Foundation. http://www. alcor.org/Library/html/newtechnology. html

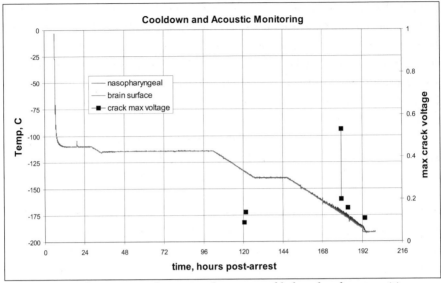

Graph indicates tissue fracturing that occurred below the glass transition temperature (-123.3°C for M22) during the cryogenic cooldown of a recent Alcor patient (2006).

distinguish the effects of chilling injury from the injury caused by warm ischemia, cryoprotectant toxicity, and osmotic shock. Moreover, chilling injury may be relatively benign compared to other problems during cryopreservation, such as the risk of ice formation and thermal stress.

Below the glass transition temperature (-123.3°C for M22) the vitrification solution turns into a glass and is limited in its ability to further contract as the temperature is further lowered, causing tissues to fracture as a result. Thermal stress not only presents an obvious obstacle to maintaining viability, but fracturing also compromises the objective of securing uniform ultrastructure of the brain. In light of the expectation that recent vitrification solutions will inhibit ice formation in cryonics patients, eliminating fracturing has become a more urgent priority for Alcor. One alternative would be to provide long-term care for patients at higher temperatures, just below the glass transition point. Another alternative would be to develop an "annealing" protocol that will inhibit or minimize thermal stress by keeping a firm control over temperature descent.[5]

Leaving social, political, and legal threats to Alcor patients aside, the final challenge to securing cerebral viability for cryonics patients is the effect of long-term care on the patient. By this point, under current procedures, viability and ultrastructure will already have been compromised. But there is no reason to believe that long-term

---

5 "Cryopreservation and Fracturing", Alcor Life Extension Foundation. http://www.alcor.org/Library. html/CryopreservationAndFracturing.html

care at liquid nitrogen temperature (-196°C) would produce adverse effects over very long periods of time (exceeding thousands of years).[6] At the temperature that Alcor's patients are currently maintained, time has effectively been halted. Open to more debate is the long-term risk of maintaining patients at intermediate temperatures (slightly under the glass transition temperature) because, at temperatures down to 20°C below the glass transition temperature, ice nucleation may still be a risk for cryopreservation. These nanoscale nucleators may not present a direct threat to patients during long-term care, but they may present a bigger challenge during rewarming of the patient in the future.

Assessing Viability

How do we know if cerebral viability is being maintained during a cryonics case? At this point most evidence for what is possible with current technologies has come from experiments on healthy animals under controlled laboratory conditions. In light of the fact that cryonics procedures do not occur under such tightly controlled circumstances, claims that viability can be secured up until the later stages of cryoprotective perfusion are highly theoretical.

Currently the only means available to cryonics organizations to get an idea about how well cerebral viability is being maintained during stabilization and cryoprotective perfusion are confined to physiological observation, temperature data, qualitative end tidal CO_2 and peripheral oxygen saturation readings and, in rare cases, pre-pronouncement and post-pronouncement blood gases and electrolytes. For example, a case where cerebral viability is maintained would typically have all or most of the following characteristics: prompt start of stabilization procedures after legal pronouncement of death, adequate cerebral perfusion generated by mechanical chest compression (or extracorporeal perfusion) and administration of vasoactive medications, and rapid induction of hypothermia.

During a number of landmark cases at Alcor and CryoCare, blood gases and temperature data have been collected that seem to indicate that viability may have been maintained during stabilization.[7] However, when reading these case reports it should be kept in mind that more subtle ischemic changes may have occurred that still present a threat to viability such as mitochondrial damage, excessive free radical

---

6   Hixon Hugh, "How Cold is Cold Enough", *Cryonics*, January 1985. http://www.alcor.org/Library/html/HowColdIsColdEnough.html
     [Note that this article presents a rather optimistic source for the time that we can expect a human to be resuscitated from cardiac arrest.]

7   Darwin Michael G, "Cryopreservation Patient Case Report: Arlene Frances Fried, A-1049", Alcor Life Extension Foundation. http://www.alcor.org/ Library/html/fried.html
     Darwin Michael G, "Cryopreservation of CryoCare Patient #C-2150", *Biopreservation Tech Briefs* (1996, no. 18)

damage, activation of apoptosis, or neurological pathologies associated with induction of ultraprofound hypothermia and extracorporeal perfusion. Consequently, blood plasma should be examined to look for more specific biomarkers of brain injury.

From initiation of cryogenic cooldown to long-term patient care, measurements of viability are no longer possible and Alcor confines itself to optimizing preservation of ultrastructure. During cooldown Alcor uses an acoustic device to monitor the occurrence of fracturing in the brain. This device uses an electronic sensor that registers vibrations that are assumed to correspond with fracturing events. After cryogenic cooldown the only available method to determine whether any ice has formed is direct observation of the surface of the brain. Naturally, during long-term care at liquid nitrogen temperature neither viability nor ultrastructure can be monitored in real time.

Discussion

One may wonder why Alcor makes such an effort to maintain cerebral viability during stabilization if it is invariably lost during cryoprotective perfusion and cryogenic cooldown. The straightforward answer is that by securing viability at an early stage, better preservation of ultrastructure can be achieved at a later stage. Cardiac arrest sets the stage for a number of pathophysiological events that may interfere with optimal circulation of the cryoprotective solution during the later stages of cryonics procedures including, but not limited to, intravascular blood clotting, production of inflammatory vascular adhesion molecules, free radical formation, and capillary and cell membrane leakage. Notable differences in cryoprotective perfusion have been observed between patients that experienced a long period of warm and/or cold ischemia and patients who received prompt stabilization and minimal transport times.

A related but more subtle issue is whether Alcor's stabilization protocol could benefit by changing the objective of stabilization from securing cerebral viability to optimizing cryoprotective perfusion. Typically one would expect that interventions that are adequate to secure viability will also confer benefits during cryoprotective perfusion, but there at least three caveats to this perspective that need to be considered.

First, there are interventions that can secure viability if executed promptly and correctly but that can frustrate cryoprotective perfusion at a later stage in the absence of such a careful approach. Ventilating a patient with 100% oxygen is an example of an intervention that might be moderately beneficial in terms of viability but can also seriously frustrate adequate distribution of the cryoprotective agent in the brain as a result of injury to the circulatory system and cell membranes (a condition known as "reperfusion injury"). Second, there are only a finite number of pharmacological interventions that a cryonics organization can be expected to do and a choice needs to be made between interventions that increase the probability of short-term recovery and a protocol that is specifically designed to preserve ultrastructure through all phases

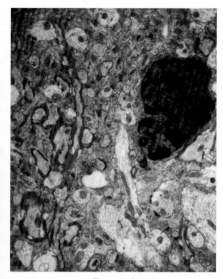

Figure 1

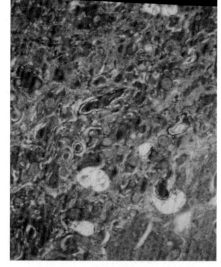

Figure 2

*Figures 1-3: In the 1980s Mike Darwin
et al. performed a number of feline
experiments to investigate the effects of
Alcor's cryopreservation procedures under
different conditions. Figure 1 shows a
control brain (cerebral cortex) that was
washed out and perfused with Karnofsky's
fixative. Figure 2 shows a brain after
cryopreservation with 3.0 M glycerol at
-196°C and rewarming. Figure 3 shows
a brain after 30 minutes of normothermic
ischemia, 24 hours packing in ice,
cryopreservation with 3.0 M glycerol at
-196°C and rewarming. Figure 2 shows
typical results after cryoprotection and
freezing: dehydration of cell structures*

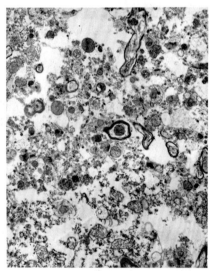

Figure 3

*but reasonably good preservation of cell membranes and intracellular architecture.
By contrast, after ischemia, glycerolization, freezing and thawing, Figure 3 shows
massive disruption of cell ultrastructure, and all that is visible in this photo (which is
representative) is disorganized cellular debris. Images courtesy of Michael Darwin.*

of cryonics procedures. This choice is especially important in light of the fact that Alcor's medications protocol reflects a normothermic recovery model to mitigate a number of pathophysiological events that should also be inhibited by rapid induction of hypothermia. Third, Alcor's organ preservation solution, MHP-2, has never been investigated for prolonged static use or in the presence of serious ischemic and reperfusion injury. In general, results obtained in a recovery model need to be validated in a model that reflects the typical patient pathologies and practical limitations of a cryonics standby team.

Should the criterion of viability of the brain be applied to the most vulnerable parts of the brain? We can imagine a scenario where a cryonics patient can be successfully resuscitated but with impaired personality and memories. For example, it is a well established fact that the CA1 region of the hippocampus is highly vulnerable to even the shortest interruptions of cerebral blood flow. This region of the brain is associated with encoding and storing memories. Does the initial start of "apoptosis" (programmed cell death) of vulnerable parts in the brain constitute a form of injury incompatible with viability of the brain by contemporary criteria? Cryonics would benefit from a deeper understanding of why certain regions of the brain are so vulnerable to oxygen deprivation to guide research into procedures that minimize injury to vulnerable cells in the brain.

Getting a better understanding of the efficacy of current procedures, and improving upon them, is one of the objectives for reviving the ambitious research agenda that cryonics pioneers Jerry Leaf and Mike Darwin pursued at Alcor. Alcor is also investigating a number of technologies that will improve cardiopulmonary support and rapid induction of hypothermia, optimize control and data collection during cryoprotective perfusion, and reduce fracturing during cryogenic cooldown.

Despite the renewed focus on evidence-based cryonics and new technologies, one of the major limiting factors in securing viability and good ultrastructure is the quality of standby and stabilization procedures. Achieving better quality requires a concerted effort between Alcor and its members ranging from forming new local cryonics groups to making substantial investments to distribute good stabilization equipment in many parts of the country. ■

CASE REPORTS IN CRYONICS

BY ASCHWIN DE WOLF

Cryonics, 4th Quarter, 2010

Introduction

The most important reasons for writing case reports are:

1. *To provide a transparent and detailed description of procedures and techniques for members of the cryonics organization and the general public.* A cryonics organization that never writes anything about its cases and procedures should be treated with more caution than an organization that does.

2. *To validate current protocol and procedures in general, and its actual implementation in particular.* A case report should not only record what happened but should be used for guidance as to what should happen in the future. A detailed case report, especially when a variety of physiological data has been collected, contains a wealth of information that can be analyzed for the team members' and patient's benefit. Cryonics cases are relatively rare (compared with other medical procedures), so we should try to learn as much as we can from the cases we perform.

3. *To serve as a medical record to assist with future attempts to revive the patient.* Although advanced future medical technologies may make it possible to determine the physiological condition of the patient down to the molecular level, it is important to provide as much medical information as possible to help in efforts to revive patients. Having a detailed record of the patient's condition prior to pronouncement, subsequent stabilization, and cryoprotection, may also help the organization in establishing the desired sequence of revival attempts.

4. *To gain more scientific credibility.* If we want scientists and physicians to take us seriously, we need to convince them that we are attempting to cryopreserve our patients in a scientific manner. Professional case reports can provide this kind of credibility.

This article will mainly concern itself with the general question of how a case report can help a cryonics organization in improving protocol, techniques and skills.

Protocol

To be able to assess the quality of patient care in a cryonics case, it is important to specify what the intended protocol was prior to writing about the case. Only if we know what the organization was *supposed* to do will we be able to assess how successful the care was. For example, if there is no mention of collecting (and analyzing) blood gases during a case this may have been because it is currently not a part of the organization's protocol, but it may also be the result of a shortage of skilled personnel, defective equipment, or other problems or deficiencies. Unless the writer of the report specifies what should have happened, it is difficult to assess the quality of preparation and performance. If preparation for the case was poor and there was no (functional) extracorporeal perfusion equipment available, the case report should not simply state that the organization did a case without substituting the blood with an organ preservation solution, but also identify and review the (logistical) errors that were made that prevented a washout in the field.

In reality there will be many deviations between the organization's protocol and what actually happens. Human cryopreservation cases are not controlled laboratory experiments, and as many people who have extensive experience doing cases know, unique situations present themselves, including frustrating events that are beyond the control of even the most skilled medical professional. Nevertheless, the inherent unpredictability and uniqueness of cryonics cases is too often used as an excuse or justification for failing to follow established protocol, or for serious errors and omissions in the care of the patient. Documenting the prospective protocol will help us to gain a more systematic understanding of what is possible (or essential) and within our control, versus that which is not.

Detail

The importance of writing detailed descriptions of the procedures and techniques employed during a case cannot be overestimated. This not only enables the reader to gain a comprehensive understanding of the techniques used, it also allows detailed analysis of the difficulties that were encountered during a case that would not have been noticed if there is only a brief mention of it. For example, instead of simply noting that medications were administered, providing comprehensive details is essential, for many reasons.

Case reports should be prepared with the possibility in mind that what may seem mysterious, or inexplicable, to the writer may be crystal clear to an expert or perceptive reader when provided with sufficient detail. Providing as much detail as possible also serves to allow for replication of the techniques used by others. This is a critical component of the scientific method. Other investigators or practitioners must be able to duplicate the procedures and obtain the same outcome. Yet another consideration is that factors not now perceived or considered to be important may become so in the future. There are many examples of this in the history of cryonics that have proved essential to improving patient care. For example, in the early days of cryonics bags of ice were used to facilitate external cooling. It was not until comprehensive and consistent core cooling data were collected that it became apparent that this technique required 6-8 hours to cool a patient to ~ +20°C (room temperature!) with the patient cooling at a rate of 0.064°C/min. Documentation of these appallingly slow cooling rates provided powerful incentive to develop stirred water ice baths which increased cooling rates to between 0.15°C/min and 0.33°C /min, allowing cooling to ~15°C within 90 minutes to 2 hours after the start of cardiopulmonary support (CPS) (see graph below).

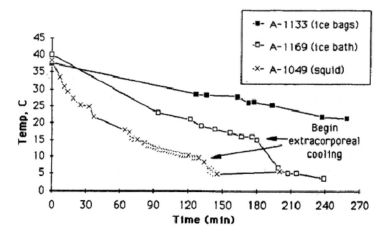

Comparison of Cooling Methods: Above are actual cooling curves for three adult human cryopreservation patients on Thumper support, using ice bags, the Portable Ice Bath (PIB), and the PIB augmented by SCCD (squid) cooling. Patient A-1133 weighed 56.8 kg, patient A-1169 weighed 57.3 kg, and patient A-1049 weighed 36.4 kg. As this data indicates, PIB cooling is approximately twice as efficient as ice bag cooling. The SCCD appears to increase the rate of cooling by an additional 50% over that of the PIB (roughly adjusting for the difference in the patients' body masses).

This example is even more instructive because continued diligent and comprehensive monitoring of cooling in multiple patients made clear other factors that were critically important to good outcome or, conversely, prohibited it. A large-framed obese male with heavy fat cover and a large amount of thermal inertia will not cool at anywhere near the rate that an emaciated, petite woman will. Evaluating the patient for fat cover and body mass index before deanimation allows reasonably accurate prediction of the cooling rate and may suggest the need for the addition of other cooling modalities such as peritoneal lavage with chilled fluid. Favorable results from application of peritoneal cooling in turn will suggest that even greater rates of cooling are possible for all patients and lead to the addition of the modality as a standard part of the protocol.

Failure to gather and promptly analyze data as basic as cooling rate precludes realization that problems exist as well as any possibility of solving them.

It is important to note that an incomplete case report doesn't necessarily indicate failure on the part of a cryonics organization. In a case where the number of team members is limited, all resources may have to be devoted to *doing* the case, instead of collecting data, or assigning an essential person to the job of taking notes. In the case of limited personnel it is better to do a good case without documentation than to document a bad case. To some degree this conflict between tasks can be avoided by having some of the team members (the team leader, paramedic, etc.) use a voice recorder with a clip-on microphone. But if the number of team members is insufficient, and data collection is not possible, this should be reported in the case report and recommendations should be made and implemented to prevent this situation from occurring again in the future. Good data acquisition and scribe work are essential for a good case report and, if feasible, should be a full-time job during a case.

Analysis

Specifying the protocol and describing the case in great detail is necessary but is not sufficient. A critical review of the information and data culminating in a list of desired changes and specific plans to address them should complement this. Ideally every discrepancy between protocol and reality that has been observed during the case should be discussed. Even in a case where stabilization started promptly after pronouncement, and the protocol was followed to the letter, there is still a lot of (physiological) data that, once analyzed, may require a change in the protocol in future cases.

To assess skills, identify critical failures, formulate solutions, and compare cases in a meaningful and valid way, a consistent and systematic format of reporting cases is essential. A typical case report should be divided into sections describing protocol, patient assessment, preparation and deployment of standby assets, the details of the case (divided in sections such as airway management, cardiopulmonary support, external and other cooling methods, blood washout, cryoprotective perfusion, and cooling to storage temperature), analysis, recommendations, and a variety of (public or non-public) appendices. Such appendices should include time-lines and graphic presentation of data, medications, cryoprotectants, and statistical analysis and comparisons to other cases.

Each case report should not only present solutions, or suggest tests and experiments to identify solutions, but provide a plan of action as to how these things can be accomplished. One approach to ensure that research and tests to validate solutions are implemented, and appropriate remedial action is taken, is to appoint an officer in the organization who is responsible for quality assurance and quality control. This individual's job will be to ensure that case reports are written in a manner consistent with the guidelines as outlined by the organization, as well as to ensure implementation of required changes.

Another critical role of case reports is to educate the organization's staff as well as consultants and, where appropriate, the patients' physicians and other health care providers about protocol, procedures and techniques. Although case reports are not and should not be a substitute for comprehensive written protocols, standard operating procedures (SOPs), and thorough training of personnel, sometimes solutions to problems can only be found in case reports where a team member was presented with an unusual problem. Consistent and systematic organization of case reports will greatly enhance the utility of case reports for this purpose. For example, if a reader wants to know about surgical techniques, and problems encountered in gaining access to the circulatory system for blood washout, consulting a case report will be far easier if they're organized in a consistent and predictable manner.

Answering Objections

One objection to writing up a case report is that it is not a controlled experiment and at best provides only anecdotal evidence. This is not the case for the following reasons.

Not all the mistakes and issues identified are of a hypothesis testing nature. For example, if a patient presents the human cryopreservation team members with a problem that could not be managed with the equipment at hand, the cryonics organization doesn't necessarily need a larger number of cases to decide to make a change to their equipment, and to start teaching employees the necessary skills.

Similarly, what may be perceived as anecdotal evidence for the cryonics organization may be a consistent finding in nearly identical settings in mainstream medicine. For example, some issues during a human cryopreservation case may be well known in hemodynamic management of potential organ donors in hospitals, or, for example, a medication in the protocol that is undergoing trial as a stroke therapy may demonstrate the same adverse effects observed during transport of a cryonics patient.

Of course, such lessons are impossible to learn without both broad and deep knowledge of medicine and the relevant research literature. Considering the ever growing number of publications and hyper-specialization, case reports may increasingly become collaborations between numbers of people with expertise in diverse areas. The individuals with the most valuable input do not necessarily have to be the ones who did the case. A physician dealing with similar issues in a neuro-intensive care unit may identify problems and propose solutions not obvious to those delivering cryonics care to the patient.

Monitoring

We don't know how our patient is going to fare in the future but we can know a lot about how our patient fared up to the point of long term low temperature care *if* we monitor his condition continuously. This starts from collecting detailed pre-mortem medical data to monitoring fracturing events during cooldown.

It is tempting to say that a case went very well if all the steps of the protocol were followed in a timely manner. This is not unreasonable because one would expect a strong correlation between an evidence based protocol and optimal care. But it is important to keep in mind that the goal of stabilization and cryopreservation is to treat the patient and not the book (as a saying in emergency medicine goes).

Without comprehensive monitoring of the patient through all parts of the procedures a case report will only document a predictable series of mechanical steps and some crude visual indicators of (relative) success at best. The things we are really interested in, like (quantitative) end-tidal CO_2 measurements, cardiac output, pH, and cerebral oxygenation, cannot be observed without sophisticated equipment.

Not only do we want to know how the patient is doing after the fact, we would also like to be able to intervene *during* a case if we observe a trend that suggests (alternative) treatment. Only in-depth reporting and analysis combined with a sound understanding of the physiopathology and available treatments will enable us to do so.

Presentation

A comprehensive list of dos and don'ts in writing case reports is not something that can be explored in this article, but some things are worth mentioning. Stylistically, a human cryopreservation report should resemble a medical or research report rather than a sensationalized adventure for the patient or the standby team. This should apply to the organization of the material as well as the choosing of words. As a general rule mainstream medical terminology should be used instead of cryonics jargon. Editorializing should be limited, and if perceived necessary, be moved to the proper section of the report. For example, jumping from a technical description of procedures to quarrelling among relatives or complaining about government regulation doesn't look very professional.

Protocol, procedures, and techniques should be the subject of the report, not people. Cryonics preparation and procedures are very demanding and exhausting for all people involved and mistakes are made and will be made. Errors should be presented as dispassionately as possible to avoid a culture of blame and personal conflict. Experience also teaches that (potential) participants are more open to transparent reporting if a case report will not single out individuals in describing procedures.

No matter how competent the writer of the report is, each report should be proofread by most or all individuals who were involved in the case and, if possible, a variety of outsiders with appropriate technical and medical knowledge, before it is released to the general public.

Patient Care

Writing case reports as presented in this article may be more demanding and time-consuming than generally has been done in human cryopreservation, but the results may improve patient care to a degree not previously seen. Ultimately, the most ambitious use of case reports will be one in which the case reports are analyzed as a series, measurements are compared, and patterns are established. Reading (and evaluating) a series of case reports in a systematic manner will even enable us to answer some very fundamental questions as to whether, or the degree to which, protocol, procedures, and techniques have improved over the years.

Providing the best patient care possible for current and future patients is the reason why cryonics organizations exist, and considering how powerful a tool a good case report can be, a responsible cryonics organization should devote considerable resources and time to writing them.

As our members and resources increase, and human cryopreservation gradually becomes a part of mainstream medicine, the successful transition from basic algorithmic, volunteer-driven care to evidence-based cryonics will be an important mandate.

Case reports and increasing caseload

One of the biggest challenges facing a growing cryonics organization is that it will also have more cases per year. This challenge is further amplified if all these cases need to be documented. As a consequence, a cryonics organization will find itself allocating an increasing amount of time to writing case reports and falling behind publication schedule. One of the most unfortunate responses to such a development would be to make an attempt to keep writing case reports in the old style but to lower standards and take short cuts.

An alternative approach is to develop a new format for case reports that allows for a shorter report but still captures the essential objectives of case reporting. One approach is to eliminate all the narrative that is not essential for following the mechanics of the case and evaluating the quality of care. In the past there have been a number of case reports with excessive narrative but little technical reporting or analysis. For a cryonics organization with a growing caseload the opposite approach should be followed. Another approach is to eliminate detail about procedures that were performed without deviations from past protocol and expectations, provided that this is made explicit in the report. As a result, case reports will increasingly read as a description and commentary on events that diverged from protocol or new observations about existing procedures.

To establish a template for such case reports the following approach can be followed. First, it is established what kind of information is essential for doing a meta-analysis of all cryonics cases. Then these parameters are reverse-engineered to create a template for writing case reports that reconcile the need for economy of expression and documenting all the relevant aspects of a case. One important advantage of producing such case reports is they permit easier consultation of the technical details of the case and still meet the fundamental objectives of writing case reports.

The history of case report writing in cryonics shows an erratic potpourri of approaches and styles. One of the most unfortunate casualties has been the objective of using case reports to improve the practice of human cryopreservation and to formulate meaningful research questions for the sciences that inform cryonics. But if systematic thought is given to the objectives of case reporting outlined in this document, steps can be taken to leave this unsatisfactory situation behind while meeting the needs of a growing cryonics organization. ■

RESUSCITATION OF CRYONICS PATIENTS

TO WAKE REFRESHED

BY MICHAEL DARWIN
Cryonics, December, 1984

One of the things that still amazes me in life is the power of exhaustion or depression to fog good judgment and distort reality. Anyone who has ever worked on a difficult and demanding project under a time limit, well into the small hours of the morning without sleep or without adequate tools knows well the frustration and despair which can quickly turn small problems into seemingly insurmountable mountains. Most of us live protected from that kind of thing. Such events are the exception rather than the rule in our lives, because in the Western World, anyway, we live lives where proper rest, food and the basic necessities of life are provided for.

Of course, this isn't true for an awful lot of the world and it's instructive to travel a bit and see how people who are sick, infested with parasites, dirty, and malnourished manage to struggle through and survive (of course an awful lot of them don't survive). What's instructive about this is to either imagine yourself or worse still find yourself in a similar bad situation and see how quickly fighting spirit departs and demoralization and hopelessness set in. I believe it was Bob Ettinger who once remarked that he had seen healthy young men succumb to shelling during World War II because they were simply too exhausted and demoralized to crawl into the trenches—to safety.

One of the great hazards of civilization is that it softens us up. We aren't accustomed to adversity and bad times and so not only is our appreciation of the goodness of life dulled, our ability to cope with stress is also diminished.

I can't pretend to be an exception to this. To a great extent I cave in and "give up" sooner than I should—especially if I'm feeling poorly, and not well rested or am badly stressed. In my work as a hemodialysis technician (someone who operates artificial kidney machines) I've seen a very large (relative to average Western experience) number of people die from chronic illness. The overwhelming majority of people, especially the old and already debilitated, just give up. They give up in large measure because they can't remember what it was like to be young, strong, and facing a full life filled with challenge and adventure. I have been sick, very sick, myself sometimes, and I can attest that it is easy to get demoralized and that it doesn't take many days of serious, debilitating illness before you forget about what it was like to be well and wonder, despairingly, if you'll ever feel that way again. For me, a good night's sleep was the best medicine to help me regain my equilibrium and during the worst of my illness I used to "live for the mornings," knowing that for a few hours after I awoke I'd have some taste of what it was like to feel well and whole—before the demands of the day wore me down again.

Unfortunately, a large number of people (probably the overwhelming majority) find themselves in just this kind of situation as they grow older and lose health and vitality. The senses fade, every activity becomes more of a struggle, and brain biochemistry shifts towards chronic depression. Growing old and becoming ill are terrible. We are aware of that intellectually as cryonicists. But we probably don't know it emotionally. I feel in a fortunate position in some ways because I have some idea, both intellectually and emotionally, of what may lie ahead. This awareness has forced me to be prepared, at least intellectually, for the possibility that I will all but forget how good life can be, and that illness and depression may seem to be unending and not worth the effort to escape from.

It's important to "gear-up" psychologically in this way because, for the time being, surviving demands that we do so. We live in a world where cryonics is not an automatic thing which we have to fight to avoid. In fact, we have to fight to keep it. As we grow older we may lose perspective, we may give up at some point because the fight may not seem worth the effort.

Unfortunately, I've seen this happen several times already to cryonicists. I know of several cases where people have let the "little" day-to-day troubles wear them down to the point where they say "what's the use" about cryonics. I've seen a few people who were "go-getters" about cryonics shift gears when sick and depressed and just opt out. Suddenly, life doesn't seem worth living anymore to these folks and they just give up.

It seems easy to be hard on these people. To criticize them for softness and lack of the "right stuff." Hard—until you've been there. The brutal fact is that it is pretty easy to break most people's spirits and, once broken, not so easy to mend them. Part of preventing that from happening is to mentally prepare in advance for the possibility of such feelings. Deep inside ourselves, hidden away, we have to make a commitment to ourselves to always try to live, to always try to fight, no matter what. That's an easy commitment to make, a much harder one to keep.

But, it can be kept. In my work in health care, as well as in my work as a cryonicist, I've seen people make that commitment and I've seen them struggle through against incredible odds and survive. Putting paperwork in order and providing for supportive people to step in and take over if you can't carry on is an important part of the physical preparation which all of us should make. Everybody should know, in fact needs to know, that there are others out there to help when the going not only seems rough, but impossible. Alcor has done that already, and we'll continue to do it. It's my great hope that even though I can become ill and worn down, ALCOR will remain young and able to help me. It is my strong conviction and ardent desire that ALCOR be that kind of organization for ALL its members.

It is my certain belief that if we can just get through the night—however long and black and hopeless—we'll wake refreshed. A good part of living to see that dawn is to never forget it's possible, even when everything and everyone tells you it isn't. ■

The Anabolocyte*:
A Biological Approach to
Repairing Cryoinjury

By Michael Darwin

Life Extension Magazine, July/August, 1977. Reprinted in Cryonics, 4th Quarter, 2008

---

* Anabolocyte is a coined word used to describe the repair device discussed here. It comes from the world anabolism (anabole Gr. meaning a rising up) or constructive metabolism and the suffix -cyte (kytos Gr. a hollow) which is a terminal combining form meaning a cell. Thus, an anabolocyte is any artificially engineered cell designed to effect biological repair.

Those interested in suspended animation in its current state must often ask the tough question: "What sort of magical repair process could possibly reverse the freeze-induced injury brought on by low temperatures?" There aren't any hard answers; only possibilities can be suggested and probabilities estimated from them. Such an estimation is still a pretty subjective thing, which this author could not put at other than "non-zero."

Actually, despite the fact that the operation of freezing someone with existing techniques depends upon some type of repair process being possible, remarkably little thought has been given the matter. Aside from a proposal by R.C.W. Ettinger in *The Prospect of Immortality*[1] that "...huge surgeon machines, working twenty-four hours a day for decades or even centuries, will tenderly restore the frozen brains, cell by cell, or even molecule by molecule in critical areas," and the suggestion by Jerome White that specially programmed viruses be used[2], the repair aspects have been totally neglected.

Before presenting my own proposed scenario I would like to consider both of the above ideas. The robot surgeon idea has obvious practical limitations in terms of physical manipulation and economic/technological feasibility. Whether it is scientifically practicable is irrelevant; that it is economically beyond the resources of the contemporary patient is enough. The viral repair idea is another matter altogether and undoubtedly will be used to repair or "add to" cells. The only problem is that it will only prove effective when there is a metabolizing cell capable of implementing the genetic instructions carried by the specially programmed virus. Many cells will not have survived the freezing process with enough structure intact to resume high

---

1   Ettinger, R.C.W. *The Prospect of Immortality,* McFadden-Bartell, 1966.

2   White, J. *"Viral Induced Repair of Damaged Neurons with Preservation of Long Term Information Content."* Second Annual Cryonics Conference, April 11, 1969. Reprinted in *Cryonics* 35:10 (October 2014), 8-17.

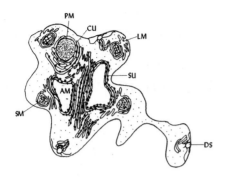

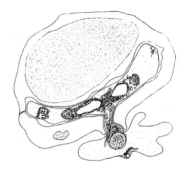

DRAWING 1: The Anabolocyte. The various parts are labelled: Conduit (CU); Program Module (PM); Synthesis Unit (SU); DS and LM are sensing and proteolysis units respectively.

DRAWING 2: The Anabolocyte breaking the junction of two capillary cells and squeezing out into the intracellular space. One of millions of such cells which would be at work in the patient.

energy metabolism and carry on normal cell functions like protein synthesis and osmoregulation. We need a mechanism capable of repairing inactive or structurally "dead" cells. Another requirement is that this approach be compatible with known or foreseeable technology and be able to act within a reasonable period of time and at reasonable cost in terms of resources. This is a very stringent set of conditions but, if we look to the emerging science of recombinant DNA technology, we may be able to "fabricate" some interesting solutions to the repair problem.

If we start with something like a normal white blood cell and assume it could be modified in most any way, we could build an ultra-miniature, self-reduplicating repair unit. White blood cells are particularly good candidates for this type of transformation because they already embody several of the properties we are seeking. They have the capacity to move through the capillary walls to reach sites of injury and/or infection, they are compatible with human physiology, and perhaps more importantly, they have some (although very limited) capacity for attaching themselves to damaged or malignant cells to either repair them or donate a lysosome and destroy them.

If we could modify white blood cells in any fashion, they could be used to crawl through the capillaries, seek out damaged cells (perhaps by following a "track" of lysosomal enzymes which are related to cryoinjury) and initiate a repair sequence.

The first of the accompanying drawings shows the anabolocyte. I have taken the liberty of assigning new names to the various intracellular organelles since in many cases they will behave differently from the original and may, depending upon our technological limitations, even be made of different materials than the original. "PM" is the Program Module and is the equivalent of the nucleus. The PM will be responsible for directing anabolocyte activities, from targeting through completion of the repairsequence. "SU" is the Synthesis Unit; it is here that new replacement organelles for the damaged originals will be fabricated. "SM" is the Storage Module which will contain high energy compound reserves and necessary raw materials that are not available on site. The Conduit, shown here as "CU," will bring newly-assembled macromolecules or building blocks to the Synthesis Unit. "DS" and "LM" are sensing and proteolysis units respectively. These last two units will be used to vector the anabolocyte and decompose damaged cell components for raw materials.

The anabolocyte may be designed to work at high subzero temperatures (say -15°C or -20°C) in the presence of some inert antifreeze agent such as one of the silicon based glycols. In any event, it will be a highly specific piece of genetic engineering designed to act autonomously and in a very precise fashion.

The second drawing shows the anabolocyte breaking the junction of two capillary cells and squeezing out into the intracellular space. There will, of course, be millions or even billions of these organisms released into the vasculature of the patient, each one targeted on locating and repairing a non-functioning cell, and most importantly, all acting simultaneously.

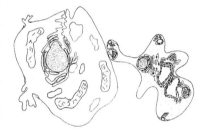 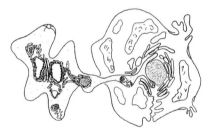

DRAWING 3: The Anabolocyte attaching itself to a damaged cell. The cell has suffered catastrophically as a consequence of being ischemic, frozen and then thawed.

DRAWING 4: The anabolocyte has begun the first step in the repair sequence, it has opened the cell membrane and has begun to appropriate nuclear information.

In drawing 3 we see the anabolocyte attaching itself to a damaged cell. This cell has suffered catastrophically as a consequence of being ischemic, frozen and then thawed. The cell membrane has been compromised, the ribosomes are dissociated, the cristae of the mitochondria have been disrupted and there is even nuclear vacoulization and rupture of the nuclear membrane. Clearly, this is what we could call our worst case injury. Looking at this mass of shattered structure, it is hard to visualize how anything could possibly restore it to normalcy.

In drawing 4 the anabolocyte has begun the first step in the repair sequence, it has opened the cell membrane and has begun to appropriate nuclear information. At this

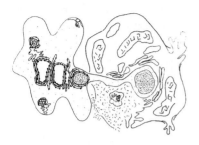

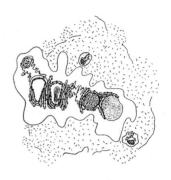

DRAWING 5: *The anabolocyte begins to pour out proteolytic enzymes which digest the old damaged structures after having sequestered the information contained in the cell nucleus.*

DRAWING 6: *The beginning steps of fabricating a new cell. The anabolocyte begins elaborating new structure into the Synthesis Module.*

juncture it is important to emphasize that this particular repair process is workable only for non-neuronal tissue. Nerve cells with information-containing dendrites and protein molecules would require an alternate repair sequence which would simply replace the defective metabolic equipment.

Once the information contained in the damaged cell nucleus has been sequestered, the anabolocyte begins pouring out proteolytic enzymes which digest the old damaged structures (drawing 5). Fortunately, nuclear information is very stable. By and large, genetic material is unaffected by conditions which are incredibly disruptive to other cellular structures. Even freeze drying, under the proper conditions, is not incompatible with the retention of genetic information.

Drawing 6 shows the beginning steps of fabricating a new cell. The anabolocyte begins elaborating new structure into the Synthesis Module, and actually step by step modifies its own structure and metabolism to conform to the blueprint contained in the original cell nucleus. The original damaged components from the "parent" cell are broken down into their component molecules and are used as raw material for synthesizing new structure.

DRAWING 7: *The finished product; a new operational cell in every way as good as the original*

Finally in drawing 7, we have a new, operational cell, which is in every way as good as the original, and hopefully contains improvements such as prolonged resistance to ischemia, immunity from aging and viral attack and just perhaps, a total lack of susceptibility to cryoinjury. ■

CELL REPAIR TECHNOLOGY

BY BRIAN WOWK, PH.D.

Cryonics, July, 1988

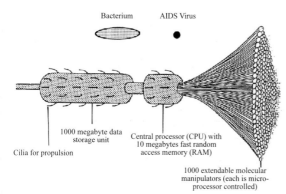

Bacterium   AIDS Virus

1000 megabyte data storage unit

Cilia for propulsion

Central processor (CPU) with 10 megabytes fast random access memory (RAM)

1000 extendable molecular manipulators (each is microprocessor controlled)

Cell Repair Unit

So you're talking about being able to put on the order of 1,000 Motorola 68000 CPU's in the volume of a bacterial cell. — Eric Drexler, Research Affiliate, MIT Artificial Intelligence Laboratory

This article will focus on the medical implications of a mature nanotechnology. In particular, it will be argued in broad technical terms why nanotechnology implies a medicine capable of reversing not only any organic disease (including aging), but also a host of supposedly irreversible injuries, including *severe freezing injury, ischemic injury,* and even *destruction of all non-brain tissues.* In short, a foreseeable future technology will be presented which would seem to give present cryonics practice a reasonable (perhaps even good) chance of success.

2006 note from the author: My primary regret about this article is that it inadequately credits Eric Drexler for first outlining the feasibility of molecular nanotechnology and its biological repair implications. Still, I believe there are some ideas, and ways of expressing ideas, in this paper that are original. Like much of what is now called nanomedicine, the capabilities discussed here are generally beyond what will be necessary to reverse cryopreservation by modern vitrification under good conditions.

Beyond Drugs

What kind of medical advances will molecular engineering bring? Simple extrapolation of present trends in biotechnology would lead one to expect a greatly expanded range of drugs and other bioregulatory compounds. Indeed, mature nanotechnology will allow inexpensive manufacture of *any* molecule that does (or could) exist in nature.

Yet a larger medicine chest is only the most obvious—and least significant—medical implication of nanotechnology. More profoundly, nanotechnology will render obsolete drugs as we know them today.

The use of drugs (simple chemicals) in medicine epitomizes the difference between today's medicine and tomorrow's. Drugs do not heal patients; *drugs merely assist patients in healing themselves.* Drugs are useless when injuries greatly exceed natural healing capacities (particularly when tissues are rendered non-functional by injury). In fact, caring for patients with drugs is not unlike trying to repair and maintain an automobile using just simple fuel additives!

If today's drugs are the medical equivalent of fuel additives, then tomorrow's nanotechnology will be the equivalent of a complete repair shop for the human body. Advanced means for engineering at the molecular level will lead not only to complex new molecules (drugs), but to complex aggregates of molecules—*molecular machines*—with unprecedented medical functions. Among these functions will be abilities to vastly augment, and even bypass natural healing processes (by repairing cells and tissues directly), thus freeing medicine from its historic reliance on innate healing capacities.

Cell Repair Systems

How can medicine repair individual cells? By learning to manipulate the most basic components of cells—atoms and molecules.

What kind of technology will allow medicine to do this? One that is not substantially different *in kind* compared to "technology" already existing in nature. Natural cells and organisms already perform extremely complex feats of molecular synthesis, manipulation, repair, and replacement as part of their normal function. As biologists gain more complete understanding of cell growth and development in the decades ahead, a variety of powerful techniques for augmenting natural healing processes will become available. Foreseeable developments include the use of synthetic growth factors and morphogens for inducing complex tissue regeneration, and even the introduction of novel genetic programs for reversing cellular and tissue injuries for which natural healing mechanisms do not exist. No doubt these techniques will have broad application in the control and reversal of ischemic and freezing injuries which are irreversible at present.

Even more powerful technologies are foreseeable over the long term. With a view toward advanced molecular engineering capabilities, this article will frame a "brute force" argument for the reversibility of almost any biological injury. It will be argued that practical devices are theoretically possible that, if necessary, could perform complete *atom-by-atom* characterization and repair of tissue.

What tools could possibly be small enough to repair cells in such detail, and how could we ever build them? The answers are: Tools like those that cells already use to repair and maintain themselves, which we will build much as cells do.

Cells maintain themselves using a variety of molecular machines (machines constructed to molecular specifications), including enzymes for fine operations and cytoskeletal structures for grosser manipulations. Nanotechnology will allow us to build any of these molecular machines (and more), and to assemble them in ways not seen in nature—ways that achieve complex medical objectives. Among these objectives will be sophisticated cell repair.

Baseline Capabilities

The development of nanotechnological cell repair systems can, in part, be viewed as the creation of artificial microorganisms for medical purposes. (Indeed, experimental usage of modified retroviruses for gene therapy today is a kind of cell repair technology.) It therefore follows that appropriately designed medical microbes, or *cell repair devices*, could *at a minimum* do anything that natural cells and their components are known to do today.

Access

White blood cells show that molecular machines can leave a patient's blood stream and move through tissues in a very general manner. Cell repair devices with non-antigenic (or immune compatible) exteriors will therefore similarly be able to reach most any cell in the body.

Viruses demonstrate that systems of molecular machinery can penetrate cell membranes and enter their interiors. More dramatically, successful transplantation of cell nuclei by today's biologists demonstrates that cells can often naturally recover from even extreme membrane and cytoplasmic trauma. Repair devices the size of ordinary organelles will therefore be able enter the interior of cells and move about freely without causing significant harm. (Note that this does not even consider the potential of repair devices to *themselves* repair structures they disturb.)

Disassembly

Digestive enzymes show that molecular machines can disassemble large molecular aggregates. Repair devices incorporating tools analogous to these enzymes will therefore be able to perform *controlled* disassembly of cell structures as part of analysis and repair processes.

Analysis

The ability of antibodies to distinguish among proteins, the ability of enzymes to distinguish among potential substrates, and many other biological processes demonstrate that molecular machines can recognize specific kinds molecules on the basis of shape and charge distribution. Cell repair devices will therefore be able to employ sets of tools for identifying and analyzing biomolecules by touch. Since larger cell structures generally contain biomolecules unique to them, repair devices will be able to similarly identify these structures by "feeling" them.

Reassembly

The molecular synthesis machinery of natural cells shows that damaged cell structures can be rebuilt and/or reassembled by molecular machines. Indeed, cell replication is direct proof that every structure in a cell can be assembled from even simple nutrient molecules by molecular machinery.

Functional Integration

The above discussion shows that every basic capability required for a sophisticated cell repair technology is already demonstrated in nature. Molecular tools already exist (and undoubtedly others are possible) that could be implemented in future medical devices to allow controlled disassembly, analysis, and repair of cell structures at the molecular level. It remains for advancing molecular technology (which at a highly advanced point will become true nanotechnology) to integrate these tools into microscopic devices capable of advanced medical functions.

The inherent feasibility of constructing such cell repair devices can be viewed in terms of their chemical stability. My article on nanotechnology (*Cryonics*, May 1988, p. 24-38) argued that progress in protein engineering (and other fields) is leading to a technology base that will eventually be broad enough to assemble molecular structures of arbitrary complexity. Therefore, as long as the cell repair hardware proposed in this article is *chemically stable,* it should eventually be *manufacturable.*

Thus we appear to already have all the basic components needed for cell repair devices, and are only awaiting the means to assemble them. In the meantime, we can use current physical, biological, and engineering knowledge to outline the possible nature of these devices—and their ultimate capabilities.

Control

Although not strictly necessary for many repair tasks, the most broadly powerful way to control the activities of a cell repair device would be to equip it with an onboard nanocomputer. Theoretical design concepts suggest that data storage densities on the order of a gigabyte per cubic micron (one thousandth the volume of a typical cell) may be achievable in computers built to atomic specifications. *This is sufficient storage to characterize an entire cell in complete molecular detail* (see **notes**). While packing a mainframe computer inside a cell may seem like overkill, knowing that this may be possible provides the security of knowing that nanotechnological cell repair systems could fix virtually anything.

Consider aging for example. We do not at present know all the changes that occur in cells with aging, although they are probably quite extensive. Regardless of how extensive, however, **none would escape detection** by a nanocomputer-equipped repair system capable of entering a cell and probing its entire molecular inventory. On the basis of such complete characterization (and general comparison with data obtained from similar young cells) onboard software could determine what repairs were necessary to return an aged cell to a youthful state. Once repairs were completed, the repaired cell would be in every way indistinguishable from a young cell. Indeed, it would once again be a young cell.

Communications

Many repair tasks (especially ones as extensive as cryoinjury repair) will require communications between widely distributed devices both within and outside of cells. Rather than lugging a cubic micron nanocomputer all over a cell to perform repairs, for example, it would seem simpler to have the computer supervise the operation of many smaller devices from a central location in the cell.

One possible communications system would use serial data channels two to three nanometers in diameter consisting of sheathed carbyne rods. Carbyne is a polymer consisting of carbon atoms joined by alternating single and triple bonds (a molecular structure exploited extensively in theoretical nanocomputer designs). Since the speed of sound in carbyne is over ten kilometers per second, a mechanical signal transmission rate of a gigabaud (billion bits per second) seems a conservative performance estimate for such channels. Many other communication schemes suitable for cell repair systems are also conceivable, such as electrically conductive channels or diffusible chemicals analogous to morphogens and hormones in nature.

As well as providing a means for coordinating repairs within the body, it should also be noted that these communications channels could be used to transfer data processing tasks to computers *outside* the body. This might be useful in instances of extremely severe brain injury (such as a day of ischemia), when inferring the correct pre-injury state becomes a problem too complicated for *in-situ* computers. A communications system consisting of just one gigabaud channel per cell could, for example, transmit a complete atom-by-atom description of a biostatic brain (assuming one byte per atom) to external computers in less than a month. Thus, data processing requirements will never be a fundamental obstacle to solving biological repair problems.

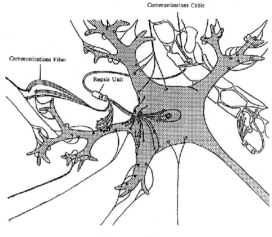

Neuronal Repair

Power

Like natural cells, cell repair devices will require power to perform their activities. For most diagnostic and repair tasks, tapping into the same chemical energy sources as natural cells (such as glucose/ oxygen and ATP) should be sufficient. As long as repair processes proceeded at a pace comparable to normal cell functions, utilization of these chemicals need not overtax natural supplies.

Repair of non-functional tissue presents a problem. Tissues with blocked circulation or failed metabolism could not naturally supply energy to fuel repair processes. One possible solution would be an active transport system, similar to axoplasmic transport in nerve cells. Fibrils originating at distant sites could penetrate inactive tissues and cytoplasm to power repair devices by moving nutrients in a conveyor system through hollow interiors. Raw materials for repairs and fibril growth could be similarly supplied.

In fact, a network of trophic fibrils raises the possibility of powering cell repair devices by an entirely *non-biological* means: electricity. Part of the fibril structure could incorporate an insulated organic conductor, such as doped polyacetylene (which could serve communications needs as well). Electrochemical processes within the repair device could then continuously recycle a chemical energy currency, such as ATP, which would directly energize enzymatic repair functions. Alternatively, nano-scale electrostatic actuators or enzymes with electric field-sensitive conformational states might be able to make direct use of electric power for performing repair tasks.

Cryogenic Operation

One particular application of future cell repair technology—recovery of today's cryonic suspension patients—will optimally require repairs at cryogenic temperatures (temperatures below -100°C). Operations best performed at these temperatures would include inhibiting metabolic enzymes (until repairs were completed), locking loose structures in place, and analyzing ice crystal positions to aid in proper restoration of mechanically disturbed cell structures. In fact, warming present-day suspension patients before disruptive ice crystals could be properly analyzed might even be fatal (i.e., lead to irreversible loss of critical identity information).

Fortunately, a variety of design possibilities exists for cryogenic repair devices. One possibility would be molecular machines similar to natural cells, but with water replaced by a cryogenic solvent. Some natural enzymes are known to retain their function in liquid ammonia, others in supercritical carbon dioxide, thus demonstrating that water does not have a monopoly on support of biological processes. Artificial enzyme systems based on natural peptides, or other polymers with protein-like conformational properties, could in principle operate in cryogenic solvents such as tetrafluoromethane, or perhaps even liquid nitrogen. Although conventional biochemistry is nonexistent at these temperatures, faster alternate chemistries could be exploited.

In fact, chemistry (in the sense of forming and breaking chemical bonds) is not even necessary for the operation of some molecular machines. The rod logic systems which underlie current (theoretical) nanocomputer designs, for example, are a clockwork of precisely-configured molecular components interacting *mechanically*, not chemically. Not only is random jostling (heat) unnecessary for the operation of such a system, it is a *handicap*. Repair devices of this sort—molecular machines resembling conventional machines on a nanoscale—would find ultra-low temperatures an ideal operating environment.

Of course, regardless of how they operate internally, repair devices will have to make chemical changes to tissues they are repairing. Yet even this does not require high temperatures in the ordinary sense. Molecular tools driven by electrical (or low-temperature chemical) actuators could provide localized kinetic energy for forming or breaking chemical bonds. Indeed, by suitably "banging" or "grabbing" target molecules it is possible to create effectively any "temperature" at a single reaction site. Thus a fairly wide range of biological repair processes could in principle be carried out at cryogenic temperatures, thereby giving future cell repair technology a greater degree of versatility—and present cryonics practice a greater chance of success.

Practical Consequences

Assuming future molecular engineering capabilities (nanotechnology), this article has sketched the outlines of a medical technology which would operate at the most fundamental level of living things—the molecular level. What would be the *practical* implications of a technology which could take apart, analyze, and repair cells like so many machine parts?

Ultimate Medicine

Disease, whether its causes be internal or external, is a malfunction of the human body—a breakdown that detracts from well-being. Curing, not just alleviating, disease has always been a difficult task for medicine: both the tools and the knowledge required to effectively repair the body have been lacking. Thus medicine has historically been (and largely still is) an uncertain art, with very limited understanding of disease processes, and even less understanding of how to intervene in them. Indeed, physicians today are in a predicament similar to that which would be faced by 18th-century engineers trying to maintain a 20th-century automobile: repairs would be crude at best, and breakdown inevitable.

Like primitive engineers faced with advanced technology, medicine must "catch up" with the technology level of the human body before it can become really effective. What is this "technology level"? Since the human body is basically an extremely complex system of interacting molecules (i.e., a molecular machine), the technology required to truly understand and repair the body is molecular machine technology— nanotechnology.

Mature nanotechnology will mean an ability to routinely design and build "machines" as intricate as our cells from scratch. A natural consequence of this level of technology will be the ability to analyze and repair the human body as completely and effectively as we can repair any conventional machine today. Nanotechnology will mean no more guesswork, uncertain cures, or untreatable organic conditions; medicine will finally be equal to the task of understanding and controlling the body in terms of its most fundamental machine components—atoms and molecules.

Future medicine will attain this degree of understanding and control through cell repair systems based on technologies and devices like those outlined in this article— microscopic devices able to roam throughout cells and tissues, diagnosing and repairing problems at the cellular and molecular levels. Since disease is a malfunction of the body, and since the body functions by means of molecular machinery, it follows that molecular-level medicine will be able to cure any disease.

This observation particularly applies to the most prevalent and deadly disease on earth today—aging. Whatever biological changes underlie aging, they must involve changes in molecules, and must therefore be amenable to control by molecular-level medicine. It seems clear that cell repair technology would allow one's biological age to be not only arrested, but reversed, and even adjusted at whim. These are the implications of a technology able to repair and maintain the body at a molecular level. *With sufficiently advanced repair technology our bodies need never deteriorate or break down as they do today.*

Injury Repair

Cell repair technology will allow a variety of powerful approaches for reversing injuries that cannot be healed naturally.

On a basic level, cell repair technology will naturally mean an ability to repair individual cells. This will be particularly important for cells which contain crucial, irreplaceable information, such as brain cells. On this level, the potential of cell repair technology appears quite broad. Even when cells are rendered completely non-functional by poison, infection, ischemia, freezing injury, and indeed any other injury, repair devices will always be able to enter cells, assess the situation, and restore the cells to a healthy condition matching an inferred pre-injury state.

On another level, cell repair technology will also mean a very general ability to *replace* cells. Cell repair devices will be able to exercise complete control over cell growth and development: they will be able to control and modify cell DNA in sophisticated ways to achieve virtually any desired growth objectives. Among these objectives will be many kinds of healing not seen in nature, such as healing of major injuries, severed spinal cords, and even replacement of lost brain tissue. More ambitiously, regrowth of lost limbs, organs, and even *entire bodies* is implicitly possible with complete control over cell growth and development. (After all, nature already demonstrates an ability to grow these items from scratch.)

Indeed, the biological repair potential of cell repair technology appears so vast that it might just be simplest to ask whether there is anything this technology *couldn't* fix.

The answer to this question becomes apparent as one contemplates the effect of increasingly extensive repairs to the body. It is possible to imagine instances of repair so extensive that the healed patient would no longer be the "original" patient. Specifically, this will occur when injuries begin to impinge on a patient's brain. Although cell repair technology appears capable of reversing any injury, it will not be able to restore brain information lost during injury. Brain information loss will pose a fundamental limitation for future medicine—and the ultimate dividing line between life and death.

Fatalities

The only causes of death for 22nd century medicine will be severe injuries *directly* to the brain. Offhand, this might not seem plausible: wouldn't, say, drowning or gunshot wounds to the heart be fatal? No, these injuries can cause cardiac arrest and ensuing coma, but they are not in themselves fatal. Oxygen starvation, cessation of circulation, even complete collapse of normal tissue metabolism does not mean a person is really dead.

Consider a patient whose ischemic (non-functional) body is recovered several hours after drowning. Although such a patient would be relegated to a morgue today, this would be unthinkable in an era of cell repair technology (or even today, with cryonic suspension available). With the basic structure of the person's brain still intact, cell repair devices could be deployed throughout the body to repair cellular injuries caused by the hours of absent blood flow. After several days of repairs conducted at deep hypothermic temperatures (to prevent further deterioration), staged restart of metabolism would be performed by selective unblocking of metabolic enzymes as the patient was warmed. The patient would then emerge from his coma in perfect health, with perhaps mild amnesia as the only remnant of what had happened. Indeed, not until decomposition led to major loss of brain structure would drowning victims, or other victims of protracted ischemia (absent blood flow), be beyond recovery by cell repair technology.

A significant point about future fatalities (one particularly relevant to appreciating cryonics) is how it will be known when patients are beyond recovery: in most cases, it won't be known. As long as some brain structure remains, it will *always* be possible to reconstruct a patient's brain and body on the basis of persisting information. The success of such reconstruction—the extent to which to the patient's life would be saved—would depend on how much memory and personality could be salvaged by the repair process. Only if complete loss of memory and personality were evident *after* repair (and perhaps not even then) would the original patient likely be regarded as dead.

Thus death (as rare as it will be) will have a radically different character in the future. There will never be "dead" bodies, only lost bodies, ischemic bodies, or amnesiac bodies following extensive injury repair. A future variation on a contemporary cliche might be, "Where there's brain structure, there's hope."

Lifespan

With disease, aging, and primitive medicine all unpleasant memories, just how long people could live in a nanotechnic era is very much an open question.

Many books about "life extension" quote 600 years as a probable life expectancy if aging were ever eliminated (a figure arrived at on the basis of "fatal" accident statistics). Yet this figure cannot be accepted as valid: it assumes fatal accidents to consist of injuries causing cardiac arrest—no consideration is given to advanced means of reversing ischemic injuries following cardiac arrest (as discussed above). Indeed, if people were routinely fitted with emergency transmitters to facilitate prompt rescue in the event of severe injury (say, within several hours of cardiac arrest), the only causes of death in an era of advanced cell repair would be immediately—and *dramatically*—destructive accidents. Just how destructive such accidents might have to be is suggested at the end of the next and final section.

Homo Perfectus

All discussion thus far has focused on the potential of nanotechnology for restoring and maintaining health. Yet technologies as powerful as those described here cannot help but invite an additional line of inquiry: What might we do to our bodies *beyond* just healing them?

Consider the potential of nanocomputers for not just repairing the nervous system, but for *augmenting* it. A nanocomputer one cubic millimeter in volume could hold one billion gigabytes of data—more information than in all the world's libraries at present. Implanting such a computer within the brain, and routing its output to visual centers, would be the ultimate in library service—all of human knowledge available for instant mental lookup.

Then there is also the *physical* side of nanotechnology. The physical capacities of our body are the result of blind choices of evolutionary development, not optimum design. These capacities are often far from the limits of what is theoretically possible.

Consider muscle function. Microstructured materials analogous to muscle tissue have been designed as part of contemporary efforts to better understand nanotechnology. One particular design consists of electrostatic motors 50 nanometers in diameter driving a matrix of fine diamond fiber. The resultant material has the tensile strength of steel, and could efficiently deliver *megawatts* of mechanical power per cubic centimeter (see **notes**). By replacing ordinary muscle with material of this sort we could (conservatively) increase our physical strength hundreds of times.

Finally, not only could we make ourselves stronger and smarter with nanotechnology, we could also make ourselves *tougher*. How much tougher? By replacing connective and skeletal proteins with covalent carbon microstructures (a necessary prerequisite for greatly increased strength) tough enough to routinely survive some of the most destructive accidents known today—even aircraft accidents.

Perhaps most remarkable of all, none of these changes would require any dramatic change in our external appearance. ■

Notes and References

1. *"So you're talking about . . ."* (at the top of this article) is a quote from "Molecular Technology And Cell Repair Machines", a talk delivered by K. Eric Drexler at the 1985 Lake Tahoe Life Extension Festival on May 25, 1985.

    My article on nanotechnology (*Cryonics*, May 1988) argued that the technology base required to assemble molecular structures as complex as cell repair devices is essentially unavoidable if technological progress continues through the next century. Relevant arguments and references will not be repeated here.

    A typical cell contains several billion macromolecules of perhaps 100,000 different types—arranged in a decidedly non-random pattern. By employing specialized coordinate systems and data structures suited to natural cellular organization, a gigabyte (one cubic micron of nanocomputer storage) should be more than adequate to hold a complete molecular description of a cell. (See the article on nanotechnology [*Cryonics*, May 1988] for a more detailed discussion of projected nanocomputing technologies.)

2. *"none would escape detection . . . ";* It is a virtual tautology that any molecular changes significant enough to adversely affect normal cell operation would not escape detection by molecular-level repair systems.

The two proposed design strategies for cryogenic repair devices (enzymes in a cryogenic solvent vs. precisely-configured molecular machinery) are respective examples of type O and type M molecular technology. Type O (organic) technology refers to molecular machines patterned after natural cells (bags of reacting chemicals), whereas type M (mechanical) technology refers to molecular machines patterned after conventional macromachines on a nanoscale (arrays of inert mechanically interacting components). Low temperature behavior is only one respect in which these two technologies differ. Further fundamental differences are explored in "Biological and Nanomechanical Systems: Contrasts in Evolutionary Capacity", by K. Eric Drexler, in *Artificial Life*, edited by Christopher Langton, Addison-Wesley, 1988.

One extremely important point made in the above essay is that type M technology is completely incapable of harmful mutation. While natural microorganisms (type O molecular machines) have a high evolutionary capacity (indeed, they have evolved to evolve), type M molecular machines will be no more capable of evolution than household appliances. (Alterations in structure would generally result in outright breakdown rather than a change in basic function.) Thus, while cell repair devices are often described as artificial "microbes" to aid in visualizing them, it should be realized that they will be more like miniature conventional machines than true life forms. As such, they will pose no danger whatsoever to the environment or other human beings (unless they are deliberately designed to do so).

Synthetic muscle with power densities of megawatts per cubic centimeter would in practice always be limited by power and heat dissipation constraints. Yet even within these constraints fantastic feats of strength would be possible. In an anaerobic burst of effort, a nanotechnological "super human" could for example lift a 4,000 pound automobile over his/her head with a body temperature rise of only 2°F, and energy consumption of 100 calories—less energy than in a typical candy bar (assuming only 10% efficient conversion). This is not comic book fantasy, but firm physical calculation. For more detailed discussion of a "muscle" design which would make this possible, see pp. 258-259, *Engines Of Creation*, by K. Eric Drexler, Anchor Press/Doubleday, Garden City, NY, 1986.

"Realistic" Scenario for Nanotechnological Repair of the Frozen Human Brain

By Gregory Fahy, Ph.D.

Reprinted from Cryonics: Reaching for Tomorrow,
Alcor Life Extension Foundation, 1991.

Abstract

Guidelines are suggested for designing realistic and defensible nanotechnological repair scenarios for the frozen human brain. A scenario is developed which is based on a) replacing brain ice with repair networks below T_g (the glass transition temperature of a system), b) carrying out gross structural repairs at temperatures in the range of about -100 to -30 degrees C, and c) carrying out most intracellular repairs at more elevated temperatures, relying in part on ordinary biological self-assembly and self-repair for carrying out much of the work required. The presently suggested scenario is intended as a rough outline that can facilitate rational discussion of the feasibility of repair. No mathematical analysis is attempted in this first specific description of "realistic" approaches to the repair of the frozen human brain.

Introduction

I. Definition

"Realistic" scenarios for repair are defined here as scenarios that might actually be applied, with appropriate modifications, to the restoration of the brains of patients in cryonic suspension. These may be distinguished from general proofs-of-principle (1,2,3) that attempt to demonstrate general feasibility without considering documented biological problems in detail, or that present the limits of the possible without considering what is most efficient, practical, and likely. No "realistic" repair scenarios have previously been proposed to the knowledge of the author.

II. Desirable Attributes of Repair Scenarios

Scenarios for repair of the frozen human brain should satisfy a number of important requirements. Although the scenario proposed here is based on the following guidelines, it does not include a self evaluation of feasibility (see "Testability" below) and does not attempt to be a fully-developed and fully-documented work.

Factual Basis. First, realistic repair scenarios must be based on what is known or can be inferred about the nature of the actual injury present in frozen brains and frozen brain tissue. This is mandatory because, by the definition above, a realistic scenario attempts to set forth specific approaches to solving the problems of repair, which is impossible if the problems are not clearly and accurately identified. It is essential to avoid addressing problems that do not exist and to avoid overlooking important difficulties that are likely to arise. Focusing on real problems is perhaps the best way to realize a technically compelling result.

Parsimony. Second, the repair scenario should be parsimonious. It should not attempt to do more than the minimum amount of work required for a satisfactory result. The reason for this is that smaller jobs are more easily and more credibly solved than larger ones, and the goal of a repair scenario is to demonstrate the feasibility of repair. The fewer the number of tasks required for repair, the more likely it is that these tasks can be accomplished. This of course does not mean that any real problem should be minimized or ignored, but it does mean that needless tasks (such as keeping track of individual sodium atoms) should not be considered. Parsimony requires distinctions to be made between what is important and what is not important.

Detail. Third, parsimony in selecting problems to solve does not necessarily imply parsimony in describing the details of the problem solving process. Too much detail is likely to be confused with fortune telling, which would be inappropriate. However, when the appearance of fortune telling can be avoided, hard detail lends reality to the scenario, particularly if it is backed up by numbers. Thus, rather than just saying, for example, "the fractures will [somehow!] be removed from the data base," it would be more plausible to spell out in detail a defensible molecular plan of attack on the problem.

Testability. Fourth, of course, the repair scenario must be physically achievable. Ideally, it should be possible to evaluate each step of the repair scenario quantitatively to test its feasibility. Each step should also be specific enough for a more general evaluation of its feasibility to be made. In short, the scenario should be testable and falsifiable in all ways possible. A recent criticism by Fahy of previous discussions of repair of frozen brains (4) focused in part on such evaluations, e.g., evaluating the feasibility of providing power for nanoprocedures at cryogenic temperatures. Although the latter criticism and many similar points will not be addressed here, a consideration of such details is important for fully-developed scenarios.

Defining The Problem: Freezing Damage
I. What Is and Is Not Considered

The repair scenario described here deliberately ignores extraneous problems such as postmortem damage, transport injury, circulatory obstruction, and previous traumatic brain damage or other devastating types of cerebral deterioration because these problems represent side issues and are not inevitable given the level of hospital cooperation that has frequently been achieved. Furthermore, legal changes could allow freezing to be carried out under much better conditions, so that fewer such problems will arise. Other types of repair scenario should if necessary (and possible) be devised to address these problems separately. However, the damage caused by cryoprotectant perfusion prior to freezing is discussed.

The repair scenario will assume conventional preservation, i.e., the brain is not fixed prior to freezing: repair scenarios for fixed brains are likely to be substantially different from what follows, for substantially different problems will be present. It will also be assumed that the "Smith Criterion" (5) is attained or bettered: grossly inadequate concentrations of cryoprotectant will produce such massive mechanical damage (6) that repair, if it is possible at all, may well depend on different principles than those described here.

The discussion that follows in the next two sections is necessarily based on limited information, some of which may be misleading. It goes without saying that more research is needed on every point discussed. The incompleteness of present information, however, does not appear to be sufficient to preclude meaningful evaluations and the development of reasonable repair scenarios. The format of the next two sections will consist of a series of statements describing potential problems followed in each case by an evaluation of the problem's likely relative seriousness.

II. Perfusion Damage and its Significance
Rabbit brains fixed after perfusion with glycerol at temperatures above 10-15 degrees C and examined histologically do not show loss of ground substance or substantial morphological alterations (6). Glycerol perfusion under low temperature conditions can, when concentrations are high (6 M), cause extensive shrinkage of the brain as a whole and of the component cells and processes, with distorted histological staining (7, unpublished observations).

Evaluation. Cell shrinkage may cause problems similar to those that occur during freezing, and will thus be considered in more detail below. Perfusion, unlike freezing, however, may remove proteins and cellular debris from the brain. Unless enormous concentrations of glycerol are used, however, extensive protein loss from previously undamaged brains appears unlikely. Altered staining implies, at worst, altered chemistry, particularly since staining is done when, presumably, all glycerol has been removed from the tissue. However, structural preservation of such brains is apparent (6,7), and it is quite possible that altered staining is the result of unusual fixation in the presence of glycerol or similar artifacts. If chemical changes have taken place as a result of glycerol exposure, these changes should be reversible due to their stereotypical nature and the identifiability of the chemically modified sites: actual information loss is not likely. Moreover, these chemical changes do not appear likely in the usual case, in which brains are perfused with lower concentrations of glycerol than 6 M.

Some chemical alterations by glycerol are likely in even the best situations. These alterations, however, primarily should be altered levels of ordinary metabolic intermediates due to the actions of enzymes on glycerol (8) or due to the differential effects of glycerol on the kinetics of different enzymes (9). As such, they are fundamentally trivial and close to being spontaneously reversible. Glycerol has apparently never been documented to denature any protein under any conditions, with the possible exception of glycerol in concentrations in excess of 95% w/w (10), a condition not remotely approached in cryonic suspension, even during the freezing phase of the process (11).

III. Freezing Damage: Significance of Different Types of Damage

1. "Biochemical/biophysical" freezing injury. Imagine the appearance of a "frozen" brain cell. Approximately 60% of the volume of the brain has been converted into extracellular ice (5). Freezing has extracted large fractions of the intracellular water and thereby reduced cell volume (12). This in turn has reduced cell surface area, which has the potential of forcing an expulsion of membrane material from the plane of the membrane (see below). The combination of cellular shrinkage, lowered temperature, and elevated glycerol concentrations may cause the following kinds of damage.

    a) Extrusion of pure lipid species from the plasma membrane, either on tethers (13,14) or as free lipid droplets in the cytoplasm (15) or in the extracellular space (proportional to the reduction in membrane surface area produced by freezing).

    Evaluation. This is a phenomenon seen so far only in plants. Shedding of lipid to free-floating extracellular droplets has not been seen even in plants. As long as any lipid extrusions are intracellular or still attached to the cell of origin, it should be clear where to redistribute the lipid on warming, if necessary. The main difficulty arises from the inability of lipid extruded in this way to spontaneously return to the plane of the membrane during volume expansion on thawing: restoration of approximately isotonic volume near the melting point causes cellular lysis in plant cells (13-15) due to inadequate membrane surface area. This should be a relatively easy problem to address and does not involve appreciable information loss on freezing.

    b) Loss of membrane proteins (possibly including hormone receptors and potassium channels) into the extracellular space.

Evaluation. Loss of glutamate receptors has been documented in brain tissue frozen without cryoprotectant (16). The number, state, and precise anatomical distribution of potassium channels in hippocampal dendrite membranes probably encodes memory to a large degree (17), so the potential loss of these membrane proteins is of concern. However, significant neurotransmitter receptor loss has only been seen when no cryoprotectant was used at all, in two papers in the literature (16). In all other cases (18), even when only low concentrations of extracellular cryoprotectant (sucrose) were present (19), all functions tested have been present, implying proper retention of membrane proteins. Even intracellular organelles do not redistribute/mix proteins to a worrisome degree after brain tissue is frozen and thawed (20). Thus, even excessive cellular shrinkage prior to freezing (caused by inadequate penetration of glycerol) superimposed on subsequent freeze-induced cell shrinkage should not subject cells to greater osmotic stress than has been shown experimentally (by freezing with only extracellular sucrose present as cryoprotectant [19]) not to cause major loss of membrane proteins.

Beyond this, however, are several other supportive observations. First, associative learning involves not just potassium channels but also changes in several other characteristic proteins that induce and maintain the alterations of potassium conductance underlying memory (17). Even loss of potassium channels should leave these remaining proteins behind, providing a clear indication of the "trained" vs "untrained" state of given dendritic synapses and/or perisynaptic regions. Second, altered K+ permeability probably involves durable chemical modification of the potassium channel, so that lost channels could be identified as "trained" or "untrained" and counted as such; improper return of individual molecules to specific synapses would likely be irrelevant as long as the proper total number of "trained" potassium channels ends up at each "trained" synapse or perisynaptic region. Finally, durability and inferability is further implied by the associative nature of memory, in which a given memory is stored redundantly in several brain regions in a number of independent forms (17,21), all of which are unlikely to be extinguished simultaneously in their entirety.

   c)   Denaturation of proteins.

Evaluation. Likely to apply, at most, to very few proteins (22). Furthermore, protein denaturation is inherently reversible (23). An apparently trivial issue.

   d)   Improper disulfide bridge formation between some proteins (24).

Evaluation. Also an almost negligible problem, for similar reasons.

   e)   Leakage of concentrated extracellular solute into brain cells.

Evaluation. Like membrane lipid loss, the main problem caused by this leakage, should it occur, would be expansion-induced lysis on thawing (25). Although the volume of extracellular space in the brain might be considered insufficient to permit lysis on warming, ultrastructural evidence of disruption of neuronal fine processes in frozen-thawed brains (26) as well as ultrastructural evidence of swelling of frozen-thawed synaptosomes (27) lends credibility to this possibility. However, this problem can be handled in principle even more easily than the lipid loss problem, simply by extruding the extra intracellular osmolyte during thawing. Not a significant problem.

   f)   Local leakage of brain cell solute to the extracellular space. This problem
        can be subdivided into leakage of small ions (primarily potassium) and small
        metabolites on the one hand and large metabolites and proteins on the other.

Evaluation. The former problem should be negligible; pumping potassium back into neurons should be straightforward (given non-leaky membranes: freeze-permeabilized membranes evidently reseal during warming and thawing [28]) and small metabolites can be resynthesized from supplied nutrients. Leakage of proteins and other large molecules is more serious. However, significant (e.g., 50%) uncorrected loss of intracellular soluble protein from cell bodies could probably be sustained without creating very serious problems, since it should be possible to institute compensatory controls over metabolic rate and membrane permeability consistent with the spontaneous ability of the cell to resynthesize missing proteins on warming. Even massive protein loss from cell bodies would not be able to erase cell identification, since cell identification will be encoded in the types of synapses the cell makes (which will be preserved [18]), by the pattern of genetic expression readable in the nucleus (which will probably also be preserved [29]), and by membrane and perhaps non-soluble cytoplasmic protein markers (which will be preserved well enough [20]).

A different kind of potential problem could result from protein loss from torn axon bundles (6,30). Severe losses of axoplasmic proteins at sites of tearing could make the identification of individual nerve fibers on both sides of tears more difficult, which may limit the ability to deduce the original connectivity of the brain. However, it is likely that a short distance away from the tear the axonal protein content should be largely unaffected by the tear, especially given the gel-like nature of axoplasm (31) and the relatively rigid structures mediating axoplasmic traffic.

Significant loss of proteins would undeniably complicate the restoration of metabolism significantly, and should be avoided to the extent possible: returning proteins to their proper sites would be comparatively difficult, and simply correcting for the losses as referred to above requires considerable metabolic "tinkering." Loss of non-proteinaceous larger metabolites once again could significantly complicate neuronal identification and would require considerable "Humpty Dumpty" work that would be best to avoid if possible. During freezing, such damage will be somewhat limited by the extracellular diffusion barriers presented by ice and high viscosity extracellular media, but during thawing the extracellular space will be progressively "stirred" by declining viscosity, thermal expansion, convection, and cellular expansion. Means of blocking this "stirring" would thus be important to deploy.

g) Precipitation of proteins and cellular buffers.

Evaluation. Little (32) direct evidence exists for this mode of injury; if it were to occur, the result would be reduced metabolic competence secondary to denatured or missing proteins or unfavorable pH's for normal metabolism. The remedies—supplying replacement buffer and/or proteins and restoring precipitated proteins and/or buffers to a soluble condition—seem fairly easy to deal with.

h) Leakage of lysosomal enzymes into the cytoplasm, predisposing to intracellular autolysis on warming (33).

Evaluation. Not demonstrated to occur. Glycerol and low temperatures can be expected to limit autolysis during cooling, and exogenous inhibitors should be able to control autolysis during warming. Not a serious problem.

i) Reorganization of membrane bilayer structure into HexII forms, i.e., cylindrical lipid tubes (34,35). This change is spontaneously reversible, in part, upon warming and rehydration, but will keep the membrane leaky in the cold. Phase separation of lipid subclasses within the membrane, producing leaks secondary to the resulting molecular packing faults in the membrane (36,37).

Evaluation. These are problems functionally comparable to osmotic or mechanically-induced leaks noted above. No direct evidence for HexII transitions exists for any mammalian system, and HexII forms appear unlikely in the presence of 3-4 M glycerol before freezing, since HexII is a dehydration form (35), and glycerol can prevent the required level of dehydration for HexII formation from taking place (11). In both HexII formation and more conventional phase separations, all membrane material remains in the membrane. The problem then becomes one of preventing additional leakage from taking place during thawing, and of redistributing solutes across membranes as needed after membrane resealing is completed. This seems achievable in principle. In the case of HexII, spontaneous reversal of the phase transition may lead to incorporation of lipid and protein into incorrect leaflets of the membrane. Controlled reversal, however, should be able to direct proper redistribution rather easily.

j) Breakdown of the structure of cytoplasm into blobs of proteinaceous material (38,39).

Evaluation. This may occur if there is a breach of the cell membrane or for other reasons that are so far poorly understood. So far, this phenomenon has been seen only in kidney, not in brain, and does not pertain to all cells, even in the kidney. If it should occur in brain, repair could be complicated, but it is doubtful that any actual information loss would occur. This change might be spontaneously reversible on warming.

2. Mechanical freezing injury. The most pressing kinds of damage are mechanical forms of damage, not only because it is this type of injury that has actually been observed in frozen-thawed brains, but also because the potential for actual information loss is much more serious than is the case for the biochemical challenges just considered. It is not yet certain that high concentrations of glycerol will prevent such injury consistently.

    Several kinds of mechanical injury could occur, including the following.

    a) Memory may be encoded in part in the shapes of dendritic trees (17); these shapes might be altered by freezing.

Evaluation. Dendritic remodeling associated with learning seems to involve massive changes such as deletion of unused synapses and unused dendritic branches (17). This remodeling is associated with the actions of many different proteins and, most likely, with considerable changes in remaining synapses (17). It is likely to be not the shape of the dendritic branchings that is important but, instead, the specific pattern of connections, and this pattern in turn is presumably responsible for the changes of shape of the dendritic trees (17). Thus, the shape changes induced by freezing and thawing should be irrelevant as long as the synapses and dendrites remain physically intact. Freezing is well known to spare synapses (18).

Although there is evidence for axonal (6) and possibly cellular (30) tearing, light microscopic evidence suggests that well-glycerolized hippocampal dendrites are not broken by freezing and thawing (6). But even considerable freeze-induced damage to dendrite branches might still leave the pattern of connections obvious from the remaining synapses. Dendrite branching patterns and their underlying biochemical correlates are biologically robust and dramatic and should retain a high degree of inferability, particularly if "stirring" is avoided during warming.

    b) Disruption of non-synaptic junctions between cells and capillary separation from the surrounding brain tissue.

Evaluation. Such problems have been observed (40), but would appear not to involve direct information loss. Such separations could tear fine processes, however, so the imperative to prevent extracellular diffusion on warming is reinforced again by such observations.

    c) Local (not global) ripping, twisting, and fraying of the ripped ends of nerve tracts by contraction of the brain cells and by the push of extracellular ice, creating debris-strewn gaps measured in microns in both length and thickness (6,30,40).

Evaluation. A severe form of damage. Reconstruction may require a certain degree of luck, i.e., the existence of positional relationships between nerve fibers in a given tract that do not vary significantly from one side of the gap to the other. Should such consistent positional relationships exist, inferring the proper connections at the site of a gap should be straightforward. However, if the positional relationships happen to be changing at the point of such a gap, additional information in the form of molecular markers that might identify individual fibers may be required for accurate inference of the pre-existing connectivity. Electrical tests across the gap may also be required to check for physiological consistency.

Should molecular markers be identical from one fiber to another, should positional relationships prove unreliable, and should electrical tests prove ambiguous, enough information for correct reconstruction may be present in the debris pattern that exists in the frozen state, considering the limited opportunities that exist for diffusion during freezing. In this event, prevention of "stirring" of the debris during warming will be critical. Finally, reconstruction might be possible based on consistent, minute size differences between fibers. Should all of these sources of information fail, however, the infrequency of these gaps and the generic effects of many connections as well as the vast redundancy of the brain may make incorrect inference of the proper connections still consistent with an adequate ultimate clinical outcome. (Clinical observations suggest that severe local damage can be consistent with maintenance of identity and personality.)

    d)   Fracture and separation of fractured halves of cells, axons, dendrites, capillaries, and other brain elements by distances in the millimeter range after the temperature drops to below the glass transition temperature (40,41). (Observations of the gaps referred to in c) above might also reflect microfractures that became "mushy" on warming and thereby resulted in molecular blurring of the fracture faces.)

Evaluation. A catastrophic form of injury, offering perhaps the greatest challenges for the design of molecular repair devices. However, this injury in itself may involve little or no actual loss of information. This is the most non-physiological type of injury and will require the most radically innovative types of repair system for its reversal. Such repair systems do, however, seem inherently possible.

    e)   Physical disruption of capillaries due to intracapillary ice formation: rupture of capillary wall, tearing of endothelial cells, stripping of endothelial cells from their underlying capillary wall material, resulting in incompetent vessels littered with emboli (40).

Evaluation. A very serious form of injury. However, no information is contained in capillaries per se. The entire capillary network could likely be cleared out and replaced with generic capillary "transplants" without any effect on the identity of the patient. Repair of the existing capillaries would require innovation on the order of what would be required to repair fractures. Reparable in principle.

    f)   Stripping of myelin from axons (40): formation of gaps between the axon membrane and the myelin, unraveling of the myelin, possible tearing of the axolemma resulting in loss of intra-axonal material at moderately low temperatures.

Evaluation. Myelin is inert, generic, non-information-containing material. Despite the types of myelin damage described, there should be no problem in inferring which regions of axolemma were previously covered by myelin and which were exposed. Myelin's function is only important under physiological conditions. Myelin repair might therefore not be necessary until the patient was restored to normal body temperature, at which point it could probably be carried out by ordinary or modified oligodendroglial cells, which lay down myelin under normal conditions. Leakage of axonal material has been considered above; it may be reduced by the presence of even a tattered myelin sheath which would act as a diffusion barrier.

Defining The Problem: Constraints on Repair

Repair scenarios must recognize that some kinds of repair would be extraordinarily difficult, futile, or even counterproductive to carry out at the lowest, most protective temperatures. For example:

I. Osmotically-induced Cellular Shrinkage

Extruded lipids and proteins cannot be reinserted into the membrane until the cell volume is once again increased because there is no room for them. Restoring cell volume while the cell is in the vitreous state would be many orders of magnitude more difficult than performing the same process at higher temperatures, and would be a seemingly ridiculous and possibly even impossible task to attempt.

II. Phase Transitions

Low temperatures and membrane dehydration per se cause membrane lipid species to crystallize or undergo HexII reorganizations. This is therefore the natural state of these lipids at the prevailing temperatures. Any attempt to reorder the membrane lipids into a lamellar phase will lead to spontaneous re-separation of these phases either at the prevailing temperatures or on warming. Thus, simply "repairing" this membrane defect at cryogenic temperatures would be futile. Introduction of alien lipid species to prevent re-separation would be problematic due to the absence of room in the membrane for such species and the need to subtract native lipid to make room. These changes would all have to be reversed later, and might create more problems than the original phase separations.

III. Denaturation

Any denatured proteins will also prefer to be denatured under the prevailing conditions. Renaturing them will only lead to re-denaturation as temperatures inevitably rise later on. Preventing re-denaturation would require special "chaperones" for each protein, whereas waiting for most denatured proteins to spontaneously renature (23), in part or completely, during warming would avoid most of the need for such artificial molecular folding-control devices.

IV. Changes in Tissue Volume: Thermal Expansion, Brittleness, & Elasticity

A fracture represents anisotropic contraction of cerebral tissue due to temperature reduction or inhomogeneous expansion during warming. Local rips in axons may arise for similar reasons. To fill in gaps caused by the inherent thermal contraction of cerebral tissue may create a problem when the temperature is raised and all of the existing structure, both the native structure and the added structure, is inevitably forced to expand: expansion lesions such as buckling and shearing of axons may replace the previous contraction lesions. It may be wiser to allow thermal re-expansion during warming to at least partially close these gaps and to effect repair only after this happens.

Likewise, many axons may be very stretched. Destretching them by adding material to them could cause the same buckling problem when warming occurs. Finally, tissue will be brittle below T_g and may be brittle even at temperatures moderately above this. Physically moving structures around under such conditions may damage them. Thus, attempting to close a fracture by physically forcing the two sides together is liable to rip structures on both sides of the gap. Thus, some repairs made below T_g could induce the need for more repairs later when the temperature is elevated.

V. Changes in Tissue Functionality

Statements have been made in the past to the effect that various cell structures, e.g., mitochondria, will be restored to a "functional state" while still frozen (3). This would, however, represent a nonsensical goal for many reasons, not the least of which is that functionality requires dilute aqueous liquid solutions, which cannot exist at low temperatures. The correct goal is to ensure that function resumes after warming to physiological temperatures, regardless of the repair pathway that must be followed during warming from lower temperatures to attain this goal.

The Repair Scenario

We will assume that the repair procedures begin at a temperature slightly below the glass transition temperature of the system.

I. Stabilizing Fractures

The first step is to stabilize existing fractures. Fractures require special treatment, and they require it from the very beginning since, as we will see shortly, the second repair step will obliterate non-organic components of fracture faces and will thus make it more difficult to match fracture faces and guide these faces together later if special precautions are not taken at the outset.

So, the very first step is to infiltrate surface fractures with specialized molecular devices which will form coatings or surface replicas of the fracture faces to molecular or near-molecular resolution. (Note that the process of fracturing releases energy that creates a very high though very brief local elevation of temperature. The first several molecular layers on each side of a fracture may therefore be somewhat melted or disordered. Therefore, absolute molecular resolution may not be attainable.) It is known from standard freeze-fracture microscopy that fracture faces can be coated below T_g with metal films that retain their structural fidelity even after the tissue is dissolved in Clorox!

Thus, the formation of sufficiently stable fracture face replicas at temperatures below T_g appears feasible and would maintain the overall geometry of the fracture faces after dissolution of the portion of the face that is ice and glass. Pores in the replicas of areas of pure ice or pure glass should be included to permit outgassing during the subsequent sublimation process (see below), which otherwise could tear holes in the replicas.

After coating of opposite fracture faces, these faces could be computationally compared to verify complementarity. After complementarity analysis, the repair system could build filaments between the faces. The filaments on each side of the fracture would be complementary to each other and would connect so as to maintain fracture face registry later when the temperature is raised. Given sufficiently strong replicas, these "guide wires" could be attached only to the replicas (the replicas in turn being tightly adherent to the fracture faces themselves at all points).

The function of the wires later would be to direct each fracture face as a whole toward the other fracture face as the gap is later closed by normal thermal expansion in such a way as to continue to ensure perfect registry of the two fracture faces as the gap narrows. Molecular "ratchets" along the guide wires could apply small forces to encourage closing where this is necessary. If the "guide wires" are built onto the replica faces at the sites of special pores, then as the gap is closed and the faces approach each other, the "guide wires" can be allowed to protrude into safe regions of tissue on each side of the gap, and/or they could be disassembled at a pace set by the narrowing of the gap.

For deeper fractures not accessible from the surface, the same process might be accomplished by excavating the vascular compartment first, pausing for fracture stabilization as fractures are encountered.

II. The Need for an Overall Orientation

The next thing to do is to get the big picture. The frozen brain contains highly shrunken cells and neuronal processes compressed between sheets of ice and pools of vitreous cryoprotectant water-solute inclusions. There may be lipid extrusions, floating debris, ripped axons, hemorrhaged capillaries, stabilized fractures, unraveled myelin, crystallized regions of certain surface membranes, extruded cell contents in the extracellular space, and other relatively gross alterations. We desire to identify and stabilize all of these lesions before significant "stirring" is permitted. This is difficult to do without large-scale cooperation of repair devices, for which a coordinate system needs to be set up, preferably one that does not in itself cause any damage.

III. Excavating the Extracellular Space

We approach the problem by capitalizing on the fact that about 80% of the brain is nothing but water and cryoprotectant (42) and that most of this exists in the form of pure ice located in the extracellular space. We first desire to remove the ice and most of the vitrified extracellular solution. This step has two important advantages. First, it creates room for the deployment of an extracellular communications complex which will be used to direct subsequent repairs. Second, it makes transmembrane diffusion in either direction ("stirring") effectively impossible when the temperature is subsequently raised.

1. General Description of Method – Our task might best be accomplished by a combination of direct excavation (done by relatively stupid molecular "jackhammers"), which creates a certain amount of local warming, and by spontaneous ice sublimation, which offsets some of the local heating due to evaporative cooling. The rate of excavation is set so as to generate net local temperatures of around -120 degrees C (i.e., about 5 to 15 degrees C below the limiting T_g for glycerol water-solute systems).

Excavation might proceed by digging out hollow tubular "mines" through the ice perhaps 1 micron or more in diameter. The insides of the "ice mines" are maintained at a strong vacuum. In a vacuum simulating that of deep space, ice evaporation rates have been shown to be sufficient near T_g to move sublimation boundaries at rates on the order of microns per day (43)! If we maximize the surface area available for evaporation while also maximizing the rate of direct excavation, it might be possible to remove extracellular ice fairly rapidly—for example, in a few months.

In doing the excavation, we are not limited to entering through the vascular system. We can enter through ice channels wherever they may be, and they will be everywhere, and larger in extent than most biological structures. We can also enter through special ports built into fracture face replicas. The cerebrospinal fluid cavities can be evacuated with bulk technologies or a combination of bulk and molecular technologies. Since the entire brain is under a strong vacuum during this process, pressure gradients that could cause mechanical failures should be minimal.

In addition to the advantages of minimizing heating while maximizing water mobilization, sublimation is also advantageous in that it is self-limiting in a favorable way. Sublimation of water, as opposed to ice, raises the glass transition temperature in the sublimed region and thus halts further sublimation. Therefore, we can remove the ice by sublimation without excessively dehydrating the glassy matrix surrounding the biomolecules of the brain, either intra- or extracellularly. Nothing but water can evaporate off at these temperatures.

Nowhere in this scheme is it necessary to pay the slightest bit of attention to documenting the locations of water molecules or extracellular solutes such as glycerol, sodium, or chloride, or worrying about their orientations. Other extracellular material, such as debris, however, poses some problems. We will return to these problems momentarily.

2. More Specific Description of Molecular Excavators – Two or more types of molecular "jackhammer" are envisioned. The first type is envisioned to attack only ice. The action of this excavator is to dislodge individual water molecules from ice and pass them to a "molecular conveyor-belt" system analogous to the conveyors used by axons to drive axoplasmic flow. The conveyor system transports water molecules to sites external to the brain. The second type of excavator removes vitreous material, such as glycerol, glycerol+water, and glycerol+salt+ water. These clumps of molecules are then passed to the molecular conveyor for transport outside of the brain.

Small molecules operating at temperatures near -120 degrees C cannot be self-powered. Therefore, these molecular devices must be attached to a power distribution source. One practical means of achieving this may be to attach the sensor-effector elements to a long mechanical rod which delivers the impulse required to disrupt the appropriate non-covalent bond once the sensing element identifies a proper target. This rod-tip association might be envisioned as a sort of "molecular steamshovel" in construction, with the ability not only to relay an impulse provided from the central power source, but also to position the effector tip in a versatile fashion using accessory positioning elements. The excavation could proceed with minimal, entirely local "computations" by following a stereotyped sequence of steps little more (and possibly less) complicated than the "computations" carried out by a ribosome.

In order for sublimation to proceed at the highest possible rate, collisions between sublimed ice and the ice vacuum interface should be minimized, since sublimed water will with some probability stick to that interface and require re-sublimation or direct dislodgement by the molecular evacuators. Without attempting to design an efficient means of proceeding with excavation so as to minimize this problem, it can be noted that simply designing the outgoing (but not the incoming) portion of the conveyor to be able to adsorb free water molecules from the vacuum would be helpful.

The energetics of both sublimation and molecular excavation should be reasonably easy to calculate. These processes might well be the most energy-intensive part of the repair process.

3. First Complication of Excavation: Avoiding Membrane Fracture – There is a fundamental problem of removing the vitreous residue from the extracellular space at temperatures just below T_g, namely, that the strengths of the non-covalent bonds holding together membrane bilayers are very much lower than the strengths of the non-covalent bonds holding together the vitreous matrix. In ordinary freeze-fracture microscopy, fracture planes often proceed along the plane of the middle of the membrane bilayer for this very reason (44). Applied to the problem of excavating the vitreous residue, this means that some method must be used to ensure that energy delivered to dislodge segments of the vitreous residue does not accidentally dislodge lipids from cell membranes.

A variety of methods might be brought to bear on this problem. One method might be to avoid regions that may contain nearby membranes as indicated by detection of membrane markers protruding a considerable distance into the extracellular matrix beyond the lipid bilayer proper. While this would lead to incomplete excavation, the opportunities for transmembrane diffusion might nevertheless be reduced sufficiently for this to be a satisfactory paradigm.

Another method might be to check obviously large dislodged chunks of residue for the presence of lipid and, if lipid is found, to separate it from most of the vitreous residue in which it is embedded and to reinsert it to its original site before proceeding. It might also be possible to design the geometry of the force application process so as to ensure that only a few molecules are dislodged at any one time, the force being applied not to the medium at large but to a very local and superficial area (e.g., the third vertex of a triangle).

4. Second Complication of Excavation: Extracellular Debris – There could be a considerable amount of extracellular debris. It is essential not to remove or damage this material, since it may be critical for inferring the undamaged state. Fortunately, the power applied per piston cycle need only be sufficient to break noncovalent, but not covalent, bonds, so extracellular debris should not be degraded by the excavation process. However, it will be necessary to fix all such debris in place, a nontrivial procedure.

Perhaps the best approach to this problem would be to erect side branches on the molecular conveyor belts. These side branches, shaped something like trees with their trunks originating on the conveyor belts, would possess binding sites and/or molecular clamps selected for the encountered debris and would bind all such debris noncovalently in place. The binding would be such as to represent the original three-dimensional distribution of the bound debris. For this type of molecular "book-keeping," it may not be necessary to completely strip the debris of surrounding glassy phase. In any case, the tree-like structure of the debris binding elements should ensure that all debris can be more-or-less locked in place during the repair process, thus permitting extracellular excavation to proceed without loss of information.

5. Third Complication of Excavation: Inadvertent Excavation – A further complication arising from this process is the possible "accidental" excavation of exposed cytoplasm/axoplasm. This can perhaps be avoided by solving the problem of excavating extracellular debris. Sensors for biological materials that permit immobilization of debris could similarly seal off cut axons and ripped cells.

As excavation concludes, the vacuum level should be reduced to ensure that additional unwanted sublimation of water (mummification) does not take place as temperature is later raised. The empty spaces can be filled with inert gas and/or with water vapor in equilibrium with the tissue at ambient temperature.

IV. Establishment of Extracellular Repair Network

As excavation/evacuation proceeds, an extracellular communication, transportation, and coordinate system could be laid down in the space made available. This system, penetrating throughout the extracellular portion of the brain and in intimate physical contact with the brain everywhere, could be thought of as a kind of "meta-brain," capable of relaying information about the brain over long distances while potentially having a volume amounting to more than 60% of the original volume of the entire brain (which is roughly the volume previously occupied by ice). This volume represents about 150% of the volume of the cellular components of the brain. The metabrain would permit all exposed lesions to be mapped and analyzed. Undamaged structures could be passed over without further action, except as they are needed to infer the proper locations of aberrant structures, such as debris resulting from ripped axons. Furthermore, the metabrain could be in contact with external computers, where most computation might occur.

V. Repair Computations for the Extracellular Space

At this point, all labile extracellular structures have been physically immobilized and a coordinate system is in place. No "stirring" has taken place because all procedures have been carried out just below T_g. All significant extracellular anatomical elements of the brain have been registered. The "wiring diagram" of the brain can now be deduced, and all damaged areas can be catalogued as to type and place. Where necessary, the loci of missing structures could be deduced at this point. For example, ripped bundles of axons are analyzed to deduce how to infer the pattern of connections between the two ripped ends based on the direct physical remains of the ripped axons and any other available information. The loci of missing cell membranes are deduced. Extracellular debris are assigned to appropriate destinations.

To this point, no actual repairs have been made and the process has been completely noninvasive as far as the actual cells of the brain are concerned. Based on the results obtained to this point, specialized repair devices are assigned to specific tasks and specific regions.

No tasks so far have involved the making or breaking of covalent chemical bonds. All excavations, sensing, and computations have been based on purely physical processes which should be able to operate at cryogenic temperatures given an adequate external power source and power transmission system.

VI. Warming above T_g

In order to proceed with repairs, warming of the brain is slowly induced. The advantages of warming are several. It induces changes in volume which permit fracture healing, it induces desirable changes in tissue pliability/deformability needed for moving structures such as cell membranes, and it permits both diffusional transport of needed molecules and the chemical reactions needed for repair.

The primary hazard of warming is not biochemical but diffusional. At temperatures as high as about -50 degrees C, virtually no enzymatic activity should be possible (22, 45). Deterioration at this temperature is likely to be due to slow intracellular diffusional processes perhaps accompanied by slow spontaneous breakdown of certain relatively rare labile molecules. Any enzymatic activity that could occur is likely to be arrested in time due to lack of available substrate or accumulated product inhibition, and thus is unlikely to proceed very long. A special class of proteins, catabolic enzymes, may pose the most serious problems. However, the fraction of enzymes represented by key catabolic enzymes is small and all such activity can be blocked by specific inhibitors.

We can at this stage also ignore problems arising from any protein denaturation that may exist. Denatured proteins are not likely to catalyze troublesome reactions and are not needed for any functional role, so there is no reason to worry about them until temperatures are brought to near-zero. At that point, many or most of them will have spontaneously renatured, or will renature spontaneously given additional warming. The remainder can be renatured and disaggregated specifically at temperatures near 0 degrees C using specialized devices for each labile enzyme. This process should be trivial enough to ignore for the present purposes, particularly since the number of denatured proteins in glycerolized frozen-thawed brains should be minimal as a fraction of the total.

Thus, the primary initial portion of actual repair, as opposed to simple survey and marking of the damage, consists of coping with diffusional processes. At temperatures between about -110 and -50 degrees C, two major types of diffusional process can be identified: the diffusional motions that blur the fracture interfaces we have previously marked and prepared for healing, and diffusional motions within cells. By removing the great majority of the extracellular space and immobilizing extracellular debris, we have precluded transmembrane and extracellular diffusion, and by forming durable fracture replicas and establishing the relationships between them, we have precluded diffusional information loss at these sites. Intracellular diffusion is relatively trivial over the short run. We therefore are able to proceed with the extracellular repair process first, and then to turn our attention to cellular interiors.

VII. Fracture Healing

Coefficients of thermal expansion and water/glycerol diffusion coefficients dictate the kinetics of spontaneous fracture healing in pure solutions. Extrapolation of available data for glycerol-water solutions suggests that spontaneous fracture healing in these solutions will first become appreciable in the vicinity of about -80 degrees C (46). Thus, we will want to heal fractures in cerebral tissue during warming from -100 degrees C to about -80 degrees C. The key issues involved at this point are a) the removal of the protective replica surfaces and b) the union of tissue on either side of the fractures. Both a) and b) pose significant problems. Removing the replica surface will tend to free bound species on each side of the gap for undesired diffusion. Uniting fracture faces could be met with steric obstacles if the repair device must go between the surfaces to repair them, since being between the two surfaces will tend to keep the surfaces apart and thus unrepaired.

But how are fracture surfaces likely to appear? Fracture surfaces will generally be cross-sections through various membrane-limited compartments (cells, myelinated axons, organelles), and planar separations between membrane bilayers. Within membrane-enclosed compartments, filamentous structures and molecular clusters such as enzyme complexes will be cleaved. In most cases, relatively free molecules such as cytoplasmic globular proteins should not be fractured, and the few that might be lost in this way can be neglected. Fractured microtubules, actin, etc. can be healed enzymatically. Steric hindrance is not a likely problem for individual molecules. Disrupted enzyme clusters can be reclustered (and will often recluster spontaneously when warmed sufficiently [47]).

In the case of membrane-bounded compartments that have been cleaved by fractures, one strategy would be to heal the limiting membrane first. It will not be destabilizing to remove replica material from membranes fractured perpendicular to the plane of the membrane because membranes can be adequately stabilized from above and below the plane of the membrane before the replica material is removed. As the naked membrane faces are brought together, they will tend to fuse spontaneously (48). This is also true for bringing together membranes fractured between leaflets. No specific chemical bonding will have to be induced to heal the major portion of the fracture.

If membrane fluidity is too low to permit good fusion at the prevailing temperatures, a small amount of specialty lipid can be added to the local area to enhance fluidity sufficiently to permit fusion to occur (49). After membrane fusion has occurred, some individual molecular species (particularly cross-linked proteins) associated with the formerly fractured area of the membrane might exist in a damaged (cleaved) form. These damaged components can be examined later, at higher temperatures, where they can be enzymatically healed (50).

The result would be a resealed compartment containing an internal plate of replica material. This material can then be disassembled from the plate molecule by molecule. As structures are uncovered by this process that require covalent bonding, they can be rotated for access, bonded, and then rotated back into proper position as healing proceeds. As healing proceeds, the liberated replica material can be passed through the healed membrane and exported to the extracellular space for removal by conveyors to outside the brain.

Some fractures are bound to penetrate through debris fields resulting from axon tearing or from myelin unraveling. The actual fracture healing in such areas should be relatively trivial, since there is no organized structure on either side of the gap that must be reconstructed. The area will consist mostly of evacuated empty space (now filled with inert gas and/or water vapor), from which removal of replica material should be particularly easy. Since all debris have been previously immobilized, repair of fractures through the debris will not endanger the information content of the region.

Note that it is the cells, vascular bed, and extracellular scaffolding whose fracture faces should be healed first. The presence of fracture replicas in gas pockets that previously consisted of extracellular ice or glass is important for maintaining the registry of cell surfaces and should be maintained until cell surfaces are safely healed.

It must be recognized that even at -80 degrees C, most relevant chemical reactions, even with the benefit of customized enzymatic catalysis, will proceed very slowly if at all (22,45). The missing energy can be made up in a variety of ways. First, heat could be liberated highly locally to permit reactions to proceed. (It could be helpful in this regard that the extracellular space has been replaced with gas, which is a good thermal insulator.) Second, exotic chemicals (perhaps including customized free radicals [51]) could be used to do the covalent bonding necessary to heal individual fractured molecules. Although this would most likely result, in most cases, in molecules containing unnatural structures, these foreign structures could be removed and corrected at higher temperatures at which the proper types of chemistry are feasible. Finally, the option exists, if all others fail, to simply hold fractured molecules together with molecular clamps until such time as they can be chemically bonded at higher temperatures.

How much time is available for these manipulations at about -80 degrees C? Although it is not possible to be certain, the normal rule of thumb would be that several months of storage at this temperature should be possible without any appreciable intracellular deterioration (52). This should be more than enough time to carry out the required extracellular repairs.

VIII. Cell Repair

1. Debris consolidation – Having healed the fractures at about -80 degrees C, the next major extracellular task is to redistribute cellular debris to their proper locations. The actual transport is simplified by the absence of extracellular diffusive barriers. Reinsertion of lipids and proteins into membranes and into cytoplasm proceeds by means of specialized transport devices, which could be individually powered by reactive chemicals supplied continuously on the molecular conveyor system from outside. Once repositioned, lipids will remain positioned through ordinary self-assembly mechanisms (given an aqueous intracellular phase and a thin layer of aqueous extracellular fluid).

Having previously mapped and analyzed all debris down to the molecular level, actual reconstruction of debris into tissue should be relatively straightforward. Intracellular proteins, once deposited in the proper sites, can be covalently bound in position or immobilized with molecular clamps. To facilitate self-assembly, the temperature may be raised to perhaps -60 degrees C for up to a few weeks (52,53) if need be, either early, late, or intermittently during the reassembly process. In cases in which debris are the result of extrusion of material from contracting membranes, their redistribution is delayed pending cell volume re-expansion. At this stage, we repair only debris resulting from tearing and the like.

2. Stabilization against diffusional/biochemical deterioration – While limited, some diffusion is possible in cytoplasm at -60 degrees C. We exploit this by introducing metabolic inhibitors at this temperature into the cytoplasm. Since we have ready access to the external surfaces of cells, we can easily deposit inhibitors at regular intervals along cell processes. The inhibitors are designed to block the action of any enzymes that permit catabolism to proceed to beyond an acceptable point. Once deposited, they can be ignored, since these relatively low molecular weight inhibitors will reach their targets by diffusion as rapidly as the normal substrates would otherwise reach these catabolic enzymes.

With the possibility of detrimental catalyzed chemical change precluded, the only further types of damage are diffusion (e.g., organelle swelling), spontaneous chemical modifications (e.g., oxidation, racemization, etc.), and structural collapse (due to declining cellular rigidity with rising temperature, causing cellular structures to sag in the absence of extracellular supports). We can ignore diffusional change at this stage because cells and organelles are all highly shrunken. Random chemical damage can be ignored at this point and will be addressed later. Minor modifications to the extracellular communications network, which can double as a kind of extracellular "connective tissue," are now made to ensure the prevention of sagging during continued warming.

In order to further prepare for warming, nanocomputer-based cell repair machines similar to those described by Drexler (1) are introduced into the cytoplasm at this time. Although they are incapable of effecting rapid repairs at -60 degrees C, their introduction at this time allows them to begin repairs at the first opportunity during warming. They may well be capable of carrying out extensive sensing and computational functions at -60 degrees C in preparation for their actual repair activities at higher temperatures.

3. Cell Volume Restoration – As noted in the discussion on mechanisms of damage, it is during thawing that many problems arise. In the present scenario, no ice is present anywhere throughout the brain and, thus, the brain never has to go through the process of thawing per se. We do, however, ultimately have to return cell volumes and cell water contents to normal. Our advantage is that we can do this in whatever manner is most desirable: we can expand cell volume at temperatures lower than would normally be associated with volume expansion during thawing (by adding both glycerol and water to the cells, we could fully expand cell volume even at -60 degrees C if we so chose), or we can expand cell volume at higher temperatures than would occur during thawing (by failing to add water to the same extent as it would be supplied by the progressive melting of ice).

The assumption we will make here is that we wish to do the former: expand the cells at temperatures lower than would exist during thawing. The reasoning is that there are many types of cellular injury which ultimately must be dealt with. If we rehydrate in a manner that simulates normal thawing, we tend to have to deal with all of these problems simultaneously. By re-expanding our cells at temperatures in the vicinity of -60 to -30 degrees C, rather than in the normal range of thawing (11) (i.e., -40 to -8 degrees C), we can take care of membrane re-expansion issues more-or-less independently of metabolic issues. We may want to favor the highest temperatures for re-expansion that do not begin to induce appreciable metabolic problems so that we can maximize membrane fluidity and minimize problems that may arise from unreversed membrane lipid phase transitions during cellular and membrane re-expansion.

Before cell re-expansion can proceed, there must be sufficient extracellular volume available for the re-expansion. We thus withdraw a portion of the extracellular communications network, much of which has already accomplished its purposes and is no longer needed. We leave in place conveyors for water and for glycerol, cellular supports, and assorted other devices.

We thus begin, at about -60 degrees C, to transport glycerol and water into the cytosol and axoplasm so as to maintain a ratio of glycerol to water that has a freezing point of about -61 degrees C. This process is carefully coordinated with the process of re-inserting extruded membrane material. As these two processes proceed, we also gradually raise the temperature, adjusting our membrane transporters to convey more and more water in comparison to glycerol so as to maintain an intracellular freezing point just below the prevailing temperature. Transport could again be powered by highly reactive chemicals introduced by conveyors.

At -30 degrees C or so, most (but not all) lost volume and all formerly extruded membrane material has been replaced. (We retain some extracellular space for the continued presence of some supporting devices.) The extracellular machinery for processing extruded material is withdrawn. The cells contain more than 6 M glycerol, a higher concentration than they began with. This is a sufficient concentration to preclude most intracellular chemistry, particularly at the prevailing temperature. The metabolic inhibitors introduced earlier have diffused to their targets and inactivated them. While cell volume expansion has proceeded, similar volume control measures have been completed for intracellular organelles. These measures have automatically included reversal of pre-existing organelle swelling. Other membrane transporters have also had sufficient opportunity to reverse ionic (Na+, K+, Ca++, Cl-, etc.) imbalances in both the cytoplasm and in organelles. They will continue to be active until brain temperature is returned to near normal values.

Volume control measures will not be entirely successful unless significant membrane phase changes have been reversed by this point in the repair process. This may happen spontaneously due to the elevation of temperature but, if not, it will be induced at this time by the temporary insertion of specialty lipid or molecules such as trehalose (54) (most likely in combination with more direct means).

4. Rehydration – At this point, the extracellular space can be flooded with glycerol-water-salt-substrate-colloid solution. This is done to maintain membrane integrity and to simplify water transport during rehydration. Colloid will preclude cell swelling in the cold without the need for vigorous ionic pumping (55).

We now reverse the direction of the membrane glycerol transporters and slowly transport glycerol to the extracellular space at the same time the glycerol concentration in the extracellular space is similarly being reduced by transport to the outside. By equating the proportion of cell glycerol removed to the proportion of extracellular glycerol removed, water activity is kept identical in the two compartments without a change in cell volume due to spontaneous diffusion of extracellular water into the cells. (Water diffusion should be sufficiently fast to preclude the need for specific— and very energy intensive—transmembrane water pumping at this stage.) At all times, the glycerol concentration within the cells is just sufficient to prevent the cytosol from freezing. Eventually, we arrive at 0 degrees C and a glycerol concentration of about 150mM. More of the extracellular communications and conveyance system is withdrawn.

Having reconstructed cellular and extracellular structures on a gross level, the vascular system is now sufficiently intact to permit cerebral perfusion to be reinstated. The brain vasculature should remain intact for days at 0 degrees C even without extensive protective modifications provided it has been sufficiently well repaired (56). The perfusate contains necessary substrates, repair machines, and small artificial cells designed to be capable of repairing natural cells under conditions of ultraprofound hypothermia (psychrophillic anabolocytes), as required. Given that organisms have been found in nature that can grow at temperatures as low as -20 degrees C (57), vigorous repairs are clearly possible at 0 degrees C, despite the very low metabolic rate of the original tissue.

These new devices as well as the previously-deployed intracellular cell repair machines therefore now proceed to correct the most critical types of continuing damage. Their activities may include, for example: myelin synthesis and replacement; bacterial and viral killing; protein reaggregation; cytoskeletal reassembly; reversal of glycerol-induced biochemical reactions; de novo synthesis of key missing proteins and other key metabolites; reversal of exotic, unnatural chemical bonds formed in order to heal otherwise intractable lesions at lower temperatures; removal of specialty lipid; restoration of normal intracellular buffering and pH; repair or removal of peroxidized, racemized, oxidized, or otherwise modified structures, resulting in their replacement with undamaged structures. Repair is powered by the chemical energy stored in the remaining glycerol present in the cells (precluding the need to otherwise dispose of this glycerol and completing the return to isotonicity) as well as by special chemical energy sources now available from the perfusate.

Almost all of the extracellular communications and general support network is now disassembled and withdrawn.

IX. Metabolic Restoration

As temperature is elevated further, oxygen is reintroduced and many metabolic inhibitors are degraded or inactivated. Necessary protein repairs are completed. Successful repair is checked by examining certain key metabolite behaviors in each significant metabolic pathway that are indicative of proper metabolic startup. Departures from expectation are diagnostic of any lingering underlying problems, which are then specifically corrected to the degree necessary. The required fine-tuning adjustments could be carried out largely by de novo synthesis of deficient proteins, by supplying inhibitory metabolites that are normally present and needed to control the overactivity of other proteins, by providing necessary protein cofactors that were previously lost, etc.

The synthesis of purely artificial proteins required for specialty tasks may also be called for. Protein denaturation is reversed artificially at this point as may be needed. [Renaturation could be accomplished by a variety of techniques. For example: a)

The protein could be completely unfolded by seizing it at the N- or C-terminal end and passing it as a straight chain through a molecular tunnel resembling the channel nascent polypeptide chains pass through as they emerge from ribosomes, then allowing the emerging protein to refold either spontaneously or in cooperation with existing intracellular folding "chaperones" (58); or b) the protein could be attached to a scaffolding whose shape is altered in such a way as to renature the protein or allow the protein to complete spontaneous renaturation when released from the scaffolding after shape alteration.] After these diagnostics and fine-tuning tasks are completed, metabolism is released from artificial control.

X. Disease Reversal and Reanimation

Brain temperature is raised to 25-37 degrees C. Cell metabolism may still be grossly abnormal in a variety of ways: it will not have been necessary to have previously reversed all details of the previously existing pathological state, but only those details required for subsequent cellular self-maintenance and self-repair. Cells "know" what their proper state is and will spontaneously establish that state provided they are viable enough to continue to exist and to repair themselves.

While this is happening, conventional medical nanotechnology will be at work on specific disease processes, reversing them, establishing proper connections to extracephalic structures, and, if need be, assisting with the provision of a new body. Given stable physiology, these curative processes, including the partial or even complete reversal of aging, can be allowed to proceed as long as needed. Very few constraints on repair exist at this point. Technologies for dealing with specific disease states will be routine and powerful and require no description here.

Once the patient has been restored to a state approaching perfect physical health, consciousness is restored.

Summary and Conclusion

A "realistic" scenario for the repair of the frozen brain is proposed. It is based on the specific details of freezing injury and on the natural resistance of most cellular constituents to freezing damage, as well as on the natural self-assembly and self-repair of living cells. It avoids the need for performing chemical reactions below the glass transition temperature while at the same time avoiding the problems of diffusive information loss on warming. Although each step has not yet been subjected to thorough analysis, each is concrete and based on known fact. The scenario is fully open to criticism, testing, and refinement. It thus could serve as a basis for future discussions of the feasibility of moderate approaches to the restoration of those frozen by today's technology.

Disclaimer

This scenario is predicated on many assumptions—such as the assumption of adequate preservation by current technology—that may be false. This scenario does not prove that cryonics can or will succeed. It may, however, facilitate discussion of that possibility. ■

References and Notes

1.   Drexler, Eric, *Engines of Creation*, Anchor/Doubleday, New York, 1986.

2.   Drexler, Eric, "Cell Repair Machines and Tissue Reconstruction: Some Notes on Computational Complexity and Physical Constraints," (unpublished document, 1/12/1984, pp. 1-53).

3.   Merkle, Ralph, "Molecular Repair of the Brain," *Cryonics*, 10(10), 21-44 (Oct, 1989).

4.   Fahy, G.M., "Molecular Repair Of The Brain: A Scientific Critique," *Cryonics*, 12(2), 8-11(Feb, 1991).

5.   Leaf, J.D., M.G. Federowicz, H. Hixon, "Appendix A: The "Smith Criterion" for adequate cryoprotection," *Cryonics*, 6(11), 38 (Nov, 1985).

6.   Fahy, G.M., T. Takahashi, and A.M. Crane, "Histological cryoprotection of rat and rabbit brains," *Cryo-Letters,* 5, 33-46 (1984).

7.   Fahy, G.M., T. Takahashi, A.M. Crane, and L. Sokoloff, "Cryoprotection of the mammalian brain," *Cryobiology*, 18, 618 (1981); Fahy, G.M., and A.M. Crane, "Histological cryoprotection of rabbit brain with 3M glycerol," *Cryobiology*, 21, 704, (1984).

8.   Burch, H.B., O.H. Lowry, et al, "Effect of fructose, dihydroxyacetone, glycerol, and glucose on metabolites and related compounds in liver and kidney," *J. Biol. Chem.*, 245, 2092-2102 (1970).

9.   Tanizaki, M.M., H.M.S. Bittencourt, et al, "Activation of low molecular weight acid phosphatase from bovine brain by purines and glycerol," *Biochem. Biophys. Acta*, 485, 116-123 (1977).

10. Bello, J., "The state of the tyrosines of bovine pancreatic ribonuclease in ethylene glycol and glycerol," *Biochemistry*, 8, 4535-4541

11. Jochem, M., and Ch. Korber, "Extended phase diagram for the ternary solutions H2O-NaCl-glycerol and H2O-NaCl-hydroxyethyl starch (HES) determined by DSC," *Cryobiology*, 24, 513-36(1987).

12. Mazur, P., "Freezing of living cells: mechanisms and implications," *Ant. J. Physiol.,* 247 (Cell Physiol., 16), C125 (1984).

13. Steponkus, P.L., M.F. Dowgert, et al, "Destabilization of isolated plant protoplasts during a freeze-thaw cycle: the influence of cold acclimation," *Cryobiology,* 20, 448-65 (1983).

14. Steponkus, P.L., D.V. Lynch, et al, "Plant cryobiology: cellular and molecular aspects of freezing injury and cold acclimation," in *Low Temperature Biotechnology: Emerging Applications and Engineering Contributions,* J.J. McGrath and K.R. Diller, Eds., ASME, New York, 1988, pp.47-56.

15. Williams, R.J., H.J. Hope, et al, "Membrane collapse as a cause of osmotic injury and its reversibility in a hardy wheat," *Cryobiology,* 12, 554-5 (1975).

16. Fagg, G.E., E.E. Mena, et al, "Freezing eliminates a specific population of L-glutamate receptors in synaptic membranes," *Neurosci. Lett.,* 38, 157-62 (1983); Wu, R., R. Carlin, et al, "Binding Of L-[H3]glutamate to fresh or frozen synaptic membrane and post-synaptic density fractions isolated from cerebral cortex and cerebellum of fresh or frozen canine brain," *J. Neurochem,* 46, 831-41 (1986). Protein loss has also been documented in other cells. For example, see Takahashi, T., S. Inada, et al, "Osmotic stress and the freeze-thaw cycle cause shedding of Fc and C3b receptors by human polymorphonuclear leukocytes," *J. Immunol.,* 134, 4062 (1985).

17. See, for example, Daniel L. Alkon's lay paper, "Memory Storage and Neural Systems," *Scientific American,* pp. 42-50 (July, 1989), as well as his papers in *Science* (226, 1037-1045, 1984; 239, 998-1005, 1988), and Alkon's book, *Memory Traces in the Brain,* Cambridge University Press, 1988.

18. *The Cryobiological Case for Cryonics,* booklet available from the Alcor Life Extension Foundation; 7895 E. Acoma Dr., Scottsdale, AZ 85260. Tel: (800) 367-2228.

19. Hardy, J.A., P.R. Dodd, A.E. Oakley, R.H. Ferry, J.A. Edwardson, and A.M. Kidd, "Metabolically active synaptosomes can be prepared from frozen rat and human brain," *J. Neurochem.,* 40, 608-14 (1983).

20. Stahl, W.L., and P.D. Swanson, "Effects of freezing and storage on subcellular fractionation of guinea pig and human brain," *Neurobiology,* 5, 393-400 (1975).

21. Kandel, E. R., and Schwartz, J. H., *Principles of Neural Science,* Second Edition Elsevier, New York, 1985.

22. Franks, Felix, *Biophysics and Biochemistry at Low Temperature,* Cambridge University Press, New York, 1985

23. Alberts, B. D. Bray, et al, *Molecular Biology of the Cell,* 2nd Ed., Garland Publishing, Inc., New York, 1989.

24. Goodin, R., and J. Levitt, "The cryoaggregation of bovine serum albumin," *Cryobiology,* 6, 333-8 (1970).

25. Lovelock, J.E., "The mechanism of the cryoprotective action of glycerol against hemolysis by freezing and thawing," *Biochem. Biophys. Acta,* 11, 28-36 (1953).

26. *Cryonics: Reaching for Tomorrow.* Booklet available from Alcor Life Extension Foundation.

27. Hardy, J.A., P.R. Dodd, A.E. Oakley, R.H. Ferry, J.A. Edwardson, and A.M. Kidd, "Metabolically active synaptosomes can be prepared from frozen rat and human brain," J. *Neurochem,* 40, 608-14 (1983).

28. Pegg, D.E., and M.P. Diaper, "On the mechanism of the protective action of glycerol," *Biophysical Journal,* 54, 471-88 (1988).

29. Houle, J.D. and G.D. Das, "Cryopreservation of embryonic neural tissue and its successful transplantation in the rat brain," *Anat. Rec.,* 196, 81A (1980); Houle, J.D. and G.D. Das, "Freezing of embryonic neural tissue and its transplantation in the rat brain," *Brain Res.,* 192, 570-4 (1980); Houle, J.D. and G.D. Das, "Freezing and transplantation of brain tissue in rats," *Experientia,* 36, 1114-5 (1980); Das, G.D., J.D. Houle, J. Brasko, and K.G. Das, "Freezing of neural tissues and their transplantation in the brain of rats: technical details and histological observations," *J. Neurosci. Methods,* 8, 1-15 (1983); Jensen, S., T. Sorenson, A.G. Moller, and J. Zimmer, "Intraocular grafts of fresh and freeze-stored rat hippocampal tissue: a comparison of survivability and histological and connective organization," *J. Comp. Neurol.,* 227, 558-68 (1984); Sorenson, T., S. Jensen, A.G. Moller, and J. Zimmer, "Intracephalic transplants of freeze-stored rat hippocampal tissue," *J. Comp. Neurol.,* 252, 468-82 (1986); Jensen, 8., T. Sorenson, and J. Zimmer, "Cryopreservation of fetal rat brain tissue later used for intracerebral transplantation," *Cryobiology,* 24, 120-34 (1987)

30. Suda, I, K. Kite, and C. Adachi, "Bioelectric discharges of isolated cat brain after revival from years of frozen storage, Brain Res., 70, 527-31 (1974).

31. Baker, P.F., A.L. Hodgkin, et al, Replacement of the axoplasm of giant nerve fibers with artificial solutions," *J. Physiol.* (London), 164, 330-54 (1962).

32. Kylin, H., "Uber die Kalteresistenze der Meeresalgen," Eer. dtsch. bor. Ges., 35, 370-84 (1917); van den Berg, L., and P.S. Soliman, "Effect of glycerol and dimethyl sulfoxide on changes in composition and pH of buffer salt solutions during freezing," *Cryobiology*, 6, 93-7 (1969).

33. Persidsky, M.D., "Lysosomes as primary targets of cryoinjury," *Cryobiology*, 8, 482-8 (1971); Persidsky, M.D., and Ellett, M.H., "Lysosomes and cell cryoinjury," *Cryobiology*, 8, 345-9 (1971).

34. Steponkus, P.L., and D.V. Lynch, "Freeze/thaw-induced destabilization of the plasma membrane and the effects of cold acclimation," *J. Bioenergetics Biomembranes,* 21, 21-41(1989).

35. Koyova, R.D., B.G. Tenchov, et al, "Sugars favor formation of hexagonal (HII) phase at the expense of lamellar liquid-crystalline phase in hydrated phosphatidylethanolamines," *Biochem. Biophys. Acta*, 980, 377-80 (1989).

36. Lyons, J.M., "Phase transitions and control of cellular metabolism at low temperatures," *Cryobiology*, 9, 341-50 (1972).

37. Quinn, P.J., "A lipid-phase separation model of low temperature damage to biological membranes," *Cryobiology*, 22, 128-46(1985).

38. Jacobsen, I.A., Pegg, D.E., et al, "Introduction and removal of cryoprotective agents with rabbit kidneys: Assessment by transplantation," *Cryobiology*, 25, 285-99, (1988).

39. Fahy, G.M., "Analysis of "solution effects" injury: Cooling rate dependence of the functional and morphological sequellae of freezing in rabbit renal cortex protected with dimethyl sulfoxide," *Cryobiology*, 18, 550-70 (1981).

40. Unpublished experimental results of Alcor Life Extension Foundation and Cryovita Laboratories.

41. Fahy, G.M., J. Saur, et al, "Physical problems with the vitrification of large biological systems," *Cryobiology*, 27, 492-510 (1990).

42. Gadea-Ciria, M., J. Gervas Camacho, et al, "Water content of various regions of the feline nervous system," *Medical Biol.,* 53, 469-74 (1975).

43. J.G. Linner and S.A. Livesey give the following calculations in their chapter, "Low Temperature Molecular Distillation Drying of Cryofixed Biological Samples," in *Low Temperature Biotechnology, Emerging Applications and*

Engineering Contributions, J.J. McGrath and K.R. Diller, Eds., ASME, New York,1988,pp.147-157.

44. Orci, L., and A. Parrelet, *Freeze-Etch Histology: A Comparison Between Thin Sections and Freeze-Etch Replicas,* Springer-Verlag, New York, 1973.

45. Douzou, P., *Cryobiochemistry*, An introduction, Academic Press, New York, 1977.

46. Kroener C., and B. Luyet, "Formation of Cracks During the Vitrification of Glycerol Solutions and Disappearance of the Cracks During Rewarming," *Biodynamica*, 10, 47-52 (1966).

47. Both proteins and membranes exist in the form they do because of the immiscibility of water and hydrocarbons. This immiscibility causes these structures to self-assemble spontaneously if permitted to do so; this is the basis of spontaneous protein renaturation and membrane assembly. Protein clusters often involve hydrophobic associations as well, but even when other contributions are more important, mis-clustering is, in principle, equally spontaneously reversible. Self-assembly can happen incorrectly, but, given a little guidance, can surely be directed to happen correctly. See also note 48 below.

48. Fat exposed to water preferentially associates with other fat if any is available. A fractured membrane presents two "greasy" surfaces to water, which is entropically unfavorable; it is thermodynamically favorable for these two cut surfaces to fuse together so as to eliminate the unfavorable water-fat interface. This tendency is, however, reduced by low temperatures (which reduce the energy cost of hydrating fat) and by solidification of the membrane. A good general discussion of these issues is given in *The Hydrophobic Effect: Formation of Micelles and Biological Membranes,* by Charles Tanford (2nd Edition, 1980, John Wiley & Sons, New York). As Tanford notes (p. vii): "The hydrophobic effect is perhaps the most important single factor in the organization of the constituent molecules of living matter into complex structural entities such as cell membranes and organelles."

49. "Specialty lipids" could be made by reducing the number of carbon atoms in the fatty acid tails of ordinary membrane phospholipids, increasing the number of double bonds (especially cis double bonds) in these tails, fluorinating the fatty acid tails, modifying polar head groups to prevent close association of the lipid tails (by preventing clumping of these head groups), or by any combination of these maneuvers. These modifications are all known to reduce the freezing points of lipids and/or hydrocarbons and hence increase their fluidity. (See also: Small,

D. M., et al, *The Physical Chemistry of Lipids: From Alkanes to Phospholipids.* Plenum Press, New York, 1986 [Handbook of Lipid Research, Vol. 4].) Specialty lipids based on such modifications should, therefore, enhance the ability of lipid phases doped with them to fuse. It does not seem likely that the specialty lipids must reverse membrane phase separations to effect membrane fusion. Even small, free molecules such as pentane or its relatives could suffice: as long as the molecule is insoluble in water and preferentially associates with hydrophobic species, it should produce the desired effect. (The fact that membranes continue to exist at low temperatures suggests that hydrophobic forces will remain strong enough at these temperatures to promote self-assembly of hydrophobic entities in an aqueous environment.) Even if a molecule such as pentane becomes volatile on warming, the membrane will not be affected, provided it becomes sufficiently fluid before the small species evaporates.

50. Evidence that it is permissible to heal some fracture damage at higher temperatures is provided by the results of Dr. Luiz de Medinaceli, who found he could regenerate rat sciatic nerves that he had first frozen and then cut cleanly at temperatures just below 0 degrees C. The nerve ends were held together by special tethers and extracellular potassium was elevated to keep the cut axons alive. Only very cleanly cut nerves regenerated well. His work was discussed in a series of papers that appeared in *Experimental Neurology*, Volume 81 (pages 459-468; 469-487; and 488-496) and Volume 84 (396-408), in 1983 and 1984. See particularly Vol. 81, pp. 469-496. His work is now being extended to human patients (personal communication).

51. As Mazur discusses in reference 12, free radical reactions can proceed relatively unabated regardless of temperature, owing to the lack of any activation energy for these reactions.

52. Meryman, H.T., "Review of biological freezing," in *Cryobiology*, H.T. Meryman, Ed., Academic Press, New York, 1966, pp 1-114.

53. Suda's papers suggest that brains will be stable at such temperatures for at least this long, and probably for much longer. See reference 30 and the following reference: Suda, I., K. Kite, and C. Adachi, "Viability of long-term frozen cat brain in vitro," *Nature*, 212, 268-70 (1966).

54. Crowe, J.H. and L.M. Crowe, "Interaction of sugars with membranes," *Biochem. Biophys. Acta*, 947, 367-84 (1988).

55. Hitchcock, D.I., Proteins and the Donnan equilibrium," *Physiol. Rev.,* 4, 505-531 (1924); Leaf, A., "Regulation of intracellular fluid volume and disease," *Am. J. Med.,* 49, 291-5 (1970); Mendler, N., H.J. Reulen, et al, "Cold swelling and energy metabolism in the hypothermic brain of rats and dogs," in *Hibernation and Hypothermia, Perspectives and Challenges,* F.E. South, J.P. Hannon, et al, Eds., Elsevier, New York, 1972, pp. 167-190.

56. White, R.J., M.S. Albin, et al, "Prolonged whole brain refrigeration with electrical and metabolic recovery," *Nature*, 209, 1320 (1966).

57. Actual growth has been confirmed at -12 degrees C, and unconfirmed reports of cell growth at -18 degrees C, -20 degrees C, and -34 degrees C are available: see Mazur, P., "Limits to life at low temperatures and at reduced water contents and water activities," *Origin of Life,* 10, 137-59 (1980). Continuing metabolism has been documented to occur at -30 to -40 degrees C by S.M. Siegel, T. Speitel, et al, "Life in Earth extreme environments: a study of cryo-biotic potentialities," *Cryobiology*, 6, 160-81 (1969).

58. For some recent references, see H. Blumberg and P.A. Silver, "A homologue of the bacterial heat-shock gene DnaJ that alters protein sorting in yeast," *Nature*, 349, 627-30 (1991).

A Cryopreservation Revival Scenario Using Molecular Nanotechnology

By Ralph C. Merkle, Ph.D. and Robert A. Freitas, Jr., J.D.

Cryonics, 4th Quarter, 2008

Advanced nanorobots will keep all human body cells in perfect repair, preventing disease and aging. Illustrated here is a cell repair robot called a chromallocyte. After the chromallocyte (in upper half of picture) locates and docks with the cell nucleus (in lower half of picture), it extends a tool-tipped robotic arm into the nucleoplasm. The job of this nanorobot is to replace old damaged chromosomes with new ones in every cell. ©2008 E-spaces 3danimation.e-spaces.com (artwork) and Robert A. Freitas Jr. www.rfreitas.com (concept/design).

We briefly outline one possible cryopreservation revival scenario using MNT (molecular nanotechnology). A full analysis will require much further work and detailed research. Our principal assumptions are that a reasonably mature MNT will exist, and that the patient has received a "good" cryopreservation by current standards, including the introduction of appropriate levels of cryoprotectants.

Pre-Repair Operations

The first question we face in designing a cryopreservation revival scenario is whether to warm the patient to provide a liquid environment before beginning, or to initiate repairs at low temperature (77 K for patients in LN2, or perhaps ~140 K for patients in the future who elect Intermediate Temperature Storage (ITS)).

The obvious disadvantage of warming before initiating repairs is that further deterioration will take place, which might result in the loss of personality-relevant information (e.g., warming might cause deterioration of synaptic or neurological structures). We know that current methods of cryopreservation cause fractures. While these fractures, like fractures in glass, are expected to produce minimal information loss, they would nevertheless create problems with structural integrity that, upon warming, could lead to further deterioration. Without some form of stabilization, warming fractures would be like slicing the tissue with incredibly sharp knives—on its face not something that we wish to do. Other forms of damage that had occurred either prior to cooling or during the cooling process might, upon warming, also cause continued deterioration of the tissue. As a consequence, initiating the repair process at low temperature is the more conservative approach.

The first step in low temperature repair is to clear out the circulatory system. This process would more closely resemble drilling a tunnel than anything else, and would require the use of molecular machines able to function at (for example) LN2 temperature (though the particular temperature could be adjusted as might be found useful).

This basic process will employ molecular machines that can operate at low temperature, and can sense and remove the kinds of materials found in the circulatory system. Fortunately, proposals for diamondoid molecular machines that operate at low temperature are common. Gears, bearings, ratchets, sliding interfaces, and the rest work quite well regardless of temperature, and detailed analyses of molecular structures bear out this claim. Unlike biological systems that typically require liquid water in which to operate, diamondoid molecular machines can operate in vacuum with no need for lubricants and at temperatures as low as we might desire.

Logistics System Installation

Coordination, communication, and power for these molecular machines can again be provided at low temperature. Designs for very compact molecular computers able to operate at arbitrarily low temperatures (specifically including rod logic, a type of molecular mechanical computation) are well known in the literature and could provide the computational power needed to coordinate repair activities. Several modes of communication are available, including molecular cables that should be able to transmit data at gigabit rates or higher (www.nanomedicine.com/NMI/7.2.5.htm). By coupling activity of onboard repair devices to off-board computational resources, the overall repair process could be guided by massive computational resources located outside of the patient, thus avoiding concerns about patient heating caused by waste heat from the computational resources required to plan and coordinate repair activities. Finally, power distribution can take place by whatever means is convenient (www.nanomedicine.com/NMI/6.4.htm), including distribution of electrical power via carbon nanotubes (which can have remarkably high conductivity).

During the repair process, various molecular inputs will be required and molecular outputs must be removed. A cryonics-specialized variant of an artificial vasculature or "vasculoid" (see www.jetpress.org/volume11/vasculoid.html) redesigned to operate at low temperatures could be installed to carry out this function. In this variant, the initial transport load would be orders of magnitude smaller than the load that a fully functional vasculoid would be required to handle in a normally metabolizing person even at basal rates. (The original vasculoid was scaled to handle peak metabolic rates.) Roughly speaking, a vasculoid is an artificial circulatory system that enables coordinated ciliary transport of containerized cargoes using a leak-tight coating of machinery on the inner vascular walls. The vasculoid appliance is readily modified to operate at low temperature, and can easily span relatively large cross-capillary breaks.

This initial stage brings medical nanodevices to within ~20 microns of any point in the brain via the circulatory system, and provides distributed power and control as well as massive computational resources located outside the tissue undergoing repair. Initial surveys of the tissue would provide damage estimates at specific sites, including a detailed mapping of fractures. A variety of imaging modalities (www.nanomedicine. com/NMI/4.8.htm) could be used to provide extensive information about the cellular structure throughout the immobilized tissue. At this stage, the external computer guiding repairs would come to possess detailed structural information of the entire system down to the cellular and subcellular level. If the cryopreservation had generally gone well, this fact would be apparent and relatively minimal analysis and repairs would be required. If the cryopreservation had produced more significant damage in some areas, this damage could be tabulated and assessed, and appropriate repair strategies could be planned. There is reason to believe that even very serious damage could be analyzed, the original healthy state determined, and appropriate repair strategies adopted (see, for example, "Cryonics, Cryptography, and Maximum Likelihood Estimation").

Fracture Stabilization

Current cryopreservation methods create fractures, some of which can have gaps that are tens or even hundreds of microns across. Unstabilized, these fractures would cause further tissue deterioration upon warming. Stabilization of fractures can be done by the synthesis of artificial surfaces specifically designed to conform to the exposed faces of the fractures. For example, we could make a stable support sheet of ~1 nanometer thickness to which arrays of hydrophilic and hydrophobic molecular surface "decorations" are attached. By making the decorations match the exposed face of the fracture, this support sheet would stabilize the fracture face on warming and prevent further deterioration. The success of this approach depends upon the ability of MNT to synthesize an appropriate support sheet—which we expect to be well within the capabilities of the technology.

Following stabilization of fracture surfaces the system temperature can be slowly increased without risk that the fractures will contribute to further deterioration. The support sheet would remain in contact with the fracture face even as the fracture face expands or contracts during warming—the thin support sheet would readily conform to such changes in shape.

Tissue Chemistry Restoration

As the temperature increases and some degree of fluidity is reintroduced into the tissue, the repair process can turn to other issues. In particular, some proteins have likely been denatured during the cryopreservation process. As most proteins should spontaneously recover, the technical challenge will be to identify those that are slow to recover and then either hasten their recovery (possibly by the use of artificially designed chaperones) or support their missing function by other means during recovery. (The recovery of many tissue types after cooling to low temperature supports this approach—if any significant fraction of proteins failed to recover, one would not expect any tissues to spontaneously survive such treatment.) In those cases where critical functionality does not spontaneously recover with sufficient rapidity, it would be possible to introduce new properly folded proteins at an appropriate temperature to take over the critical functions that have been compromised, and then let the tissue recover by itself later on, once it has resumed normal functioning. Re-denaturation of proteins can largely be avoided by delaying repairs to higher temperatures in a series of stages depending on which repairs are needed at various temperatures.

The cryopreservation process and the changes prior to cryopreservation have likely caused imbalances in the concentrations of specific chemicals. Concentrations of sodium, potassium, other ions, ATP, glucose, oxygen, and many other metabolites and chemicals are likely not at desirable values. Concentrations of cryoprotectants might or might not be at desired levels for the particular temperature, so it might be useful to remove cryoprotectants employed during the cryopreservation and replace them with newer cryoprotectants that have more desirable properties. As the tissue becomes more fluid, concentrations of any specific chemical can be measured and adjusted. Direct access to cells surrounding the capillary lumen is available, and the use of tubular probes (which could be introduced from the luminal vasculoid face once the liquid environment becomes sufficiently viscous to allow such probes to penetrate) would provide direct access to the intracellular contents of cells 10 or 20 microns from any capillary. Concentrations of reactive molecules such as oxygen and other reactive metabolites would be kept low until later in the recovery process, with metabolism also kept on hold during this time.

The support system and external computer would have essentially total control over the concentration of all chemical compounds in all cellular and even subcellular compartments in the recovering patient. The control system would adjust these concentrations as needed to minimize damage, both during the re-warming process and also later while metabolic activities were being re-established.

Fracture Sealing and Comprehensive Cell Repair

At some higher temperature, with sufficient fluidity for tissues to flow and reduce strain, the fracture faces can be brought together and the support sheets removed and exported from the body. One simple conceptual mechanism for bringing the fracture faces together involves using biologically inert "strings" attached to specific matching sites on two support sheets that are stabilizing the two opposing faces of a particular fracture. Pulling the strings tight draws the opposing fracture faces together. Even fracture gaps as large as 0.5 millimeters can be accommodated, since all the individual support sheets in a large block of tissue can be simultaneously manipulated as an incremental three dimensional global strain release network to slowly heal the breaks.

Once the system is liquid it becomes possible to introduce other medical nanodevices to deal with specific forms of damage, including pre-existing damage—like the presence of lipofuscin or other undesired intracellular or extracellular junk, nuclear mutations or epimutations (http://jetpress.org/v16/freitas.pdf), damaged mitochondria (which could simply be removed and replaced with new, functionally correct mitochondria), and a wide range of other conditions.

Patient Wake-up

After the patient has been repaired, stabilized and warmed to conditions of moderate hypothermia, metabolic activities and concentration gradients appropriate to a healthy functional state can be re-established. The vasculoid increases its transport activities to levels appropriate for a healthy human under normal conditions. The vasculoid can then be removed (in accordance with the sequence described in the vasculoid paper) and the patient is now fully restored but unconscious. Finally, the person is gently ramped through mild hypothermia up to normal body temperature with initiation of consciousness and full awareness of surroundings. The patient is now awake and healthy.

References

Cryonics 4th Quarter 2008, in which this article was originally published, was a special issue on Molecular Nanotechnology (MNT) and cryonics. Other articles in that issue include "The importance of MNT to the cryonics community," "Interview with Robert A. Freitas and Ralph Merkle," and a summary of the December 2008 "Alcor Scientific Advisory Board Meeting."

Other published literature on revival includes:

- Robert C.W. Ettinger, *The Prospect of Immortality,* Doubleday, NY, 1964.

- Jerome B. White, "Viral-Induced Repair of Damaged Neurons with Preservation of Long-Term Information Content," Second Annual Conference of the Cryonics Societies of America, University of Michigan at Ann Arbor, April 11-12, 1969, by J. B. White. Reprinted in *Cryonics* 35:10 (October 2014), 8-17.

- Michael G. Darwin, "The Anabolocyte: A Biological Approach to Repairing Cryoinjury," *Life Extension Magazine* (July-August 1977):80-83. Reprinted in *Cryonics* 29:4 (4th Quarter 2008), 14-17.

- Thomas Donaldson, "How Will They Bring Us Back, 200 Years From Now?" *The Immortalist* 12 (March 1981):5-10.

- K. Eric Drexler, *Engines of Creation: The Coming Era of Nanotechnology*, Anchor Press/Doubleday, New York, 1986, pp. 133-138.

- Brian Wowk, "Cell Repair Technology," *Cryonics* 9 (July 1988).

- Mike Darwin, "Resuscitation: A Speculative Scenario for Recovery," *Cryonics* 9 (July 1988):33-37.

- Thomas Donaldson, "24th Century Medicine," *Analog* 108 (September 1988):64-80 and *Cryonics* 9 (December 1988).

- Ralph C. Merkle, "Molecular Repair of the Brain," *Cryonics* 10 (October 1989):21-44.

- Gregory M. Fahy, "Molecular Repair Of The Brain: A Scientific Critique, with a Response from Dr. Merkle," *Cryonics* 12 (February 1991):8-11 & *Cryonics* 12 (May 1991).

- "Appendix B. A 'Realistic' Scenario for Nanotechnological Repair of the Frozen Human Brain," in Brian Wowk, Michael Darwin, eds., *Cryonics: Reaching for Tomorrow,* Alcor Life Extension Foundation, 1991.

- Ralph C. Merkle, "The Technical Feasibility of Cryonics," *Medical Hypotheses* 39 (1992):6-16 [shorter version of next referenced article].

- Ralph C. Merkle, "The Molecular Repair of the Brain," *Cryonics* 15 (January 1994):16-31 (Part I) & *Cryonics* 15 (April 1994):20-32 (Part II).

- Ralph C. Merkle, "Cryonics, Cryptography, and Maximum Likelihood Estimation," First Extropy Institute Conference, Sunnyvale CA, 1994.

- Ralph Merkle, "Algorithmic Feasibility of Molecular Repair of the Brain," *Cryonics* 16 (First Quarter 1995):15-16.

- Michael V. Soloviev, "SCRAM Reanimation," *Cryonics* 17 (First Quarter 1996):16-18,

- Mikhail V. Soloviev, "A Cell Repair Algorithm," *Cryonics* 19 (First Quarter 1998):22-27,

- Robert A. Freitas Jr., "Section 10.5 Temperature Effects on Medical Nanorobots," in *Nanomedicine, Volume I: Basic Capabilities,* Landes Bioscience, Georgetown, TX, 1999, pp. 372-375.

Neural Archaeology

By Thomas Donaldson, Ph.D.
Cryonics, February, 1987

Recently Alcor conducted some very important experiments. They are important not because they answer any questions, prove or disprove anything, or even tell us much directly. They are important because they are the very first studies of their kind carried out by cryonicists. They may in fact be among the few studies of their kind at all.

What Alcor has done is to produce micrographs, both on a light level and on an electron microscopic level, of several different regions of dog brains undergoing warm ischemia. That is, these brains were subject to periods of no blood flow and then examined to see the state of the neurons. The periods in question were 2 hours, 12 hours, and 24 hours. Qualitatively, these brains were not in a good state. Mike Darwin himself refers to their contents as "just debris." My own feeling on seeing the Alcor micrographs is that our understanding is still too rudimentary to draw conclusions. To obscure the matter more, for instance, there is one reference to successful cell cultures of gray matter taken from the human cerebrum 2 to 3 hours after death (Z. Wroblewska, D. H. Gilden et al, *J Comparative Neurology,* 16(3), 295-306 (1975)). DNA will also survive in ischemic neurons for at least 2 hours (N. Becker, *Amer J Pathology*, 38, 587 (1961)). All this work needs extension, replication, and clarification.

Not many years ago cryonics experienced a very positive event. Someone from outside cryonics (Eric Drexler) came to understand our ideas on cellular repair and their importance. I think they are important, and I think Eric has done a service in both spreading them around and tying together all the thinking people have done, both in the electronics industry and in biology, about "nanotechnology." What these ideas give us, of course, is some idea about how repairs can be done.

But there is another side to cryonics, and that is the issue of whether the information survives at all. Without the information we can't really think of bringing anyone back, no matter what our technology. (Of course, behind that point about survival of information lies another point, about whether the information is sufficient: just what is this identity we want to preserve? But for purposes of this article, I'll simply say that survival of information is the second fundamental issue with which cryonics must deal).

Many cryonicists might hope for a similar "win" about survival of information to the one we've just had with nanotechnology. I'm going to argue that we can't really expect that "win" until it's irrelevant to us, that in fact the nonexistence of such a "win" is fundamental to the whole cryonics idea.

We would all like "proof" that cryonics will work. There will never be proof that cryonics will work. Certainly, individual people will be revived. Some of them (we hope a very large percentage) will actually come back as the same people as those who "died." There will certainly be proof that we can successfully freeze human brains and definitively preserve personality, identity, the "soul", or what have you. But those things aren't cryonics, they're just particular technologies. They don't really embody the key idea.

The really key idea in cryonics is the idea of freezing (or otherwise preserving) people when we don't know if we can ever revive them. Of course, we intend to figure out later whether we can do this. We intend to succeed in reviving them. But before we've actually done so, we certainly can't prove we will succeed. And funny thing, after we've done so, the proof will be irrelevant. If we know how to bring somebody back as a fully functioning human being after an hour of ischemia, why should we ever bother to go to the added expense and trouble of freezing them first? That would be bizarre and unnecessary.

If you're involved in cryonics, you've got to make your peace with the unknown, because it will always be there. You've simply got to make your peace with it.

Before cryonics, there was "death." After cryonics, there are a host of pathologies. Brains ischemic for 12 hours are one instance of a pathology. We have many others, and yet others piled on top of them. Brains ischemic for less than 12 hours, brains poisoned with cyanide, with nerve gas, with botulin toxin. Brains hacked into pieces. Brains improperly frozen or improperly revived (in that are thousands of different pathologies not yet even named!). Brains fried in radiation. Brains taken over by nanotechnological machines. Brains subject to Gaucher's disease, Alzheimer's disease, kuru, dementia from AIDS, Kreutzfeldt-Jacob disease. . . and so on and on. The cryonics proposal is to treat everyone with these conditions as a permanent patient, until means are found to bring them back.

We do this not just because it is humane and liberating (yes, it is humane and liberating. It's even in the highest tradition of medicine. But I'm not going to argue that). We do it because we know of at least one technology which makes it possible to treat people as permanent patients (I mean permanent). Of course, that technology is cryonic suspension. Currently we know of no other technology, but it won't change matters if another one comes along. It is even likely that another one will come along. But we do have to be clear that the effects of cold are a fundamental empirical premise. We also have to be clear that cryonic suspension isn't the same as suspended animation. It only looks the same.

The word "nanotechnology" doesn't provide us with a magic wand we can wave over all such problems to transform them into a solution. It doesn't do so because the preservation of information will always be a fundamental issue. For most frozen patients we're unlikely to even have proof that their identity survives. This is because the problem of recovering identity isn't the same and can't be the same as the problem of how memory is stored. The second problem is a solvable problem in neurophysiology. The first problem is a problem in nerve cell archaeology: to infer from whatever clues remain at hand what the memory was before. This discipline doesn't yet even exist. It has been inaugurated by the recent Alcor work

To do neural archaeology it's not just necessary to understand the physiology of memory. Life is not nearly so easy. We have to understand the entire workings of nerve cells and all the other brain cells, to such a degree that we can predict in advance how they will respond if stressed in different ways: by ischemia, by poisons, by radiation exposure, by hostile nanotechnology. We have to understand every single pathological condition, and have a detailed picture of the sequence of events occurring in brain cells subjected to these pathologies, second by second, straight down to total autolysis. This is a fundamentally infinite task. True, the brain is a finite system. But the number of possible stressors and the damage they can cause to the brain is inexhaustible.

Often in medical periodicals people will publish reflective articles about the future of medicine. They are usually insipid. Well, cryonics is the future of medicine. I don't mean just that people will someday be frozen and that gerontology will rejuvenate us so that we live indefinitely long. I mean that we're going to see a change in boundaries. All of the deaths that we now know of as deaths, and simply abandon, will become pathological conditions, to be studied as problems with the aim of a cure. The future of medicine consists of finding ways to recover poorly frozen patients with Alzheimer's disease and an hour of warm ischemia.

We already have a class of diseases called iatrogenic diseases. These are conditions which result from medical treatments. Antipsychotic drugs, for instance, cause a neurological condition called tardive dyskinesia, which consists of violent facial tics. These conditions are not the same as malpractice, at all. What has happened is that our treatments simply aren't perfect. We'd like to think that we'll have perfect freezing and perfect rejuvenation. But that can't happen either. Even if things go well for most people, for some people things will go badly. They will become medical cases. Some people will go to their doctor for rejuvenation, and wake up 200 years later because they reacted badly to the treatment.

Solving the problem of neural archaeology is like curing or preventing all diseases. It won't happen. (Give me a particular disease, and it will be either cured or prevented. But that's not the same thing.)

But What If The Information Isn't There?

The existence of at least one way to put people into stasis has one more consequence. We can say that a condition is incurable (meaning permanently incurable, not just incurable by present technology) if the information is permanently lost. Without any means to put patients in stasis, doctors must decide what is curable and incurable in a hasty fashion. Nobody can afford to wait. But with cryonic suspension, there is no hurry at all. We simply don't have to decide that someone is gone until we have full and complete understanding of what happened to them. Before cryonics, the patient was assumed dead unless proven otherwise; after cryonics, we assume that the patient is alive unless proven otherwise.

To prove that someone is gone must necessarily take a long time. This is the point where we have to make our peace with the unknown. The key fact is that we have barely begun to study this subject. We have only a few micrographs, with a small number of stains. We lack biochemical data. We lack many more studies, using many more stains. For instance, osmium tetroxide is a common stain for electron microscopy. This chemical binds to lipids in cell membranes. If it isn't present in a cell region, this should tell us that the cell membranes have missing lipids. Are these all lipids, or only particular lipids? Are there other structures which remain? We lack a knowledge of the chemistry/physiology of this degradation. Even following a dog brain at intervals of (say) 15 minutes, watching the structures change, would tell us a lot about what's happening. In fact, even for this ONE pathological condition of prolonged ischemia getting a complete account of what happened would take lifetimes of scientific work.

About 10 years ago I looked through the literature with neural archaeology in mind. I wrote up some of what I found in my bibliography (A Brief Scientific Introduction to Cryonics). This bibliography is of course very out of date. But there is one thing I never said much about in it, and that fact is fundamental to what we are now doing. The truth is, every single paper I quoted was written with some other aim in mind. Nobody was seriously trying to study the physiology of ischemia at 2 hours. These authors hadn't imagined the idea of studying that. In fact, they'd all probably react with outrage to someone quoting them as I did. They were always interested in something else, and the information I wanted just fell out. It is reported that DNA is recoverable from brains at 2 hours warm ischemia. We need studies of DNA in brains. There are stains for DNA we might use. It is also reported that lysosomal enzymes don't actually play a large role in events during warm ischemia. A fascinating fact, if true. There are known stains to localize these enzymes. Who has done this work? Who will do this work, other than cryonicists?

But the question with which I began this section contains much more than just an expression of doubt. Right now, we don't know enough to say. But it is certain that if we never look for remains of memory in these brains, we'll never ever find them. We've barely begun to look.

It's in the dynamic of cryonics that every patient stored will come back in some form. Why not? If you have spent 300 years to clarify this patient's problem, it would be senseless to just throw them away.

There are two special objections to neural archaeology deserving of an answer.

1. *Brain cells are on such a small scale compared to archaeological objects that the available room for the same kind of special inference is too small.*

This statement presupposes that the only kind of archaeological inference possible consists of examining the parts of the fragments we find. For instance, archaeologists might look at fragments of wood, and date them using radiocarbon dating techniques. However, archeology does not only look at parts of parts. The first thing done in examining an archeological site is to carefully plot the relation of all the fragments to one another. Debris has a structure too. We discover this structure by looking at the relations of its parts to one another, not just by looking at the parts. (Archaeologists in Central America complain constantly that valuable artifacts are taken away and sold, with no record of where they were found, in relation to what). If a protein has two degradation parts, we can learn a lot by knowing where these parts are found in the remains of a cell.

In fact, one way of looking at cryonics is that it is simply a way of making such a detailed record. Here is a patient's brain, in the condition it was when we lost him.

Furthermore, it's not clear or obvious that we can't examine some of the parts. Decomposition products of brain chemicals can be specific indicators that they were there. Enough DNA fragments can tell us an entire genome. Proteins and polypeptides in nerve cells can be 10,000 to 100,000 daltons molecular weight or more. Even if fragmented, the fragments can give us much information.

2. *If we make such a reconstruction of a patient from debris, will the patient be the same person?*

This question, of course, is the question about identity (or the soul) with which every committed cryonicist is obsessed. It is right to be obsessed. It is fascinating to watch, because the fact that we are obsessed by it tells us about the future of humanity. When we take over, no joke, the newspapers will have pages devoted to the problem of identity every day of the week. (No longer aging now, but instead identity!) As for answering the question, I don't know. We can do this to animals, and if they pass all tests we'll say they have come back. But animals, of course, aren't aware (?) or at least can't tell us so. It seems to me a fundamentally unknowable question, akin to asking if someone else has self-awareness.

But some things can be said. For instance, if memory is stored in proteins, and if these undergo constant turnover, then exactly what is the difference between this renewal process and recovery of memories from protein fragments? Your memories wouldn't even be the same molecules from day to day. Some patients have ischemic episodes from which they recover. During these they show fleeting symptoms exactly like those of stroke patients (if this happens to you, see your doctor immediately. You may soon have a real stroke, and something can be done about it before it happens). No such patient has ever claimed that they were fundamentally different while this went on. It is not easy to draw any lines here. It will become far less easy in the future.

If we take seriously the proposal that our souls are patterns of organization, then it must follow that these souls are recovered when we do this archaeology. Isn't the pattern of organization recovered? I cannot think of any experimental difference between the notion that I would be the same person after recovery and the notion that I am the same person as I was when I was 8 years old.

The Unknown As A Fundamental Problem

But there is a fundamental practical problem, not to neural archaeology but to the issue of knowledge. I've just argued that only cryonicists would even think of doing the kind of studies we'd need. This comes down to making peace with the unknown. You see, even cryonicists aren't going to get any answers for a long time on any of these death pathologies. And when we do finally get answers for some of them, we'll discover many others we haven't even imagined. We won't just find out about ischemia. We're much more likely to discover many new varieties of ischemia, some of which we understand and others we do not.

It's obvious what is happening. Medical conditions aren't all studied with equal intensity. We don't notice the same amounts of money going into cystic fibrosis research as into cancer. As societies we rank these conditions according to how immediately pressing they are. We then work on them in proportion. This must therefore mean that we will always have a vast number of medical problems for which study has hardly even begun. "Death" isn't really unique here. It's a commonplace that we know of many more diseases now than 100 years ago. Heart disease is now intensively studied, while in 1886 it received little attention. If a medical condition is unstudied, we can't be surprised that very little is known about it.

It is exactly these as yet unstudied problems for which cryonic suspension is intended. When thousands of scientists and doctors work in their laboratories to find a vaccine for polio, we know that the vaccine is imminent. It won't be hard to convince anybody that help is coming. Why would so many work on the problem unless they expected imminent success? Why should one lone scientist work on something else, when he knows that his own unaided efforts will make little progress with the problem? It is under exactly these conditions, when everyone agrees that success is imminent, that cryonic suspension will soon become useless. Cures will be found and the problem will vanish overnight. Yet a vast number of unstudied problems will remain, all summed up in a few words: death, fits, ague. Once there was only "cancer", until we studied it and found a thousand kinds, all different. More than most, cryonicists believe that problems can have a technical solution. But that is simply not the belief of most people. Among cryonicists, even many longtime cryonicists who I feel should know better, there is an easy assumption that provable suspension and revival of brains will solve our problem. I believe strongly that work to suspend brains should be pursued. But I will also say that mere technical problems aren't really the key issue. If you want to be suspended, you'll have to make your peace with the unknown. The problem is that to all of those people out there, it is not obvious that aging will be curable. It is not obvious that their diseases will ever find solution. It is not obvious that we can raise the dead.

You think that all we have to do is to convince people that we can freeze and store them. But they believe that all their problems are fundamental aspects of human existence. What a pointless procedure to take a dying man and plunge him 200 years into the future so that he can die there! What fantastic nonsense, that the human life cycle will ever change! What we have to do to make cryonics spread is to change public attitudes to the unknown. That's much harder to do than just to prove suspension of brains. And it's the unknown for which cryonics is intended. If we knew how to cure this man's problem, we would not freeze him in the first place. And the unknown always dances just one step ahead of us, always out of reach.

What Do We Do Now?

We have many pressing problems. Current dog experiments at Cryovita and elsewhere focus rightly on the most probable case. That is one in which we capture the patient in a hospital, apply CPR or even ECMO,[1] and therefore both cool and oxygenate their brains. The ischemia experiments don't even apply to this case. But even for this case they provide a baseline. We can think about doing a similar series for dogs treated parallel to the way human hospital patients are treated. This would give us valuable feedback about our procedures. Furthermore, it's not quite the same as current dog experiments, which involve rapid cardiopulmonary support rather than HLR treatment with drugs. We need more work like the recent Cryovita model of no oxygenation, to find drug regimens which will better protect patients treated in this likely way.

Unfortunately money and time are very short. However, I believe that we should continue the ischemia experiments, too, although with lesser priority. My reason is that all members face a significant risk of freezing in poor conditions. The risk of autopsy

---

1   "ECMO" stands for "extracorporeal membrane oxygenation," a technique of rapid cooling while supplying oxygen to the tissues to minimize tissue deterioration.

alone is enough to merit work on ischemia. What we need is much more work to define what is happening to ischemic brains. For light microscopy, we need a greater variety of histochemical stains. We need work done at smaller intervals, particularly in the earlier stages of ischemia. We need attempts at cell culture, to bound (for instance) the times at which isolated brain cells can recover. (The no-reflow phenomenon, and all the difficulties in restoring circulation, won't play any role in recovering isolated cells. It seems to be an assumption that brain cells won't survive. This is not an experimental fact.) We need to correlate electron-microscopic stains with their chemical affinities and work out a historical account of what has happened to these cells.

What will come of such a study? I don't know. But then, this article is about making peace with the unknown. There are very few references for our question. We have to provide them for ourselves. It's called pioneering, which is exactly about making peace with the unknown. ∎

CRYONICS, CRYPTOGRAPHY, AND MAXIMUM LIKELIHOOD ESTIMATION

BY RALPH C. MERKLE, PH.D.

Cryonics, 2nd Quarter, 1995

This paper was published in the Proceedings of the First Extropy Institute Conference, held at Sunnyvale, California in 1994. Some changes have been made to this version. A more annotated version is available on Ralph Merkle's Cryonics Pages. http://www. merkle.com/cryo/cryptoCryo.html

Introduction

Most people, if they think of cryonics at all, think of Woody Allen in *Sleeper*, Sigorney Weaver in *Aliens*, or Mel Gibson in *Forever Young*. The hero, after spending decades or centuries in the deep freeze, thaws out gradually and somewhat painfully. Rather stiff from the cold, the warmth of the new era slowly penetrates into their chilled limbs until they at last stretch and look about the world with renewed interest and vitality.

Not!

The damage done by the cryonic suspension (and the probably poor condition of the patient before the suspension even began) are quite sufficient to insure that nothing even remotely resembling these scenarios will ever take place. First, there are fractures in the frozen tissues caused by thermal strain—if we warmed our hero up, he'd fall into pieces as though sliced by many incredibly sharp knives. Second, suspension is only used as a last resort: the patient is at least terminal, and current social and legal customs require that the patient be legally dead before suspension can even begin. While the terminally ill patient who has refused heroic measures can be declared legally dead when he could in fact be revived (even by today's technology), we're not always so lucky. Often, there has been some period of ischemia (loss of blood flow), and the tissue is nowhere near the pink of health. The powerhouses of the cells, the mitochondria, have likely suffered significant damage. "Floculent densities" (seen in transmission electron microscopy) likely mean that the internal membranes of the mitochondria are severely damaged, the mitochondria themselves are probably swollen, and cellular energy levels have probably dropped well below the point where the cell could function even if all its biochemical and metabolic pathways were intact. The high levels of cryoprotectants used in the suspension (to prevent ice damage) have likely poisoned at least some and possibly many critical enzyme systems. If the cryoprotectants didn't penetrate uniformly (as seems likely for a few special regions, such as the axonal regions of myelinated nerve cells: the myelin sheath probably slows the penetration of the cryoprotectant), then small regions suffering from more severe ice damage will be present.

All in all, our hero is *not* going to simply thaw out and walk off.

And yet the literature on freezing injury, on ischemia, and on the other damage likely caused by a cryonic suspension forced me to conclude that cryonics would almost surely work: how can this be?

Molecules and people

Fundamentally, people are made of molecules. If those molecules are arranged in the right way, the person is healthy. If they are arranged in the wrong way, the person is unhealthy or worse. While a surgeon's knife does indeed rearrange molecular structure, it does so only in the crudest fashion. The living tissue itself is what really arranges and rearranges the intricate and subtle molecular structures that underlie life and health. When the tissue is too badly damaged, when intracellular levels of ATP are too low to provide the energy the tissue needs to function, when its own internal structure is disrupted, it can no longer heal itself. Today's surgical tools, gross and imprecise at the cellular and molecular level, can no more aid in this process than a wrecking ball could be used to repair a Swiss watch.

Technology advances, though. The Third Foresight Conference on Molecular Nanotechnology (Palo Alto, 1993) was attended by about 150 research scientists, chemists, computational chemists, physicists, STM researchers, and other research scientists from a range of disciplines. By a show of hands, almost all think we will develop a general ability to make almost any desired molecular structure consistent with physical law, including a broad range of molecular tools and molecular machines. Over half think this technology will be developed in the next 20 to 40 years. A medical technology based on such molecular tools will quite literally be able to arrange and rearrange the molecular structure of the frozen tissue almost at will. The molecules in frozen tissue are like the bricks in a vast Lego set, bricks which in the future we will be able to stack and unstack, arrange and rearrange as we see fit. We will no longer be constrained by the gross and imperfect medical tools that we use today, but will instead have new tools that are molecular both in their size and precision. Repair of damage, even extensive damage, will simply not be a problem. If molecules are in the wrong places we will move them to the right places, hence restoring the tissue to health.

Information theoretic death

This ability, awesome as it will be, will not let us cure all injuries. Before we can move a molecule to the right place, we must know what the right place is. This is not always obvious. Consider, for example, what happens when we cremate a person and stir the ashes. There's more than damage. We can't tell where anything was nor where it should go. We haven't a clue as to what the person looked like, let alone the structure of the tissues in their nervous system. This kind of damage will be beyond even the most advanced medical technology of the future. A person who has been cremated is truly dead, even by the criteria of the 21st or 22nd century.

This true and final death is caused by loss of information, the information about where things should go. If we could describe what things *should* look like, then we could (with fine enough tools, tools that would literally let us rearrange the molecular structure) put things right. If we can't describe what things should look like, then the patient is beyond help. Because the fundamental problem is the loss of information, this has been called *information theoretic death.* Information theoretic death, unlike today's "clinical death," is a true and absolute death from which there can be no recovery. If information theoretic death occurs then we can only mourn the loss.

It is essential that the reader understand the gross difference between death by current clinical criteria and information theoretic death. This is not a small difference of degree, nor just a small difference in viewpoint, nor a quibbling definitional issue that scholars can debate; but a major and fundamental difference. The difference between information theoretic death and clinical death is as great as the difference between turning off a computer and dissolving that computer in acid. A computer that has been turned off, or even dropped out the window of a car at 90 miles per hour, is still recognizable. The parts, though broken or even shattered, are still there. While the short term memory in a computer is unlikely to survive such mistreatment, the information held on disk will survive. Even if the disk is bent or damaged, we could still read the information by examining the magnetization of the domains on the disk surface. It's not functional, but full recovery is possible.

If we dissolve the computer in acid, though, then all is lost.

So, too, with humans. Almost any small insult will cause "clinical death." A bit of poison, a sharp object accidentally (or not so accidentally) thrust into a major artery, a failure of the central pump, a bit of tissue growing out of control: all can cause "clinical death."

But information theoretic death requires something much worse. Even after many minutes or hours of ischemia and even after freezing we can still recognize the cells, trace the paths of the axons, note where the synapses connect nerve cell to nerve cell— and this with our present rather primitive technology of light and electron microscopy (which is a far cry from what we will have in the future).

It is interesting to note that "The classical methods for tracing neuronal pathways are histological methods that detect degenerative changes in neurons following damage.

These staining methods provide a remarkably accurate picture of neuronal projections in the central nervous system" [5, page 262]. Such degenerative changes typically take days or weeks to develop. In many cases, the actual nerve fiber need not be present at all: "Some injuries, such as the crushing of a nerve, may transect peripheral axons but leave intact the sheath that surrounds it. In such injuries the sheath may act as a physiological conduit that guides regenerating axons back to their targets"[5, 264]. Thus there are multiple sources of information about neuronal connectivity, the actual neuron being only one such source.

If we can tell where things should go, then we can in principle (and eventually in practice) restore the patient to full health with their memory and personality intact.

Clinical trials to evaluate cryonics

How can we tell if information theoretic death has taken place? How can we tell if someone has been so injured that they are beyond all help, both today and in the future? The medically accepted method of evaluating any proposed treatment is to conduct clinical trials: try it and see if it works. The appropriate clinical trials to evaluate cryonics are easy to describe: (1) Select N subjects. (2) Freeze them. (3) See if the medical technology a century (or more) from now can indeed revive them.

The clinical trials are ongoing (contact Alcor at 480-905-1906 if you wish to join the experimental group—no action is needed to join the control group), but we don't expect the results to be available for many decades. Which leaves us with a problem: what do we tell the terminally ill patient prior to the completion of clinical trials?

This is not an entirely novel situation for the medical community. Often, new and promising treatments are undergoing clinical trials at the same time that dying patients ask for them. There is no easy answer, but in general the potential benefits of the treatment are weighed against the potential harm, using whatever evidence is currently available as a guide.

In the case of cryonics, the potential harm is limited: the patient is already legally dead. The potential benefit is great: full restoration of health. The medically conservative course of action is to adopt the strategy that poses the least risk to the patient: freeze him. If there is any chance of success, then cryonic suspension is preferable to certain death. This is also in keeping with the Hippocratic oath's injunction to "do no harm." If cryonics were free there would be no dilemma and no need to examine its potential more carefully: we would simply do it. It is not free, and so we must ask: how much is it worth? What price should we pay? Part of this question can only be answered by the individual: what value do we place on a long and healthy life starting some decades in the future?

We will leave these rather difficult questions to each individual, and confine ourselves to a simpler question that is more accessible to analysis: what is the likelihood that current suspension methods prevent information theoretic death?

For information theoretic death to occur we would have to damage the neuronal structures badly enough to cause loss of memory or personality. The structures that encode short-term memory seem particularly sensitive: they are likely not preserved by cryonic suspension. The electrochemical activity of the brain is stopped when the temperature is lowered significantly (as in many types of surgery that are done after cooling the patient) so it is certainly stopped by freezing, with probable loss of short-term memory. But human long-term memory and the structural elements that encode our personality are likely to be more persistent, as they involve significant structural and morphological changes in the neurons and particularly in the synapses between neurons. Thus, we would like to know if the structures underlying human long-term memory and personality are likely to be obliterated by freezing injury.

The evidence available today suggests that the freezing injury and other injuries that are likely to occur in a cryonic suspension conducted under relatively favorable circumstances are unlikely to cause information theoretic death.

Not all cryonic suspensions are conducted under "favorable circumstances;" some circumstances have been decidedly unfavorable. When should we give up? How much damage is required to obliterate memory and personality in the information theoretic sense? What level of damage is sufficient to produce information theoretic death?

Cryptanalysis

Which brings us to cryptanalysis: the art and science of recovering secret messages after they have been deliberately distorted and twisted, ground up and then ground up again by a series of cryptographic transformations carefully designed to obscure and conceal the original message. In cryptography, the person who wants to send a secret message transforms it. The Caesar cipher, for example, changed each letter in the message by "adding" a constant. "A" becomes "C", "B" becomes "D," etc. Modern cryptographic systems are more complex, but the principle remains the same.

Of course, enciphered messages are meant to be deciphered. We know that each step in the scrambling process, each individual transformation that turns "Attack at dawn!" into "8dh49slkghwef" is reversible (if only we knew the key....). Surely this makes freezing and ischemia different from cryptography! However, the basic "transformations" applied in a cryonic suspension are the laws of physics: a physical object (your body) is frozen. The laws of physics are reversible, and so in principle recovery of complete information about the original state should be feasible.

Reversibility strictly applies only in a closed system. When we freeze someone, there is random thermal agitation and thermal noise that comes from the rest of the world: this source of random information is not available to the "cryptanalyst" trying to "decipher" your frozen body (the "encrypted message"). In cryptanalysis, though, we don't know the key (which, as far as the cryptanalyst is concerned, is random information mixed in with the plaintext). The key can be very large: "book codes" use an agreed on piece of text (such as a book) as the key to the code. In addition, some cryptographic systems add random information to the plaintext before encryption to make the cryptanalysts job more difficult.

So the question of whether or not we can revive a person who has been frozen can be transformed into a new question: can we cryptanalyze the "encrypted message" that is the frozen person and deduce the "plain text" which is the healthy person that we wish to restore? Are the "cryptographic transformations" applied during freezing sufficient to thwart our cryptanalytic skill for all time?

It is commonplace in cryptography for amateurs to announce they have invented the unbreakable code. The simple substitution cipher was once described as utterly unbreakable[1]. Substitution ciphers can be broken quite trivially, as we are now aware.

This weakness is not confined to amateurs. The German Enigma, to which the Nazi war machine trusted its most sensitive secrets, was broken by the Allies despite Nazi scientists' opinions that it was unbreakable[1].

It is also well known that erasing information can be much more difficult than it seems. The problem is sufficiently acute that DoD regulations for the disposal of top secret information require destruction of the media. (This poses an interesting question: if a person with a top secret clearance is cryonically suspended, is this a violation of security regulations? Would their cremation be required to insure destruction of the information contained in their brain?)

Against this backdrop it would seem prudent to exercise caution in claiming that freezing, ischemic injury, or cryoprotectant injury result in information theoretic death (and hence that cryonics won't work). Such prudence is sometimes sadly lacking.

Rotor machines and Maximum Likelihood Estimation

We now consider a particular method of cryptanalysis, the application of Maximum Likelihood Estimation (MLE), and discuss how it might be applied to frozen tissue.

The purpose of MLE is to determine the most probable configuration of a system, given many individual (and possibly correlated) observations about the state of that system.

MLE has been applied to World War II rotor machines[2]. While the connection between cryptanalysis of rotor machines and inferring the neuronal structure of frozen tissue might at first be obscure, the parallels are often compelling.

Rotor machines are designed to "scramble" the characters in a message by transforming each individual character into some other character. Rotor machines use a more complex transformation than the Caesar cipher. In particular, they use a series of *rotors*. Each rotor, which resembles a hockey puck in shape, is a short cylinder with 26 contacts on each face (for a total of 52 contacts on the rotor). Each contact on one face is connected by a wire to a single contact on the other face. If we assign the letters A through Z to the contacts on one face, and do the same to the contacts on the other face, then connecting the "P" on one face to a battery might make a voltage appear on (for example) the "H" on the other face. A single rotor thus is a hard-wired permutation of the 26 letters.

In the illustrations, we will pretend that the alphabet has not 26, but only 5 characters: A, B, C, D and E. This will make the examples that follow much more manageable. The reader should be aware that real rotor machines have the full 26 characters and contacts, and that we use 5-letter rotors only to illustrate the concepts.

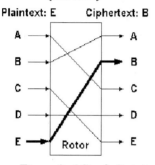

Concept of a WW II rotor machine (one rotor)

Plaintext: E   Ciphertext: B

Figure 1: A Single Rotor.

A single 5-letter rotor is illustrated in figure 1. The illustration shows the input "E" as active, producing an output "B."

If we put several rotors next to each other (like a stack of coins), the contacts on one rotor will make electrical contact with the contacts on the adjacent rotor. If we apply a voltage to the letter "E" on the first rotor in the stack, we will be able to read off the voltage from some contact on the last rotor. The electrical signal, instead of going through a single wire in a single rotor, will have travelled through several wires in several rotors. Connecting the 5 contacts on the last rotor to 5 lightbulbs, we can see at a glance which output has been activated by our input signal.

If we just stack several rotors together and pass an electrical signal through the stack, the result is actually no more complex than a single rotor, i.e., one rotor with the proper wiring would produce the same permutation as a series of rotors. The value of using several rotors becomes apparent if we rotate individual rotors by different amounts, thus changing the electrical connections in a complex and difficult to analyze fashion. Various mechanical contrivances have been used to move the different rotors by different amounts, but the important point here is that the result is a complex and changing network designed to defy cryptanalysis.

The application of MLE to cryptanalysis of a multi-rotor system is rather interesting. We assume, for the moment, that the series of motions that each rotor goes through is known (which is usually true for such machines) but that the pattern of wiring in the individual rotors is unknown. Thus, we don't know which contacts on opposite faces of the rotor are connected, although we know the general structure of the machine.

Rotor machines usually came with a set of pre-wired rotors. By selecting which rotors were used and by setting the initial rotational position of each rotor in the machine, the user could select a unique and hopefully difficult-to-cryptanalyze cipher. In what follows, we will simply assume that the permutation described by the wiring of each rotor is initially completely unknown, and will not attempt to take advantage of the fact that each permutation was in fact drawn from a relatively small set of possibilities.

The information typically available to the cryptanalyst is the ciphertext. Fundamentally, to determine the plaintext from the ciphertext, the plaintext must contain redundancy. In English, for example, "e" is more common than "b." If the cryptanalyst proposes a set of wirings for the rotors and says "Aha! this is the solution!" then we would expect, upon deciphering the ciphertext, that there would be more "e"s than "b"s. If, when we deciphered the message, we found that "e" and "b" were equally common (particularly for a long message) then we would likely conclude that the cryptanalysis was incorrect.

More generally, if the frequency distribution of the 26 letters obtained by "deciphering" the ciphertext with a proposed solution is "smooth," i.e., if the distribution could reasonably have been produced by chance assuming that all 26 characters were equally likely, then the proposed solution is almost certainly wrong. If, on the other hand, the "plaintext" produced by a proposed solution is "rough," i.e., the distribution of letters has the unlikely peaks and troughs of English text, then the proposed solution is very likely right.

It would seem, however, that to use this "smooth" versus "rough" method, we would have to try all the different possible rotors until we found the right ones. The wiring in a single rotor encodes one of 26! different permutations, and three such rotors encodes 26!*26!*26! different possibilities. Simple exhaustive search would be rather expensive.

The problem that we face (common in cryptanalysis) is that the possible keys are discrete, and different keys produce very different results. Thus, a "small" change to a single rotor might produce a big (and hard to predict) change in the deciphered message.

This can be overcome by mapping the discrete cryptanalytic problem into a continuous cryptanalytic problem.

In the discrete case, either "a" is connected to "c" or it is not. There is no halfway about it, no partial connection. In the continuous problem, we will represent our state of knowledge of the rotors by allowing "partial" or "probabilistic" connections. We might have a 40% chance that "a" is connected to "c," and a 60% chance that "a" is connected to "e." Or there might be a 20% chance that "a" is connected to "c," a 33% chance that "a" is connected to "e," a 12% chance that "a" is connected to "b," and a

35% chance that "a" is connected to "d."

More generally, we can assign probabilities that any letter is converted to any other letter. For our 5-character alphabet, we can assign a probability to the connection between "a" and "a," "a" and "b," "a" and "c," "a" and "d," and finally "a" and "e." This would give us a vector of probabilities, such as: (10%, 20%, 30%, 40%, 0%). Instead of percentages, we will adopt fractions, so that the preceding vector will be denoted by (0.1, 0.2, 0.3, 0.4, 0.0).

If we wish to describe the connections between all five input characters and all five output characters, we will need five vectors. Thus, we can describe a single rotor using a 5x5 matrix, as illustrated in figure 2. The particular rotor described in figure 2 is actually a specific real rotor (the rotor described in figure 1), for each row and each column of the matrix has a single 1 with all other entries being 0. The "1" in row A column C means that the input A is connected by a wire to the output C. This matrix notation lets us describe all possible real rotors.

Ciphertext

	A	B	C	D	E
A	0	0	1	0	0
B	1	0	0	0	0
C	0	0	0	0	1
D	0	0	0	1	0
E	0	1	0	0	0

Plain
Text

Figure 2: A 5x5 matrix describing the rotor from Figure 1.

Ciphertext

	A	B	C	D	E
A	0.2	0.2	0.2	0.2	0.2
B	0.2	0.2	0.2	0.2	0.2
C	0.2	0.2	0.2	0.2	0.2
D	0.2	0.2	0.2	0.2	0.2
E	0.2	0.2	0.2	0.2	0.2

Plain
Text

Figure 3: A 5x5 matrix describing a rotor about which we have no information.

The great advantage of this notation is that it also lets us describe our uncertainty about a rotor. For example, if we don't know which wire is connected to what (the state of affairs when we begin cryptanalysis), then we could use the matrix of figure 3. In this matrix, all the entries are 0.2. That is, any input is equally likely (a priori) to be connected to any output. We don't know what's connected to what, and this uncertainty is captured by the matrix. The reader should note that this matrix does not correspond to any "real" rotor. In some sense, it describes the probability that a specific physical rotor is the "right" rotor (physical rotors are rotors whose matrix has a single "1" in every row and column, with all other entries being "0").

How does this help solve our original problem? Yes, we can now use the three "we don't know what's connected to what" rotors of figure 4 as the rotors in our machine, but what does this gain us? How do we "decipher" the ciphertext, and how do we decide if the resulting "plaintext" is smooth or rough?

When we decipher a given letter with a physical rotor, the result is another letter. When we decipher C we get A. When we decipher a letter with a matrix, we get a probability distribution over all letters. When we decipher C we might get a 20% chance of an A, a 10% chance of a B, a 30% chance of a C, a 15% chance of a D, and a 25% chance of an E. In vector notation, we get (0.2, 0.1, 0.3, 0.15, 0.25). When we decipher many letters with a physical rotor, we get a probability distribution over our alphabet. When we decipher many letters with a non-physical matrix, we also get a probability distribution over our alphabet. We know how to measure "roughness" and "smoothness" in a probability distribution: if all the letters are equally probable, the distribution is smooth. If the letters are not equally probable, the distribution is "rough."

Our method of cryptanalysis is now clear. We start by assuming non-physical rotors (as in figure 3) which represent our initial state of knowledge: all permutations are equally likely. We can "decipher" the ciphertext with these rotors, and compute the distribution. Initially, of course, the resulting "plaintext" distribution is smooth. We can now make a small perturbation in our matrix. We might, for example, make the connection between A and C slightly more likely, while making other connections slightly less likely. We can again decipher our ciphertext with this new (slightly modified) rotor. If the distribution of the resulting plaintext is still smooth, we're no closer to the answer. If the distribution is somewhat rougher, then we're moving in the right direction.

In short, we can now make small changes and ask "Are we moving in the right direction?" If the distribution of plaintext is rougher than it was, the answer is "yes!" If the distribution of plaintext is smoother than it was, the answer is "no!" Instead of playing a game of hide-and-seek where you only know if you've found the answer when you actually stumble on it, we're now playing a game where we can take a few steps and ask "Am I getting warmer or colder?" As the reader might appreciate, this makes the cryptanalysis much easier.

There is actually greater sophistication in picking "good" directions than is described here, but the additional mathematics involved is all based on the same concept: we can tell when we're getting warmer or colder, and move in the appropriate direction.

This type of method was used to successfully cryptanalyze rotor machines with three independent rotors over an alphabet of 26 characters on a rather small computer in the late 1970's[2]. A larger computer should be able to handle more than three rotors, although as the number of rotors increases, the cryptanalysis rapidly becomes more difficult. Generally, methods like this either succeed or fail completely. If there is sufficient information for the algorithm to start moving in the right direction, it will usually succeed. If things are so confused that it can't even make an incremental improvement, then it will fail utterly amid data that is totally confusing.

This appears to be a special case of a more general phenomenon. Hogg et. al. [7] said "Many studies of constraint satisfaction problems have demonstrated, both empirically and theoretically, that easily computed structural parameters of these problems can predict, on average, how hard the problems are to solve by a variety of search methods. A major result of this work is that hard instances of NP-complete problems are concentrated near an abrupt transition between under- and overconstrained problems. This transition is analogous to phase transitions seen in some physical systems."

Maximum Likelihood Estimation and cryonics

How might this be applied to cryonics? In general, frozen tissue can be analyzed to determine its structure. The most information that can usefully be obtained about the frozen structure is the location of each atom. (Purists might argue that we also need information about electronic structure, but the electronic structure can almost always be inferred from the locations of the nuclei. For those few cases where this might not be the case, some additional information might be used, e.g., the state of ionization of an atom). Future technologies will almost certainly be able to give us information about the frozen tissue that approaches this limit: we will know the coordinates of essentially every atom when we begin our "cryptanalysis." Even today, SPM (Scanning Probe Microscopy) methods already image individual atoms, thus demonstrating the feasibility in principle of this kind of analysis. Economically producing a sufficient number of sufficiently small instruments able to scan a sufficiently large volume should be feasible, based on published proposals for molecular manufacturing systems[3]. The kind of information this gives us is shown in Figure 4.

The computational load implied by this approach is enormous. Again, extrapolation of future computational capabilities strongly supports the idea that we will have more than enough computational power to carry out the required analysis, even when it quite literally entails considering every atom in our brain[4, 6].

Analysis of the frozen tissue will, on a local basis, allow the recovery of what might be called *local neuronal structure* or LNS. If the suspension took place under favorable circumstances, the LNS will be substantially correct with little ambiguity; that is, we will be able to assign a single interpretation based on local information (e.g., this synapse connects this neuron to that neuron; this axon carries information from one well identified location to another well identified location, etc.). Under adverse circumstances, the LNS will become increasingly ambiguous. An axon might have one of two possible targets, which cannot be fully disambiguated based only on local

REMARK	Atom	X	Y	Z
REMARK An example of the Brookhaven (or Protein Data Bank)				
REMARK file format. This file format includes the type of				
REMARK atom, the X, Y, and Z coordinates, and other				
REMARK information (not shown).				
REMARK				
REMARK	Atom	X	Y	Z
HETATM	1 C	4.345	1.273	-12.331
HETATM	2 C	4.588	2.559	-13.195
HETATM	3 C	5.207	1.273	-11.095
HETATM	4 C	4.587	-0.015	-13.194
HETATM	5 C	2.967	1.273	-11.724
HETATM	6 N	3.431	2.503	-14.246
HETATM	7 C	4.375	3.884	-12.439
HETATM	8 N	6.121	2.503	-13.491
HETATM	9 O	4.947	-0.028	-10.418
HETATM	10 O	4.947	2.575	-10.419
HETATM	11 C	6.673	1.273	-11.440
HETATM	12 C	4.375	-1.339	-12.437
HETATM	13 N	3.431	0.041	-14.245
HETATM	14 N	6.121	0.041	-13.490
HETATM	15 O	2.836	-0.028	-11.011
HETATM	16 C	1.894	1.272	-12.781
HETATM	17 O	2.836	2.574	-11.012
HETATM	18 C	3.585	1.271	-15.031
HETATM	22 C	2.982	3.838	-11.807
HETATM	23 C	7.069	2.560	-12.244

Figure 4: Frozen tissue at low temperatures can be fully described by listing the coordinates and types of the atoms.

information. Which axon a synapse is connected to might not be distinguishable based on the remaining local structure. This will result in a situation where the LNS will not be a single, specific neuronal structure, but will instead be a set of possible structures with initial probabilities assigned based on local information.

Our experience with MLE suggests that ambiguous local neuronal structure can be disambiguated by global information (just as ambiguous information about a single rotor can be disambiguated using the ciphertext and the redundancy of the plaintext). As in cryptanalysis, the fundamental observation is that neuronal structures are redundant. We can use this redundancy to correct errors or omissions in the LNS.

We consider as an example the neuronal structures that process visual information (not least because this system has been extensively studied, and hence we have some reasonable idea of what's involved).

The retina is exposed to photons which describe the visual scene. This information is processed initially in the retina, then transmitted along the optic nerve to the lateral geniculate nucleus and from there to the primary visual cortex in the occipital region. The output coming from the primary visual cortex is highly characteristic: the image has been processed and basic image elements have been isolated and identified. From our point of view, the interesting thing is that certain types of input to the retina (a spot of light, a line, a moving line, etc) produce characteristic outputs from the primary visual cortex. We have, in short, "plaintext" (the input to the retina) and "ciphertext" (the output of the primary visual cortex), a great deal of knowledge about which "plaintext" can correspond with which "ciphertext." and some knowledge about the structure of the "key" (the possible structures of the neural circuits in the retina, lateral geniculate nucleus, and the primary visual cortex).

Given that we have knowledge derived from the frozen tissue about the LNS in the retina, the lateral geniculate nucleus, and the primary visual cortex, we can then enter "plaintext" (images on the retina) and observe the resulting "ciphertext" (neuronal outputs from the primary visual cortex). If the "ciphertext" is inappropriate for the "plaintext," we can incrementally modify the descriptions of the LNS and see if the resulting plaintext-ciphertext pairs become more or less reasonable. If the result is more reasonable, we are moving in the right direction and should continue. If the result is less reasonable we are moving in the wrong direction and should stop and try some other direction.

More generally, the brain has many cortical areas connected by projections. The processing in each cortical area and the information that can pass along these projections are characteristic of the function being performed. When inappropriate responses are observed, we can incrementally change the relevant LNS in an appropriate direction (e.g., we can change the initial probability vector which describes the state of the LNS by taking a small step in the multi-dimensional hyperspace).

The high degree of redundancy in the brain is evident from many lines of evidence. One of the more dramatic is the ability of the embryonic and infant human brain to correctly wire itself up. Initially, the "wiring diagram" of the brain is quite rough. As the brain receives input, the growing neurons utilize the characteristic patterns of neuronal activity to quite literally make the right connections. Individual neurons can determine, based only on local information, that they aren't wired up correctly. They will either change morphology (often dramatically) or (in the case of roughly half the neurons in the growing brain) will actually die.

The same redundancy that allows the growing human brain to wire itself up can be used to verify that we have correctly inferred the neuronal structure of the frozen brain. If the characteristic neuronal behavioral patterns (simulated, of course, on a computer) are inappropriate, then we have somehow erred in our analysis and need to incrementally modify the LNS until it is appropriate.

This approach will let us start from a state of partial knowledge of the original neuronal structure (perhaps caused by significant delays in the start of suspension combined with an inadequate suspension protocol) and successively improve that partial knowledge until we have fully reconstructed a neuronal structure consistent with the original data.

If there has been so much damage that we are unable to infer sufficient local structure to allow even an incremental improvement in our description of the system, then this approach will fail. Published work on the cryptanalysis of multi-stage rotor systems has already demonstrated an ability to infer the wiring of the rotors even when there is no knowledge at all of the wiring in the intervening stages. In the case of the frozen human brain, there is typically a wealth of information about the neuronal wiring (or LNS) unless the structures involved have quite literally been obliterated.

Or, as experience with erasing top secret media has demonstrated, it's hard to get rid of information when sophisticated means of data recovery are employed. And we'll have *very* sophisticated means of data recovery available to us in the future. ■

References

1. *The Code Breakers*, by David Kahn, Macmillan 1967

2. *Maximum Likelihood Estimation Applied to Cryptanalysis,* by Dov Andelman, 1979, Ph.D. Thesis, Stanford Dept. of Electrical Engineering.

3. *Nanosystems: Molecular Machinery, Manufacturing, and Computation,* by K. Eric Drexler, Wiley 1992.

4. *The Technical Feasibility of Cryonics,* by Ralph C. Merkle, Medical Hypotheses 39, 1992, pages 6-16.

5. *Principles of Neural Science*, third edition, by Eric R. Kandel, James H. Schwartz, and Thomas M. Jesse, Elsevier 1991.

6. *The Molecular Repair of the Brain,* parts I & II, by Ralph C. Merkle, *Cryonics,* 1994; Vol. 15 No. 1, pages 16-31 and Vol. 15 No. 2, pages 18-30.

7. *Phase transitions in constraint satisfaction search,* Tad Hogg et. al., http://www.hpl.hp.com/shl/projects/constraints/

INFORMATION STORAGE AND COMPUTATIONAL ASPECTS OF REPAIR

BY TAD HOGG, PH.D.
Cryonics, 3rd Quarter, 1996

Cryonic suspension is an attempt to preserve enough of a person's body, after death by current standards, to allow future technology to restore the person to health. This preserved physical structure may not in itself be sufficient for future repair, due to the damage caused by suspension, especially if the suspension is delayed. So people planning for suspension might improve their chances of eventual revival by saving additional information about themselves in the form of records separate from their bodies [1-3]. But, what should be saved, and how? Before discussing these questions in sections 2 and 3 below, it first helps to better understand why saved information could be useful.

Why Save Information?

Three distinct technical abilities are required for repair [4]: 1) observe, in sufficient detail, the preserved structure, 2) compute what changes need to be made, and 3) manipulate the structure to make these changes. The scale of these operations (e.g., molecular or cellular) will depend on the amount of suspension damage.

Technologies required for these steps could develop at different times. In cases where the second step is the bottleneck, additional information could shorten the time until repair becomes feasible. This is because the second step is primarily one of information processing: determining the original (healthy) physical structure from the (damaged) preserved structure and whatever other records about the person are available. Such records should include descriptions of the person and the suspension method.

There are two important aspects of using information for repair. The first is whether the information uniquely determines the original structure, up to changes that don't matter for preserving identity. The second is the computational problem of actually finding such a structure, and planning a series of physical changes to construct it. Even when there is a unique structure, the time needed to find it by searching through the enormous set of possible structures can mean, in practice, the original structure cannot be found. This remains true even with much more powerful computers [5], with the possible exception of (so far, hypothetical) quantum computers [6, 7].

To reduce the required computation time, sophisticated heuristics can guide the choices made during the search. These procedures consider only a few changes at a time and estimate whether each of these changes gets closer to solving the problem. At each step a change that seems to get closer to a solution is selected [8]. This method sometimes gets stuck where none of the changes can improve the situation. In these cases one must make a few changes that temporarily make things worse [9]. Even though these heuristic methods are not guaranteed to find a solution quickly, they often work quite well, and are much faster than examining all possibilities [10,11]. Heuristics are especially effective when they use plenty of information about the solution. Thus even when there is enough information to determine structure uniquely, additional information could be very important for reducing the computational search.

This is particularly significant because there are abrupt transitions in the quality, solvability, and required search time in large computational problems as information is added [10, 12, 13]. This contrasts with the gradual improvement one might expect from experience with small problems. That is, there is some essential amount of information beyond which the problem most likely has a unique solution, and below which the problem has extremely many. In this latter case, the chance of finding the correct reconstruction would be very small. Moreover, problems near the transition tend to be the hardest to solve: these would be the cases for which even the best future technology would have the most difficulty. For the computational problems associated with tissue repair we don't know where this information threshold is. But its existence means a little extra information, especially giving a wide variety of constraints, can help a lot in some otherwise marginal cases.

External records can also help evaluate the quality of a repair. In fact, this might be the only way to determine when the repair is complete, instead of "just" producing a similar, healthy individual. Even if it doesn't help a particular case, this evaluation could help improve future repairs by showing what information is sufficient for repair with a given level of technology.

Other reasons to maintain records include the information's value to you [2] and providing your preferences for various repair options that may be, from a purely technical point of view, equally likely to work [14, 15].

To help make these ideas more concrete, the use of information in a simple repair problem is illustrated in BOX 1. While this artificial example shows the essential computational issues, repairing damaged tissue will be much more complicated. For instance, the constraints provided by the information won't always be so clear-cut. Instead they'll assign probabilities to distinguish likely from unlikely original structures [12]. Also, errors in the records or their interpretation could give conflicting constraints. Learning how to interpret the information properly will be one of the major tasks to complete before repair can proceed. Because we lack this knowledge at

BOX 1 – A Parable of Coins

To illustrate how information can help, let's consider a very simple repair problem. Suppose instead of repairing a suspended person you are "repairing" a "preserved" sequence of ten coins. You want to reproduce the original sequence of heads and tails. For the sake of illustration, we'll suppose some additional records are available. Although the details are artificial, these records show how different types of information can be combined to improve the reconstruction.

When the sequence was preserved it was inside a box preventing examination of individual coins, though some properties could be determined with the crude technologies then available. Now you can directly observe the "damaged" (preserved) sequence, call it D, and turn over individual coins, corresponding to the first and third steps in the repair process. Suppose you observe

$D = $ H H T H T T T H H T

with H and T denoting heads and tails, respectively.

You now need to deal with step two, i.e., figure out which of the 1,024 possible sequences was the original one, the undamaged sequence, call it U.

If all you knew was that each coin was tossed during preservation, you couldn't determine U from D: all possibilities would be equally likely. Fortunately you have some description of the preservation process and the original sequence. It turns out there were two preservation methods used for these boxes of coins: shake the box vigorously ("cremation") or bump it gently ("suspension"). The records tell you this particular box is a result of the gentle method. They also note that the original sequence had a property called "balanced," determined by an old, crude measurement process which you find described in a library. To use this information, you must relate it to the condition of individual coins, a level of detail that wasn't available when the sequence was preserved. You do this through a series of experiments.

First, you reproduce, as closely as possible from the available descriptions, the preservation methods used and examine the damage caused. You find that vigorous shaking results in a random flip of each coin. The gentle method, call it G, always turns over exactly five coins, leaving the other five unchanged, but which five are changed varies randomly from one experiment to the next. This already greatly reduces the repair problem: you now only need to figure out which five coins were turned over, that is, you have to determine which version of G was used in going from U to D. In this case, with G consisting of exactly five flips, there are 252 possibilities.

Furthermore, examining other undamaged coin boxes shows original sequences always have the same face showing for each neighboring pair. That is, the first and second coin must both be heads or both tails, and similarly for the 3rd and 4th, etc. This constraint leaves 16 possibilities.

Finally, you study other cases that are balanced, a property observed to apply originally to the sequence you are repairing. You find this means the number of heads in the first half of the sequence is the same as in the second half. This leaves only 6 possibilities.

This is all the information you have, so each of these remaining possibilities is equally consistent with everything you know. It now remains to actually find one of the consistent possibilities. Conceptually, the simplest approach is to go through all

1,024 possible sequences until you find one that satisfies all the constraints. However, this method isn't feasible for long sequences because the number of possibilities grows extremely rapidly. For instance, with just a thousand coins there are so many possibilities that, even if every atom in the observable universe were a separate computer checking a trillion possibilities per second since the Big Bang, almost all the choices would still not yet have been examined. Instead you use a heuristic search method turning over a single coin at each step combined with a test for getting closer to a solution expressed as a penalty for violating each constraint.

The first constraint requires that we turn over exactly five coins in going from U to D. So as a penalty you count the absolute difference between five and the actual number of coins you must turn over to get from U to D. (Since U and D are ten bits in length, the number of bits that must be turned over to get from U to D will be between zero and ten and the penalty, therefore, will be a number between zero and five.) For the second constraint, you count a penalty point for each neighboring pair in U showing opposite faces. Finally, for the third constraint, you count a penalty point for the discrepancy in the number of heads in the first and second halves of U. Smaller penalties mean the constraints are closer to being satisfied. A sequence consistent with all the constraints has zero total penalty.

As a start, we will guess that

$U = D =$ H H T H T T T H H T.

In this case, no coins at all are turned over in going from U to D, whereas 5 coins are supposed to be turned over, so we have a penalty of 5 for the first constraint. For the second constraint, among neighboring pairs in U, the 3rd and 4th coins, the 7th and 8th and the 9th and 10th have opposite faces, giving a combined penalty of 3. For the third constraint, U has three heads in the first half and two in the second, for a discrepancy penalty of 1. So the total penalty for this choice of U is 5+3+1 or 9. With this measure in mind, you modify (flip coins in) U so as to reduce the penalty. For example, flipping coins 6, 7, 3, 5 and 10, in that order, results in decreasing penalties of 8, 7, 4, 3 and 0, respectively.

The final result,

$U =$ H H H H H H H H H H,

is one of the six sequences that satisfy all the constraints.

How well have you done? In this example, the odds are 1 in 6 that you reproduced the original sequence exactly, much better than the odds of 1 in 1,024 you started with but still not perfect. You may actually have done even better if, among the five incorrect reconstructions, there are a few with the "same identity" as the original.

As an analogy with repairing suspended people, the three constraints for the coins correspond to different sorts of information. The first constraint involves damage caused by suspension. The second constraint is a property of all undamaged sequences, analogous to information about healthy tissue structure in general. Finally, the third constraint is specific to this individual case, analogous to a description of a person's preference or memory. The repair calculation required both the saved records and new experiments to interpret those records. This illustrates how the usefulness of information is a combination of the quality of the records themselves and the capability of future technology.

present, we can't know for sure whether the computation is feasible [5]. Instead we're forced to rely on more general feasibility arguments [10, 11, 12], realizing that these are suggestive, not definitive.

What Should Be Recorded?

Current knowledge of the physical basis of identity and memories, and how much change is tolerable, is rather limited. So it's impossible to say what records will definitely be useful; however, there are some reasonable suggestions. To help eliminate incorrect reconstructions and cross the solvability threshold, it's best to save a variety of characteristics that distinguish you from others, especially information that cannot otherwise be inferred in the future. Variety provides many different constraints for the repair process which in turn can lead to effective search heuristics.

Information of a more general nature should also be useful. This includes the microscopic nature of memory storage, requirements for healthy cells, structural changes that preserve identity, and the effectiveness of different repair options. We currently lack the means to determine this information. Fortunately this sort of information applies to all people, so it can wait to be provided by future technology. This is also true for determining how records relate to physical properties of tissue structure. Thus, information that currently appears to have no value, because we don't know how it relates to physical structure, could be useful in the future.

Types of Information

There are two types of individually distinguishing information. The first describes physical structure and the second is mental or cognitive. These impose different requirements on future technology for their use and also differ considerably in the ease with which they can be obtained now.

If damage is relatively minor, it may be sufficient to restore the tissue to biological viability. This would require detailed knowledge of the nature of healthy tissue and the types of physical damage that occur during suspension. Some limited studies along these lines already exist [16, 17], though much remains to be done. Records of the suspension, such as measurements of temperature and chemical concentrations vs. time, can help with this type of repair, and also indicate the quality of the suspension [18].

Medical diagnostics, such as MRI scans, give physical measures of the original healthy tissue structure. Currently this sort of information is expensive to obtain and probably lacks enough resolution to help discriminate among different individuals at the scale where repair needs to take place. Nevertheless, as these technologies improve they could provide useful information. In fact, even if current measurements appear to have insufficient detail, future improvements in their interpretation could make them useful for repair. Taking this to an extreme, some of this physical information could also be obtained during repair through a series of simulations [12].

For more extensive damage, the repair process may need to use records of mental characteristics. This information is much easier to obtain at present than the physical information described above. However, using such characteristics for repair will be more difficult because it requires learning how these properties relate to the underlying physical structures that encode them.

Suggestions for Individual Records

A variety of easily recorded information is given in the following list. Being specific, and elaborating the reasons for responses, will best help distinguish yourself from other, similar people.

1. Memories
   - memories of people and events, e.g., a diary
   - memories elicited by photos, music, stories, odors, etc.
   - events that happened to you but you don't remember, e.g., some of your childhood events as described by older relatives; these may nevertheless have made physical changes so the memories are there but just not accessible
   - knowledge and skills you have, e.g., languages

Even trivial sorts of memories you don't really care whether you keep could be useful. What habits do you have? What is your typical day like?

2. Personality
   - preferences: what you like or dislike, e.g., about people, books, art, music, movies, places, rituals, and foods
   - your interests and hobbies
   - psychological tests such as those used to help identify career interests and personality preferences [19]; more important than the answers themselves are the reasons for your answers, i.e., use the test questions as prompts to describe yourself
   - jokes you find funny or not
   - views on current events and policy choices
   - personal philosophy on ethics
   - the relation of individuals and society, etc.

3. Individual psychophysical behavior
   Most psychophysical experiments require laboratories to conduct. But there are

some easily available records, such as voice and handwriting samples, and reactions to illusions known to differ among people [20].

4.   Writings, publications, artistic and music compositions, presentations, etc.

These can be memory aids, especially in conjunction with descriptions of the background behind each item. With sufficient quantity, their statistical properties, e.g., of word choices, can help distinguish you from others as in studies of disputed authorship [21], and the relationship of word choices to brain structure [22].

5.   People who know you

Other people who know you well could give additional information. If they are much younger than you, they may also be available during repair to provide information, such as suggestions of which available repair options you would want. Alternatively, if they are also suspended, the constraints provided by knowledge you have of each other could allow the repair computations for the whole group to proceed even if they would not for each individual considered separately.

6.   Preferences for reanimation

As repair technology develops, a variety of options will become available. For instance, whether to attempt a reasonable repair as soon as possible or wait for further improvements to give an even better reconstruction. Repairs could also introduce physical or mental changes. To help select among these options, a record of your preferences, and your reasons for them, would help [14, 15].

What physical changes might you like as part of the repair process? For instance, if you currently wear glasses, would you like the shape of your eyes corrected? Or to provide more familiar context for adjusting to future society, would you prefer minimal changes? At the other extreme, would you want to start with whatever is currently fashionable at the time of repair, even if very different from what you're used to now?

Repairs capable of using records of your memories or personality could also make changes in them. What are your thoughts on this? Suppose some memories can't be restored completely. Would you prefer to have the lost memories "filled in" with a "best guess," to be repaired without them and make a choice after reanimation, or wait in suspension a bit longer in the hope that better technology or the interpretation of additional records will allow complete repair?

What if there are conflicting records from different times in your life [1, 3]? For instance, suppose you enjoy bird watching at age 20, and leave extensive records on this hobby, but lose interest later in life. Should these records be used for repair even though they are obsolete, and could result in a mixture of memories and preferences from different times in your life?

As another example, languages are continually changing: the common idioms, word choices and accents in the future could be quite different than those of today. Would you prefer to have new language skills added during reanimation, if possible, or gradually learn them afterwards?

More generally, what to you constitutes an adequate repair? What physical or mental changes would you be willing to tolerate if they meant an earlier reanimation? If other people you know are also suspended, would you prefer to wait until some of them can also be repaired?

At present, the eventual options are unclear, making it difficult to answer these questions. So you may find it makes sense to rely on the best judgments of people in the future, based on their experience with other repairs. In that case you might record the trade-offs as you see them now as a guide to choices you might have made. At some point, the options may become more clear and you could then state more specific preferences. Of course, because of the uncertainties of future technology, these preferences should be viewed as guidelines rather than strict requirements.

How Should Information be Stored?

Information storage requires selecting a durable storage medium for the records and placing them in a stable long-term environment. Archival storage environments are provided by various companies, and arrangements for their use can be made through cryonics organizations [2, 23]. For the storage medium there are various choices, with different trade-offs among known physical durability, cost, storage capacity and type of information they can readily contain [24, 25].

Paper has remained legible for centuries if carefully stored and is particularly good for recording text. But paper is bulky and less suitable for images and sounds. Microfilm offers a compact alternative archival storage medium, currently in widespread use.

Another option is digital storage. This has the advantage of compact storage for a wide variety of information, including text, photos, video and sounds. For instance, a large amount of information can be stored on CD-ROM, equivalent to the text in hundreds of books. Individual recorders are available for around $1,000, and $10 per disk [26, 27], although for making just a few CD-ROMs a cheaper way is to use companies that create CD-ROMs from data you provide. As with other technologies the cost should drop substantially in the next few years.

Can digital media preserve information reliably for long periods of time? Just as with paper, the media eventually degrade due to, for example, heat or moisture. Unfortunately, in spite of some experiments, the long term reliability of CD-ROM's has not been tested fully [28]. Still, many types of information, such as English text, have a great deal of redundancy so losing a few bits is unlikely to make it completely unreadable. And any future technology capable of detailed examination of preserved tissues will also have much greater capability for recovering damaged information from digital media than is currently available.

With digital storage you might also worry that file formats rapidly become obsolete [24]. This is unlikely to prevent using the information for repair because reference libraries should maintain descriptions of the common formats in use today, to aid future historical research. Furthermore, even if the exact format descriptions are unavailable, redundancy in stored information makes interpreting digital data a much simpler task than computations to repair tissue in microscopic detail. Nevertheless there are some easy ways to minimize this difficulty. These include using simple widespread formats such as plain ASCII, using several different formats and some easily described files to provide a check on the correct format. You should also record, on paper, a summary of the contents, as well as describe the file format and programs used.

Digital information can also be readily copied from one physical medium to another as technology improves, providing easy migration during your lifetime. After suspension this copying process would need ongoing institutional support. One such proposal is described in BOX 2.

BOX 2 – A New Option for Digital Storage

Record storage is a natural complement to maintaining people in suspension. A simple option for digital records is currently under construction as part of a larger effort to expand the Alcor pages on the World Wide Web at http://www.alcor.org by Ralph Whelan, Steve van Sickle, and others.

This will include public information about people in suspension. It will also accept, via electronic mail, comments from their friends for archival storage. Some of these additional records may be useful for repair. This system will also allow members to save digital records for themselves prior to suspension.

Some practical issues need to be resolved for this service. These include privacy of the records, the size of the files (text shouldn't be a problem, but images, video and sound files can use up storage very rapidly), changes or corrections (e.g., new reanimation preferences) and an institutional structure to ensure the digital records are replicated and copied to better media as they become available. Nevertheless, this proposal to use the Web and electronic mail for creating digital records is an important new storage option. Its simplicity of use should also help overcome people's procrastination since individual records can be constructed a little at a time.

In addition to individual storage, you can also use existing archival services provided by libraries for newspapers, books, and other public materials maintained for historical or reference purposes. If you are a writer, your publications in these sources are likely to be maintained as part of a larger archival effort. You could then save, on paper, a list of your publications. Currently library archives are mostly paper and microfilm, but a large effort is underway to find suitable archival storage methods for digital data [29], including World Wide Web documents. The results of this effort should, in a few years, also provide another format suitable for individual use.

While there are many options, a reasonable choice is to use paper or microfilm for the most important textual records, collect the larger records digitally during your lifetime while you can continually upgrade to better archival media, and then transfer the information to a stable environment, within the limits of reasonable expense.

Finally, remember one of the real benefits of external records: redundancy. Make copies, perhaps in multiple formats, to save.

Summary and Afterthoughts

A key step in repairing suspension damage is determining the physical changes required to restore healthy function. With current suspension methods, it's likely this will involve substantial information processing. While a great deal of information exists within the preserved tissue, additional records could simplify the computation required for repair. Many types of individually distinguishing information can be obtained easily and saved for this purpose.

Technologies able to interpret and use these records, especially descriptions of memories and personality, raise many intriguing questions beyond the repair process itself [1, 14]. As an extreme example, this may allow people to readily change many aspects of themselves, mental as well as physical, that we currently regard as fixed and part of what defines a person. This could include changes in personality, preferences and memories. In such a world, the concept of what constitutes a person and the range of changes that can be made without losing one's identity will be very different from what they are today. This raises an ironic possibility: from that future perspective a precise match to the original person may appear less important than it does to us now. Such an expanded view of personal identity could allow some repairs to be judged adequate in preserving identity even if they would not be so regarded from our present perspective. This in turn could encourage people to proceed with repairs for cases that were previously thought to have too little information for adequate reconstruction, even without any additional improvements in technology or available information.

This discussion highlights a key purpose of suspension: preserving individual information. From this point of view, the required information can be shared between preserved structure and external records, so that records can compensate for some suspension damage. This also raises the question of how much information is required to determine a unique individual, and whether it could exist entirely in external records [30]. This emphasizes the philosophical view that, fundamentally, our identities are not tied directly to our functioning bodies, nor even to the preserved physical structure of these bodies, but rather to whatever information is required for accurate reconstruction [31]. Whether this in fact is the case is a difficult philosophical question. Seeing how additional information helps with repair could provide a strong empirical grounding for addressing this question. ■

Notes

[1] R. Ettinger, *The Prospect of Immortality,* Sidgwick 1964

[2] S. Bridge, "Memory Storage for Cryonics Patients," *Alcor Phoenix* 2(8) 4 (1995)

[3] M. Perry, "Coping with Imperfect Preservation," *Alcor Phoenix* 2(4) 1-3 (1995)

[4] R. Merkle, "The Molecular Repair of the Brain," *Cryonics* 15(1) 16-31 (1994) also at http://merkle.com/merkleDir/ techFeas.html. For another proposal, interleaving the three repair steps, see M. Soloviov, SCRAIVI Reanimation, *Cryonics* 17(1) 16-18 (1996)

[5] T. Donaldson, "It's Not at All So Easy," *Cryonics* 15(3) 37-39 (1994), and 16(3) 2-3 (1995)

[6] D. DiVincenzo, "Quantum Computation," *Science* 270,255-261 (1995)

[7] T. Hogg, "Quantum Computing and Phase Transitions in Combinatorial Search," *J. of Artificial Intelligence Research,* 4,91-128 (1996) also at http://www.cs.washing-ton.edu/research/jair/abstracts/hogg96a.html. See also cryonet messages 6110 (21 Apr. 1996) and 6130 (30 Apr. 1996) [32]

[8] S. Minton et al., "Minimizing Conflicts: A Heuristic Repair Method for Constraint Satisfaction and Scheduling Problems," *Artificial Intelligence* 58,161-205 (1992)

[9] S. Kirkpatrick et al., "Optimization by Simulated Annealing," *Science* 220,671-680 (1983)

[10] T. Hogg, *Cryonics* 15(4) 3-4 (1994)

[11] R. Merkle, "Algorithmic Feasibility of Molecular Repair of the Brain," *Cryonics* 16(1) 15-16 (1995)

[12] R. Merkle, "Cryonics, Cryptography and Maximum Likelihood Estimation," *Cryonics* 16(2) 13-20 (1995) also at http://merkle.com/cryptoCryo.html

[13] T. Hogg et al., "Frontiers in Problem Solving: Phase Transitions and Complexity," *Artificial Intelligence,* 81 (1-2) (1996). See also ftp://parcftp.xerox.com/ pub/dynamics/constraints.html

[14] M. Perry, "Thinking About Reanimation," *Alcor Phoenix* 2(3) 1-2 (1995)

[15] R. Cheney, *Alcor Phoenix* 2(5) 5 (1995)

[16] As an example of constraints on brain organization, see C.-C. Hilgetag et al., "Indeterminate Organization of the Visual System," *Science* 271,776-777 (1996) also at http://www.psychology.ncl.ac.uk/www/hierarchy.html

[17] An example of current studies of the molecular basis of tissue damage is J-Y. Koh et al., "The Role of Zinc in Selective Neuronal Death After Transient Global Cerebral Ischemia," *Science* 272,1 013-1 016 (1996)

[18] M. Perry, "Toward a Measure of Ischemic Exposure," *Cryonics* 17(2) 21 (1996)

[19] For example, D. Keirsey and M. Bates, *Please Understand Me,* Gnosology Books, 1984. See also http://www.bae.uga.edu/other/david/HTM L/myers-briggs.test. html.

[20] For a discussion of audio illusions, see P. Yam, "Escher for the Ear," *Scientific American* 27 4(3), 14 (March 1996)

[21] F. Mosteller, *Applied Bayesian and Classical Inference: The Case of the Federalist Papers,* 2nd ed., Springer-Verlag 1984. Some software for analyzing text is at http:// crl.nmsu.edu/users/CRLfolks/dunning.html

[22] P. Wallich, "Senile Words," *Scientific American* 274(6), 26-28 (June 1996)

[23] J. Strout, cryonet message 5541 (5 Jan. 1996) [32]

[24] J. Rothenberg, "Ensuring the Longevity of Digital Documents," *Scientific American* 272(1) 42-47 (Jan. 1995)

[25] J. Strout, cryonet message 5558 (1 0 Jan. 1996) [32] and follow-up messages.

[26] G. Wasson, "Feel the Burn," *MacUser* 86-94 (Jan. 1996)

[27] J. Seymour, "Create Your Own CD," *PC Magazine* 99-104 (Apr. 9, 1996)

[28] For information on CD technology and reliability, see http://www.cd-info. com

[29] M. Hedstrom, "Digital Preservation: A Time Bomb for Digital Libraries", http://www .uky .edu/-kiernan/DL/ hedstrom.html

[30] R. Merkle, "Uploading: Transferring Consciousness from Brain to Computer," *Extropy* 5(1) 5-8 (1993). See also http://sunsite.unc.edu/jstrout/uploading/MUHome-Page.html.

[31] M. More, *The Diachronic Self: Identity, Continuity, Transformation,* at http://www.primenet.com/-maxmore/disscont.htm, part of which appears in M. More, "The Terminus of the Self," *Cryonics* 15(4) 25-35 (1994)

[32] The cryonet archive is available at http:// www.access.digex.net/-kfl/les/cryonet/ with message 5541 in file 5541.html, and similarly for other message numbers.

[33] I thank Steve Bridge and Ralph Whelan for their suggestions, and Ralph for also preparing the illustrations.

PERSPECTIVES ON CRYONICS

A Message for Terminal Patients

By Saul Kent
Cryonics, October, 1984

"We are all terminal and we are all going to die sometime. So why should a terminal illness be different from a terminal life? There is no difference, and I would suggest that the most positive thought for any patient is to concentrate on perpetuating life. First and foremost, whether the patient is a mechanic or a United States Senator, he or she must have motivation for living—if the life force is to prevail over illness or infirmity."

For many years, the author of the above quote was indeed a United States Senator. He was also an Army officer, lawyer, and State Attorney General. He attained wealth, fame, and a place in history. His name: Jacob K. Javits.

A few years ago, Javits was stricken with Amyotrophic Lateral Sclerosis (ALS)—a disease that disables the victim by reducing the ability of motor neurons to deliver chemical messages to muscles.

ALS is known as Lou Gehrig's disease because it killed the great baseball player while he was still in his 30s. There is no known cure.

The Javits quote was taken from an article entitled "When Should Doctors Let A Patient Die?" in the August, 1984 issue of *Discover* magazine. It is symptomatic of the confused, irrational thinking that prevails among virtually everyone on this planet.

Advice For Terminal Patients

Javits tells patients suffering from terminal diseases to "cheer up" because in the end we are all going to die—not just those of us who are suffering from "incurable" diseases. The bitter truth is that life has been designed to be of short duration. That the seeds of our destruction are contained within us and that we are condemned to "count the days" until our "inevitable" demise.

In light of this tragic situation, it's a good idea to tell patients suffering from terminal diseases to have a positive attitude toward life. Incessant brooding about death is depressing and counterproductive—even for a terminal patient. To be tormented by the anticipation of a future event is to be paralyzed in the present.

A Positive Attitude

There's solid evidence that a positive attitude can not only bring pleasure to individuals on the brink of death, but can actually extend their lives. Feeling good about yourself and about your life can help you to recover from life-threatening diseases and injuries—even from diseases considered "incurable."

So it's good to have a positive attitude toward life. But such an attitude must be rooted in the value of one's own life, not in the knowledge that other people are going to die. It's absurd to be told to cheer up simply because everyone around you is also going to die. Anyone with feeling and compassion for others is likely to be profoundly distressed by such thoughts.

A Matter Of Degree

Moreover, it's even more absurd to equate the prognosis of a patient suffering from a terminal disease with that of a young person in perfect health. While it's true that we're all in a terminal condition, there's a tremendous difference in the extent to which we're terminal.

Like it or not, we're not all in the same boat...some of us—such as Jacob Javits—are in small, battered lifeboats that are about to sink, while others are in large, well-fortified ships with heavy artillery. Terminal patients like Javits are faced with almost certain death in the near future, while others can look forward to many decades—perhaps even centuries—of healthy, productive life.

Although everyone is terminal, some of us are clearly more terminal than others.

"Forgetting" About Death

Javits' advice to terminal patients is to "forget" about the fact that they're dying. As he puts it:

"The greatest therapy is to forget about terminal illness. Everyone is terminal. That is the great message that can perpetuate the useful life of the patient and be of solace and comfort to the patient's family and friends. What is really worthwhile in life is the excitement and the expectation of living, and the giving and the receiving which is, after all, life's essence."

Unfortunately, this bit of advice is not only absurd, it's also criminal.

An Impossible Task

It's absurd to tell a terminal patient to forget about the fact that they're dying, because it's simply impossible for them to do so. The terminal patient—by necessity—lives and breathes death because he or she is utterly consumed by the dying process.

Terminal patients are reminded of their condition during every waking moment of their lives—either by pain and suffering or by their inability to perform the simplest of tasks.

This point is illustrated by Javits when he describes his current condition: "I am now confined to a wheelchair because my leg muscles are inadequate, and I need a ventilator to help me breathe, though it uses only room air. The critical thing in keeping alive, in my estimation, is to keep my mind in order and functioning. Fortunately, ALS does not seem to compromise the brain or the intellectual ability of the stricken individual."

The fact that Javits is able to think clearly while in the grips of a fatal disease is fortunate, but it also makes it impossible for him to forget that he's in a wheelchair with a ventilator and that he's moving closer and closer to death.

Why Forgetting Is Criminal

The reason that Javits' advice to patients to "forget" that their condition is terminal is criminal is that forgetting precludes the possibility of taking positive action. If it's true that a positive attitude is essential for survival, it's even more important for you to take positive action when you're faced with death.

Right now, the only possible action against death is Cryonic Suspension. Jacob Javits and other terminal patients have the option of making preparations to be frozen after clinical death. They can preserve their bodies under the best available conditions for reanimation in the future. To do so, however, they'll have to face the fact that they are about to die.

An Unperfected Technology

One reason that people like Jacob Javits aren't rushing to sign up for Cryonic Suspension is that it is an unperfected technology. Most scientists dismiss its use for today's patients as "unwarranted," "premature," or "certain to fail."

Another problem is that most people don't understand the concept of death— which they probably believe to be an absolute condition—rather than the end point of a long, gradual process. As a result, they are unable to understand that it's possible to be brought back to life after "death."

The final problem is that Cryonics is not accepted in Society at large. To prepare to be suspended is thus to stand out in the crowd...to flaunt the established order by choosing a highly unorthodox procedure. No doubt some people decide not to be frozen simply because they're afraid of what other people will say about them. They fear embarrassment more than they do death.

We're All Going To Die

Which brings us back to Jacob Javits. If Cryonic Suspension was an established part of today's medicine, there's little doubt that Javits would go for it. He obviously wants very much to live and he has a great deal to live for.

His message that all of us are in a terminal condition is an important one, but it's misdirected. Patients suffering from terminal diseases are well aware that all of us are going to die because they've already begun to experience the last stages of the dying process. What they need is help, not consciousness raising.

Those of us who are still in "good" health, however, need to be reminded of the fact that we're all going to die. It's so easy to imagine that you're never going to die when you're strong and productive.

What we need to learn from terminal patients like Jacob Javits is that our days are numbered—no matter how young or healthy we may be. That we are moving perilously closer to death with every tick of the clock and that death can come at any moment.

The Prospect Of Immortality

Once we fully understand the crisis we're in, those of us who truly want to live will begin to appreciate the remarkable opportunity that stands before us.

In 1964, Robert Ettinger put forth the revolutionary idea that all of us living today have a chance at physical immortality. Since then, millions of people—who failed to comprehend the urgency of this message—have died. Even today, only a handful of pioneers have seen the light...the overwhelming majority of people continue to believe that they must grow old and die—despite compelling evidence to the contrary.

My book *The Life Extension Revolution* was written to present the scientific evidence that aging and death are not inevitable consequences of life. Since then, scientific breakthroughs have continued at an unprecedented rate. Today, the prospect of immortality is brighter than ever before in history.

A Time For Action

The only pertinent questions that remain are: Will you and I become immortal? Or will we die...as part of the last generation of mortals?

Cryonic Suspension offers a chance for immortality to everyone on the planet—even those who are old and dying.

The support of research in the life extension sciences offers us the opportunity to increase our chances for immortality dramatically...the opportunity to achieve immortality within our lifetime!

The time for action is now! Tomorrow may be too late! ∎

THE DEATH OF DEATH IN CRYONICS

BY BRIAN WOWK, PH.D.[1]

Cryonics, June, 1988

"**cry on'ics**, n. the practice of freezing the body of a person who has just died in order to preserve it for possible resuscitation in the future, when a cure for the disease that caused death has been found."

— Webster's New Twentieth Century Dictionary

"CRUEL, CRAZY, 6£ A MONTH TO COME BACK FROM THE DEAD"

—front page headline from the British tabloid, *Sunday Mirror*.

This article is about a problem in cryonics. Perhaps *the* problem in cryonics. It is a problem which has dogged cryonics since its inception, and which has caused incalculable grief since then.

Unlike so many of the problems which confront cryonicists, I believe that it is a problem for which cryonicists have only themselves to blame.

The problem to which I refer is the perception of cryonics as the freezing of dead people, and all the corollaries that perception implies. How often have cryonicists struggled with impressions (be they conscious or unconscious) that cryonics is a sacrilegious, ghoulish, or Frankenstein-like practice when they try to explain the concept? How often have cryonicists had the impossible task of trying to overcome the notion that cryonics entails supernatural resurrection when they try to explain its scientific foundations? Problems of this sort (arguably the most serious public relations problems of cryonics) can all be traced back to the fundamental problem of cryonics being perceived as the freezing and storing of dead people.

In this article a strategy is proposed for attacking this problem at its root. The strategy outlined does not require any scientific breakthroughs, political lobbying, new laws, or the breaking of existing laws. And it does not require any change in cryonics practice at all. What it does require is a fundamental change in the way cryonicists think about cryonics, and especially in the way cryonicists attempt to communicate it to others.

---

1   This classic paper has been revised and updated to bring it into compliance with modern usage, e.g., "cryopreserved" instead of "suspended", etc.

The Problem

At first glance it may not seem that there is a solvable problem here at all. If cryonics patients must be legally dead before they are cryopreserved, and if once cryopreserved all metabolism has irreversibly (for the present) ceased, then are not cryopreserved patients, at least in some limited sense, dead? The answer is no.

A large share of public relations problems are directly attributable to cryonicists' own confusion about this issue. This article is an attempt to solve this problem by first thoroughly examining the concept of death, and then proposing some consistent standards for dealing with death in a cryonics context.

Semantics

Words evolve to describe particular realities. When reality reveals itself to be something other than expected (as it often does), communication can become difficult. Problems of this sort can be remedied in two ways: the meaning of old words can be modified to suit new realities, and/or new words can be coined.

The word/reality synchronization problem cryonics faces today concerns the meaning of the word "death." "Death" seems to have two broad meanings in people's minds. First: the cessation of brain function. Second: the irreversible loss of life. Historically, our medical limitations have been such that these two definitions were equivalent. This of course is not the case today (and it will be less so tomorrow), and so begins many a tale of cryonics PR woe.

Clearly the meaning of the word "death" must be better defined. In fact, there is no doubt that it will be better defined as advancing resuscitation technologies obsolete old meanings in ever more minds. Notwithstanding, it is to the advantage of cryonicists to expedite this change as rapidly as possible.

The meaning of the word "death" can be brought back into sync with reality in one of two ways. Cryonicists can either retain death as meaning the loss of brain function, and accept that death can be reversed. Or cryonicists can reject death as meaning loss of brain function, and retain death as meaning the irreversible loss of life. It is the proposition of this article that the second strategy is far superior to the first.

It is true that in most minds death is still strongly associated with the loss of brain function. However, death is more correctly identified with the irreversible loss of life. In other words, if the meaning of death must be clarified (and it must), it will be far easier to drop the association of death with loss of brain function than to introduce the idea that death itself can be reversed (with all the complex qualifications that statement entails).

Defining Death

I therefore propose the following firm definition of death.

Death: the absolute and irreversible loss of life, which occurs in human beings when their brain structure is destroyed.

Thus, no one is ever dead until their brain structure is gone. (Of course, death will not be quite so clear cut for future medicine; exactly how "much" a person dies will depend on how much brain structure is lost during injury. Nevertheless, retaining death as a "black and white" idea is fine as a first-order approximation.)

The value of defining death in this way is that it is completely independent of any particular level of medical technology. With this definition, dead is dead, now or ever.

New Terminology

Having better defined the criteria for death, it is necessary to introduce some new terms to fill the vacuum in the lexicon that has been created in the process. In particular, medical terms are needed to describe the vast expanse of time between cessation of heartbeat and breathing (the classic signs of death) and real death.

Conventional medicine currently uses the terms "clinical death" and "biological death" to fill this void.

However, I believe something more descriptive is necessary for cryonics purposes. For one thing, it's necessary to adopt a terminology that does not in any way suggest an element of death (and all the emotional and intellectual baggage such an association will invoke) when discussing conditions other than real death. Also, cryonicists need a terminology that will be applicable to conditions far beyond what physicians today would ordinarily consider as clinical death (such as biostasis, or protracted ischemia). The traditional workhorse for this task in cryonics has been "deanimation." "Deanimation," however, has always struck me as vague, crude, contrived, and in fact like just another name for death. I would like to suggest some more precise alternatives. In particular, I would like to borrow some possible terms from the medical lexicon of the 22nd century.

With mature cell repair technology, future medicine will be able to recover anyone whose critical brain structure (brain structure encoding basic identity information) remains intact. Whether their heart has stopped, their brain function ceased, or indeed whether they are frozen solid will not matter. As long as critical brain structure is intact, patients will always be recoverable. In fact, it is likely that future medicine will adopt a rather innocuous, almost casual jargon to refer to many conditions we still equate with death today. Below is a table of some of these conditions in their various grammatical forms.

Condition or Event	Present Terminology	Future Terminology
clinical death or biological death	death, legal death	ametabolic coma, or biostatic coma (when in biostasis)

What is the purpose of these definitions and redefinitions? Quite simply: the elimination of misunderstanding. Since cryopreserved patients are being transported to distant future medicine, cryonics simply cannot be understood without viewing its patients and their conditions from the perspective of future medicine. And from such a perspective, cryopreserved patients are not dead. There is therefore no reason ever to refer to cryopreserved patients as dead (and bring upon ourselves all the suspicion, confusion, and metaphysical baggage that that word invokes).

Should cryonicists be saying, then, that cryonics patients are alive? No. I believe this would be unwise because "alive" is most often taken to mean the presence of integrated metabolism. Instead, it is perhaps best to say that cryopreserved patients are in an ametabolic or biostatic coma, and as such deserve the same regard and care as any patient who is alive (i.e., metabolizing) but comatose and facing an uncertain prognosis.

Some may say that cryonicists are not justified in stating the status of cryonics patients so confidently because cryonics is not yet proven. I disagree. It is a convention of present medical practice that whenever the status of a comatose patient is in doubt, we treat them as viable patients until it becomes certain that recovery is impossible. Why should cryonics patients not enjoy the same benefit of the doubt?

Thus, by honestly and consistently characterizing the condition of cryopreserved patients in the proper medical terms—the future's—it is possible to significantly ameliorate one of the greatest perception problems facing cryonics.

Defining Cryonics

There remains one serious impediment to implementing this strategy. Nowhere have I ever seen cryonics defined as anything other than the preservation of clinically, legally, or otherwise dead people—even by cryonicists themselves. This is despite the fact that defining cryonics as freezing dead people (even people dead only by present standards) is inherently absurd.

Why? Because to define cryonics as freezing legally dead people means that cryonics—the very idea of cryonics—is to freeze people after legal death. Defining cryonics in this way means that even given the legal opportunity to do otherwise, cryonicists are people who believe in waiting for an arbitrary, deleterious physical event (cardiac arrest and ensuing ischemia) before even considering freezing someone. Clearly this is not what cryonics is all about.

Sooner or later (probably later) there will come a time when cryopreservation (even by imperfect means) will be performed as an elective medical procedure for terminal patients. Will this no longer be cryonics? On the contrary, it would be ideal cryonics—exactly the idea that cryonicists had in mind all along. Indeed, cryonics (now or ever) is not about preserving dead patients, but about preserving terminal patients. The fact that cryonicists currently must wait until cardiac arrest occurs naturally is merely an artifact of our present legal system, not an inherent component of the idea of cryonics.

Thus the final step to eliminating death as an element in cryonics is to correctly define cryonics as cryopreservation of terminal patients. This leaves a pure, untainted vision of what cryonics is really all about; a vision of a technology not for "handling," or "dealing" with death, but for *avoiding* death. A technology for living people who want to stay alive.

Proposed Guidelines

Successfully communicating this vision will require overhauling many old ideas and habits cryonicists have when discussing cryonics. Listed below are just a few of the most important guidelines that will have to be followed to rid cryonics of its death-related imagery.

- Never use the single words "death," "dead," "die," or "died" to refer to any condition other than complete destruction of the brain. When we say someone is dead we should mean they are dead—permanently and absolutely irrecoverable. All other uses of these words should be prefixed with appropriate qualification, such as "clinical" or "legal." (I, for one, am tired of seeing "the D word" constantly in quotation marks. Following this rule will make such ambiguities unnecessary.)

- Even better, avoid words like "death" as much as possible, except to emphasize that death is what cryonics attempts to prevent. (For example, as an alternative to "clinical death" use the terms "cardiac arrest," or "ametabolic coma.")

- Consistently emphasize that the purpose of cryonics is to save the lives of dying patients, not to "save" people who have already died. Legal restrictions prohibiting cryopreservation until after legal death are a transient impediment to this goal to which cryonicists must adhere at present, but which should not be depicted as inherent in cryonics. There is no reason to characterize cryopreserved patients as dead (quotations notwithstanding) at any point in a cryonics discussion.

- Rather than saying a patient to be cryopreserved has just died, or "deanimated," just say they require cryopreservation. (E.g. Alcor will not cryopreserve you when you die, Alcor will cryopreserve you when you require cryopreservation to keep you from dying.)

- Rather than saying a patient in cryopreservation is dead, just say they are in cryopreservation. The term "in cryopreservation" (with any luck) will gradually replace "being dead" as a social designation for cryonics patients. Similarly, the term "biostatic coma" should rightfully replace "death" as the medical designation of the condition of cryonics patients.

- Finally, never depict cryonics as an "alternative" to burial and cremation. Cryonics is in the life-saving business, not the undertaking business. There is no reason to ever introduce negative, death-related imagery like interment methods when discussing cryonics. Cryonics is a life-saving technology, not an interment procedure. Cryonics is not "in competition" with undertakers any more than any other field of medicine that prevents people from dying is. (Imagine a physician who intends to place a brain-injured child in a drug-induced coma to improve the chance of recovery saying to the parents: "I believe you should consent to this procedure because even though recovery from the coma is a long-shot, his chances are still better than with burial or cremation."!!!)

Presenting Cryonics

A typical presentation of cryonics today will begin by defining cryonics as the freezing of dead people (perhaps with "clinical" or "legal" qualification) and then, of necessity, engage in long explanation of why "dead is not dead." This approach is highly inefficient, suspicion-arousing, and most importantly misses the most important idea of cryonics.

Understanding contemporary cryonics practice requires appreciating two basic ideas. First, that freezing with present methods is probably not fatal (assuming access to future medicine). Second, that "death is a gradual process," or, more properly put, ischemic injury following cardiac arrest is a gradual process that probably does not kill patients for at least several hours (assuming access to future medicine). Of these two, the first is by far the most important.

If cryonicists can credibly argue that a living, functioning person might be able to survive freezing with present technology, and thawing with the future's, then a complete case will have been made for cryonics. After making this case, it can be examined how to implement cryonics to save today's terminal patients, and note the present legal problems of performing this procedure on a legally living patient. It can then be explained that this isn't a major concern because the legal declaration of death seldom means a person is dead from the perspective of future medicine (or even today's), so let's go ahead and do this procedure even after cardiac arrest.

The most important point here is that the second idea is only relevant to our present legal environment, and is not intrinsic to cryonics. Ischemic injury (so-called death) is only a certain class of injury that patients may or may not have when they are cryopreserved.

Thus the reversibility of advanced clinical death (read: ischemic injury) is simply not the big cryonics issue it is usually made out to be. Ischemic injury is not inherent in the basic idea of cryonics. If anyone says to you, for example, that they don't think cryonics will work because legally dead people cannot be revived (as arbitrary as that belief is), then just turn the argument around and ask them why they aren't aggressively seeking legislation so that it won't be necessary to wait until legal death to cryopreserve dying patients.

Of course, some readers may say this is all moot because as long as cryopreservation looks like death, and cannot be implemented until after legal death, its identification with death is going to be prominent in people's minds. That may very well be the case, but it is not the point. The point is to not concede to anyone's irrational premises, and suffer the long-term consequences of doing so. For cryonics this means that cryonicists should not be arguing that "dead is not dead," death is reversible, etc., but instead be arguing unflinchingly that cryopreservation patients are not dead, period.

How successful this strategy will be remains to be seen. Yet I believe it rests on a truism: one that says that people who disagree on the definition of death are inherently less crazy than people who claim they are going to bring the dead back to life. If this is indeed the case, cryonicists may be able to do away with some major communication problems. ∎

WHY SUSPENSION MEMBERS NEED MORE THAN MINIMUM FUNDING

BY SAUL KENT
Cryonics, November, 1989

[Note: The current minimum numbers are higher but the lesson has not changed. Eds.]

Perhaps you first heard about cryonics on TV, or in an article you read. If so, you may have learned (in that initial encounter) that the "cost" of cryonic suspension is $100,000.00 for whole-body suspension and $35,000.00 for neuro suspension.

You now know, I suspect, that those figures represent the *minimum* amounts of money charged for suspension, not necessarily its true cost. When I say this, I don't mean that minimum funding is inadequate in any way, or that Alcor will not be able to fulfill its contract with you. That's not my intention at all because I have great confidence in Alcor's ability to meet all its commitments and obligations.

The True Costs Are Unknown

My real purpose in calling your attention to Alcor's minimum charges for suspension is that it is vitally important for you to understand that the true costs of suspension are unknown and that current charges (by any cryonics organization) are only vague guesses about the costs of the procedure.

What's so difficult (you may ask) about determining the cost of suspension? After 22 years of suspensions, why can't anyone come up with the right cost figures? What's the problem?

The problem is that—on the indefinite time scale of cryonics—it's only been a little while since we started placing patients into suspension and we've had relatively little business during this period. Most important of all, we're completely in the dark about the costs of reanimation.

Why Reanimation Costs Have Been Neglected

The possible costs of reanimation have just begun to be discussed within Alcor. After all, the idea of even mentioning the subject seemed rather self-indulgent when Alcor's existence was being threatened by "bombing raids" from a half-crazed coroner, the prospect of criminal charges from a half-witted district attorney, and public cries that cryonics is "illegal" from health department officials trying to convince the authorities to put us out of business.

When you're struggling to fight off the yahoos, there isn't much time to contemplate the future—especially the possible costs of technologies that don't yet exist, or the possible constraints of a society that's likely to be radically different from ours. Besides, cryonicists have always been so giddy at the thought of actually being able to challenge death that we've never really been concerned about how to pay for it. An oft-quoted remark among cryonicists goes something like this: "If I'm lucky enough to come back young, fair, and debonair, I won't care if I don't have a dime."

What isn't considered is the possibility that Alcor may not have enough dimes to bring you back at all. Or that you may have to remain frozen for an extra century or two while Alcor comes up with the spare cash to get you back on your feet again.

Fantasies About The Future

A common fantasy is that money won't be a factor in the super-abundant future. That everyone will be so wealthy and magnanimous that patients will be brought back to life routinely, regardless of cost.

The problem with this notion is that it is highly speculative, perhaps more so than the idea of being brought back at all. And that if we're successful as we expect to be, there may be millions of patients in suspension awaiting nanotech revival. So if you don't give Alcor enough of your money, you could find yourself at the end of the line.

Next is the idea that nanotechnology will make reanimation so simple and inexpensive that it will be "a piece of cake" to make us young and healthy again. This is possible. It could happen that future physicians will be able to turn us into immortals with ease, but I prefer not to bet my life on it.

Great Expectations

It isn't that I don't have great expectations about the future. I do. I think we'll be able to transform ourselves into true superbeings with incredible powers. That eventually we'll become more different from our current selves than we are today from non-human primates. And that someday in the not-too-distant future we'll have truly godlike powers. But I don't think it will be easy. And I don't think it will be inexpensive. Here are my reasons.

The Political Struggle

In the past two years, Alcor has come up against a formidable array of political opponents who have sought to crush us. The fact that we've been able to fight them off successfully has been due—in large part—to the availability of money from Alcor members to pay legal expenses. We now know that California agencies such as the Cemetery Board and Health Department first began to think about putting us out of business in 1981, after the Chatsworth scandal in which cryonics patients were abandoned by the Cryonics Society of California. If they had hit us hard at that time, it would have been difficult for us to survive.

Our political problems aren't about to disappear anytime soon. We're out to change the world in radical fashion. . . . And soon! Right now the established order is based upon aging and death and is run by deathists who have no intention of changing their ways without a struggle. Cryonics is more explosive than any other idea in history because it threatens the entire fabric of society.

Many outsiders assume that our strongest opposition comes from organized religions threatened by the fact that we are working to actually deliver a promise (life after death) that they rely upon heavily. But we've had far more opposition from scientists and doctors threatened by our unorthodox behavior than from religious leaders. I think we can count on continued opposition from the scientific establishment for quite some time and I don't think the religionists will leave us alone much longer either.

The Bureaucratic Mentality

We've also been attacked by mindless bureaucrats threatened by our insistence on doing things that don't fit neatly into the fixed categories that govern their lives. The inflexibility of bureaucrats—especially in government—has always been a problem with anything new, but never has there been an idea (like cryonics) that threatens so many bureaucrats in so many different places. We've already had our share of trouble with officials having authority over matters of health statistics, medicine, scientific research, law enforcement, zoning, disposition of bodies, transportation, and customs.

These problems are far from over. Since cryonics involves every aspect of human life, we can expect a long series of painful collisions with officials whose primary concern is to avoid conflict with those who have authority over them.

Threatening the Financial Establishment

I also think we're on the verge of disturbing some of the most powerful bureaucrats on Earth—the officials who control the financial system that regulates the lifeblood of government itself—the flow of money. These are officials who not only play by the "rules of the game," but are the ones (along with the bankers, industrialists, and politicians who stand behind them) who actually make the rules.

Sometime soon, the financial establishment will discover that cryonics is likely to mess up their system. They're going to find that cryonics disrupts the orderly flow of assets from one generation to another, that it raises serious questions about the values behind the distribution of wealth, and—most frightening of all—that it is leading to accumulation of large amounts of capital in the hands of radicals who not only want to change the system, but who want to overthrow the species.

The Most Revolutionary Idea In History

Once the financial establishment begins to understand the full implications of cryonics, they will begin to cause us serious problems. Once the American people begin to appreciate what's up our sleeve, they'll begin to make demands (of their leaders) that will cause them (and us) a great deal of difficulty. Once the idea of cryonics takes hold, it will lead to political, economic, social, and religious turmoil throughout the world.

Although I firmly believe that cryonics will lead to many problems, I am also confident that, in the end, we will prevail, and that many of us living today will enjoy longer, healthier, and happier lives in the future.

I believe this because cryonics is the most revolutionary idea in history. The prospect of achieving an indefinite, extended, healthy lifespan—with full control over aging, injury, and disease—will alter our values and behavior in ways that will benefit everyone, including our opponents. I think that when enough of us know for sure that it's really possible for us to live in prosperity for centuries, we'll make sure it happens.

It Will Take Money

But it will take money. . . lots of money. Money for research, money for education, money for lawyers, and money for political action. There's simply no way of predicting the extent of the opposition we'll have to face, what we'll need to defend ourselves, or the length of time we'll have to fight. What we cannot afford to do (at any time) is underestimate the financial strength we'll need to succeed.

That's one reason why it is not a good idea to rely on minimum funding for cryonic suspension. We've already had several political crises that required a good deal of money from Alcor. If several members had not provided Alcor with the resources to fight these battles, the organization could have been destroyed, and with it the hopes and dreams of every member.

Developing Suspended Animation

Another reason to raise your funding above the minimum is the need for cryonics research to improve our methods of suspension and, eventually, to develop full-fledged suspended animation. The best way of improving your odds of reanimation is to help Alcor improve its suspension methods. The sooner Alcor improves these methods, the better your protection will be against loss of life, and the faster we can become too powerful to destroy.

Developing Reanimation Technology

Alcor will be aided in its quest for improved suspension methods by private companies, and when suspended animation has finally arrived it will be offered (along with other medical treatments) in clinics and medical centers throughout the world. When it comes to reanimation, however, things may be different.

There may be little or no interest on the part of companies (or governments) in research to develop reanimation technology for patients frozen under poor conditions with imperfect methods unless there are larger numbers of these patients and enough money available to justify such research.

While it's true that the development of nanotechnology will lead to ultra-small machines capable of repairing tissue damage from injury, disease, and aging, it will be necessary to modify these machines to deal with the special problems of reanimation. Nanotech systems to repair the tissues of frozen patients suffering from multiple types of injury will have different requirements than systems designed to repair living patients.

It's quite possible that the impetus to develop nanotech repair systems for patients in suspension will be lacking, unless Alcor takes the lead. After all, if Alcor (and other cryonics organizations) aren't concerned about these patients, then who will be? It may be that Alcor will have to spend a great deal of research money over a great many years, perhaps decades, in order to develop and perfect such systems.

Identity Reconstruction

It also may be quite expensive for Alcor to bring suspension patients back to life, especially those who have suffered severe brain damage. The ability to reconstruct an individual's identity is likely to be a formidable task (even for nanotech repair systems), which could require long and costly research and involve highly sophisticated techniques.

Right now we believe that the major component of identity is memory, but we have little or no knowledge of other cognitive, electrical, chemical, and structural factors that may be involved in determining the subjective feeling of being (and continuing to be) oneself, nor do we even have a clear picture of how memory contributes to identity, except to say (with some degree of confidence) that the more of our memories we retain the more likely we are to remain ourselves.

In my opinion, questions revolving around the issue of identity will be one of the major areas of study in the future, with many biological, medical, psychological, and philosophical implications. How long it will take to identify the physical components of identity is unknown, but it may prove to be an exceedingly complex task.

The Burden May Be On Alcor

Once again, it is not my intention in bringing up the potential problems of reconstructing the identity of those who suffer brain damage before (and during) the suspension process to cast any doubt whatever on the value of cryonics. On the contrary, I have great confidence that it will become possible to reconstruct the identity of most patients suspended with current techniques. But it may take a long time, it may prove to be quite expensive, and the burden of doing much of the research may fall on Alcor.

Although we don't know the degree to which the burden of identity reconstruction research will fall on Alcor, we do know that the more money Alcor has the better equipped it will be to perform whatever research is needed (and to motivate others to do this research) in the future. A strong, wealthy Alcor is your greatest assurance that your interests in staying alive (and in coming back to life after being suspended) will be looked after.

Money To Re-Enter Society

If it becomes possible to bring you back to life (after cryonic suspension), you'll need money to get you back on your feet again. If you don't have any, it will probably make it difficult to do so and may even postpone your reanimation. (A future government may not look too kindly at having to bear costs of your re-introduction into society, especially if there are a great many other suspended patients who need this kind of assistance.

Right now, there is a law (the Rule Against Perpetuities) in most countries (including the U.S.) which makes it illegal for Alcor to set aside money for this purpose. To help solve this problem a new organization called the Reanimation Foundation is currently being set up in Liechtenstein, which has no Rule Against Perpetuities (more about this in a later article). However, it's quite reasonable to expect that — when cryonics becomes acceptable—the Rule Against Perpetuities will be revoked or changed to make it legal (and perhaps even mandatory) for Alcor (and other cryonics organizations) to contribute to the costs of re-introducing reanimated members back into society.[1]

Once again, the more money Alcor has, the more it will be able to contribute to the costs of putting you back on your feet again.

The Inescapable Conclusion

The inescapable conclusion is that minimum funding should not be relied upon to purchase your ticket to a future life, and that every penny that you contribute to Alcor will help solve the formidable problems that stand in the way of your reanimation.

To look at it from a slightly different perspective, just consider what the word "minimum" means. According to Webster's New Universal Unabridged Dictionary, "minimum" is defined as "the smallest quantity, number, or degree possible or permissible."

Minimum standards for nutrition involve the consumption of just enough vitamins (and other nutrients) to avoid vitamin deficiency (and other) disease. This is far less nutrition than you need for optimal health and longevity. The same principle holds for cryonics. If you consider cryonics essential to your survival, it is imperative for you to make every effort to increase your funding as much as possible above the minimum. If you think cryonics is "a matter of life and death," the extent to which you provide funding for your own suspension (and reanimation) is a clear-cut indication of the degree to which you value your own life.

Do It Now!

Cryonics is definitely "a matter of life and death" for me. I know that my life is likely to depend on the success of cryonics and that the urgency to succeed becomes more and more compelling with each passing day as I grow older. I've already provided Alcor with funds (in the form of life insurance) that are far in excess of the minimum needed for my own cryonic suspension and I intend to contribute more funding as long as I am able to.

What about you? Isn't it time you added to your funding? It isn't just that Alcor needs your money. It does, but the truth is that you need your money even more than Alcor does! When you're in suspension, you won't have any earning power... perhaps for a hundred years or more. Doesn't it make sense to put away as much money as you can while you're still able to?

My advice is: Do it now! And keep on doing it until it's time for you to be suspended! Although the ultimate payoff on your investment may not come until you're reanimated, you'll be more than amply rewarded by observing the growth of Alcor in the coming years. ■

Footnote:
1   Since the publication of this article, the Reanimation Foundation has been closed to new members. However, some states have modified or dropped the Rule Against Perpetuities, and some Alcor members have developed trusts based on these new laws. Contact Alcor for more information.

CONSERVATIVE MEDICINE

BY MICHAEL DARWIN
Cryonics, July, 1990

con–ser–va–tive: adj. 1 PRESERVATIVE . . . 3 a: tending or disposed to maintaining existing views, conditions, or institutions: TRADITIONAL b: MODERATE, CAUTIOUS . . . [1]

— *Webster's New Collegiate Dictionary*

Sometimes it's the little things that make all the difference in the world. For as long as I can remember cryonics has been described as a "radical undertaking," as a "long shot gamble," and as something that most "scientists (read 'conservative scientists' or 'establishment scientists') scoff at" and call "irresponsible."

It's a funny thing, but to a great extent we've been our own worst enemies in trying to promote cryonics because we've allowed the media and the establishment to write our promotional literature[2] and, much worse, to shape our very thoughts. I think that we have paid a very high price for this. Just how high we are only now beginning to fully understand.

Before I get to the reason for this article, I'd like to talk a little about an example of our failure in this respect which can't be talked about too much. It should serve as an indicator of just how badly we can hurt ourselves by buying into the wrong semantics.

Almost from the start we went wrong. The first mistake was allowing cryonics to be described as the practice of freezing the dead. This was a mistake because dead is dead; the dictionary definition of death is the correct one: death: a permanent cessation of all vital functions: the end of life. It goes without saying that you can't raise the dead. And in fact, we don't claim to be able to do that either, and we never really ever have. What Ettinger said in 1964 and what we've been saying ever since is that there is something wrong with medicine's definition of death. It is fundamentally flawed because it defines death not in any absolute sense, but only as a function of medicine's ability or lack thereof to restore function. Thus, the medical definition of death as

---

1 I have left out the definitions of conservative which relate to politics.

2 One thing which to my knowledge Alcor has never done, and which used to irritate me when I saw it done by other cryonics organizations, was to use media stories about cryonics as promotional literature. In my 23 years of involvement with cryonics I have yet to see a single media story I would consider suitable for the purpose of telling anyone about either Alcor or cryonics. The media always manages to screw up some key element of what we are about; and all too often they have all of them screwed up!

"irreversible cessation of heartbeat/breathing and/or brain function" fails because it doesn't go deep enough; it begs the question. What constitutes irreversible? What are the absolute limits to resuscitation in a theoretical sense, as opposed to the practical matter of what a physician can do right now? These were issues that were never directly addressed and on which we never challenged our critics.

If we had it to do all over again, those of us who've been around from the beginning (or nearly so) would probably not make the mistake of allowing suspension patients to be called "dead" or "frozen dead" or cryonics to be described as the practice of "cadaver freezing" or "freezing the dead." Had we taken the tack of pointing out the inadequacy and shallowness of existing function-based criteria for pronouncing death, and challenged the medical and cryobiological communities on a fundamental level, things would probably have gone a lot better for us. There would be fewer people who were (and are) frightened or put off at the "ghoulishness" of freezing dead people; and the intense, morbid revulsion some people experience at the very mention of cryonics would certainly not be there nearly as often as it is now. In fact, had we played our cards right, the intense morbid revulsion would be reserved for those who did anything but place terminal patients into cryonic suspension.

And of course it goes almost without saying that the strong religious objections that have plagued us from the very start of the program could have been completely sidestepped by the simple expedient of pointing out that suspension patients aren't dead! And what's more, we agree that it is not possible for people to "resurrect the dead."

I first noticed this difference when discussing my experience with resuscitation cases as a dialysis technician many years ago. When I would talk about an experience in resuscitation I noticed that people were perfectly happy to hear such stories as long as the patient didn't become a cadaver at the end of them (i.e., when the story was about a success). In fact, many people I spoke with who were very uncomfortable in talking about death were actually reassured in talking about successful resuscitation.

From the start, we should have fought tooth and nail the image of cryonics as something done to dead people or to us "after we die." We didn't. I was looking back through my clipping files recently and I came across an article written about me in 1970 entitled "Teen Wants To Be Frozen After Death." I can remember quite well that I was pleased about that article at the time it appeared and that I thought it did a fair job of telling people what we were all about. Indeed, I can remember describing cryonics as something that "would be started as soon as I was pronounced dead . . ." I was not alone. The file is full of clippings from around the world with similar quotes and headlines. No wonder people think we're crazy. Death is a dreaded word, loaded with finality, irreversibility, and anxiety. In hindsight it is easy to see that portraying cryonics as a post-mortem procedure was in effect putting an impossible barrier in the road to its acceptance.

The above insight has caused me to think deeply about other aspects of our public relations and the way we communicate about cryonics to those around us. I have become very sensitive to the words reporters and hostile scientists use to describe cryonics to the public. In short, I've become very careful not to buy into their oppressive world view of us. About a year ago I was called up by a reporter for some publication or other and during the course of our conversation she quoted me a statement made by a university physician to the effect that cryonics was a radical, unproven treatment which should not be allowed.

I was almost ready to agree with the first half of that statement (i.e., that cryonics is radical and unproven) and then go on to defend why radical and unproven things should be allowed when I got to thinking about cryonics in the context of the words "radical," "unproven," and "medicine." I came to a very surprising conclusion which I've used in almost all my public speaking since, and which I think is worth sharing because I have observed the powerful positive effect it has had on the wide range of people I've used it on, and in particular because of the wonderful effect it has had on hostile medical doctors: either silencing them or putting them uncomfortably on the defensive.

The insight is a simple one: cryonics is *conservative* medicine in almost every sense of the word. At first glance this wouldn't seem to be the case at all. Normally we think of conservative as being defensive of the status quo, as being preservative of the existing order of things. And in one sense, the political/institutional sense, cryonics is certainly not conservative of the status quo. But in a more important sense, in the medical or biological sense of the word, cryonics is truly conservative medicine.

It is often said that the first dictum of medicine is to "do no harm" to the patient. This does not mean that a physician can literally do no harm; incising a patient's abdomen to remove an inflamed appendix causes some additional harm to the patient in the short term, but it averts long-term disaster. Rather, the dictum means that you should not administer treatments which worsen your patient's overall condition or prognosis. I believe this is a sound dictum and I believe it is universally accepted by competent physicians of good will. It is also a conservative dictum in the truest sense of the word since it seeks to confine treatments to those which conserve the patient's life and health.

The issue at the beginning of this article is really the issue of "when is death?" If you are equipped with the right tools, it is easy to demolish the simple-minded function-based criteria used by cryobiologists and many physicians to define death. All of their attempts to do this will always have reference to function-based criteria which in turn are always related to current technical limits. With the right examples it is easy to destroy these arguments. One such example points up the relative and changing nature of function-based criteria: 50 years ago anyone whose heart stopped beating from a heart attack or electric shock was pronounced dead; today many of those people are resuscitated. Were people who "died" of heart attacks 50 years ago really dead if they could be resuscitated today?

There are other, even better analogies that can be used and I think it is worthwhile to digress a bit and discuss them. The difference between our definition of death and their definition is simple. We define death in the following way: death: irreversible loss of the critical structural information which encodes identity. By this definition you are only dead when it is no longer possible to deduce your functional state from your nonfunctional state. Try using few simple analogies to make this point:

A photograph or a printed document has a function, which is to communicate information (people have functions too: blood circulation, reproduction, thinking, happiness . . .). If we tear a photo or a page of text into several pieces it is no longer functional and thus by current medical criteria it is "dead" (it helps to actually do this to a piece of paper while explaining). But here's the catch: the pieces or the "debris," if you will, completely describe the functional state. Thus, if you have some tape and a little time you can restore the document or the photo to a functional state. With better tools you could perfectly restore it.

On the other hand, if you burn the document or the photo and you stir the ashes, then you experience an irreversible transition and, given what we know of physical law, it is impossible to restore the debris to the functional state. I have found this example a very powerful one to use, because it can be easily understood by almost everyone and because it forces our critics to deal with the issue of remaining structure after legal death and freezing. This is something they are ill-equipped to do, and at which they invariably fail at doing because we know much more about those issues than they do and what's more, the facts support our position better than they do theirs!

The point is, once you destroy their function-based definition of death and shift it to a structure or information-based definition, you put the critics in a very difficult position. That position is simply that at the very least, patients in cryonic suspension may not be dead.

Indeed, the most intellectually honest of our critics will always, when pressed, say something like "Well, it's not possible to say absolutely that cryonics won't work, but in my opinion the odds are so small that it is a waste of time . . ."

And with that remark our critics have conceded the argument.

Why is this so, you may ask? Well, lets look at the issue of cryonics as conservative medicine again. A physician, when faced with a situation where a patient has experienced a cessation of vital functions such as heartbeat and breathing which he either cannot reverse or more often chooses not to reverse (as in the case of "no-code" or "do not resuscitate" patients), is faced with two choices:

1. He can assert that the nature of the patient's malfunction is such that no technology, present or future, could ever reverse that malfunction. Here he is asserting in effect that the skills of contemporary medicine as embodied in his practice of it can

never be improved upon, or at best cannot be improved upon sufficiently to rescue this patient. He can thus abandon his patient and allow him to be incinerated or used as food for soil organisms.

2.   He can take a course of action wherein he uses the best available technology to prevent the patient's condition from deteriorating further (accepting added damage from the preservation process), thus allowing the patient to continue forward movement in time to a point in the future where medical knowledge may be more sophisticated and the patient may be considered rescuable.

Which of the above two alternatives is conservative and cautious and which is radical and irresponsible?

Human beings consist of a unique pattern of atoms. That pattern does not disintegrate all at once upon cessation of heartbeat and breathing. At what point in the dissolution process of that pattern of atoms human identity is lost we simply do not know at this point. It is a radical, arrogant, and unconscionable act of intellectual chauvinism for a physician to abandon his patient and allow him to be destroyed before he can answer the question of when in the dying process identity is lost and what constitutes irreversible injury.

The logical, rational, and above all conservative thing to do is to preserve as much of the patient as possible and defer any decision to abandon the patient and destroy him until it is possible to determine with a high degree of certainty that the patient truly has experienced an irreversible loss of the critical structural information which encodes his identity (i.e., has died).

I think it is very important that we stop allowing ourselves to be cast as the radicals, as the people who are taking unreasonable and unreasoned "risks" and/or as people who are engaged in "far out," "extreme," or "irresponsible" behavior. The facts are otherwise. WE are the CONSERVATIVES. We are the people who are being cautious, who are saying "look, we cannot be sure this patient is really not going to be salvageable in the long run, so the only reasonable thing to do is to get him into a stable, unchanging state in the least injurious way we know how and continue working on the problem in the meantime." That's conservative medicine.

I have used this strategy many times now and it is incredibly effective at putting our critics on the defensive and destroying their authoritarian credibility. I think cryonics can profit a great deal from a wider application of this tactic. I urge each and every one of you to give careful consideration to adopting this strategy when you talk about cryonics in the future because it is nothing more or less than the honest truth.

After all, it never hurts to tell the truth.

Especially when you're right. ∎

BINARY STATUTES, ANALOG WORLD: BURKE'S PARADOX AND THE LAW

BY STEVEN B. HARRIS, M.D.
Cryonics, June, 1989

As Mayor of the Munchkin City
In the county of the Land of Oz,
I welcome you most regally. . . .

But we've got to verify it legally
To see (to see)
If she (if she)
Is morally, ethically,
Spiritually, physically,
Positively, absolutely,

UNdeniably
AND reliably

DEAD. . . .

— The Munchkins

As coroner I must aver
I've thoroughly examined her —
And she's not only merely dead,
She's really most sincerely dead.

— The Coroner of Oz

Though no man can draw a stroke between the confines of day and night,
yet light and darkness are upon the whole tolerably distinguishable.

— Edmund Burke

The conundrum which struck the political philosopher Edmund Burke more than two centuries ago remains with us today. The condition we term "night," does indeed turn into the condition we call "day," and it does so with no sharp dividing line between the two. And yet, we all agree nevertheless that "night" and "day" are clearly different states.

What is more, this sort of thing happens all the time. Our world contains numerous examples of processes in which "state A" is transformed smoothly and continuously into a somewhat different "state B." Wet becomes dry, for example. One kind of weather verges imperceptibly into another. Organisms grow and change form, and so on.

None of this is necessarily a bad thing, and in fact it is continuous change which keeps planet Earth from becoming boring. Transformation is interesting and pleasant to watch, and it is even more pleasant to watch if it is observed passively with no attempt to classify what one is seeing. But when one begins to think. . . .

This essay will argue that language and its penchant for classification is the tree of "knowledge" which forever disturbs the Eden of human tranquility. Whenever we humans talk, we mark out lines and boundaries in continuous natural processes. Our words do that for us. The boundaries which words create may or may not be there in actuality; we draw them in anyway, because classification and analysis are essential to the human thinking process.

But line-drawing can also lead to trouble. This essay is about the kind of trouble to which it can lead.

Part I. Black and White—and Gray

Let us begin our discussion of the boundaries produced by language by considering a very ordinary transformation in the universe we live in: that of a black cup of coffee being sweetened. Since "black coffee" means, by definition, a cup of coffee with no sugar or cream in it, such a cup of coffee does not start out sweet. Nor does it become sweet if one adds a single sugar crystal and stirs. Nor if one adds two crystals. Or three. But if one has the patience to continue adding sugar crystals one by one, then by the time one has added the many thousands of crystals of sugar in several tablespoons of sugar, one will have arrived at a "coffee state" which will be judged sweet by any drinker whose palate is in working order.

So far, so good. The reader will notice that the cup of coffee has now become an example of the kind of state change of which we spoke in the introduction. State A (not sweet) has been transformed to state B (sweet). But now suppose we ask a naive question: At what point does the cup of coffee become sweet? There is no question that it does make the transition, but suppose what we want to know is which sugar crystal does it?

A little thought will show that the answer is not clear, for the issue is a very subjective one. The problem is that there are many intermediate quantities of sugar which, if added to a cup of black coffee and stirred, would produce considerable disagreement among drinkers as to whether that particular cup deserved the label of "sweet." The judgement of sweetness is, in fact, quite literally a matter of taste, and varies between persons. It would thus be fair to say that in the matter of sweetening a cup of coffee, NO particular sugar crystal does the deed. As sugar is added slowly to it, a cup of coffee does not become sweet as an event, but rather as a process. "Sweet" and "nonsweet" are tolerably distinguishable at the extremes, as Burke would have said, but "no man can draw a stroke between them" when one is changed slowly to the other.

Judging a Cup of Coffee Objectively

Or can they? Let us suppose now for the sake of argument that a certain society is unhappy with the state of affairs in the transformation of a black cup of coffee into a sweet cup of coffee. Perhaps it is a society of chronically anxious people—the sort of people who are uncomfortable with ambiguity. If a society does not like the judgement of sweetness in a cup of coffee to be a subjective one, is there anything which can be done to make things more objective? More. . . scientific?

Without doubt, a society could certainly go through the motions of being scientific. It could, for instance, begin by defining "sweet" in terms of the sugar concentration in coffee. That would in turn allow an exact calculation of the point at which a given cup of coffee became "sweet" as sugar crystals were added, and it would even allow people to identify the exact crystal which pushed things "over the line." The only problem with this formal approach, needless to say, is that the decision of where to define the "sweet" concentration in the first place would necessarily remain a matter of personal opinion. A line might be drawn and labeled "sweet," but it would have to be done subjectively. Thus, an anxious society would only end up back where it started.

Or perhaps it would be more correct to say that scientifically it would end up where it started—but perhaps not politically. Sweetening a cup of coffee, like most occupations, is subject to the addition of the trappings of science, even if it is not subject to the full methods. For unfortunately the more instruments one has and the more numbers one generates, the more objective any process may seem, whether it actually is or not. Thus, although it might not be possible to be more objective about the sweetness of a cup of coffee, it might indeed be possible to fool oneself and others that one is doing so. In anxious societies, after all, formality can be important.

Practical Applications

Are there societies which would try to do such a thing, then? We now consider an actual case. For those who found the above example amusing, consider, in place of a cup of coffee, the fluids of a human body. In place of crystals of sugar, consider instead molecules of ethyl alcohol. And in place of the term "sweet," consider the term "intoxicated."

In short, consider the matter of drunken driving enforcement. Here, of course, society is faced with a terrible problem. For any given concentration of alcohol in the blood, the amount of driving impairment for different persons will vary significantly. Even the average amount of impairment will vary in a smooth and continuous fashion with increasing concentration of alcohol, so that there still remains the subjective task of deciding how much performance-impairment is acceptable, and how much is not. Unless one simply outlaws having any alcohol in the blood at all while operating a vehicle (as is intelligently done in Sweden), the idea of "drunk driving" is one in which there is subjectivity at every turn.

So what is a society to do? Well, needless to say, things become easier for all concerned if one can pick a semi-arbitrary blood alcohol concentration and label persons who fall to one side of the line as "intoxicated." Labels do make a difference—in law they often determine at least what charges are filed. Thus, if a man is brought to court on a charge of "driving while intoxicated," for instance, the burden of proof falls on the defendant once the magic blood alcohol numbers have been given. In other words, once the term "intoxicated" has been applied, the legal defense now has the burden of going through the arguments about subjective standards and gray areas, while all the time the jury is thinking about what a clever job the defense lawyer is doing in order to try to get off a guy who has been scientifically proven to have been drunk.

The Law in General

For the benefit of all those readers who feel emotionally so strongly about the issue of drunk driving that they had difficulty with the preceding discussion, it should be pointed out that it is the nature of human law in most cases to draw lines in spectrums of continuous processes, and the legal definition of "drunk driving" is only one of a million examples. The laws of men are binary, for they recognize just two states: legal and illegal. Unfortunately, the nature of the world, by and large, is smoothly continuous, and that contrast leads to interesting situations.

One can get a parking ticket for parking 24 feet from a hydrant, for instance, but not 26 feet. One can be put in jail for buying liquor the day before one's 21st birthday, but not a day later, and so on. It isn't that anyone seriously believes that a parked car is significantly more a threat to fire safety at 24 feet from a hydrant than 26, or for that matter that any one is significantly more mature at exactly 21 years old than a day shy of that age. It is just that one has to draw the line somewhere.

And, of course, one does. The mild paradox of Edmund Burke which opened this essay has much application to the law. The most flagrant violations of the law are often obvious, yet at the same time objective places for marking lines of illegality often do not exist. Indeed, almost everyone passes through a phase sometime during the process of growing up where they first come to realize the basic unfairness of drawing binary legal lines in a continuous world. But just as surely, the resultant cynicism soon passes for people of normal intelligence once they come to realize a bit later that there really isn't a better way to do things as long as any laws at all are to be made.

In the real world, the legal system attempts to obviate the basic unfairness of "line-drawing" in a number of ways. These include 1) having multiple categories of gravity for offenses, 2) only prosecuting the more flagrant violations, and 3) having a system of lawyers skilled at making juries see the possibility of grey areas in the law. The result is a system that works on the whole, but which may be a nightmare in any individual case. For of course multiple categories of crime still do not perfectly mirror a continuous world; and sometimes overzealous police or politically motivated prosecutors decide to prosecute violations that are not so flagrant; and finally the presence of grey areas often means that the skill of the lawyer, rather than the guilt of the accused, determines the ultimate verdict.

Part II: Law and Language

The above discussion is meant to prime the reader for the major problem to be discussed in this essay. It is this: there are times when line-drawing is necessary and fair, others where it is necessary and unfair, and still others when it is both unnecessary and unfair but where the fact is not recognized because the lines have been mistaken for reality. The law is a profession dependent upon language, and as intimated earlier, one of the reasons why the utter subjectivity of most law is not more apparent is that the subjectivity of law is well hidden in the nature of language itself.

As noted in the introduction, when speaking about the universe we live in we run immediately into difficulty when describing continuous transformation and change. The very act of labeling a state or an object with a particular word, is equivalent to drawing a mental line around it which some other words dare not cross. When one says "sweet," or "drunk" or "daytime," for instance, one is marking out a linguistic territory that has borders, even if those borders are ill-defined ones that may shade into a twilight zone of doubt when examined closely.

The act of "naming" things tends to encourage and foster the practice of putting mental borders on processes and states where there may in fact be none in reality. When this happens, and the map (language) is confused for the territory (reality), the arbitrary lines we draw may be erroneously taken for real. The resulting unedifying semantic debates about such things as whether or not a cup of coffee "really" is sweet, or the man "really" is drunk, or the person "really" is an adult, in the absence of any natural definitions of "sweet," or "drunk" or "adult," is one of mankind's more enduring pastimes and follies. It was a folly recognized in Buddhist philosophy 2,500 years ago, but one which seems destined to be with us forever.

S. I. Hayakawa, famous popular explainer of the study of semantics, has this to say about a related situation:

> *The habit of trusting one's definitions. . . is one of the most stubborn remnants of primitivism to affect us. It does not matter if the verbal associations are beautifully systematic, as among the neo-Aristotelian reformers of modern education, or random, as among the uneducated. Words, and whatever words may suggest, are not the things they stand for, and education that fails to emphasize this fact is more than likely to leave students imprisoned and victimized by their linguistic conditioning, rather than enlightened and liberated by it.*

To people so imprisoned, it inevitably appears that if certain individuals have a name in common—say "criminals"—they must have the "essential attribute" of "criminality" in common, while "noncriminals," of course, do not possess that "attribute." The profound sense that there is something different between people who have been in jail and those who have not is one of the most cherished beliefs both of the respectable rich and the respectable poor. Similarly, as mentioned earlier, Jews are supposed by many to have in common the attribute of "Jewishness," which distinguishes them from non-Jews. Now what is this "Jewishness"? Define it any way you like—take Hitler's definition, or anyone else's—and from that point on it is not necessary to examine Jews. You know what they are like without even looking, because you have what Aristotle called "knowledge of universals," which "is more precious than sense perceptions and than intuition."

Hayakawa's invocation of Aristotle here is in recognition of the ancient idea in philosophy that mental attributes of things (such as man-made classifications) were to be given some of the same sort of respect as the more measurable and continuous attributes such as (for instance) dimension and texture. Aristotle's "universals" are created by the classificational lines and boundaries which language draws, and the essential question these linguistic boundaries create is always one of how objectively real they are.

Aristotle's ideas in this regard are actually rather mild in contrast to those of his teacher Plato, who had taken the idea even a step further and decided that the common classificational attributes of objects were to be given all the respect. Plato, in fact, had decided that the attributes of objects were the only reality there was, and that the individual objects themselves were merely shadows or illusions. Thus, for Plato (as an example) no individual table was real, but "tableness" as an ideal essence or attribute, had a real existence. Similarly, for Plato, there were no real horses, but only various imperfect manifestations of an ideal "horsehood," and so on.

The Roman Catholic Church was eventually to find many of Plato's philosophical ideas useful. Thus, for example, in the Roman church, individual priests came to be seen as only imperfect manifestations of an ideal "priesthood," and so on. The early Christian church was also influenced (through early Christian writers such as John the Evangelist) by the philosophy of the Greek Stoics. The Stoic school held that the material universe was pervaded by a kind of ordering "force" (Logos), which was identified with mind, deity, soul, and (most importantly for our discussion) language. Following Platonism, then, many of the idealistic (linguistic) attributes of objects were given a separate metaphysical reality in Christian thought. Following the Stoics, language itself became somewhat deified ("the word" = "God"), and complicated liturgical formulas involving language were held to influence objective reality, such as the "transubstantiation" of sacraments, etc. Formal linguistic "line drawing" ceremonies ("spells") are important in both religion and magic. In fact, the magician's "hocus pocus" is really the hoc est corpus of the Roman Catholic eucharist in disguise.

The Law Again

Classical Roman Law (from which our law is derived) was constructed under the influence of certain aspects of Greek philosophy, and therefore contains many Stoic and Platonic ideas. Especially Platonic is Western law's infatuation with the separate "reality" created by words and labels, such as "intoxicated," "criminal," "adult," and so on.

Both religion and law in Western society have thus acted historically to perpetuate the myth that language and terminology may create some special objective change in the universe. In fact, if one is under the influence of Plato in this fashion (either directly or indirectly), one may be tempted to believe that one's mental classifications of things are enforced by separate metaphysical characteristics of objects which correspond with the language that one uses.

Some examples of this are needed to illustrate. Let us examine now in detail what kinds of world views this philosophy can lead to.

Part III. Putting Lines in Biological Transformations
Gestation

As a first example, let us begin with a transformational process with which religion and the law must contend. Consider a fertilized human ovum, which has few of the characteristics ordinarily associated with a baby. To call a fertilized ovum a "baby" would be akin to calling a cornerstone and a set of blueprints a "building," or to calling two teaspoons of soda and a recipe, a "cake." These are things we do not do. However, it is also true that an average of eight and a half months after conception, a living organism is normally born which is universally regarded by society as a baby and a human being. A smooth and continuous process has happened between these two events of conception and birth. "State A" has been transformed into "state B," with never a clear dividing line between the two. The cup of coffee has become sweet.

The law, which is zealous about protection of "persons," and "babies" of course has a problem here. If it is persons (babies) that one wishes to protect under the law, then one is forced to ask an embarrassing question: when is it exactly that the fertilized ovum becomes a baby or a person? At this point, it should be apparent to the reader that the question is essentially a matter of taste, as in the matter of the coffee. However, as also in the example of the coffee, many other approaches to the question have historically been taken by anxious persons and societies with an intolerance of ambiguity.

The Fundamentalist Christian churches, notably, have provided several "answers." In typical Platonic fashion the early Christians had come to see the "essence" of human beings in metaphysical terms. Aristotle had thought that humans possessed separate "souls" for each of the three linguistic quantities of "life," "locomotion/animalness," and "humanity" which he recognized in humans. The later Christians however, under the influence of Greek philosophy and myth, had long since pared the essence of humanity down to just one economical "spirit," which was thought to not only confer "humanity," but also personal identity. Accordingly, it seemed natural to assume that a fetus objectively became a "person" (a linguistic term) when it received a human spirit.

Interestingly the word "spirit" is associated with "breath" or "breath of life" in most ancient languages. In Hebrew and Greek, spirit and breath are the same word. [A little known fact is that the historical reason why people say the blessing "Gesundheit" (good health) to sneezers, is it was once thought that a sneezer momentarily blew out his own soul, putting himself temporarily at risk for demonic possession of his untenanted body]. Thus, it seemed natural to equate the drawing of the first breath of life with "personhood." This attitude prevailed in the early church, and throughout most of the Middle Ages miscarried fetuses which did not draw breath were not even buried in hallowed ground by Roman Catholics, but were simply discarded without a second thought.

Sometime later, of course, after conception was more thoroughly understood and therapeutic abortion became a controversial issue, the Roman Catholic Church announced that "ensoulment" occurred at the precise moment of fertilization. By this time however (and unfortunately for the Catholic Church) the world had turned protestant and humanistic. Abortion was outlawed for a time, but eventually in 1973 it became legal everywhere in the United States.

The result of this ruling was literally screams of bloody murder from certain factions, and a history of protest with which the reader will be familiar. Especially loud were protests from American Christian Fundamentalists, a religious category defined by its inability to live with ambiguity, as previously illustrated by its lobbying activities against the theory of evolution. What most disconcerted the antievolutionists in the case of Darwinism, interestingly, was precisely the idea that apelike primates could change gradually into humans, without any clear dividing line between the two. This "Burkean" paradox was too much for the fundamentalists, who craved to know the precise moment when the First Man appeared, and wanted to know his name and address.[1]

In the United States the law, which was not controlled by the Catholic church, and which lacked a "soul detector," was at an impasse. To the law, pregnancy was a huge biological grey area, and so the law did what it usually does when faced with a large grey area: it proceeded to draw arbitrary lines. Specifically, in "Roe vs Wade" the U.S. Supreme Court drew legal lines at conception, three months after conception, six months after conception, and birth. During each of the three resultant intervals the State's interest was defined. The rationale for the six month demarcation was presumably that this was close to the time of theoretical viability outside the womb (and still is not too far away from it even in 1989). The three month line presumably had something to do with the time when any responsible person who was going to have an abortion should have had it already. But in any case, the Court did not explain its reasoning for any of the times given.

In doing this the Court interestingly came in for the same sorts of arguments that most people learn in adolescence to avoid when speaking of law, and such protests serve as a nice illustration of the basic frustration with binary law which lies just under the surface in all of us. Specifically, the three and six month legal lines were denounced by fundamentalists as "arbitrary"(!)—as though arbitrariness were somehow not the nature of all laws when dealing with grey areas in transitional processes. There was also much protest about the fact that the law regarded fetal status as changing completely with the comparatively short process of birth—a protest which under the circumstances was equivalent to protesting the fact that the law regards a person in violation just a few miles per hour over the speed limit, but not a few under. Even more incredibly, this sort of protest was made by people who wished the law to similarly

---

1   I've been hard on the fundamentalists here, but scientists can be just as silly about drawing linguistic boundaries where there are none in reality. When someone finds a fossil skull with a brain volume of 700 cc's, for instance, there is enormous pressure to name it Homo something rather than Australopithecus something. After all, who wouldn't rather be the paleoarcheologist who found the oldest man, instead of just the one who found one more late ape? Archaeologists are forever talking about putting a baseball cap on such and such a creature, and taking it on the subway without having anyone scream; a measure of the crudity of thought-experiment to which one will descend to if the result will allow one to justify using the taxonomic term one wants to use.

change the legal status of genetic material after the comparatively short process of fertilization—an illustration of the illogical lengths to which people will go when attempting to enforce a metaphysical agenda.

Death

To this point we have discussed issues which have been in the news, and which impinge on cryonicists as citizens, but which do not affect cryonics per se. We now move on to a subject which affects cryonics directly and inescapably.

It is seldom realized that the issue of death is potentially as politically explosive as the issue of abortion. The reason is that many scientifically sophisticated persons now realize that in the case of death we again deal not with an event, but with a smoothly continuous transformation process from state A to state B. Human beings come into existence a little bit at a time, as the abortion issue has taught us. Unfortunately for the long-term future peace of mind of cryonicists, humans go out of existence in the same way.

A living organism is a package, or pattern of information. Certain atoms in the package may be changed (replaced) as metabolism goes on, but the organism retains its identity throughout this process, just as (for example) a volume of a novel would retain its identity even if its pages are replaced with photocopies. Today we know that certain living organisms can be dehydrated, or even frozen at nearly absolute zero (processes which stop all metabolism), and yet can still be revived as long as their building pattern is not damaged. "Life" is not metabolism, it is information.

The great difficulty in speaking of the destruction of organisms, is the word "death." If "life" is information, then "death" may be usefully defined as the complete loss of information. Thus, a man who has been cremated is pretty clearly dead, because the information is gone. But what shall we say about a child who has fallen through the ice on a river and "drowned" an hour ago? Or two hours ago, or ten hours ago? In all of these cases, most of the information is certainly still present, even though heartbeat and respiration have long since ceased. Although only the child in the first instance can be revived with the technology of 1989, to use this fact as part of a supposedly "objective" definition of "death" would be chauvinistic to our present age. A generation ago, after all, none of these children would have been revivable, and there is no reason to think that things will not change again in the future. In fact, we expect that they will change as resuscitation technology improves.

A human who has decayed to a skeleton is dead. There is an absolute objective difference between life and death, then, but the transition between them is ordinarily a slow one, with no clear dividing line. Again we are confronted with the paradox of Burke. And once again in the issue of death we must deal with people who have little tolerance for ambiguity, and who wish to use the institutions of language and religion and law to draw an arbitrary line in a continuous process.

The law's interest in the matter, of course, is obvious. If a society is unable to define the difference between life and death, it cannot even define the difference between murder and simple mutilation of a corpse. Historically, then, the law has been forced to draw a line in the process of cessation of vital functions, albeit a somewhat arbitrary one. A convenient place to do so up until the mid-twentieth century was at the point when "internal motion" (heartbeat and breathing) ceased, in what physicians of today call "clinical death." This point was convenient because it not only marked the limit of "viability" (hope of return to normal function), but also because it was associated with the religious connotation of breathing as being associated with the presence of the spirit.

In the middle of the twentieth century, however, things began to become complicated. Doctors learned how to restart hearts with electrical cardioversion, and CPR and heart-lung machines now began to make it possible to maintain persons for variable lengths of time without any intrinsic heart or ventilatory function at all. Worse still, the concept of "brain death" was found inapplicable to acute situations, because it was found that the diagnosis could only be made in retrospect at a time when the brain had already been almost completely destroyed. Brain death thus did not help in line drawing unless people were satisfied with drawing the line well after the fact.

The law did what it could. In California, death was redefined as the "irreversible cessation of circulatory and respiratory function." Unfortunately the word "irreversible" promised difficulty, since it made the time of death highly variable among individuals whose hearts had stopped, and also because the diagnosis of death in theory could not be made for some time after clinical death without an attempt at resuscitation which was inappropriate for many people (folks with terminal illnesses, etc.) Thus, the California law was widely ignored by physicians, who continued to pronounce people (whom they did not wish to resuscitate) dead when their hearts stopped, just as they had always done.

Cryonics

The danger inherent in the above state of things ought to be apparent to any cryonicist. Although legal lines may be initially drawn somewhat arbitrarily, they do have the virtue of being easily identified and complied with—indeed that is their purpose. But where a line is not clearly drawn in a process which itself is murky, the law becomes worse than useless. The word "irreversible" implies a functional definition of "death" and a functional test. You can't tell if function is "irreversible" in many instances unless you try to reverse it! If the test (attempted resuscitation) is not done, it is impossible to imagine how one is to tell the legal status of anyone for a very long time after their hearts have stopped. This being the case, the matter of when to prosecute for suspected violations of law in this area would seem to be completely arbitrary.

A well known method of social control is to pass laws with such a structure as to guarantee universal violation, then enforce them selectively against undesirables. Although physicians involved in standard medical practice may never be prosecuted for violation of the law's new definition of death (though in violation of it every day), it is entirely possible that physicians (and nonphysicians) involved in cryonics may be.

To make things worse, all of the above legal problems are complicated by a religious overlay. Many religions conceive of death as a sharp event which takes place when the soul leaves the body. The religious confusion generated in the last 25 years by the changing technological definition of death is to be gauged by the proliferation of stories about people whose souls left their bodies during clinical death and then were jerked back by resuscitation (one envisions a sort of Platonic/metaphysical elastic paddle-ball for the souls of folks who are resuscitated several times). Thus, many people are convinced that death does occur as an event sometime after the heart stops, and therefore that murder of a person already in cardiac arrest may indeed be theoretically possible. And once the possibility is admitted of a crime for which there are no hard and fast defining criteria, then the way becomes open for prosecution (or persecution) of people who just seem vaguely "up to no good."

Thus, it might be entirely possible for a jury of believers to convict on the "impression" that someone was "alive" or "dead" when they underwent a given cryonics procedure, in somewhat the same fashion that an Inquisitorial tribunal might have judged persons guilty of heresy in the Middle Ages.

Part IV. Transitional Ceremonies

All societies have ways of dealing with gradual social changes in which status would otherwise not be clear. Some of these social functions are grouped under the heading of "rites of passage," and they are often elaborate. An example is the puberty ceremony in many cultures (for example, the bar mitzvah in Jewish culture) in which adolescents are formally accepted into society as adults.

In areas where the status of a social transition or the new status of an individual would not otherwise be immediately clear to the average member of society, ceremonies may be especially ornate. Examples here are marriage ceremonies and award ceremonies of various kinds. Under many circumstances, the ceremony itself often becomes part of the new status of the individual, and one consequently sometimes sees ceremonies performed in this context even when they make little physical sense. For example, one sees empty coffins buried sometimes when missing persons are declared formally dead.

Transition ceremonies and rites of passage are only extensions of our definitional language. They are used to draw lines in continuous processes so as to minimize confusion and anxiety in a society. As in law, they seem to be necessary. Also as in law, however, they become dangerous when the people who perform them come to believe that their words make an objective change in reality. An official pronouncement of marriage by a priest is such a transition ceremony. An official pronouncement of death by a doctor is such a transition ceremony. The danger comes when a society forgets that the one is no more an indication of an objective physical change than the other.

Conclusion

We began this essay with a scene from the 1939 MGM production of The Wizard of Oz. In the scene, Dorothy's house has come down in The Land of Oz on top of the Wicked Witch of the East, crushing her. The Munchkins are still anxious, however, and they need absolute assurance that the wicked witch is dead by all possible definitions. In the movie this assurance is at last provided by the Munchkin coroner, who draws himself up importantly (he is four feet tall), produces a huge death certificate, and makes the formal pronouncement. The all-important social line must be drawn even in Munchkin Land.

Sad to say, as we look about us here in Southern California in the year 1989, we find that things are not that much different here than in the wildest fantasies of L. Frank Baum. The Dark Ages, we must remember, were only 25 generations ago. We live in a pretty crazy society, still bound up with intellectual baggage from a magical and mystical past—and its way of looking at things is sometimes completely irrational. Our job now is to find ways of dealing with it. A sense of humor is helpful, particularly if one is confronted with a coroner who seems straight from the Land of Oz, or assorted Munchkins who have begun to worry about whether a person whose heart has stopped is only merely dead, or is really most sincerely dead.

Cryonics has passed a threshold of some sort in this past year, and we really aren't in Kansas anymore. Courage is now required, and brains, and heart. Let us hope that we find that these things were always within us, whether we knew it or not. ∎

WHY A RELIGIOUS PERSON CAN CHOOSE CRYONICS

BY STEPHEN W. BRIDGE

Cryonics, 2nd Quarter, 1995[1]

"Why on God's Green Earth would someone want to be frozen and come back later?"

"I guess I am of the mind that Death is natural and something I look forward to because of my belief in God and an afterlife."

"How does God fit into cryonics? Or does He?"

These are some of the questions that a friend asked me last year; but they are not new. I have been asked variations on these questions many times in my 18 years in cryonics. They may be the same questions you get from your friends and family; or you may have these questions yourself. One is always admonished to avoid the topics of religion and politics at a party; people just feel too strongly about them. I recognize that is true, and I may be wading into a deep and tangled swamp by tackling this subject at all; but it is too important to ignore.

Some cryonicists and many interviewers assume that only an atheist can become a cryonicist, that religion and cryonics are totally incompatible. This is completely untrue. The reasons that one person chooses cryonics may be very different from another person's reasons.

Some people have gone so far as to say that the success of cryonics will mean the destruction of religion. I think such a viewpoint is nonsense. Changes in some religions, yes; just as many religious groups have adapted in various ways to knowledge of the solar system, birth control, transplant technology, and in vitro fertilization. Certainly more of Alcor's suspension members are atheists than are religious. Often these non-religious people have stepped away from the mainstream in many areas of life and are willing to look at and adopt new ideas more quickly than others. However, as cryonics matures and seems more likely to work, more traditionally religious people have also decided they want the expanded possibilities for life in the future that cryonic suspension will be able to offer.

---

1   Originally published as "Frozen Souls: Can a Religious Person Choose Cryonics?"

The first and most important point to make is that in most ways cryonics has nothing to do with religion at all, any more than do penicillin or heart transplants. Cryonics is a technology to help keep people alive. The entire history of medicine is about helping people live longer and healthier, and most religions (with rare exceptions, such as Christian Science and some small "faith healing" Christian sects) have embraced and advanced medical knowledge. Some of the finest hospitals in the world are owned and managed by Catholics, Jews, Methodists, Seventh Day Adventists, and other religious organizations.

Cryonics is NOT about bringing the dead back to life. We are not talking about performing miracles. The entire point of cryonics is that physicians of today often pronounce patients dead at a point when doctors of the next century would consider them alive and would cure them. At some point real death occurs; but we think we may actually be preserving life (rather than reversing death) when we suspend patients.

It is a basic tenet of cryonics that what criteria we use to label people as "dead" at one point in history are not the same criteria we use for that label at a later point. A simple example is the modern ability to revive humans from several minutes of no circulation or breathing—a condition that was routinely labeled as permanently dead in the early part of this century. From that point of view, many thousands of people have been "revived from the dead."

If we use the word "death" to mean a permanent cessation of function, it is currently impossible to specify the exact instant when a patient crosses that line. Every year researchers make great strides in their abilities to resuscitate seemingly "dead" individuals, and we are a long way from reaching the limits of this technology. For example, how can we know what to label someone who is in a coma? One patient may have a nearly destroyed brain but have a heartbeat, while another may appear brain dead for months and suddenly wake up with all his memories. Each case may appear the same even to experienced neurologists, yet the outcome is quite different. People often ask where the "soul" goes when a person dies and is frozen. If we wish to revive that person in the future, will the soul still be there? I suggest that these people need to ask that question about the people who are already being revived from "death-like" experiences.

Excellent examples are the many children who have been revived from cold water drownings after thirty minutes underwater—no respiration, no circulation, no brain waves. They appear to be dead, and fifty years ago any physician would have labeled them that way and would have made no attempt to revive them. Yet now they can survive such conditions. The record is 66 minutes underwater by a 3-year-old, with full recovery, no apparent brain damage. The child had no electrical activity for an additional two hours after being pulled out of the river. Did the "soul" go somewhere and come back? Did God want the child to survive?

Robert Ettinger, in his original book about cryonics, *The Prospect of Immortality*, pointed out that "no one seems to make an issue" of where the children's souls went while they appeared to be dead. They were just happy to have their children alive. Ettinger then goes onto point out:

"Why, then, should anyone be concerned about the souls of the frozen? The mere length of the hiatus can hardly be critical; in God's view, 300 years is only the blink of an eyelash, and presents no more difficulty than 2½ hours.

"Except quantitatively, then, the problem is not new, and the religious communities have already made their decision. They have implicitly recognized that resuscitation, even if heroic measures are employed, is just a means of prolonging life, and that the apparent death was spurious."

Another kind of medical rescue now possible is a "suspended animation" brain surgery for aneurysms. A medical team lowers the patient's body temperature to about 50 degrees F, shunts the blood out of the patient's brain, and performs bloodless surgery on the brain for about 50-60 minutes. There are no brain waves during this time. The team then warms the individual back up and restarts the cerebral blood flow. The patient survives with his memory and personality (and presumably his "soul") intact.

One cryonics laboratory, building on what Alcor did several years ago, can now take a dog, begin cooling it, replace all the blood in its body with an organ preservation solution, cool it to about 3-4 degrees above freezing, and hold it at that temperature for nearly six hours. At that time the dog can be warmed and his blood reintroduced, and he survives. He still answers to his name and he knows the same commands as before. We assume that surgeons will apply similar techniques to many human operations in the next decade.

What this proves as much as anything is that we don't know much about life and death. It seems apparent that physicians of the late 21st Century will define the point of death much differently than most people do today. A doctor from the future traveling back to today would no doubt be saddened by the hundreds of thousands of patients we call dead when he could see they were repairable with future knowledge. If this is true, then we should consider them "alive" now, and arrange to get them to that doctor in the future.

Cryonics should be viewed as an extension of clinical medicine, not a new kind of dead-body storage. The entire purpose of this technology is to save lives. From that point of view, religious beliefs are irrelevant as far as cryonics is concerned. Cryonics success would not prove or disprove Christianity, anymore than heart transplants or other life-saving treatments do.

Assuming there is a God and assuming that God created humans, then God also created our brains. He (or She) also created our curiosity and the desire to explore the limits of our existence. God apparently allowed us to develop CPR, antibiotics, heart transplants, brain aneurysm surgery, and other medical advances. It appears that if this is God's creation, it is our duty to continue to explore that creation and find out what our human limits are. From this point of view, if cryonics works, God meant it to and meant us to explore it. If it doesn't work, then God didn't mean it to. As with heart transplants and other medical advances, God doesn't tell us in advance. Humans have to explore for themselves.

One of the interesting things about religious arguments is that almost everyone has their own opinions based on what they were taught; but many extend those opinions to saying they know what God's plan or purpose is. I don't believe anyone can know that. Anyone who did would by definition BE God. All we can do is our best and try to help each other. I choose to do so right now by helping people stay alive—or at least by giving them as much of a chance as possible.

Because of this sort of reasoning, Alcor and other cryonics groups have sometimes attracted suspension members who are religious. This has given us the chance to ask them about their beliefs and often to speak with their religious leaders about cryonics. (I will point out that no religious group has—as far as I know—stated an official position on cryonic suspension. The following ideas are from individual members and religious leaders.)

For example, the members of one conservative Christian family believe that God wants them to stay alive as long as possible to spread the Word. Choosing cryonics for them means doing God's work.

Orthodox Jews, Seventh Day Adventists, and some other religious groups believe that the Bible says nothing about a person's soul floating up to Heaven when he dies. They believe the Bible tells us that when you are dead, you are completely DEAD— until the Resurrection, which means the revival and reconstitution of the physical body, including the soul. Therefore, you may as well stay alive as long as you can; when God is ready for the resurrection, it won't matter if you're alive or dead—or frozen.

There are several reasons to believe that the Catholic Church in the next century will actually view cryonics with favor. As far back as the late 1960s, a Catholic priest was photographed blessing a capsule at the Cryonics Society of New York. On at least two occasions in the 1980s, television interviewers added Catholic ethicists to cryonics programs to provide "the other side;" and the ethicists decided that they saw no conflict with Church teachings.

At some point in the late '80s, the case of some frozen fertilized embryos in Australia brought an official Vatican reaction (I don't recall if this was an official statement of the Pope, though). Fertility researchers had already proven that human embryos could be frozen in liquid nitrogen, thawed, transplanted, brought to full term, and produce normal, healthy children (the first in 1984, now many thousands worldwide). The Church's position was that these fertilized embryos had souls, were humans, and destruction of them was murder. This seemed to imply that liquid nitrogen on its own was not inimical to "soul storage."

Several years ago, I had a conversation with a prospective member who had spoken to his priest about cryonics and had gotten an interesting answer. I have since asked at least one other Catholic priest about this and was told that the answer had theological merit.

Today, if a Catholic is in a hospital with an illness for which life-saving treatment is available, some theologians would argue that for the Catholic to refuse that treatment would be willful death—suicide. God chooses when you die, not you, and God has given you a way to survive through medicine. By extending that argument, if cryonics could be shown to work—to save lives—then choosing not to undergo cryonic suspension when current medicine cannot save you could also be considered willful death. Neither priest could find anything inherently wrong with cryonics as a potential life-extending technology.

A firm answer on this question cannot be given yet, because cryonics is still experimental. Perhaps these people in cryonic suspension should be considered alive or perhaps they should be considered dead. We won't know for a very long time. But if they are really dead, then God has already taken care of their soul and it doesn't matter. A person can lose nothing spiritually by trying cryonic suspension. God does not punish people for trying to stay alive.

Back to those questions at the beginning of the article: One of the most often heard comments about cryonics, from religious and non-religious people alike, is that "death is natural." There are at least two ways to reply to that. You may recall Katherine Hepburn saying to Humphrey Bogart in *The African Queen*, "Nature, Mr. Allnut, is what we were put on this world to overcome." It is our "nature" to overcome what is "natural." "Natural" is running around naked in the woods eating roots and grubs. Our human nature (whether given by God or evolved) has led us to build homes and churches, make tools and clothing, and invent air-conditioning, surgery, libraries, bifocals and hearing aids, Cadillacs, digital watches, and gourmet restaurants to make our lives easier, longer, and more interesting.

Another approach is to point out that rape and murder and war are also "natural." Does that mean we should not try to prevent them? Does that mean that God wants us to rape, kill, and bomb? Or are these actions things we must learn to overcome? If so, then why not learn to overcome dying?

In the 1800s, many whites in the American South told black slaves that their conditions were the "natural, God-given" state of things. Further, they said that African people were naturally inferior and destined by God to be slaves of the superior descendants of Europeans. In fact, slave owners made a great deal of noise about how slaves were happier being slaves, about how slavery made them better people, even brought them closer to God. This was the equivalent of giving seminars in how to be a happy slave instead of showing them how to be FREE.

Likewise today, why give ourselves seminars in how to be happy that we will soon die? Let's learn how to be free of death instead.

"Why on God's Green Earth would someone want to be frozen and come back later?"

That's the easy one. I don't particularly want to be frozen and come back—I want not to die in the first place. But if my condition is so poor that all other options are closed to me, I want to be placed into cryonic suspension so that I can continue my existence.

The question should be, "Why do you want to live indefinitely?" The answer is both easy and complex: Because I like being alive, in this form and in this identity. Because life is good and infinitely varied. There is much more to learn and experience and explore of this universe (this "creation," if you prefer) than we can do in thousands of years. Living includes thinking and studying and learning, maybe in other parts of the galaxy, comparing my observations with beings much different from myself. Perhaps people who can live a very long time will spend a lot of it examining and defining the meaning of human existence, the nature of the universe, the relevance of religion, and the existence of God. Are religions elaborate lies or tricks we have played on ourselves to remain sane in the face of death? Or does one of those hundreds of sets of beliefs that people swear are "true" actually reflect the reality of our existence before and after the event we call death?

If today we are dying and do not choose cryonic suspension—and if it turns out that this existence is all there is—then we lose the bet and no more choices are possible. If we choose to be suspended and can be revived again, we can continue to look for the answers. Death and "going beyond"—if such a thing can happen—will always be options.

Cryonics itself is only a technology, not a religion. For some people, cryonics may be part of a philosophical approach (which includes immortalism, life extension, space travel, and other ideas) that fills the psychological space in their brains that others may use for religion. But for most, cryonics will fit into their philosophical framework in the same way that heart surgery and chemotherapy do—as a medical technology which may extend their lives.

I don't know if cryonic suspension will preserve life or not. I think it is likely, based on my understanding of science; but I have no guarantee. However, if it turns out that my life only exists in this physical reality, then I want to prolong that reality for as long as possible.

I am not saying this to persuade you that my beliefs are correct. Religion or lack of it is very personal, and my beliefs certainly need not have any influence on yours. Besides, mine may change again over the next decade. But I want to remind you that there are many approaches to life and philosophy that can co-exist with the choice of cryonics.

I also want to inform all prospective suspension members (and to remind the current suspension members) that Alcor's official policy is to take no position on the relationship of cryonics to religion, whether Christianity, Judaism, Islam, or any other belief. Individuals make their own decisions on the correctness and acceptability of cryonics, based on whatever criteria they consider important. Alcor's approval of suspension membership is not related to an individual's religion or personal belief system. Please note Alcor's "Non-Discrimination Policy" at the end of this article.

We welcome your further thoughts on these issues, especially if you can discuss how cryonics might fit in with Islam or other religions with which Americans are less familiar. If you are not yet a suspension member of Alcor, do some thinking about how important living is to you. If it seems a lot more important than dying does, you may wish to make cryonic suspension arrangements, so your safety net is in place. You might make that decision based on your religious beliefs, on a desire to fill some part of your own empty "religion slot," or for reasons based completely on logic and science. Whatever causes you to make this choice to live, we welcome you.

Appendix: Non-Discrimination Policy

The Alcor Life Extension Foundation believes that every person has a right to choose and arrange for his or her own cryonic suspension and to enjoy its possible benefits of greatly extended lifespan. To this end, the Alcor Life Extension Foundation does not discriminate against any person on the basis of race, religion, color, creed, age, marital status, national origin, ancestry, sex, sexual orientation or preference, medical condition, or handicap.

However, nothing in this statement prevents Alcor from avoiding any situation that genuinely threatens the health or safety of Alcor employees, volunteers, patients in suspension, or the public, or from requiring reasonable medical evaluations in some instances where a genuine threat to health or safety may be suspected to exist, or where the legal status of an individual with regard to mental competency may be in question. ∎

CRYONICS AND EMERGENCY MEDICINE

BY THOMAS DONALDSON, PH.D.
Cryonics, 1st Quarter, 1999

I will begin with a simple statement: Yes, I do think that we'll someday find means to revive most of those suspension patients frozen with current methods, now or in the past. Revival of patients suspended by future methods will be even easier. However, all of human history suggests that revivals will not occur within just a few years, and they will certainly not occur at any one given time. If theoretical ideas tested only by computer need no revision, current scientific ideas about memory are close to correct, money for the required research becomes available instantly, everybody cooperates, no one stands up to oppose the changes, and no one insists on proof before we can proceed . . . then means to revive suspended patients will arrive quite soon.

Yet to assume that everything will go so smoothly is simply to dream. To believe that we might specify repair processes based on nothing more than computer studies looks to me like the belief of a novice programmer; since he can easily write flawless "Hello" programs, he assumes he can write a million-line program totally without bugs.

Then too, explicit reports of suspensions published by cryonics organizations suggest that patients will not be revived by only a few repairs. We already know that such patients have experienced a wide range of conditions, from those whose brains alone were straight-frozen, to those suspended under the best conditions according to current knowledge (which may be mistaken!). Repair must deal not with one kind of problem but with many. We will not simultaneously solve every problem of reanimation, regardless even of how far we develop the suspension process itself.

No, improving cryonics-style procedures to the point of reversible suspended animation will not alleviate *all* of our problems. How many people will decide, *in full health,* that they want to enter suspended animation? They would be helpless for an unknown length of time, and would arrive in an unknown world missing all of their friends and requiring their extensive re-education. Given these likelihoods, the choice of suspended animation while healthy looks almost as irrational as the choice of cryonic suspension in a similar condition*. (Yes, some people would subject themselves to either one, but not many).

Beyond the rationality of this choice, there is the price tag. Few people would happily decide to spend in excess of $75,000 without prolonged deliberation. Certainly reversible suspended animation will be no less expensive than this, and so its cost will affect the circumstances under which someone might choose it. Again, most people would probably not submit to suspended animation (or cryonic suspension) until near the end of a terminal illness.

Here we encounter our main problem: death does not follow a schedule. Cryonicists die by accidents that occur thousands of miles from their cryonics society, they die suddenly in the apparent peak of physical health, and they die all alone in their private homes and apartments. Even in cases for which their time of death is predicted, they may doubt that prediction, holding out until the very last minute. If we had true suspended animation, they might take this option before death, but they also might only come to that decision in circumstances which made their suspended animation just as difficult as many cryonic suspensions today.

We will not have completed our research if we only go so far as reversible suspended animation. For emergency medicine we need much more: the equipment to perform suspended animation must become portable. Ideally, such equipment must allow *only one person* to carry out a full procedure. Facilities able to carry out suspended animation must become easily accessible on very short notice. And we'll *still* have to work out just how to deal with patients who have experienced cessation of breathing and heartbeat many minutes before the suspended animation team arrives. Yes, if a deanimation is expected, we *might* avoid these difficulties, but not all deanimations will be expected—ever.

What this means is that even if 21st Century Medicine succeeded in its basic aim of perfecting reversible suspended animation, cryonics organizations such as Alcor would still be far from obsolete. Full suspended animation might demand as much research to extend its practical application as was necessary to develop it in the first place. And we must never forget that we will *inevitably* find ourselves in situations where the patient is so damaged or long deanimated that suspended animation would not be feasible. We will always need some form of cryonic suspension as a safety net. ∎

* It may still prove useful in special cases, such as the need to move someone from one hospital to another because the other hospital has devices the prior one lacked. Some uses will require further development, since the first versions of suspended animation will probably leave a revived suspendee needing time (and money) to recover. Once fully developed, we might see its use in space exploration. We might also see suspensions for economic or justice reasons: people choosing suspension until "revival" of the industry that employed them, or suspension as an alternative to jail.

ETHICS OF NON-IDEAL CRYONICS CASES

BY BRIAN WOWK, PH.D.

Cryonics, 4th Quarter, 2006

Cryonics can be defined as the low temperature preservation of people who cannot be saved by medicine today until they can be revived and treated in the future. While the idea is simple, it involves many complex issues. This article will address only one of them: the question of to whom cryonics technology should be ethically applied, and when.

Ideal Cryonics

A truly ideal cryonics case might consist of a patient with a terminal disease consenting to placement in reversible suspended animation until treatment is possible. However such perfected "medical time travel" is still hypothetical since no technology exists for long-term suspended animation that is demonstrably reversible. In that sense, all cryonics cases today are "non-ideal" because the preservation method itself is not proven to work.

Nevertheless, even if the final result of cryopreservation is uncertain, an "ideal" cryonics case can still be defined as one in which the survival status of the patient is not in doubt at the time cryopreservation begins. This could be achieved by connecting an anesthetized living patient to a heart-lung machine to maintain blood circulation as temperature was lowered. In practice this cannot be done because cryonics is not an approved medical procedure.

Cryonics deals with this problem via the mechanism of legal death. When an illness is terminal, legal death may be declared on the basis of cardiac arrest (heart stoppage) even though resuscitation is still possible. It is therefore possible to be legally dead, but biologically viable, for a short period of time. It is during this period of several minutes that "ideal" cryonics cases can be performed under existing law. This window of time is also used by conventional medicine for harvesting living organs for transplant in cases of donation after cardiac death (DCD).[1]

The cornerstone of ideal cryonics is the idea of "Standby." Standby is the process in which a team of cryonics technicians wait at bedside for the heart of a terminal patient to naturally stop beating, at which time legal death is declared. Legal death in this context means that further care by conventional medicine is not appropriate. The

---

1   L. Whetstine, S. Streat, M. Darwin, D. Crippen, Pro/con ethics debate: When is dead really dead? *Critical Care* 9 (2005) 538-542. and Cryonics Commentary.

team then artificially restores blood circulation and begins cooling. This stabilizes the biological viability of the patient. Although difficult to achieve in practice, the goal of standby is to maintain the same biological viability in a cryonics patient as would exist if cryonics were an elective medical procedure, not a post-mortem intervention.[2]

Non-ideal Cryonics

A non-ideal cryonics case occurs when cryonics stabilization procedures, such as cooling, are begun long after resuscitation by contemporary medicine is impossible and thus biological viability is believed to have ceased. Such cases, which account for more than half of all cryonics cases, are often the result of unexpected legal death. Non-ideal cases may involve hours, or even a day or more, of clinical death without intervention.

In extreme cases, a non-ideal cryonics case may involve salvaging and freezing brain tissue that has been subjected to both trauma and decomposition. Use of chemicals to prevent freezing damage (cryoprotectants) is often impossible for non-ideal cases, which adds freezing damage to damage already caused by a lengthy period of clinical death.

Interestingly, the general public perception of cryonics seems to be that all cryonics cases are "non-ideal" as described above. It is widely believed that cryonics companies receive patients the same way that funeral homes receive bodies, many hours or days after legal death. The concept that cryopreservation can ideally be begun at bedside, with little or no brain injury by conventional criteria at the start of the procedure, is generally unknown.

Rationale for Non-ideal Cases

The biological rationale for non-ideal cases is that death is a process, not an event. It is generally known that clinical death can be reversed for up to 4 to 6 minutes after the heart stops before the brain is believed to die. It is less well known that this limit can be extended to as long as 15 minutes using experimental resuscitation methods.

In some animal models, up to 60 minutes of clinical death at normal temperatures has been reversible, with most damage confined to a particular area of the brain (CA1 region of the hippocampus). Even hours after blood circulation stops, living cells can still be retrieved from brains assumed to be long dead by contemporary medical standards. The brain does not suddenly fall apart when it is deprived of oxygen. These

---

2   B. Wowk, "Cardiopulmonary Support in Cryonics," monograph published by the Alcor Life Extension Foundation (2003).

facts have been discussed at length in cryonics literature.[3,4,5,6]

Why, then, is it believed that people go out "like a light" when the heart stops? Many important functions do stop suddenly. When the heart stops beating, the brain runs out of energy, and all brain electrical activity stops after about 30 seconds. But people can and have recovered after far longer periods without any brain activity. This is because people are not really light bulbs. The structure and chemistry of the brain ultimately determines whether someone can be revived. Brain function does not matter. The brain is like a computer hard drive, not volatile electronic memory.

Whether a clinically deceased person can be revived depends on whether whatever is wrong with the structure and chemistry of their brain can be set right. Today nothing can be done about repairing structure, and setting chemistry right is limited to re-supplying oxygen, nutrients, and a few simple drugs. Whether a patient lives or dies when blood circulation is restored depends on whether the brain can naturally recover from damage that accumulated during the interval without oxygen.

Future technologies for molecular repair of the brain will be able to directly reverse structural and chemical changes caused by long periods without oxygen, making resuscitation after hours of clinical death theoretically possible. A century from now, doctors may speak of the critical need to treat cardiac arrest within the first 4 to 6 hours rather than the first 4 to 6 minutes as they do today.

In the limiting case of a technology capable of completely general molecular repairs, restoration of a healthy state would always be possible. Whatever repairs were necessary to repair/reconstruct a functional, biologically healthy brain and body could always be performed. What would happen is that long periods of clinical death followed by repair would result in varying degrees of memory loss about prior events. If decomposition were severe enough, "repair" would result in a new person. How much memory loss is required before the original patient is considered deceased? It is a tradition in medicine that if brain function can be restored, the original patient is considered recovered despite amnesia. This custom seems likely to continue in the future whenever clinically deceased patients can be restored to consciousness, even when the repaired injuries were severe.

Ethics of Non-ideal Cases

The ethical justification for non-ideal cryonics cases begins with the ethical justification for cryonics generally, which is that medicine should not be limited to treating

---

3   "The Cryobiological Case for Cryonics," monograph published by the Alcor Life Extension Foundation (1988).

4   T. Donaldson, "A Brief Scientific Introduction to Cryonics," monograph published by the Alcor Life Extension Foundation (1976).

5   T. Donaldson, "Neural Archaeology," *Cryonics*, February, 1987.

6   T. Donaldson, "Prospects of a Cure for "Death"," *Cryonics*, May, 1990.

conditions that can only be treated in real-time with a certain outcome. Any remedial strategy that is scientifically defensible, even if requiring very long time scales, is a legitimate strategy for protection of human life. Cryonics under ideal conditions is scientifically defensible.[7,8,9,10]

If it is stipulated that performing cryonics under ideal conditions can be ethical, what of the non-ideal cryonics case? Clearly there are degrees of biological decay that will obliterate so much of the original person that future repair will not recover the original person. This state has been called information theoretic death.[7] But short of complete destruction of a person, how can information theoretic death be determined?

Present medical practice is to suddenly stop care of patients that reach certain stages of illness, and destroy them. This is done by a legal and social ritual that strips them of personhood. That ritual is legal death. The sudden transition from living patient to "remains" is so inculcated in popular culture that the very idea that a person without blood circulation or brain function could still be a person is unthinkable. In reality, there is no sudden loss of personhood when the heart stops, only a relatively sudden loss of ability to be resuscitated by current technology. That loss used to occur at the very moment the heart stopped. Now it occurs after 4 to 6 minutes. If post-resuscitation cooling is used, it can be over 10 minutes. Drug interventions show promise for extending it to 20 minutes. Eventually nanomedicine will extend it to hours. There is no sudden moment at which a brain, or person, ceases to be viable.

The idea that human life is something that disappears slowly hours after clinical death, even as disposal rituals are already underway, is an aspect of biology that is rarely examined because the implications are so disturbing. Yet the availability of technologies for stabilizing patients for indefinite periods of time (cryonics) forces hard examination of this issue.

Michael Darwin has called cryonics "conservative" medicine that is in keeping with the medical ethical imperative, "First, do no harm." A triage process that commits viable patients to destruction certainly does harm, at least to the patient concerned. Thus "do no harm" would seem to require the cryopreservation of any patient with remaining brain structure until such time as tools become available to adequately examine and reconstitute the patient.

According to this paradigm, almost all conditions now considered "death" are actually disease states in which future treatment would result in resuscitation, albeit

7   R. Merkle, "The Technical Feasibility of Cryonics," *Medical Hypotheses* 39 (1992) 6-16.
8   J. Lemler, S.B. Harris, C. Platt, T.M. Huffman, "The Arrest of Biological Time as a Bridge to Engineered Negligible Senescence," *Annals of the New York Academy of Sciences* 1019 (2004) 559-563.
9   "Scientists' Cryonics FAQ," monograph published by the Alcor Life Extension Foundation (2005).
10   "Scientists' Open Letter on Cryonics." http://www.evidencebasedcryonics.org/scientists-open-letter-on-cryonics/

with varying degrees of loss of memory of prior events. No patient would be left behind. No patient should be left behind based on short-sighted judgments.

The Best and Worst of Cryonics Ethics

It is ironic that what some might call the noblest ethical statement in cryonics—the "no patient left behind" doctrine —can lead to the worst ethical criticism of cryonics. Cryopreserving "bodies" in states of severe deterioration appears scientifically indefensible. Doing so in exchange for money appears ethically indefensible. Which view is correct?

It may be that they are both correct, depending on circumstances. Most people who arrange for cryonics do so while young and healthy. They plan for, save for, and consent to cryonics many years in advance of need. Many specify in their signup paperwork that "any biological remains whatsoever" are to be cryopreserved, consistent with the "no patient left behind" doctrine. They do so in full knowledge that there is a line of deterioration beyond which cryonics cannot work.

But they elect not to guess at where that line might be. Since funds have been set aside long ago, proceeding with cryonics under poor conditions is not a financial hardship or decision burden on family or society. It is a matter of personal planning and choice, and even medical ethical idealism. Were the "no patient left behind" doctrine ever to be accepted by society generally, with common funding mechanisms established, it would arguably be ethically superior to the current system of discarding patients whenever contemporary medical capability is unable to meet their needs. The expense would be small compared to total lifetime medical expenses in the industrialized world.

The most serious ethical problems of non-ideal cases arise in the context of "last minute" cases. A "last minute" case is a case in which a cryonics organization is contacted when legal death is imminent, or has already occurred, for a non-member of the organization.

These cases typically involve distraught families, high emotion, lack of informed consent, and even lack of patient consent when the patient is unconscious or already legally deceased. Families are faced with the decision of paying a large amount of money for something they do not understand, is not likely to work, and that cryonics organizations can barely defend. Such cases conform to the worst negative stereotypes of cryonics preying on grieving families for financial gain. "Last minute" cases are rarely accepted by Alcor for many of these reasons.

Two Ideas, One Word

The word "cryonics" is actually a name for two different ideas. The first idea is that human cryopreservation under ideal conditions today could be reversible in the future.

The second idea is that medicine should never leave patients behind; every patient beyond the capabilities of contemporary care should be cryopreserved instead of destroyed, even if found in poor condition. The distinction is necessary because it is possible to agree with the first idea even while not accepting the second. The first idea is a scientific proposition, while the second is a philosophical imperative.

For those who advocate the broader second view of cryonics, it is important to remember that non-ideal cases can be an expression of both the best and worst of cryonics ethics. It is the responsibility of cryonicists to ensure that non-ideal cases are handled with the highest ethical standards. This is best done by upholding "no patient left behind" as an ideal of medicine and personal planning, while discouraging sale of cryonics under poor conditions where no prior cryopreservation plans exist. ■

Let's Talk About Cryonics

By Ralph C. Merkle, Ph.D.
Cryonics, 4th Quarter, 2009

Introduction

Alcor has grown over the years, and the rate of growth has varied dramatically. In our best year we grew by 44%, in our worst we shrank by 4%. In 2009 our net gain was 38 members—somewhat more than 4%.

Growth is good. A higher growth rate is better. More members means more resources for everything we do. Research and development, legal rights, legal expenses, conferences, operating rooms, publications, the web site, public relations, lobbying—everything.

Which has created great interest in the cryonics community in ways to increase growth. Everyone has an opinion, many of the opinions differ, and it is sometimes difficult to say which opinions are better.

People Talk About Ideas

Rather than attempt to review all the ideas about what drives (or doesn't drive) the growth of cryonics, it seemed more useful to focus on one of the few areas where there seems to be broad agreement: personal contact. Alcor members come in clusters. California and Florida have many members. North Dakota has few. The United States has almost 800 members. There are 27 in the U.K. France has none. Statistically it is very unlikely that two Alcor members would be closely related, but there are siblings, spouses, and even whole families signed up. If joining Alcor was a decision made entirely independently by each person who thought about cryonics, we would not see these clusters.

But we do see clusters, and we see them because people form communities. Ideas spread from member to member in these communities. You meet people at work, in clubs, in schools, at conferences, on the web—we swim in a sea of friends, acquaintances, co-workers, relatives, colleagues and others. You talk with them about the iPhone and the Nexus One, the Super Bowl, whether to get a Mac or a PC, which type of chocolate is best—almost everything we do we talk about. If we hear an idea, and it seems to make sense to us, we adopt it as our own.

Growth is a good idea for many reasons. More members means greater strength as an organization and a better chance that all of us will survive. Each new member brings a new set of skills, a new set of capabilities, new resources. Alcor needs medical and paramedical personnel, lawyers, accountants, administrative support, computer experts, investment advisors, handymen, writers, … In short, Alcor needs all the skills that any modern organization needs if it is to thrive and grow.

More members means more influence at the polls. More members means a better chance that the EMT who shows up after your heart attack has heard of cryonics and will follow the instructions on your Alcor ID tag. More members means a better chance that the hospital you are in will cooperate with Alcor when the time comes, because someone on the staff has a friend whose uncle is an Alcor member.

More directly, if your friends and loved ones know you are signed up with Alcor then they will better know what to do in an emergency. If everyone around you knows what you want, then the odds that you will be cryopreserved are much better. If you keep it a secret, when the time comes no one will know what to do—they might not even realize they should do anything at all.

If you persuade a friend or relative that signing up with Alcor is a good idea then that's one more friendly face when you wake up in the future. And even if you don't succeed, they'll know what you want and what to do in an emergency. It's also fun talking about cryonics—you'll find that your own knowledge and understanding grows deeper as you talk about the issues with others, and that talking about things that matter to you is more interesting than talking about the weather. And there's always the sheer altruistic pleasure of persuading someone to do the right thing—not for any particular reason, but just because that seems to be part of what being human is all about.

If every member of Alcor persuaded one or two of their friends or relatives that cryonics was a good idea; and if those friends and relatives persuaded one or two of *their* friends and relatives, and so on; then Alcor would grow exponentially—which helps us all.

What to Say

What do we say when we talk with people about cryonics? What do we need to know, what are they likely to be curious about, and what do they need to know that they don't know they don't know?

The single most important piece of advice I can give you is: read the FAQ!

Alcor's website working group has done a fantastic job on Alcor's web site. The FAQ, in particular, is truly excellent. The main FAQ is at http://www.alcor.org/FAQs/index.html and the Scientist's Cryonics FAQ is at http://www.alcor.org/sciencefaq.htm. I recommend them both.

The FAQs are remarkable because of the breadth and scope of the topics they need to cover to provide a balanced picture of cryonics. From cryobiology to nanomedicine to neuroscience to finance to the soul, the FAQs have it all. Whenever we hear a common question, we add it to the FAQ. It has become quite formidable—and it continues to grow.

Just as important as the FAQ are the instructions on how to sign up at http://www. alcor.org/BecomeMember/index.html—which methodically goes through all the steps in the process. If we want people to sign up, they have to know how.

But before someone can sign up, before they can think about cryonics, they have to hear about it. And more than hear about it, they have to hear about it in a context where they decide it is worth thinking about and asking about. The most likely way this will happen is if someone they know talks with them about it. This means you.

Starting a Conversation

How might such a conversation start? There are a million ways. At lunch one day in the company cafeteria I was sitting next to an acquaintance who said, out of the blue, that he had just heard about cryonics. "Who would be dumb enough to do that?" he asked, to which I replied "me." Flustered, he said, "I'm so embarrassed…" (he's a very polite sort of person, and would never have dreamed of deliberately offending anyone). Which, of course, led to a discussion of cryonics—and his position on the subject promptly became more favorable just because someone he was talking to was actually signed up.

It's often that simple. As long as cryonics is something "they" do, for unknown and mysterious motives, then it's easier to dismiss. If a friend or relative learns that *you* do it, then suddenly most of those imagined scenarios collapse. Cryonics is now something that someone they know has actually signed up to do. It's part of their world, just like that new web site you suggested they try, or the new restaurant that has *fantastic* salads.

If someone brings up the subject, that provides an obvious opportunity to jump in and discuss it. If such an opportunity doesn't spontaneously occur, there are many other approaches. There's the direct approach—"I signed up with Alcor—they freeze people. If I'm ever in an accident or something, make sure to call them. The number is right here on my bracelet." No need to tell them *they* should sign up—not just yet. Just let them get used to the idea that *you* signed up, and if there's ever any problem they should call Alcor. Most of the time, the response will be to look at your bracelet and perhaps start reading it. "It says push 50,000 U Heparin—what's that?" At this point, you can talk about cryoprotectants and ice blockers—or they might ask "Doesn't it cost a bunch?" at which point you can talk about life insurance and how inexpensive it can be. Or they might ask a few polite questions and not express much interest, in which case you can let the topic slide. Some people take time to get used to cryonics— and if you know the person there will be plenty of time in the future to mention it in small, easily handled bites.

More indirectly, you can talk with people about life extension. That latest study you read about in *Cryonics* magazine that shows that calorie restriction slows aging—you can mention it and ask, "Would you like to live longer? If they could figure out why calorie restriction worked and develop a medical treatment (something that didn't involve being hungry all the time) would you want to use it? If you could stay healthy, how long would you want to live?" If they are uncomfortable with the idea of a long and healthy life, no need to bring up cryonics when it looks like they don't even want to live! But if they express interest in a long and healthy life, you can say things like "Medical technology is getting better all the time. We might even be able to revive someone who was cryopreserved" and see how they respond.

Most people are receptive to a discussion *about* cryonics, but can be sensitive if you try to *sell* them on cryonics. Usually, you won't persuade someone to sign up in one encounter. Pick one area of confusion or a single reason they wouldn't consider signing up, and discuss that. This is seldom threatening, as they usually have other reasons for not signing up which you don't have to disturb—at least, not in that conversation. And, of course, when they examine this one reason for not signing up, they find it doesn't actually make much sense.

Common Arguments Against Cryonics

Often you will hear an argument against cryonics that is logically the same as an argument in favor of suicide—which makes it easy to explain why it is not a very good argument. Perhaps the classic was a conversation around a table when the reason for not signing up was "I wouldn't have any friends in the future." What he didn't know was that everyone else around the table was signed up. When he gave his reason we all smiled and said, "We'll be there!" Scratch one reason for not signing up!

Another argument you will often hear is that cryonics would be great if it worked, but it doesn't work. The most common form of this argument is to say, "but it has never been done, therefore it is impossible!" It often takes some time to convey the obvious fact that flight to the moon was "impossible" in 1940 but that did not make it impossible in 1969. There's a first time for everything—arguing that something hasn't been done before is not an argument that it can never be done, nor even that it is unlikely or will be expensive. No one built a stored program computer until the 20th century, but now they are ubiquitous.

It is actually very hard to make a well-founded argument that no future technology—no matter how advanced—could ever revive someone who was cryopreserved today. Anyone who has even a modest idea of what technologies are likely to be possible in a few centuries will see how hard it is to support this argument. The simplest counter to this argument is the "sweep of history." An ancient Roman who time-travelled to our day would be awed by our technology—flights to the moon, heart transplants, transatlantic flights, and the internet to mention just a few. So too would someone from our day be amazed by the commonplace a few centuries from now. For us to dismiss cryonics is like an ancient Roman dismissing heart transplant surgery.

Picking a specific reason for dismissing cryonics and countering it is based on the assumption that most people have a finite list of reasons, and that people are more amenable to logical persuasion if you only ask them to make a small change in their world view (also known as "salami tactics.") If, over time, all their reasons are addressed they often switch from "I don't want to sign up because ....." to "Yes, I really should sign up." Once in this latter mental state people can still procrastinate for years—but they will generally enjoy conversations about cryonics and are likely to sign up at some point.

Not everyone can be persuaded by reason and friendly discussion. Some people seem to have a deep seated emotional bias against cryonics. They are entirely comfortable with some facile-sounding reason for not signing up—and can become quite agitated when you show their "reason" is entirely irrational. Some of these people are even sufficiently self-aware to acknowledge that they have an emotional bias and don't care about logic, evidence, or reason—they don't want to do it and that's that! For the most part, once you have identified such a person, just leave them be.

Sometimes the list of reasons is very short. One person had decided cryonics was a good idea, but literally was not aware that it could be funded inexpensively through life insurance. When he heard that final piece of information, everything clicked and he signed up.

Who to Talk With

Perhaps the most obvious rule of thumb is to talk with people who seem interested. Cast your net wide and let those who are interested come to you. If you let everyone know you are interested in cryonics, most people will discuss it politely and then move on to other subjects. Occasionally, someone will be more interested. Talk with them, and listen to their concerns. Address them at a pace they can handle, and give them time to absorb the new ideas. If you are the only person in your school, or at your job, or in your club who is signed up, let everyone know about it. If someone is interested and wants to talk more about it—follow up and talk with them.

There is also the role of social pressure. While still the exception, there are environments where the majority opinion is both that cryonics is likely to work and that being alive in the future is a good idea. In these environments it is much easier to persuade people they should sign up. In a casual conversation with three or four people—only one of whom is not signed up—the subject can be raised, discussed and analyzed in a context where the social instincts of the lone holdout are to go with the crowd. This can be quite effective, particularly if it can be repeated over time.

Conferences, parties, or other social events involving food, movies, conversation, talks, and good friends where there is a significant percentage of cryonicists in attendance can often be used effectively for this purpose. And, of course, they are fun.

Conclusion

Persuading people to sign up is a fascinating hobby. The discussions span most of human knowledge and often cut to the root of what it means to be human. Every year the evidence in favor of cryonics gets stronger and the number of supporters goes up. Even if you never persuade one other person to sign up, you have clarified your own understanding of your own views and told everyone what you believe in and what you want—which could save your life when the time comes. And if you persuade just a few other people, then you have improved everyone's chances for survival—theirs, yours, and ours. ■

How to Protect your Cryonics Arrangements from Interference by Third Parties

By Rebecca Lively, Attorney at Law
Cryonics, 1st Quarter, 2010

On December 15, 2004, Orville Richardson signed up with Alcor Life Extension Foundation, Inc., to have his body cryopreserved in the event of his legal death. This was not a simple matter for Orville. When Orville signed up with Alcor, he paid an upfront lump sum payment of $70,000. He also had to read and fill out at least three lengthy legal agreements expressing his intentions. Ultimately, before Orville's arrangements with Alcor could become final he had to gather two witnesses and a notary and attest to his wishes publicly.

On February 21, 2009, Orville Richardson was embalmed and buried. Orville had not changed his mind about his arrangements prior to his legal death. Orville did not want to be buried and the people who made the arrangements to bury Orville knew it. Yet, despite the contracts he had signed, the money he had paid, and the people he had told, no one stepped in to protect Orville's wishes or inform Alcor of his legal death.

How did Orville go from a signed up cryonicist to embalmed and buried six feet underground? Unfortunately, Orville did not do enough to ensure that his cryopreservation would begin as soon as possible after his legal death. The unfortunate truth is that the family members of cryonicists often pose the greatest risk to a prompt cryopreservation. Orville's expressed wishes for cryopreservation were ignored by his own brother and sister after he became unable to take care of himself.

Accordingly, it is critical for cryonicists to manage the risk that family members pose to a successful and prompt cryopreservation. The purpose of this article is to suggest legal and practical strategies to minimize the risk of unsupportive family members and to limit the amount of time which passes between legal death and the start of cryopreservation procedures for as many cryonicists as possible.

While a precise description of the laws and policies in every state and country is far beyond the scope of this article, the below categories are intended to point cryonicists in the right direction to avoid devastating conflicts with their arrangements. However, nothing can replace hiring a knowledgeable and cryonics-friendly attorney in your jurisdiction.

I. Sign Up With a Provider

The September 1989 issue of *Cryonics* magazine contained a survey of 109 people who identified as "cryonicists." Of the respondents, 34% indicated that they were not signed up with any cryonics organization. While this percentage has likely improved in the twenty-plus years since the survey was taken, it is safe to assume that at least some of the intended readers of this article have not yet signed up with a cryonics organization despite identifying as cryonicists.

Obviously, the first and most important step toward cryopreservation is signing up and arranging funding. The excuses for not signing up are varied and range from not having family support to not being able to decide which cryonics organization to sign up with to not having the money to being "young and healthy" and waiting until you "need" cryonics to sign up.

Regardless of the reason, if you are not signed up for cryonics, your best case scenario at legal death involves suffering ischemic damage while a friend or loved one makes last-minute arrangements for your cryopreservation. Of course, the more likely scenario is that such last-minute arrangements will not be possible.

Being "young and healthy" is no excuse either. First, young and healthy people die every day. Second, the best time to arrange for life insurance to fund your cryopreservation is when you are young and healthy. Locking in the relatively low life insurance premiums generally available to the under-forty set is reason enough to arrange funding and sign up as soon as possible.

If you can't decide which organization to sign up with, just flip a coin. This may sound like a cavalier way to make such an important life decision, but years of indecision could lead to your legal death before arrangements are made. If you change your mind after you have signed up with one organization, just switch. Nothing says you cannot continue to research your options after you have signed up with one organization or another.

While signing up with a cryonics provider seems like the simple and obvious solution, it is the most important step you can possibly take toward ensuring you are cryopreserved at the time of your legal death.

II. Designate a Guardian

Orville knew his family was not supportive of his decision to be cryopreserved. Indeed, the brother and sister who cared for Orville after he was unable to care for himself admitted in court documents that they "tried to talk [Orville] out of" his plan to be cryopreserved and "emphatically told him they would have nothing to do with his plan."

Since Orville knew that his family did not support his cryonics arrangements, he should have taken steps to prevent them from making decisions if he ever became incapacitated. Instead, when Orville began showing signs of dementia in 2007, his sister easily obtained an appointment as his guardian. Once she was appointed as his guardian, she had complete decision making authority regarding Orville's medical care and treatment.

This could have been prevented. Most states allow you to execute a medical power of attorney to designate who should oversee your medical affairs in the event you become incapacitated. These states also generally allow you to specifically disallow a potential guardian. In addition, you can specify what decisions your guardian is and is not permitted to make and provide specific restrictions. Using a medical power of attorney, a cryonicist could do three important things: (1) select a fellow cryonicist as their medical guardian; (2) prohibit hostile friends and relatives from serving as medical guardians; and (3) restrict an appointed medical guardian to make choices in consideration of your cryonics arrangements and to notify your cryonics provider if you are near death.

Authorized medical power of attorney forms (also known as health care proxy or designation of guardian in the event the need arises) differ by state and country. You may be able to find the appropriate form for your jurisdiction by searching your state government's website or the website of a hospital doing business in your state. At a minimum, most forms contain a space for the designation of a guardian and an alternate. Most forms also require two witnesses and a notary. Your witnesses cannot also be designated as guardians. In the United States, an appropriate form should specifically address the HIPAA privacy laws as they apply to your guardian.

III. Execute a Living Will

A Living Will is a legal document which provides specific direction to health care providers in the event that you are terminally ill. Coupled with the designation of an appropriate guardian, a Living Will can ensure that your cryonics provider will be contacted and any necessary protocols will be followed prior to your legal death. Your Living Will can also dictate your wishes regarding the removal of life support measures under various circumstances. If it is your desire to be removed from life support, it is recommended that you specify that your health care providers should wait to remove life-sustaining treatment until your cryonics provider's support staff is on hand to begin any necessary protocols as soon as possible after your legal death.

Like all other legal documents, a Living Will is a state-specific document. However, in most states the witness and notary requirements are similar to the designation of a guardian. For that reason, it will probably be convenient for you to execute a Living Will at the same time as your medical power of attorney.

IV. Add a "No Contest" Clause to Your Will

Looking back to the unfortunate situation with Orville Richardson, the question remains: If his family was so intent on having him buried, how did Alcor ever discover that Orville's wishes were ignored? The answer is simple, Money. Remember the $70,000 that Orville prepaid to Alcor—his family called requesting a refund.

The unfortunate and sad truth is that many challenges to cryonics arrangements are motivated at least in part by the money at stake. Because cryopreservation is funded in some manner which is usually payable at death, family members often have a desire to access the funds earmarked for cryopreservation. If the cryopreservation does not occur, they reason, the money will go to them. Had Orville ensured that the money could never be available to his brother and sister, perhaps they would have chosen to honor his wishes.

A critical step toward controlling the purse strings of your estate after your death is executing a Last Will and Testament. A Will dictates the disposition of your assets and property and can also reiterate your cryonics-related wishes. Your cryonics paperwork most likely included a document stating that it is your desire to be cryopreserved. For this reason, it is *critical* that your attorney be aware of all of your cryonics paperwork so that you do not unintentionally supersede your cryonics documents with your new Will.

Most states recognize a special Will provision called a "no contest" or "in terrorem" clause. This clause states that if anyone interferes with your Will, they forfeit everything which is granted to them by your Will. While the issue has never been litigated, this provision could easily be drafted to extend to interference with your cryonics arrangements. A creative lawyer may even attempt to draft a provision which provides for an inheritance on a sliding scale based on the amount of time which passes between your legal death and your cryopreservation.

The primary caveat to using a "no contest" clause to financially incentivize your family to follow your cryonics arrangements is that you have to leave them something substantial in your Will in order to make it worthwhile for them to abide by its terms. Leaving a family member very little in your Will makes a "no contest" clause a worthless protection, because they will not mind risking their small inheritance for the chance at the big "payday" that might result if they prevented your cryopreservation. However, assuming you have something to give, a "no contest" clause can be a substantial motivator for an otherwise reluctant family member.

A "no contest" clause is subject to a probable cause exception in many states. The probable cause exception allows a person to collect under your will despite challenging it if they had probable cause to do so. Probable cause is determined by the court and cannot be determined until after a challenge has been made. For this reason, a person challenging a Will despite a "no contest" clause takes a substantial risk of disinheritance. At this time, "no contest" provisions are not enforced in either Florida or Indiana.

V. Change Your Contingent Beneficiary

Most cryonicists fund their cryonics arrangements using a life insurance policy listing their cryonics provider as the beneficiary. However, a problem arises when you list a family member as contingent beneficiary or when you do not list a contingent beneficiary. Contingent beneficiaries collect from the life insurance policy in the event that your cryonics provider cannot perform your cryopreservation or you change your mind and cancel your agreement with your cryonics provider. If no contingent beneficiary is listed and the contingency is triggered, the funds from the policy will pass to your estate and be distributed under your Will or by the laws of intestacy.

Life insurance policy contingencies create an incentive for family members to challenge your cryopreservation if they have hope of collecting the insurance proceeds. Cryonics life insurance policies can be several hundred thousand dollars. That amount of money is enough to sway almost anyone, especially a family member who is skeptical of your arrangements.

It is critical to remove any financial incentive to challenging your cryonics arrangements. For this reason, you should name a contingent beneficiary who is entirely unrelated to you. Your contingent beneficiary will never know that they are your contingent beneficiary unless the contingency is triggered. This contingent beneficiary should be an established charity organization. An established charity organization is the ideal choice because it is very likely that they will still exist if the contingency is ever triggered. Moreover, they will have no reason to believe that they are in a position to benefit from your estate or that your estate even exists.

VI. Tell People About Your Arrangements

All of the legal forms in the world cannot guarantee that you will be cryopreserved if you put them in a drawer and do not tell anyone they are there. Make several copies of every cryonics related document that you sign and give them to trusted individuals. Tell those individuals where the originals are located. At a minimum, keep a copy of your paperwork in at least four places: (1) with your cryonics provider; (2) in a clearly marked folder where you keep other important documents; (3) with the person you have designated as your guardian; (4) at your attorney's office. Keep the forms up to date and ensure that any old forms are destroyed.

In addition to making sure your legal forms are not buried in a desk drawer, let other people know about your plans in general. If the unthinkable happens and your right to cryonics is litigated in the probate court, you should ensure that witnesses are available to testify and say, "he told me that he wanted to be cryopreserved on many occasions." Additionally, telling friends and family about your arrangements ensures that your cryonics provider will be promptly notified in the event of an accident or illness. An additional option is to go the extra mile and make a video of yourself explaining your wishes and desires. This video can provide further evidence of your strong desire to be cryopreserved.

VII. Conclusion

In the end, the Iowa Appellate Court has ordered that Orville Richardson will get his wish to be cryopreserved. However, well over one year has passed since his burial in February 2009. The damage that has occurred in that time is an unthinkable disaster that no cryonicist should endure. This disaster may have been prevented if Orville had taken the proper steps to prevent his siblings from having medical decision making authority, made his last wishes known, and removed all financial incentives to hindering his cryopreservation.

The ultimate outcome of the Orville Richardson legal case is hopeful and the precedent it has set will help future cryonicists. However, the presence of supportive legal precedent will not save you from the ischemic damage which will occur while you wait for a court to rule. Do not become the next cryonics legal battle. If you have already put the time and money into signing up with a cryonics organization, put in a little bit more effort and safeguard your arrangements in as many legal and practical ways as you can. ■

(Editors' Note: Orville Richardson was finally cryopreserved [straight-frozen as a neuro] in August 2010, after embalming followed by 18 months of ground burial. Low-resolution CT scans done at the time showed a surprisingly normal-looking brain, at least to the imaging resolution of ~2-5mm, though this of course says nothing about the brain's ultrastructure. See photo below.)

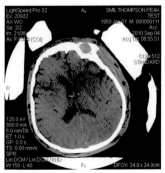

Orville Richardson,
contrast-enhanced brain scan image.

DEBATES WITHIN CRYONICS

But What Will The Neighbors Think? A Discourse On The History And Rationale Of Neurosuspension

By Michael Darwin
Cryonics, October, 1988

You cannot do just one thing.
— Zen proverb

This article expresses my own views and opinions and not necessarily those of Alcor. This article came about as a result of urging by Dr. Mike Perry to respond to an article on neurosuspension by Dr. Paul Segall of the American Cryonics Society, which appeared in the March, 1987 issue of the *ACS Journal*, the relevant portions of which are reproduced below.

From the *American Cryonics Society Journal,* March, 1988

THE NEUROPRESERVATION CONTROVERSY
Owing to the lack of public acceptance of neuropreservation, ACS and Trans Time biomedical scientists are advising the small number of their clients who are opting for this service that at the present time it is a much less secure method of preservation than whole-body freezing. While the public image of whole-body suspension is improving, neuropreservation is widely regarded as both ridiculous and gruesome, despite scientific arguments to the contrary. This unfavorable image and its consequences are very real, regardless of the validity of the supporting evidence.

There are also, however, some good scientific reasons to preserve the whole body rather than just the brain. The most important derives from cloning experiments in amphibians, which suggest the possibility that not every adult cell contains the entire genome, but merely most of it. Early stage embryos have nuclei that can give rise to adult organisms following nuclear transplantation, but transplanted adult nuclei have never allowed development past the early tadpole stage.

Perhaps certain genes are eliminated during maturation in a given cell, and these may be different for each cell type. Although there are arguments to the contrary, until we can clone a human (or at least a vertebrate) from a single cell, or until we can read the entire human genome and compare it to that of a fertilized human egg, the question cannot be entirely resolved.

While it is certainly better to preserve the brain or head rather than nothing, whole-body preservation means more biological information is rescued, and that it will be there when and if needed. Since it has not yet been determined exactly how much information is needed to revive or reconstruct an individual following cryonic suspension, whole-body suspension makes more sense from a strictly scientific point of view.

Coupled with public revulsion at the idea of neuropreservation, this makes whole body preservation even more desirable. Of course, it is more expensive. One way to offset the expense is to obtain a life insurance policy for the additional cost of whole body as compared to neuropreservation. This policy might cost only $10-30 a month, depending on the age and health of the member, and could be abandoned once cryonics established a greater degree of public acceptance, and it is ascertained scientifically either that a whole human could be constructed from a single adult cell, or that the human genome as it exists in a single adult cell is as informationally complete as that in an early-stage human embryo.

If techniques for whole-body reversible cryonic suspension are developed, one could convert to a whole-life insurance policy despite any unfavorable changes in health. Those insured only for neuropreservation could find themselves uninsurable should reversible cryonic suspension become closer during the next ten to fifteen years.

Promoters of neuropreservation contend that it is easier to cool and perfuse just the head rather than the whole body. However, because the circulatory system is designed to deliver a maximum amount of flow to the brain, one can cool the head by both core and surface cooling. Since the attachment of the head to the body does not alter the rate at which the head can be frozen, it makes little difference, using current cryonics techniques, whether or not the head is attached.

— Paul Segall, Ph.D.

Introduction

Cryonics is not just a technical or scientific undertaking completely isolated from social, political, and emotional considerations. In fact, there are no disciplines which are isolated from human considerations. On the other hand, some areas of scientific and technological endeavor touch human values far more intimately than others. Of all human undertakings, cryonics is one of the most sensitive and powerful. It deals with the fundamental and basic values upon which human civilization rests: personal immortality, health, well-being, the quality and quantity of life, and the structure of powerful human institutions such as religion and philosophy. Above all, cryonics deals with the most frightening and unsettling area of human experience: death.

Until recently, the public perception of cryonics was that of preserving one's body (as a unit) for rescue and repair by the presumably more sophisticated medicine of tomorrow. Recently, this perception has been shifted somewhat by the controversy surrounding the suspension of Alcor member Dora Kent. A difficult and alien idea, namely that of having one's body frozen at "death" was perhaps made even more difficult and alien by suspension of just the patient's brain (contained within the head).

The fundamental questions raised by Dr. Segall would seem to be: "Should we carry out neurosuspension?" and, "Is the social cost worth the benefit?"

I will state at the outset that I don't think it is possible to answer those questions in any objective way. We simply don't have sufficient information to make any hard and fast assertions, since the outcome will be determined by enormously complicated social and political processes about which we have little information. However, this is not to say that we cannot discuss the pros and cons in a thorough and thoughtful way so that everyone can draw their own conclusions from the information now available.

Some History and Background

It is ironic that the intellectual seed upon which modern cryonics has been built was a "neurosuspension" story by science fiction writer Neil R. Jones.[1] Robert Ettinger, the father of the cryonics movement, was no doubt significantly influenced by Jones' story *The Jameson Satellite* in which the hero, Dr. Jameson, has his body rocketed into earth orbit after death for perpetual, deep-frozen preservation. After millennia in orbit, Jameson's body is happened upon by a technologically advanced race of immortal beings with robot bodies, known as the Zoromes. The Zoromes remove Jameson's brain from his body, install it in an immortal Zorome body and invite him to join them in their never-ending interstellar adventures. Jameson's terrestrial body is discarded.

It was the publication by Doubleday of Ettinger's *The Prospect Of Immortality* in 1964 that launched the cryonics movement. The scenario for cryonics presented in Ettinger's book is almost exclusively that of preservation of the whole body, although Ettinger does acknowledge the primacy of the brain as the repository for personal identity and does discuss treatment of the brain in isolation in passing.[2] The extent to which Ettinger considered and perhaps discarded the option of neurosuspension when he conceived of cryonics as a practical program is unknown. In any event, the cryonics movement began as a program focused exclusively on preservation of the entire body, not just the brain or head. How and why did neurosuspension evolve as an option—an

---

1   Pohl, Frederik, *The Way the Future Was,* Ballantine Books, New York, 1978. pp. 44-45.
2   Ettinger, R. C. W., *The Prospect of Immortality,* Doubleday, New York, 1964. p. 31.

option which accounts for ten of the sixteen patients now in suspension and for nearly one-third of those signed up for cryonics protection?

The idea of suspending just a patient's brain is an obvious one. All of modern neurophysiology and neurology indicate that the brain is the repository of memory and personality. High spinal cord injuries demonstrate that neurological disconnection of the brain from the body does not destroy either consciousness or identity. The startling head transplant and isolated head perfusion experiments conducted by Dr. Robert J. White at Case Western Reserve University have demonstrated that consciousness, learned tasks, and personality are preserved intact in the isolated head.[3,4] It therefore stands to reason that the brain constitutes the critical repository for memory and identity. Preservation of the brain should thus be sufficient to preserve the individual.

However, the obviousness of this proposition is a long way from a decision to implement it in a practical way. In the early 1970's a handful of cryonicists began to have deep and troubling concerns about the logistic feasibility of cryonics in the absence of broad public acceptance and particularly in the face of public indifference and even hostility. I was one of the people who was most deeply affected by these concerns and I was certainly among the most vocal in expressing them. I was not alone.

My concerns were based on years of first-hand involvement in cryonics from a practical rather than a theoretical standpoint. At the age of 13 I had become involved with the Cryonics Society of New York (CSNY) and I remained involved with CSNY throughout its decline and ultimate disintegration.

All of the CSNY patients were ultimately removed from suspension and disposed of by burial or cremation. This was an extremely demoralizing and frightening experience. When I first became involved in cryonics, I had a great deal of confidence in the solidity and workability of existing organizations. This confidence was based in large measure on an inadequate understanding of the enormous difficulties involved and on an unrealistic appraisal of the size, resources, and competence of the organizations then in existence, on the basis of their literature.[5]

As I grew to understand the magnitude of the task of maintaining patients in suspension over a period of decades or centuries in a world beset by cyclical military and economic catastrophes, I became even more demoralized. Cryonics was a fundamentally new undertaking. Not only was it faced with the basic problems of economic, social, and political instability over a long time course, it must also confront many unknowns of a more mundane nature including potentially catastrophic short-

---

3   White, R. J., et al, "Primate cephalic transplantation: Neurogenic separation, vascular association," *Transplantation Proceedings,* 3, 602-4 (1971).
4   White, R. J., et al, "Cephalic exchange transplantation in the monkey," *Surgery,* 70 135-139 (1971).
5   *Cryonics Reports,* 4, issues 1-12 inclusive, 1969.

term problems resulting from errors in legal, financial, or administrative judgments. Many of these judgments would necessarily be made in a vacuum—without the invaluable resource of past experience to draw upon.

Indeed, the failure of CSNY and the Cryonics Society of California (CSC) were case studies in how not to run cryonics organizations. While the failure modes of each organization were radically different, both suffered from errors in administrative and technical judgment which are obvious only in hindsight. Some of those errors are worth recounting because they were very important in subsequent cryonics efforts which led to creation of the neurosuspension option.

A major error that was not at all obvious at the time was accepting patients for suspension who were already legally dead and for whom the next of kin were pursuing suspension. The relatives of such individuals rarely, if ever, had a full or even adequate understanding of cryonics and were making their decision on the basis of emotional pressures and misinformation, and almost always in the absence of adequate financial resources. Such patients created almost unimaginable problems of every kind and their suspensions accomplished nothing so much as to create bitterness, bankruptcy, and ruined lives.

In the early days of cryonics it was not at all obvious that this would be the case. No one could (or at any rate no one did) foresee that the relatives of these patients would become embittered and hostile when the reality of the situation fell short of their expectations. Lack of sound business sense and the failure of economies of scale to materialize put an enormous burden on early organizations. There was virtually no cash flow and absolutely no political or financial leverage to provide insulation from powerful outside forces.

Care of the patients was difficult—more difficult than anyone had imagined. The early horizontal units which were designed for mobility and ease of handling proved an engineering nightmare requiring extraordinary maintenance and delivering abysmal economy. The second generation vertical MVE units which replaced them were reliable, but very difficult to handle and almost impossible to transport safely or economically. The MVE units also required specialized quarters and handling equipment—a building with high overhead ceilings, appropriate zoning, and a gallows or overhead crane.

The upshot of all of this was that cryonic suspension was a labor-intensive and costly undertaking with a number of unusual and inflexible requirements. In short, it had high start-up costs both in terms of technology and labor.

My awareness of these problems made me realize that in the absence of broad acceptance of cryonics (and the resource base such acceptance represented) very large amounts of money would be required on an individual basis to insure any reasonable chance of long-term survival for a patient in suspension. Additionally, easy transport and low visibility would be impossible for patients in suspension, and over a long time course, hostility and adverse conditions of one sort or another might necessitate many moves. The decline of a civilization (such as the decline of the Spanish and British Empires) can occur within the space of several decades and the outbreak of war would necessitate even more rapid relocation. From my perspective in 1974 such untoward events seemed not at all unlikely over a time span of 100 to 200 years (my personal timescale for possible revival of patients frozen under good conditions at that time). My evaluation of the world in the intervening 14 years has served only to increase my concerns about the likelihood of these potential problems.

Sometime during the summer of 1974 I came to the conclusion that the chance represented by cryonics was simply not worth the tremendous effort demanded. Too many things could go wrong and while the things we knew about and had experienced already seemed bad enough, the problems we hadn't yet experienced and couldn't anticipate were probably much worse. Youthful optimism notwithstanding, I was ready to throw in the towel.

I shared my doubts and fears with a valued colleague. Shared is a misnomer— delivered as a raging statement of frustration and despair probably better sums up the communication. My colleague, being a thoughtful and rational man, made a powerful and simple suggestion. He prefaced it by asking a number of leading questions which caught my interest.

What if there were some way to decrease by orders of magnitude the logistic problems associated with cryonics, while at the same time greatly reducing the cost— perhaps by as much as an order of magnitude? Furthermore, what if it were possible to make cryonics flexible and bring its execution within the realm of "do-ability" by even a single individual? Would I reassess my decision to abandon ship?

His solution to the problems was to cut to the core of what cryonics was really all about—personal survival. And the bare essential for personal survival is the brain. I wish I could say I was immediately persuaded of the rationality of this idea, but the truth is it took me several days to think over the implications and lock onto it. I did not reject it out of hand, but I do not recall enthusiastically embracing it either.

My introduction to neurosuspension took place in Augusta, Georgia. Unbeknownst to both my colleague and myself, others in the cryonics community were arriving at the same conclusion for many of the same reasons nearly 2,500 miles away.

During the summer of 1974 my colleague and I journeyed to Southern California to assess the state of cryonics there. We planned to meet with Robert Nelson, President of CSC, and tour CSC's facilities. We also planned to meet with Fred and Linda Chamberlain of the Alcor Foundation and Manrise Corporation.

The meeting with Nelson did not go well—he was evasive and deceitful and we were not allowed to tour CSC's storage facilities. Evidence I gathered on that trip strongly suggested that CSC had already succumbed to the problems that plagued CSNY and that our solution to the logistic and financial nightmares had arrived too late to benefit any CSC patients.

The meeting with the Chamberlains went far better. We had corresponded with them at length and thus were somewhat prepared for what we found: two energetic and highly competent people who had virtually single-handedly revolutionized cryonics by developing the first perfusion system, the first training and procedural manual, and the first real scientific approach to perfusate design.

Our meeting with the Chamberlains was at their home in the foothills of the San Gabriel mountains, north of L.A. The house was secluded and tucked away amidst dense foliage and the grounds were patrolled by two well-trained German Shepherds. During the course of our outdoor meal we began to discuss the problems associated with cryonics in earnest. Gingerly we broached the issue of neurosuspension. This was the first time we had discussed this idea with anyone else. What would the response be? Fred and Linda seemed to take the idea in stride. They evinced no reaction other than to discuss the pros and cons calmly and add to a number of points we made. As we finished our meal, Fred and Linda looked at each other knowingly and then Fred said that he had something he wanted to show us before the sun went down. We were led to a small storage shed at the back of the property. Inside was the prototype of their first perfusion machine (already obsolete) and a number of other odds and ends used in developing the suspension capability they had put together.

Immediately inside the door and to our left were two nearly waist-high cardboard boxes, one of which Fred proceeded to open. Deftly he extracted an LR-40 cryogenic dewar. This, he explained, was the storage unit his terminally ill father was going to be placed in. Both Fred and Linda eyed us expectantly. It was very clear at that moment that not only had they considered the problems in the same light we had—and arrived at the same conclusion—they had every intention of acting on that conclusion.

I cannot speak for my colleague, but I was both dumbfounded and excited. Here was the answer to so many problems. Here was a workable way to practice cryonics.

For Fred and Linda there was little choice but to pursue the neurosuspension option for Fred's father. The financial resources were simply not there to allow for whole body suspension. If Fred Jr. (Fred's father) was to have any chance at making it into the future, this was going to be it.

Two years later, in July of 1976, Fred Jr. became the first cryonics patient to be placed into neurosuspension.[6]

The Chamberlains' decision to pursue neurosuspenson for Fred Jr. and for themselves was based not only on the logistic considerations I have outlined above

---

6   *Alcor News,* 1. August, 1976.

but also on financial and cryobiological considerations. Treatment of the patient's brain (head) in isolation meant an opportunity to better control the introduction of cryoprotective agent (CPA), to minimize exposure time (and thus toxicity) to the CPA, and to achieve better control of cooling (again with the consequence of less CPA toxicity and less damage due to prolonged exposure to high subzero temperatures while the whole body is cooled).

Treatment of just the patient's brain also meant that storage and long-term care could be pursued without high overhead and exorbitant start-up costs. There would be no delay in going to liquid nitrogen storage while a costly custom whole-body dewar was ordered and no need to pursue storage in a specialized structure. There was economy and flexibility of an unprecedented degree.

Objections and Answers

The above is, I think, a fairly reasonable evaluation of how and why neurosuspension came to be. And yet, despite the many advantages cited above, neurosuspension has not become the exclusive or even the dominant method of suspension in the cryonics community as a whole. Why is this? In the following pages I will attempt to answer that question by critically evaluating many of the objections to neurosuspension that have been made since the procedure was first implemented in 1976.

The most frequently cited objection to neuropreservation is aesthetic. People associate decapitation with death and generally regard invasive or dismembering procedures as repugnant.

This is a largely irrational objection. It does, however, have strong roots in past human experience. Traditionally, decapitation or removal of the brain has been associated with the end of life rather than its beginning. Additionally, human beings, as they are currently configured have a very limited capacity for self-repair. Mutilating or amputating injuries in higher vertebrates are not reversible. There is thus strong social pressure present to avoid such injuries. In addition to being catastrophic when they do occur, they are also uncommon.

Such injuries are catastrophic because they cause profound functional losses and these losses translate into loss of sense of self. If a man can no longer work due to a dismembering injury, his social self is profoundly injured as well as his somatic self.

An answer to this objection is relatively easy. Clearly any technology capable of reversing extensive cryoinjury (as currently experienced by suspension patients) by making molecular-level repairs should be able to rebuild or regenerate any dismembering injury, including replacement of the entire body. As a minimum, transplantation of the patient's brain into an anencephalic clone should be possible. Much recent work supports the ability of the spinal cord to be regenerated, and clinical treatments for transecting spinal injuries are acknowledged by many experts to be no more than a decade or at most two decades away.

Closely related to, and perhaps even an extension of the aesthetic objection is the social objection. In short, what will other people think and what impact will this have on cryonics and cryonicists?

Will society tend to view neuropatients as hunks of tissue rather than as people? Will the seemingly gruesome or outlandish nature of neurosuspension polarize people against cryonics who would not have been hostile otherwise? This is a difficult question to answer. On the surface the answer would seem to be: "Yes." Most people find the notion of storing isolated brains, or worse still, isolated heads, gruesome. And yet, there was and is no widespread, grass-roots reaction against Alcor or any neurosuspension, including that of Dora Kent. Despite all the recent publicity, much of it luridly orchestrated by the local press, there has been not one single piece of hate mail received by Alcor. Early on in the media circus, Chief Deputy Coroner Dan Cupido said the Riverside Coroner's office had received exactly zero complaints or calls from concerned citizens.[7]

The mood in the national media seemed to be one of humorous japing. Neurosuspension was simply too outrageous to be taken seriously. That may well be an unexpected bonanza. One thing is very clear: there was no widespread public outrage or outcry.

Where the courts and the educated person or professional is concerned, the case seems clearer. Alcor's February 1st victory in the Dora Kent case[8] is proof that competent, thoughtful people can and will respect neuropatients as more than just specimens. The declarations of the scientists who came forward to support Alcor also attest to this.

A more subjective but perhaps more valid assessment is the reaction of the local community to Alcor staffers when they make purchases using Alcor checks or are otherwise recognized. In every case people have been supportive, have recognized the Coroner's actions as a witch-hunt, and have often remarked to the effect "Why don't those people just leave you alone. . . ?"

Paradoxically, neurosuspension in the form of the Kent case may have acted to increase Alcor's overall level of credibility with the people that count. Since the publicity surrounding Dora Kent's suspension and subsequent disappearance, a number of politically powerful and intellectually influential people have become associated with Alcor. This has been in no small measure because Alcor had put the brass tacks aspects of patient care ahead of harder-to-quantify social considerations.

What the long run will hold is impossible to know at this point. But two things are clear: First, if Dora Kent had been a whole-body patient she would have been

---

7   Cupido, D., Personal communication.
8   Babwin, D. "Thawing of Heads Blocked," *Riverside Press-Enterprise*, February 2, 1988. p. B-1.

autopsied long ago. Second, due to economic considerations most cryonics patients today (not just those at Alcor) could not have been placed or maintained in suspension if it had not been for the neurosuspension option.

The first and simplest of the scientific/technical objections to neurosuspension raised by Dr. Segall is that "since the attachment of the head to the body does not alter the rate at which the head can be frozen, it makes little difference, using current cryonics techniques, whether or not the head is attached."

This statement is true only if a decision is made to disregard the proper cooling of the patient's body during descent to -79°C. Unless the patient is allowed to freeze uniformly, he or she will experience shell freezing. Shell freezing occurs when the outside of the patient freezes solidly before the interior of the patient freezes. Subsequent freezing and expansion of the interior water deforms the frozen, rigid outer shell of material, causing it to crack and promoting intracellular freezing.

The mass and diameter of the head allow it to be cooled far faster than the mass of the patient's body, and to avoid shell freezing careful control between surface and core temperatures is required. A decision has to be made as to whether or not this will be between oral and brain surface temperatures or between rectal and abdominal surface temperatures. Dr. Segall fails to make this clear in his article.

Dr. Segall also leaves unaddressed the issue of the longer perfusion times required to introduce (and presumably remove) cryoprotective agent (CPA) in whole body patients. As Dr. Perry's paper elsewhere in this issue indicates, whole body patients will experience roughly a 60% longer exposure of the brain to toxic CPA because of the "high flow" nature of cerebral circulation as compared to the remainder of the body.[9] Additionally, the logistics of handling whole body patients and the thermal inertia they represent to the cooling bath mean that they will experience even longer periods of relatively high temperature exposure to CPA than their neurosuspension contemporaries.

Another common technical objection to neurosuspension also voiced by Dr. Segall is that not all of the information necessary to reconstitute the individual is present in the brain or head.

This objection can take any of a number of forms. The most common and perhaps the most valid is that the body is somehow possibly a repository of critical but currently unappreciated identity information. There are two broad categories of the argument. The first and the simplest is the "discarded genome" argument which states simply that not all of the genetic information needed to reconstitute the individual is present in somatic or body cells.

In other words, some of the genes involved in development and differentiation

---

9   Perry, R. M., "Mathematical analysis of recirculating perfusion systems, with application to cryonic suspension." *Cryonics* 9, (Oct, 1988). A revised version is available in this book.

are discarded or lost in body cells and are present only in embryonic tissue or sex cells (some nematodes are known to discard up to 70% of their genome in this way[10]). This argument is fairly easy to dispose of. The only "evidence" that adult mammalian somatic cells don't have the full genetic complement is that efforts to clone mammals and other vertebrates from adult body cells have so far failed. Of course, this does not necessarily mean that the information is not there—it may be simply be turned off or otherwise made inaccessible.

By contrast, there is a considerable body of evidence that human (and other vertebrate) somatic cells are totipotent (i.e., contain the organism's entire genetic blueprint). Unlike the previously mentioned nematodes who discard most of the genome in body cells, adult human cells show the same number of chromosomes as do embryonic cells or fertilized ova and a number of studies have shown relative constancy of DNA content in a wide range of somatic and embryonic cells.[11,12] Several decades of extensive genetic manipulation of adult somatic cells have also not disclosed any noticeable absence of information. Additionally, the results of Gurdon with the cloning of frogs also suggest strongly that most somatic cells are totipotent.[13] The view that adult somatic cells contain all of the genetic information necessary to reconstitute the individual has thus become widely and generally accepted.[14]

Additionally, certain disease states such as cancer often lead to the expression of fetal genes in somatic tissues. Colon cancers will often produce fetal proteins, and fetal hemoglobins are produced in other types of malignancies similarly unrelated to the blood producing tissues. These abnormalities suggest that the genome is conserved in adult cells, but is not normally expressed. In other words, the information is there but, like a book on a shelf in a library, is not currently in use.

But even if there were wholesale loss or deletion of genetic information from brain or other body cells, is this a serious obstacle to resuscitation of neurosuspension patients? The answer is a resounding "No!" The problem could be addressed in any of a number ways. The simplest would be to take samples of various organs and tissues (including reproductive organs if they are available) and preserve them with the patient. This is done almost routinely by Alcor when carrying out neurosuspensions[15]).

The second solution is to get such "generic" genetic information from other people.

10   Tyler, A., "Gametogenesis, Fertilization, and Parthenogenesis." *In Analysis of Development* (V. H. Willier, P. A. Weiss, and V. Hamburger, eds.), W. B. Saunders, Philadelphia, 1955. pp. 170-212.
11   Mirsky, A. E., and Ris, H., "The deoxyribonucleic acid of cells and its evolutionary significance," *J. Gen. Physiol.,* 34, 451-462 (1951).
12   Swift, H., "Quantitative aspects of nuclear proteins," Internat. *Rev. Cytol.*, 2, 1-76 (1953).
13   Gurdon, J. B., "The cytoplasmic control of gene activity," *Endeavor*, 25, 95-99 (1966).
14   Tyler, A., and Tyler, B. S., "Informational molecules and differentiation," In *Cell Differentiation* (O. A. Schjeide, and J. de Vellis, eds.), Van Nostrand Rheinhold Co., New York, 1970. p. 97.
15   Darwin, M. G., Leaf, J. D., and Hixon, H., "Case report: the neuropreservation of Alcor patient A-1068." *Cryonics* 7, 15-28 (1986).

Clearly that part of the genome necessary to carry out day-to-day operation of the brain has to be in the patient's brain cells. Recent experiments with various nerve growth factors have also demonstrated that aged, adult nervous tissue can be induced to undergo cell division, sprouting, and remodeling with stimulation by relatively simple chemicals.[16] This indicates that genes coding for growth, development, and differentiation of brain cells are also present in adult neurons—even aged adult neurons.

If other critical body genes are missing, copies can be obtained from other people. Indeed, this may even be desirable in many instances. I, for one, would like a number of new genes including ones for stronger muscles, nondefective veins, a much better looking face, improved cholesterol metabolism and so on. In fact, I hope for a much better body all around. The point is that much of the genetic information which makes us up is almost certainly not essential to conserving our identity. It is not identity-critical. Much of our genome is probably not only not essential to survival, but contrasurvival.

These objections and their answers bring us to the second class of "loss of identity-critical information" objection. That objection can best be best summed up as the Stradivarius Objection (SO for short). SO enthusiasts believe that the body may be like a Stradivarius violin. Very easy to understand and reproduce in outline, but possessed of subtle and identity-critical properties which are not yet appreciated.

In this worldview bodies are like violins played by masters (or yokels for that matter). They are not just their genome, rather they are the complex interaction of genome with environment and brain with body with environment. . . . In other words, a person's peripheral nervous system, immune system, heart, lungs, and so on all interact with each other in complex ways to produce the person.

A simple example of this would be someone with a hyperactive thyroid. Such a person will be temperamentally different than someone without a hyperactive thyroid. Similarly, someone with exceptionally fine peripheral nervous connections may have certain skills and abilities that others lack. SO people believe that such subtle and possibly random connections and interactions all go to shape or make up the essence of the person. Many of the connections and positions of cells in the body which determine the character or function of the brain may thus be lost if the body is discarded. For instance, it is known that the interconnection of nerve cells in the spinal cord and brain are not determined completely by genetics but by other, "random" influences. The most visible evidence of the randomness of some of our features is that fingerprints are not identical in identical twins. Similarly, sexual orientation, aggressiveness, and so on are also sometimes at variance in animals or people with exactly the same genetic make-up.

---

16   Maier, F., "A second chance at life," *Newsweek*, September 12, 1988. pp. 52-61.

SO advocates argue that there may be subtle, as yet unappreciated identity-critical information present in the body. They view the organism as a unit, not as any one of its parts.

The SO objection is a more difficult one to answer and in fact can probably not be answered with 100% confidence given the state of today's knowledge and experience. Am I to any significant degree my kidneys or my little finger?

Despite the fact that no one has undergone a head transplant or been fitted with a regrown body, the questions raised by the Stradivarius Objection proponents are not totally unanswerable. As usual, a host of modern pathologies and medical treatments provides some indirect, but very powerful and persuasive insight.

People with high spinal cord injuries do not suddenly cease to be themselves or experience changes in their personalities unrelated to the disability inflicted by such a currently irreversible medical catastrophe. Despite the fact that their brain is disconnected from their central nervous system, such people are obviously still the same people. Multiple organ transplant recipients also demonstrate continuity of memory, personality, and identity. Such patients do not take on the character or personality of the donor of the tissue. While they often experience profound improvement in well-being, they do not cease to be who they were. Indeed, it can be argued that such changes enhance their personhood and allow them to be more of who they are.[17]

Less conclusive are the results of primate head transplants, such as the work conducted by Dr. Robert White of Case Western Reserve University in Cleveland, Ohio. I have spoken with Dr. White about the results of his monkey head transplants and he has told me that not only do the animals regain consciousness but their ability to repeat learned information (such as sound-eyeblink responses) is intact.[18] Obviously, monkeys are not people and they cannot verbalize any more subtle emotional or cognitive problems.

In short, nothing in contemporary medical experience suggests that replacement of the body with a healthy, functioning duplicate or even with another "generic" human body will have any catastrophic impact on personal identity. But there is a deeper point here. It is the brain that senses and responds to the body. It is the brain that holds memories of what was and what is. And it is the brain that decides. If we awake with a body that is not the Stradivarius we remember, we will be able to fine tune and to make changes. Indeed, for many of us the nightmare is not that we will waken without the body we had, but rather that we will waken with it. We want more and will be disappointed (but grateful) if what we have now is all we get.

Yet another objection is that neuropatients may come back without bodies at all or otherwise with substandard hardware.

---

17 Ibid.
18 White, R. J., Personal Communication.

This objection can be answered easily and straightforwardly: If tomorrow's medicine cannot regrow or replace the body, revival won't be possible in the first place. Existing preservation techniques cause serious damage which will require nearly complete control over life at the molecular level to repair. Any technology capable of repairing and rebuilding individually damaged brain cells will be able to clone or regrow a new body around the existing (repaired) brain. Concerns about the inability to regrow bodies are like concerns about being unable to build a bottle rocket if you can build a Saturn Five. As a worst case, new bodies could be produced the old-fashioned way, by fusion of gametes and production of an anencephalic infant body which could then be supported until it had matured to a sufficient degree. (The brain is immunologically privileged, so rejection would not even have to be solved to overcome this problem.)

A variant of the previous objection is that it may not be possible to reconnect spinal cords.

A variety of lower vertebrates such as the salamander, A. Punctatum, can reconnect severed spinal cords[19] and there is a growing body of evidence that higher mammals can do the same.[20] Limited experimental regeneration of the spinal cord is already a research reality. Even mainstream popular science magazines such as *Discover* are beginning to run review articles summarizing recent progress in this field.[21] Today's whole-body suspension patients experience complete, multiple severance of the spinal cord and brain due to cooling-induced differential contraction and the resultant fracturing. Ice formation in the brain may also occasionally sever long processes. These injuries must be reversible by any technology that seeks to revive today's patients. A corollary of such a capability is the ability to repair severed spinal cords.

Finally, there is the delayed revival scenario.

This scenario holds that the technology required to revive some (if not all) suspension patients will be equal to reviving whole body patients first since "all of them is already there." In other words, it is easier to repair than to replace. This argument has both strengths and weaknesses. First, let's look at the strengths. For a patient who is young, suffering from a "simple" disease like leukemia or muscular dystrophy, and who is suspended using only slightly damaging techniques, revival might occur decades or even a century or so sooner than if he went the neurosuspension route.

This argument may very well be valid. For this reason both Alcor and I recommend that people provide for the likelihood of improved suspension techniques and suspension while comparatively young. Unfortunately, such a scenario does not

19   Pietsch, P., and Schneider, C. W., "Brain transplantation in salamanders: an approach to memory transfer," *Brain Research,* 14, 707-715 (1969).

20   Marx, J. L., "Regeneration in the central nervous system," *Science*, 209, 378-380 (1980).

21   Kluger, J., "The Miami project," *Discover*, September, 1988. pp.60-70.

describe the average person entering suspension. Current suspension techniques are damaging, and the vast majority of people who need suspension are old and suffering from multiple organ system failure. To act as if this were not the case now would seem very foolish. It makes sense to prepare for the worst (and most likely) scenario and hold the best (and currently least likely scenario) as a contingency to be exercised when it is appropriate to do so.

But for those suspended now or in the foreseeable future, a case could be made that neuropatients will be revived first because it will be much more difficult to "repair" than "replace." Many people object to regeneration of the body because it will be made up of different material. Repair thus implies that the original molecules are retained, the original "stuff" which makes the person up. What will happen in the case of an elderly person in need of enormous structural overhaul? Having to deal with complicated repairs laden with philosophical issues may greatly delay revival! Certainly no one today tries to repair worn out and broken parts in either complicated or simple equipment—they are replaced because it is cost-effective and faster by far to do so.

Conclusion

The foregoing objections to neurosuspension are all that I have commonly heard. Despite the prevalence of whole-body suspension members in the cryonics movement as a whole (2/3 as a best guess) there has, to my knowledge, never been any thorough argument for the rational basis of the procedure. The many challenges offered by advocates of neurosuspension over the years have gone unanswered.

Two of the three existing cryonics organizations have dealt with the issue by simply not offering neurosuspension and restricting its discussion.

Where does all of this leave us? Clearly the Dora Kent case demonstrated that the Judiciary will take the issue of a frozen patient's rights seriously—even if the frozen patient happens to be an isolated head. Nowhere in all the media coverage was Dora Kent ever reduced to the status of a tissue specimen. Nor were the reporters, many of whom were not the brightest or most reflective of creatures, unable to grasp the essence of what we were doing. Most surprisingly, the reporters failed to raise the host of so-called "insurmountable objections" they were expected to raise. It was a "given" that if science could thaw out and rejuvenate an 83-year-old lady's diseased and damaged brain, it could find or clone a body to put it in. Clearly, the absence of Dora Kent's body hasn't hurt her brain. Not with the media, not with the courts, and not with the scientists who stepped forward to support Dora Kent and Alcor.

The recent positive reaction of media to the announcement by Dr. Timothy Leary of his plans for neurosuspension[22,23,24] also attest to the fact that neurosuspension presents no overwhelming public relations obstacles.

Finally, what the whole issue of neuro vs. whole body reduces to is a decision about what's important. Cryonic suspension has been likened to escaping from a burning building. This analogy is a correct one, with an added condition being that the escape is being made from a fourth-story window using a rope of knotted towels and bedsheets. In such a situation a decision has to be made about what's important to save. The antique bedroom furniture, the grand piano, even the family jewels must all be weighed against the urgency of the situation. Obviously, what is important to save in such a crisis is yourself. Everything that we know about biology and medicine indicates that the human brain is the human being. When an individual decides to take more than that (particularly in light of the uncertain legal, financial and political status of cryonics today) they are taking a potentially very large added risk. Each individual must weigh this risk and decide. For some of us it has been an easy decision.

Alcor and I started down the neurosuspension road because it was the rational and moral thing to do. It offered us an opportunity to save the lives of those we loved when we would otherwise have been unable to do so. If history later demonstrates that it was the wrong thing to do from a "political" or "greater good" standpoint, I hope we are not judged too harshly. For the fact is, it was really the only thing we could have done and still remain human.

It's strange how things work out. Who would have ever dreamed that cutting off your mother's head could be the ultimate act of caring love and the best chance of saving her life?

It is a strange, strange world. ■

---

22   Fulcher, Robb, "1960's Guru turns on to frozen head idea," *Riverside Press-Enterprise*, September 16, 1988.

23   Saavedra, Tony, "Timothy not Leary on cryonics: '60s drug guru wants head frozen at Riverside lab," *San Bernardino Sun*, September 15, 1988.

24   Martinez, Marilyn, "Acid test for a cool head: Forward thinking Timothy Leary will have brain frozen after his death," *Los Angeles Herald Examiner,* September 16, 1988.

THE NEUROCRYOPRESERVATION OPTION: HEAD FIRST INTO THE FUTURE

BY STEPHEN W. BRIDGE

Cryonics, 3rd Quarter, 1995

At the conclusion of most tours here at Alcor, I end up in the Patient Care Bay with an awestruck visitor staring at the 9-foot tall Bigfoot dewars. They really are an inspiring sight—both a non-final resting place for some of the smartest people on the planet and an audacious symbol of what might be the most optimistic idea in human history. Many of these visitors come to Alcor with little knowledge of cryonics, or even of life extension, aging reversal, nanotechnology, or any of the other wonders we envision. By the time we get to the big climax of the tour, their minds are spinning. Then they ask, "Wait a minute, I thought there were twenty-nine patients. But you said there are only eleven in these big cylinders. Where are the others?"

I then point at the two huge concrete vaults on the opposite wall. "Well, you see, 18 of our patients chose to have only their heads frozen. We call this neurocryopreservation."

The most common reaction is a stunned pause with eyes growing to the size of saucers. For them, the entire building has just melted into surreality, like Salvador Dali's clocks, sculpted in ice. A few people laugh in surprise or nervousness. A small number look queasy or disgusted. And occasionally, if I have done my job well and set up the visitor with descriptions of the repairs that will be possible in the future, the visitor will say, "Oh, that makes sense. You can just grow a new body for the brain."

Our readers' reactions are probably very similar. Some of you may be reading an issue of *Cryonics* for the first time; you may be reading in detail about cryonics itself for the first time. But even for people who have been involved in cryonics for many years, the issue of "how much should you freeze" can be disconcerting. It certainly took me a couple of years before I could throw off my instinctive reactions and appreciate the idea that the brain is the most important part (and perhaps the only necessary part) to preserve.

The most basic step in understanding neurocryopreservation is one on which we can all agree: our memories, personalities, and most of the other critical parts of our identities are in our brains. People can have heart and lung transplants and still be the "same person." Even someone paralyzed from the neck down thinks of himself as having the same identity. On the other hand, someone else who has lost her memory may look like the same person, and we may even use the same name for her; but clearly her identity is missing.

The primary keys are our own unique experiences, which create in us memories different from anyone else's. Each individual in a set of identical twins has the same genetic makeup and similar birth environment; but from birth on they are separate beings which experience life and acquire memories from their own unique perspectives.

There is no such thing as a "brain transplant;" a brain transferred into a new body would be a "body transplant." We are our brains.

This same understanding means that freezing the body of a patient whose brain had been removed and destroyed, or destroyed within the skull by disease or injury, would not save the identity of that person. With only the physical information in the rest of the body available, we could possibly use the DNA and chemical information to create a clone (an identical twin) with, in effect, total amnesia; but we couldn't reproduce the original memories and identity. We might be able to recreate many of those memories from the writings of that person and from memories of experiences which might be shared with family and friends; but that would be more a new creation than a "re-creation."

So, are we planning to revive neurocryopreservation patients as "heads on a plate," with tubing and wires sticking out? No, of course, not. Neurocryopreservation patients will be revived with a full body, young and healthy, just like the whole body patients. Actually, I used to say that no one would want to be "just a head;" but the variety of human existence is such that almost certainly someone will eventually think that a bodiless existence sounds deeply fulfilling. Not me, thanks.

"Young and healthy"—think about that. Many of Alcor's whole body patients were age 65 or older when they were placed into cryopreservation. They had cancer, heart disease, and considerable problems from basic aging. There is no point in reviving people and curing their cancer but not curing their aging. I don't want to be both near-immortal and painfully aged anymore than I want to be a head-on-a-plate. So, if cryonics works at all, aging will be reversed.

Sound difficult? Perhaps, but no more difficult than the basic concept of cryonics repair itself. If a technology can be developed to repair the injuries added to patients by our imperfect freezing processes, it will most likely have to work by making at least some repairs cell-by-cell. Aging is not magical; it involves misarrangement of molecules, just like everything else that can go wrong with us. If we can repair cancer and heart disease in the cells of these frozen patients, we can surely learn to make all their cells healthy again. And healthy equals young, for all practical purposes.

It may turn out that growing new bodies for whole-body patients is even simpler than repairing them cell by cell. Look at what our bodies can do already. We can all grow skin over a cut. Our bodies can recover from the massive trauma of heart bypass surgery. Young children can often regrow a fingertip severed in a car door. The repairs possible in the future will be more extensive, because the field of medicine is putting a tremendous emphasis on accomplishing them. For instance, within 25 years, spinal injuries may not be paralyzing or fatal. Researchers are making steady progress in regrowing the connections in crushed or severed spinal cords.

Our understanding of how cells operate and grow is expanding rapidly. Someday we will learn why the child can regrow that fingertip and use that knowledge to regrow entire missing limbs. At that point, we won't need organ transplants from deceased donors—we will simply have new copies of our own hearts or livers grown for us, with genetic flaws eliminated. Eventually physicians may develop such fine control that they can spot the damage early on and renovate the injured organs from the inside out, with no replacement necessary.

We all grew a body once. One tiny cell's molecular machinery and DNA instructions combined the chemicals available (supplied at first by the mother's womb and later by the grocery store) and eventually assembled them into us big people. These instructions are not lost when we become adults; the DNA is still there. Considering this everyday miracle, growing a new, improved copy of your body for your brain (i.e., you) to occupy seems almost easy.

So if the final outcome will be the same, what are the advantages and disadvantages of neurocryopreservation vs. whole body cryopreservation?

Let's start with the easy one: cost. Alcor requires a minimum cryopreservation funding donation of $120,000 for whole body cryopreservation and only $50,000 for neurocryopreservation. (Each option carries a $10,000 surcharge for members outside the United States.) That's a pretty large difference for most people. Even if you are funding your cryopreservation with life insurance, the premiums are obviously higher for the larger policy.

Why the difference in cost? The upfront expenses of both types of suspensions are similar. Even in a neurocryopreservation we need the complete circulatory system so we may perfuse the patient's brain with chemicals to protect the cells from cooling and freezing damage. The head and the body are not separated until after the cryoprotective perfusion has been completed. We do save some expense on a neurocryopreservation by clamping off the circulation to the lower body, so we require less total solution. The real difference is in storage costs. All of the patients are stored in liquid nitrogen at -320 F. No matter how well insulated, liquid nitrogen is constantly evaporating and returning to the air. We have to add more nitrogen to the dewars each week. Alcor has to pay a local supplier for this liquid. One of our steel Bigfoot dewars boils off about 12-15 liters of nitrogen per day, whether it contains one whole body patient or the maximum of four. Each neurocryopreservation dewar (inside a concrete vault) holds nine patients and loses nitrogen at only half the rate of the whole-body units. This means the nitrogen cost per neuropatient is only about one-ninth of the cost per whole-body patient.

There are many other factors in the storage costs that are more evenly divided between neuro and whole-body patients, so the total difference is not 1/9; but it is still large. To ensure enough principal in the Patient Care Fund so that the earnings can cover expenses, we invest $70,000 (at least) of the cryopreservation funding for whole body patients. We only have to invest about $17,000 to achieve the same result for neuropatients.

Neuropatients are also easier to transport in an emergency. The Bigfoot units are about nine feet tall, weigh almost 2 1/2 tons, and take several people to move. However, we can quickly move the neuropatients to small, individual dewars that can be placed in the back of a van or pickup truck and handled easily by two people. You might not at first think of that as an advantage, since taking care of the patients is a rather passive activity. However, we were certainly glad that Dora Kent was a neuropatient in 1988 when the Riverside Coroner wanted to autopsy her already frozen head. She was out of the building when the Coroner's deputies arrived. (Alcor later obtained an injunction against the Coroner to protect Mrs. Kent and to prevent future attempts to seize patients.) You can imagine your own paranoid scenarios about possible legal problems or natural disasters in the future when the neuropatients might have a transport advantage (except it's not "paranoid" on the days when they really are out to get you).

There may be at least one repair advantage to having a complete body to work with. Certainly a whole body patient takes more total information along into the future, although it is still hard to say how significant the added information is. For some people, the pattern of nerve growth development in the body may be very important to their identity—for a dancer or musician, for instance. On the other hand, enough of that information may be encoded in brain development that the same result can be achieved either way. We don't know yet; so we can't say for sure if you are risking anything by leaving your body behind.

Neurocryopreservation may convey a significant upfront biological advantage, however. If the cryopreservation team can concentrate on just the brain, and not worry about the best cryopreservation methods for the liver, muscles, and intestines, more sophisticated techniques may eventually be developed that result in a higher level of brain preservation. Certainly, a tight focus on the brain today results in shorter perfusion times; and once the freezing process begins, the smaller package of the head can be more rapidly cooled to temperatures where the biological and chemical activity are halted.

One important consideration for cryonicists is which method will result in less time in cryopreservation. Cryopreservation patients can no longer make their own decisions. Their vulnerability means that time in cryopreservation is time at risk. But I can see nothing credible which convinces me that one method will result in resuscitation sooner than the other. In fact, my personal guess is that the technology to repair a body cell by cell and the technology to grow a new body will occur at about the same time and involve nearly the same processes. Besides, in both cases the most important limiting factor will be the same and will be the hardest task by far: the brain must be restored to proper function and consciousness.

Finally, there are the possible social disadvantages of having only your head frozen. No, I don't mean that telling people of the future you were once a neuropatient will get you fewer dates. "I was always a head of my time" will still be a good way to start a conversation. The problems may occur with your less imaginative friends and relatives today. Let's face it: no matter how logical I make neurocryopreservation sound and how many advantages it may have, we've all seen too many movies about the French Revolution and other kinds of sharp-edged activities which made it pretty clear that a head without a body had no future at all. The concept of cryonics is hard enough to explain and sell to most people on its own, even without explaining how the missing bodies will be replaced.

So you have to decide what's important to you. If you can afford whole body cryopreservation, and you feel it is either a truly better option, and you just can't deal with the alternative—or you can't deal with telling people about the alternative, then your choice is easy. However, if you cannot afford $120,000 in cash or life insurance, then you have to start working on that old logic circuit in your brain. Start talking with your family and friends about cryonics and cell repair right away so they get used to the basic concept. Then when you spring frozen heads on them later, they may not see it as such a strange idea.

Either way, you cannot totally avoid the idea of neurocryopreservation. You see, we at Alcor long ago decided that no matter which method was truly the best, burial was infinitely worse than either. So we have this important clause in our Cryonic Cryopreservation Agreement—"Emergency Conversion to Neurocryopreservation." Basically, this says that if the economy totally collapses or the legal climate turns against cryonics or some other calamity occurs so that we can only save or afford to maintain the neuropatients—then everyone will become a neuropatient. All Alcor cryopreservation members have to agree to this in their Cryopreservation Agreements. We're adamant about maintaining whole body patients in whole body cryopreservation and we'll do everything we can to meet that obligation. But if the choice is between burial/cremation or switching everyone to head-only, there is no doubt in our mind what we will do. We haven't spent all of these years protecting our patients just to surrender when the going gets tough.

So how do you choose which kind of cryopreservation you want now, and how do

The two questions that everyone wants answered but that they really don't want to ask:

1. *So, umm, how do you, uhh, you know ... remove the head?*

Actually, we think of it as removing the body. And you already know the answer. Since evolution and genetic technology have failed to come up with neck zippers, pop tops, or screw-off heads, we have to use a scalpel and a surgical saw, just as a surgeon would use for amputating a leg. No way around it.

2. *What do you feel like when you do that?*

Perhaps the most important thing that all medical and emergency workers must learn is that one often has to do unpleasant procedures to save someone's life. A surgeon does not enjoy removing a child's leg which has been mangled in an accident; but the surgeon knows his level of technology is not good enough to save the leg—only to save the life. To do nothing would certainly condemn the child to death. So the surgeon does what he has to do and knows it is the only choice he has.

It is not much harder emotionally to perform a neurocryopreservation than a whole body suspension. We don't know if cryonics will work in general or if it will work for the particular acquaintance, friend, or relative we are trying to save today. But like the emergency workers and the surgeon, we know that not to act at all means sure failure. We do the best we can for our patients, even if that rescue work requires that we perform emotionally difficult tasks like removing their bodies. We do this because we care about them and want to see them alive and healthy again someday. And we do it because we want that same attitude to be present if our own turn for suspension should come.

you keep your future options open? You must compare your definition of "ideal" with what you can afford. One of the biggest unknowns in the future is how much the true cost of cryonics will be as it becomes more popular. Some things will grow more expensive, some probably less. But the strength and continuation of your cryonics organization will be one of the most critical factors, and possibly the true key, as to whether or not you stay in cryopreservation. Doing the minimum possible as a member is not a survival characteristic.

I recommend you consider the solution I have chosen myself. At least for the next ten years, in these early days of cryonics, if you can afford $120,000 in insurance or other funds, then plan for that amount but choose neurocryopreservation. If it happens that you need to be suspended in the next decade, instead of spending money on keeping all of that extra mass frozen, let those extra funds go toward research, marketing, legal funds, and otherwise making sure your organization can thrive. If you're still kicking up your heels in ten years, and Alcor is so rich and powerful that your measly extra thousands won't make a bit of difference, then you can reconsider. If it won't harm your organization, you could switch your choice to whole body and take the extra information along. If you want whole body cryopreservation today, I recommend funding it at a level of $200,000, for the same reasons. For insurance, the difference in premiums won't be that much; and it could make all the difference in the world to your cryonics group—which could mean all the time in the world to you. ■

THE CASE FOR WHOLE BODY CRYOPRESERVATION

By Michael B. O'Neal, Ph.D. and Aschwin de Wolf

Cryonics, July, 1990; Expanded edition Cryonics, February, 2014; slightly revised June, 2014 for publication on Alcor's website

Introduction

This article presents a number of reasons for preferring whole body cryopreservations over neuro cryopreservations. For those of you who may be new to cryonics, a whole body cryopreservation, as the name implies, involves the cryopreservation and long-term care of the entire patient. Neuro cryopreservations are similar to whole body, with the exception that only the patient's brain (encased within the cranium, that is to say, normally the whole head) is placed in long term care.

The intent of this article is not to dispute the validity of neuro cryopreservations. The authors believe that a neuro cryopreservation is certainly immensely preferable to no cryopreservation at all and we fully support Alcor's policy of conversion of whole body patients to neuro cryopreservation in emergency situations.

We are disturbed, however, by the ease with which many Alcor members seem to reach the conclusion that full body cryopreservation is simply a waste of liquid nitrogen and money. Of Alcor's nearly 1,000 members approximately one half are whole bodies and one half are "neuros" [1]. Even allowing for the economics of the situation, we find it surprising that such a large percentage of Alcor members choose the neuro option [2]. Each of us must decide for ourselves whether the additional cost of a full body cryopreservation is justified by the perceived benefits. Any informed decision can only be made after careful consideration of the benefits and costs of each option. The Alcor publication: "Neuropreservation: Advantages and Disadvantages" [2] attempted to do just this. The authors of that article, however, seem to be biased in favor of the neuro option. As evidence of this conclusion we would point out that of the 17 paragraphs in the document only 4 seem to present advantages of the whole body approach (paragraphs: 1, 9, 14, 17). To be fair, articles have appeared in this and other publications [3] which favor the whole body approach. Even Mike Darwin's excellent pro neuro cryopreservation article, "But What Will the Neighbors Think?!" [4], devotes substantial space to a balanced treatment of the questions surrounding neuro cryopreservation.

Merkle's Wager Revised

Before discussing specific technical and social arguments, there is one abstract argument that can be made in favor of whole body cryopreservation that follows the same logic as Ralph Merkle's restatement of Pascal's wager in approaching cryonics. But instead of applying his argument to the rationality of choosing cryonics, we will apply it to the forms of cryopreservation being offered.

This exercise requires us to make a number of assumptions. We need to assume that cryopreservation is conducted under optimal conditions for both cryopreservation options and that there are no other obstacles (e.g., logistical or legal) to resuscitation. The focus here is on how much information preservation is required for complete survival of the person. As can be seen in the table below, whole body cryopreservation will lead to complete survival for the simple reason that it is the most comprehensive cryopreservation option available—at least as it pertains to the person as a physiological being. In the case of neuropreservation, only the brain (usually contained in the head) is preserved. Regardless of how much information we need to preserve, the person who has made whole body arrangements will do fine. In the case of neuropreservation, the reductionist argument about the brain sufficiently encoding identity must be correct to achieve the same outcome as whole body cryopreservation.

	Neuropreservation Is Sufficient	Neuropreservation Is Insufficient
Neuropreservation	Complete Survival	Incomplete Survival
Whole Body Cryopreservation	Complete Survival	Complete Survival

Now, what if we would relax our assumptions a little and allow for some degree of ischemia or brain damage during cryopreservation? It strikes us that this further strengthens the case for whole body cryopreservation because the rest of the body could be used to infer information about the non-damaged state of the brain, an option not available to neuropatients.

Whole Body Cryopreservation and Identity

First, it is by no means clear that the body does not contain information critical to the revival of the person. We do not mean by this statement that we reject the fact that the human brain holds a person's mind and personality. What we do mean is that reconstruction of the person as they were immediately prior to cryopreservation may be very difficult, or impossible, without the body.

Most everyone agrees that DNA does not completely specify a person. The argument of those who have selected neuro cryopreservation seems to be that DNA plus the information contained in the brain does specify all of the important aspects the person. But can we really be completely sure of this?

Let us consider the case of identical twins—naturally occurring clones. Since they developed from the same original cell, their DNA sequences are identical. However, twins are not exactly the same. For example, they are not always the same height and they do not have the same fingerprints. Some of these differences, such as height, may be directly attributed to environmental factors such as nutrition and health care. Other characteristics, such as fingerprints, seem less related to environmental factors and suggest that DNA programming may only specify general patterns, with the specifics arrived at in some other fashion. In fact, in recent years the study of epigenetics, which looks at how genes are switched off and on by environmental and other factors and can explain at least some of the differences in the way twins develop, has become a major research focus. Regardless of how these differences arise, it should be clear that a person's physical characteristics are not fully determined from DNA alone.

"So, what is the point?" you might ask. "Surely all of my memories plus an almost identical body would still be me." Perhaps. But what if the details of the central nervous system are not fully specified in the DNA programming?

The typical scenario for reviving a person cryopreserved using today's primitive technology involves reconstructing the person using cell by cell (or molecule by molecule) repair techniques. If whole body procedures were used, the person's entire central nervous system would be preserved. This preservation would not be perfect. There would be damage, perhaps even fractures to the spinal cord. It has been suggested [2, page 3] that because of the likelihood of these fractures there is little reason to prefer a whole body cryopreservation. This argument ignores the fact that repair of a damaged system, even a spinal cord, is likely to be much less complex, and more accurate to the original, than an unguided reconstruction based on DNA alone.

This leads us to conclude that without the original body to serve as a guide, it may not be possible to smoothly "interface" the neuropatient to a (re-grown) body. As mentioned above, the fact that "identical" twins (naturally occurring clones who share the same DNA) are not, in fact, identical proves that DNA does not fully specify our physical form. Thus it is at least plausible to postulate that the differences between our original bodies and cloned bodies may complicate the process of integrating a neuropatient's existing brain and head to a newly cloned body. Even if an approximation of the original connections can be designed, the new body may not "feel" right due to the subtle differences that are sure to exist between the original body and a re-grown one.

Of course we are not claiming that a revived neuropatient wouldn't be the same person if he or she were integrated with a cloned body. After all individuals, such as

Christopher Reeves, can survive as the same person for many years after injuries that deprive them of use of their bodies—but no one would claim that these individuals' lives aren't dramatically changed by such incidents. Similarly, skills may have to be relearned by neuro patients after resuscitation. For individuals such as athletes and musicians, where exceptional physical abilities comprise a significant portion of their self-identities, relearning these skills could be tremendously frustrating. Even those of us who are far less physically talented may find relearning how to type, fly fish, ride a bike, or even walk, quite annoying.

Our second point is that the existence of the body may help reduce personality and memory loss caused by a less than perfect cryopreservation.

The physical characteristics of our bodies strongly influence who we are. Our actions also strongly influence the condition of our bodies. We can think of our bodies as a crude physical backup of lifestyle choices, and hence personality. Careful examination of our bodies can reveal the answers to many questions, such as: Did we lead a sedentary life or were we physically active? What kind of diet did we consume? What kind of physical accidents and ailments did we suffer from? What led to clinical death and how old were we when clinical death occurred?

Modern anthropologists can infer much about the lives of our ancestors, and answer many such questions, working only from the clues available from our ancestors' skeletons. How much more information could be gleaned by future experts working with advanced technology and well preserved bodies?

Many people in the cryonics movement have pointed out the need to keep records and memorabilia to back up crucial memories. While this is certainly a good idea, it should be pointed out that information of this type cannot entirely replace the information stored in our bodies, since there is always the chance that our bodies contain important information that we are unaware of. For example, a person may suffer from an undiagnosed medical condition that greatly impacts his or her life. Complete molecular preservation of the body by definition gives us the most complete information about the history of our body and its interaction with the brain, regardless of our current level of understanding.

Recently, research has been conducted to understand the "microbiome" and the alleged interaction between gut bacteria and the brain. One does not need to believe that the microbiome is part of the (peripheral) nervous system to recognize that its preservation (and gut bacteria in particular) may provide clues about the brain, (past) mental states, and could be useful to resolve ambiguous brain repair challenges.

One could argue that in the vast majority of cases most information available from an examination of the body would be known to the person and therefore be available in the patient's brain. Even if some memories are apparently destroyed by a poor cryopreservation, many traces of them may remain. Surely, during patient reconstruction, these partial memories will be discovered and enhanced, making whatever personality / lifestyle information that may be contained in the body redundant.

This argument overlooks the very real possibility that technologies to repair a patient's brain may be developed that do not require or provide an understanding of the personality and memory information contained in that patient's brain. This is a very important point. Reconstruction and repair of a brain does not necessarily imply access to the memories it contains.

Perhaps the best way to understand why this is true is to look at "neural net" computers. The connectionist machine or neural network is composed of a large number of simple processing elements that are highly interconnected. These elements are modeled after biological neurons, the basic components of the human brain. Information in such systems is not stored in discrete locations, as is the case in conventional computers, but instead is stored as weighted connections between large numbers of processing elements (i.e., nodes). Machines of this type are often trained to recognize and classify particular patterns.

We can imagine a neural net where the connections between nodes are represented as electrical currents that flow through wires. Our particular machine has been in storage for a long time. When it was being placed into storage some of the wires came loose from their connections. We may repair the machine by reconnecting the wires to their proper connections (assuming we can tell where the loose wires belong). After completing these repairs we should have a fully functioning machine. Of course, we have no idea what patterns it has been trained to recognize. It would, in fact, be very difficult to try to determine what the machine knows without turning it on, since its knowledge exists only as connections between nodes.

The parallels with repair of a human brain after cryopreservation are clear. Just because we can repair a brain does not mean we will understand the person contained in that brain. The point of all of this is that it is unreasonable to expect that during repair memory traces from a damaged brain will be automatically detected and enhanced. Instead, the availability of the original body may prove invaluable in helping the person to reconstruct his or her life by providing a familiar physical environment to ease the transition into resuscitation and by providing physical reminders of memories which may have been partially lost.

Subjectivism and Identity

Alcor members who have made neuropreservation arrangements are often perplexed by the choice to make whole body arrangements. "Surely, a technology that is powerful enough to repair the damage associated with the cryopreservation process should be able to grow a new rejuvenated body." In turn, the advocate of whole body cryopreservation rejects such reductionism of identity to the brain and points out that the body is also part of one's identity and that it should be possible to rejuvenate and enhance one's existing body. Who's right? The problem with this question is that it assumes that questions about identity have objective answers and that ultimately this argument will be settled in favor of neuro or whole body cryopreservation.

We believe that this whole framework of looking at the issue may rest on the mistake that identity is an objective property of a person and excludes subjective preferences. To illustrate this point, let's compare an ascetic philosopher whose life completely revolves around abstract ideas and a professional body builder whose living and passion depends on the exact shape of his body. The philosopher may even abhor his body and would not be interested in its continued existence if technology permits. The body builder, on the other hand, is quite keen on preserving his body exactly in the state it is and hopes to resume some advanced form of bodybuilding after resuscitation. In this example identity, self-image, and preferences are closely linked and no objective theory of identity is going to render a clear verdict on who is thinking "correctly" about identity.

It is easy to see how issues concerning identity, self-image, preference, and survival can confuse matters. For example, people who have lost their limbs or lower part of the body, and still lead meaningful lives, are often used as "proof" that preserving the brain is sufficient for identity. But such an example is more testament to our instinct for survival and the resolve to live life at its fullest despite trauma or disease. It does not mean that such people do not regret having lost these faculties and would not want them back if possible. Identity can be lost, restored, and created. In a sense, identity involves decisions we make and is not fixed.

It is also important here to note that some contemporary thinkers are moving away from the idea that identity (or the mind) is confined to the skin and skull. Increasingly, we store vast amounts of personal information that is important, or even essential, to our functioning as a person outside ourselves. This position is called "the extended mind." It is not some vague spiritual notion about the mind but recognizes the role of external objects in the functioning of our mind and identity. Looking at the issue of identity preservation from this perspective makes even the whole body option look limited because it does not take into account all the external objects and information outside of us that have become part of our person and self-image. For example, a Facebook account can be considered part of one's identity and it is not realistic to remember everything that one posted, liked, and shared. So it is not part of one's brain or body but it can be considered a part of one's identity and life history. We should not be surprised, then, that an increasing number of Alcor members are paying more attention to saving information and objects in addition to their own brain or body.

Of course, in the case that the brain is so severely damaged that the body might contain some kind of clues of its original state, this kind of subjectivism does not apply. Preservation of the whole body would simply provide more information about the brain.

Quality of Preservation

One of the most persuasive arguments in favor of neuropreservation is that this option will produce a better cryopreservation. The reasoning here is that when the cryonics organization can exclusively focus on the brain (or just the head) a better outcome will result. Perfusion times are shorter, (abdominal) edema does not present a challenge, and, in the case of isolated head perfusion, better venous return of the cryoprotectant is possible.

A rejoinder to this argument is that one does not need to choose neuropreservation to receive these advantages. One could preferentially cryopreserve the isolated head and after this procedure cryopreserve the rest of the body. In fact, as of this writing, the default procedure at the Cryonics Institute is to perform cryoprotective perfusion with a vitrification agent for the upper body and give the rest of the body a straight freeze. At Alcor it is possible to execute a contract that provides for separate cryopreservation of the head and the body. So it is not accurate to say that one needs to exclude the cryopreservation of the body to get a superior cryopreservation.

Although it is indisputable that isolated head perfusion reduces cryoprotectant exposure time and accelerates cooling, it should be kept in mind that the (alleged) superiority of neuropreservation only holds when cryoprotection procedures remain sub-optimal. If ischemia is minimized and a cryoprotectant was developed that was non-toxic, issues such as exposure time would be less relevant. When you make cryopreservation arrangements you do not just need to assess the technology available at the present time but also consider technological advantages in the future. It should also be stressed that as more people choose whole body cryopreservation, cryonics organizations have a greater incentive to perfect this procedure.

We should also mention that it is possible to get the (alleged) technical advantages of neuropreservation without the bad PR (see below) associated with this procedure if one would just preserve the brain. Whereas many people are repulsed by images of isolated heads, the sight of an isolated brain is relatively common in the media and popular science. Brain preservation reduces long-term costs even more than neuropreservation. We suspect that many people would feel more comfortable with a cryonics organization offering brain preservation than with a cryonics organization offering neuropreservation.

Public Perception of Neuropreservation

Cryonics is a radical concept. As a group we would do well to consider the fact that no individual or organization can survive in isolation. We need the cooperation of others—doctors, lawyers, pharmaceutical companies, liquid nitrogen suppliers... the list is almost endless. Without these people, we are already dead. The concept of neuro cryopreservation is even more radical than the idea of whole body cryopreservation. Decapitation has historically been associated with death, not life, and thus can elicit a very strong emotional reaction. This seems to characterize one of the author's [O'Neal's] family's views of cryonics. Most of his family does not object to the idea of his being cryopreserved at death. In fact, his sister has agreed to be the executor of his estate. The family's biggest concern was that he would choose the whole body option. Most of O'Neal's family members, like the vast majority of "reasonable" people, believe that it will never be possible to restore a person from a "frozen head," and find the notion extremely repulsive. Note use of the word "believe" in the previous sentence. The scenarios generally envisioned for the restoration of neuropatients have been described to O'Neal's family members in some detail, including the apparent necessity of nanotechnology to restore both whole body and neuropatients cryopreserved under today's imperfect conditions. They seem to intellectually understand the arguments, but at some deep emotional level they still don't "believe" it will ever be possible to restore a patient from neuro cryopreservation. At some point it seems that the energy devoted to trying to convince individuals that neuro cryopreservation is reasonable would be better spent first securing buy-in from a larger segment of the population that the underlying concept of cryopreservation itself is reasonable.

The importance of having the support, or at least acceptance, of family and friends concerning our desire for cryopreservation should not be underestimated. There are situations in which hostility towards cryonics by family members has led to substantial delays in the application of stabilization and cryopreservation protocols, and some members have even failed to enter cryopreservation at all due to the objection of family members. Members may be wise to consider whether choosing the whole body option could help ameliorate any resistance that may exist within their own families, as this could have a direct impact on their own cryopreservation.

It is also important to carefully consider the negative PR that can result from cryopreservations involving removal of the patient's head, regardless of whether the body is stored or discarded. A relatively recent example of such negative PR is the controversy surrounding the cryopreservation of baseball player Ted Williams that followed from the publication of Larry Johnson's book *Frozen*. It is, of course, difficult to precisely quantify what damage, if any, Alcor experienced as a result of this episode. The authors do note that membership growth at Alcor has slowed dramatically in recent years. One could argue that the negative PR surrounding unfounded allegations about "disrespectful" treatment of William's remains—specifically his head—may be a contributing factor to reduced membership growth.

The authors' personal beliefs are that Alcor, and the entire cryonics movement, would be better served if future members were more strongly encouraged to consider the advantages of full body cryopreservations. Given the obviously deep rooted resistance to neuropreservation, why should we throw another psychological roadblock in our path? Cryonics is a hard sell as it is and expecting people to embrace the conceptual argument in favor of cryonics and also not have a visceral response to the idea of neuropreservation (and Alcor's isolated head perfusion procedure in particular) makes things unnecessarily difficult. In fact, if a person's first exposure to cryonics is through a sensationalist account of a neuropreservation case, a substantial number of them will no longer be in the right mindset for a dispassionate examination of the cryonics argument.

One logistical/safety argument in favor of neuropreservation is that the much smaller volume and storage container will make transfer of the patient easier in an emergency situation (such as a natural disaster). It is undeniable that it is easier to move a neuropatient (let alone an isolated brain), but this is a double-edged sword because this also means that it is easier to remove or steal a patient. Past experience is not a good indicator of which scenario is more likely to occur in the future.

The issue of paramount concern for each of us as individuals is to be cryopreserved at clinical death, and for cryonicists as a group is to increase public acceptance of cryonics—ultimately leading to the establishment of the right to choose cryopreservation as an elective medical procedure for critically ill patients. Once the public and the law acknowledge our right to cryopreservation, then recognition of neuro cryopreservations as a valid option will be much easier. Neuro cryopreservations could be presented as an intelligent fallback position, to be used under circumstances that preclude whole body cryopreservations, rather than as a primary option.

Whole Body Cryopreservation, Suspended Animation, and Medicine
Ultimately, the aim of a credible cryonics organization should be to perfect the cryopreservation process. If we can offer true human suspended animation, all arguments about the cryopreservation process itself causing damage will no longer be relevant in assessing the feasibility of cryonics. If we can place critically ill patients in suspended animation, the "only" challenge is to develop a cure for their disease (and, in most cases, rejuvenate them).

It is our belief that as cryopreservation techniques approach the level of true human suspended animation (no ice formation, no cryoprotectant toxicity, no fracturing, etc.), the decision to retain only the head and to discard the rest of the body will appear increasingly strange. It is unlikely that mainstream medicine will choose to adopt neuropreservation once reversible whole body cryopreservation has been achieved—at least not until ALL of the issues related to revival of neuro patients (e.g., growing a new body and integrating the patient with that body) have been fully and reliably solved. Until that level of advanced technology is achieved, the concept of "do no harm" will almost certainly yield a decision to practice cryonics in its whole body form. Even given that technology exists for reviving neuro patients, neuropreservation may continue to be eschewed by mainstream medicine based on the concept of avoiding any unnecessary risk to the patient or the view that neuropreservation does not constitute a "respectful" treatment of the patient.

This brings up another argument in favor of choosing whole body cryopreservation. The more popular whole body cryopreservation becomes, the more Alcor can claim to not just serve its own members but to be involved in developing human suspended animation, which may have many other applications such as long-distance space travel, military medicine, and perhaps even as an alternative for the death penalty.

Neuropatients Have No Fallback Option

Another point we'd like to make in this section is that whole body patients have a fallback position that neuro patients do not. One of the primary reasons that whole body cryopreservation is more expensive than neuro cryopreservation is that substantially more money is set aside for long term care of whole body patients than for neuro patients [3]. The rationale for this is straightforward: whole body patients require more physical space inside the storage dewars and more liquid nitrogen for cooling than do neuro patients—they simply cost more to maintain.

While Alcor is very conservative in the financial assumptions used to calculate the amount of money set aside for long term patient care—assuming only an annual 2% real return on investments (return after accounting for inflation), it is always possible that these assumptions may prove too optimistic. For neuro patients there are few options for lower cost storage. Whole body patients, on the other hand, could always be converted to the less costly to maintain neuro state, should long term patient care funding prove inadequate to meet the actual costs incurred. In fact, Alcor cryopreservation contracts have long included a conversion to neuro provision for members selecting the whole body option.

Most Alcor officials agree that, in light of the possibility that one might want to switch from neuro to whole body arrangements in the future, it is wiser to get coverage sufficient for whole body cryopreservation. A welcome consequence of this is that if long-term cryopreservation and resuscitation turn out more expensive than anticipated, the member would not immediately drop below the amount required for long-term care and resuscitation.

Practical Considerations

As mentioned in the previous section, whole body cryopreservation is substantially more expensive than neuro preservation. Currently (January 2014) Alcor charges a minimum of $80,000 for a neuro cryopreservation and $200,000 for a whole body cryopreservation. And these minimums are likely to increase in the future.

While most members fund their cryonics arrangements via life insurance, the cost of a whole body cryopreservation—equivalent to the cost of a middle / upper middle class home in many parts of the country—is substantial. As time passes and members age, the minimum cost of (whole body) cryopreservation generally increases, while the insurability of members tends to decrease—making cryopreservation expensive for the sick and elderly, and whole body cryopreservation unaffordable for many. One of the authors (O'Neal) has encouraged Alcor to consider a number of changes to increase the affordability of whole body cryopreservations. These include: (1) allowing greater flexibility in funding options beyond life insurance and irrevocable trusts, such as bequests; and (2) adopting less conservative assumptions on the rate of return for whole body long term patient care funds compared to long term patient funds for neuro patients.

An advantage of including cryopreservation funding in a will is that, after clinical death, a member no longer has need of a house, car, or other assets. Some older members who may have substantial real assets but live on limited incomes and are no longer insurable would probably welcome the option of paying for part of their cryopreservation minimums via a bequest.

The problem with wills, of course, is that they can be easily changed by a member—often up to the moment of clinical death. Even after a member is declared legally dead, his or her will can be contested. The end result is that the money for the member's cryopreservation is not "guaranteed" in the sense that life insurance proceeds are. Since cryopreservation is an expensive undertaking and the existing organizations are relatively small they simply cannot bear the risk associated with performing cryopreservation procedures in which payment is questionable.

However, there is a middle ground that dramatically reduces risk for the cryonics provider while enabling members to cover (part of) their cryopreservation minimums via a bequest. Essentially, the upfront costs of patient stabilization, transport, cryoprotective perfusion, and cooldown could be paid via a guaranteed mechanism—insurance policy, prepayment, irrevocable trust, etc.—while the long term patient care funding (over ½ the cost of a whole body cryopreservation) could be provided via a bequest. Thus, a whole body patient could be cryopreserved with little or no financial risk to the cryonics organization as long as funds sufficient for neuro cryopreservation (including long term care), plus a small additional amount to cover possible conversion from whole body to neuro, were provided by insurance, trust, or some other guaranteed means. If the additional funding required for long term whole body patient care, funded via a will or other means, were to fail to appear in a reasonable period of time the patient could simply be converted to a fully funded neuro patient.

Another potential approach for making whole body cryopreservation more affordable would be to adopt less conservative investment return projections. Instead of assuming a very low risk 2% rate of return, projecting a 4% or 5% return while adopting somewhat more aggressive investment strategies might be a reasonable strategy given the fact that whole body patients can always be converted to neuro patients should the projected rates of return fail to materialize.

Given that neuro patients do not have the luxury of a fallback position, it is critical that investments for neuros meet or exceed expectations. Because whole body patients do have the conversion to neuro option, failure to meet projected returns on investments would have far less dramatic consequences. If whole body patients' investments underperform, once a certain minimum level of funds is reached, they could be converted to fully funded neuro patients—no worse off than the other neuro patients and no financial burden on the system. Since every whole body member has already agreed to neuro conversion, no change to the existing (or past) cryopreservation agreements would be needed to implement such a policy.

Conclusions

The authors have presented an "abstract" Merkle's Wager style argument and two technical arguments for preferring whole body cryopreservations to neuro cryopreservations. The first argument described a theory that information contained in the brain and DNA is necessarily incomplete and that the information loss incurred from disposal of the majority of the body may be critical. The second argument postulated that in cases of memory loss, the existence of the body might act as a crude type of memory backup and trigger recall of partial memories that might otherwise be lost.

Five additional non-technical/social arguments were presented. First, in some cases, selection of the whole body option may increase the level of acceptance of cryonics by friends and family members—which could have a direct effect on the likelihood that a member will receive a smooth and rapid cryopreservation—and decrease the chances that his or her wishes concerning cryopreservation will be contested by antagonistic family members. Second, whole body cryopreservations appear less likely to generate the kinds of sensational news coverage which can lead to potentially damaging PR as was the case with Ted Williams (and much earlier Dora Kent [6]). Third, whole body patients have a backup plan that neuro patients do not, in that whole body patients can always be converted to neuros if the funds to support long term patient storage ever prove insufficient. Fourth, as Alcor's cryopreservation procedures begin to approach the level of reversible human suspended animation, whole body cryopreservation will most likely become the procedure of choice in mainstream medicine. Fifth, the issue of identity has a subjective component and what may be important to one person (preserving one's body) may not be important to others.

The cost differential between whole body cryopreservation and neuro preservation was discussed and a number of approaches that Alcor might adopt to help make cryopreservation, especially whole body cryopreservation, more affordable were presented.

In the final analysis each of us must weigh the costs and benefits of both approaches. For the authors, the potential benefits of a whole body cryopreservation far outweigh the additional costs. We find whole body cryopreservation to be the most conservative form of cryopreservation. The procedure is conservative in a technical sense since it retains the maximum amount of information concerning the patient by storing the patient's body. The whole body procedure is also conservative in the social sense as it avoids the negative perceptions associated with decapitation and seems far more "reasonable" to the general public than neuro preservation. Whole body cryopreservations are also more conservative than neuro preservations in that whole body patients always have conversion to neuro as a fall back option in times of financial or other difficulties. ■

Endnotes

1. As of December 2013, there were 971 Alcor members. Of these 482 were whole body members (49.6%), 449 were neuro cryopreservation members (46.2%), 26 were "neuro with whole body" (2.7%), and 14 were "open option" (1.4%) — Alcor Membership Report, December 2013.

2. It should be noted that during the 24 years that have elapsed between the original version of this paper and its revision the percentage of Alcor whole body members has actually increased. In 1990 two thirds of Alcor members were neuro cryopreservation members. Today the numbers of Alcor whole body and neuro members are roughly equal.

3. As of January 2014, $25,000 is set aside for neuro patient long term care versus $115,000 for whole body patient long term care [5].

References

[1] "The Alcor Survey 1988-9 (Part I)" by Max O'Connor and Mike Perry, in *Cryonics*, Vol 10(9), September 1989, page 42.

[2] "Neuropreservation: Advantages and Disadvantages," Alcor publication NEUROPRE 9-88.

[3] "The Neuropreservation Controversy" by Paul Segall, in *The American Cryonics Society Journal* Vol 5(2), March 1988, pages 4-5.

[4] "But What Will the Neighbors Think?!: A Discourse on the History and Rationale of Neurosuspension" by Mike Darwin, in *Cryonics*, Vol 9(10), October 1988, pages 40-55.

[5] "Alcor Cryopreservation Agreement – Schedule A: Required Costs and Cryopreservation Fund Minimums." http://www.alcor.org/BecomeMember/schedule A.html

[6] "A Timeline on the Events Surrounding the Cryonic Suspension of Dora Kent" in *Cryonics*, 9(1), January 1988, pages 1-7.

RESPONSIBILITY, PROBABILITY, AND DURABILITY

BY THOMAS DONALDSON
Cryonics, July, 1989

Recently Steve Harris and Mike Perry[1] have discussed estimates of the probability of our revival. Their efforts have been very useful not as numerical estimates but as discussions of the issues involved. After all, few readers would attach exactly the same numbers to each issue.

But there is an assumption lying behind both of these estimates which deserves examination. Some of the factors Steve and Mike raise we can easily think of as appropriate issues to which to apply the notion of probability. Others, however, are far too bound up with our own actions. It's reasonable to ask, first of all, whether the idea of probability means anything at all in that context.

Here is an example of the problem I'm raising, with the issues raised to an absurd level just for clarity. A new gambling house sets up in Reno. The owner undertakes to bet with everyone about whether or not he, the owner, will do his laundry tomorrow. Bets are made today and close at 6 PM. (Perhaps gambling houses already operate this way?) Do we, then, expect a rush of clients?

The problem with this bet is that he, the owner, has some control over whether or not he does his laundry. Not only are the dice loaded, but he gets to pick, after all bets are laid, which loaded die to use. Computing probabilities only makes sense when the events bet upon are known to be random. For Mike and Steve, this means that our actions can have NO effect upon the outcome. I don't mean "only a very little." NO means none at all, zilch, zero. Why zero? Because our actions now are seeds, not just "observational errors" which lead nowhere. Once we admit that our actions can influence these events, how do we predict by how much and when?

Within a very wide range, what happens to us is our responsibility. We are not passive bettors on the outcome of events. I mean this both in the narrow sense of I, me, myself, and in the broader one of cryonicists generally. How can I (myself) affect my frozen fate 100 years from now? Well, for one thing I can choose my cryonics society. I can try to make its officers not only honest and competent as individuals, but operating within a constitution which keeps them honest and competent or throws them out of office. And I can provide enough resources so that evasive action is possible when

---

1   See *Cryonics*, May, 1989, 36-53.

any threat appears. Third, I can try to arrange that equipment, supplies, and competent people will be available when I'm declared legally dead. And of course last of all I can try to create other cryonicists.

But of course someday I will be frozen. What control do I have then? Not directly, but through other cryonicists who succeed me. We have all joined together for a journey across time. If anyone is revived 50 years from now, even with technology far in advance of ours and in another country, it will strengthen my chances. I believe the important part to remember about Mike and Steve's social catastrophes is that every one of us is putting out effort to see that they do not occur to us.

That qualification gets to the gist of my point in this article. It is wrong for us either individually, or as a class of people (cryonicists) to take occurrence of world-wide or even Solar System-wide events as necessarily our own personal fate. It is wrong and far worse than wrong. Habits of mind which identify ourselves with the general fate of humanity assume an abdication of that exact responsibility we must take over our own fate. Putting our fate into a model of passive probability assumes our own passivity.

Some people made money hand over fist during the Depression. They did so not by preying on others but by providing needed services, just as people do today. Many German Jews escaped Hitler, by an agility of mind which told them that now was the time to leave a place where their family had lived for centuries. We want to choose a cryonics society agile enough that when the mobs come to loot the facility, they find only empty dewars and bare offices; when the nanotech beasties come for us, we meet them with a nanotechnological immune system which consumes them. We very much should not identify our own fate with that of "society" or "mankind" or even the Earth (cryonics societies should found offices off the Earth as soon as that becomes possible). Didn't we become cryonicists because we proposed to escape that which all the philosophers said was the common fate of all mankind? Floods, earthquakes, meteor impact, major war, mobs searching for us in every cranny, how could we be fazed by such trivialities having once adopted our major goal?

It is, after all, not as if we have only five minutes to prepare for such events. Haven't you noticed that cryonics is a very long term project? Every year we should all look up from our local cryonics tasks and think about dangers over the longer term. No cryonics society, for instance, has a constitution which satisfies me completely. There are other issues too. Part of our responsibility consists exactly of foreseeing problems which now look far away. To be immortal means to be farseeing.

Finally, since both Mike and Steve discuss the Fermi problem as an indicator of our future, I have a few words about that. One scientist closely involved with the search for ETI summed the matter up: the fact that we don't see anyone else says something unknown about the existence or the intentions of an advanced society.

Currently we live in an apocalyptic age, when myths of total worldwide destruction lie on everyone's mind. Before nanotechnology, it was nuclear war. Before then (a long time!) it was poison gas. That's a highly biased view of the facts: what about the other possibility? Children can look on adults and wonder how they can eat asparagus and forego so much candy. We don't really know what we will grow into, either as individuals or as a member of humanity. We can't even estimate probabilities for events we haven't ever imagined. That's one of the most fascinating parts of cryonic suspension. Whatever we become in 1,000 years it's certain that every one of us would surprise ourselves if we could see it now. ∎

THE "I" WORD

BY RALPH C. MERKLE, PH.D.
Cryonics, August, 1992

The right to live is widely recognized. "Life, liberty, and the pursuit of happiness" is enshrined in the Declaration of Independence. From the biblical "Thou shalt not kill" to the legal prohibition against ". . . the unlawful killing of any human being with malice aforethought, either express or implied by law," the value of life is upheld, protected, and exalted.

There is no "right to immortality." Those who seek it are mocked and ridiculed, or at best ignored with the tolerant amusement we reserve for small children and the simple minded.

So is cryonics simply a method of saving lives, or do we want to proclaim loudly that it is the path to immortality?

If the former, we are supported by all the philosophies of the earth and by the laws of all countries. If the latter, we are held up to derision and contempt by most philosophies, and defended by no law.

According to the dictionary, death is "a permanent cessation of all vital functions." If cryonics works, then by definition such a permanent cessation has not occurred; only a temporary and reversible cessation, not sufficient (according to the generally accepted definition) to let us say the person is dead. Therefore, if cryonics has even a modest likelihood of success, then blocking a cryonic suspension or interfering with the activities of a cryonics organization endangers human life. This is a very powerful defense of cryonics.

According to the dictionary, immortal is "not liable or subject to death." At the moment, we are most definitely "subject to death." Indeed, it is difficult to imagine the circumstances that would make us immortal in the commonly accepted sense. Safer, certainly. Longer lived, certainly. But immortal? Not subject to death? Under any conditions? No.

Should we, then, proclaim that we seek "immortality" when the dictionary definition is incompatible with what we know of the physical laws that govern the universe? Or should we seek simply to stay alive?

What's the difference? If we seek to be immortal or we simply want to stay alive, will we not act the same, regardless of our goal? We'll still be careful crossing a street. We'll still run from a burning building. We'll still go to the doctor with a broken leg, and take antibiotics for an infection. What's the difference?

There is a difference: if we simply want to stay alive, we can secure the sympathy and support of the world. This increases our chances of staying alive.

If we seek to be immortal, we earn the scorn and derision of much of the world. This decreases our chances of staying alive.

Cryonics is about using future medical technology. Will future medical technology make us immortal? Not according to the accepted definition. Will it keep us healthy for a long time? Almost certainly. Does cryonics make us immortal? No more than an ambulance might. Cryonics is simply a way of getting to a hospital in the 21st or 22nd century that can heal our injuries.

When we go to the hospital for a tumor, do we say, "They're going to remove the tumor! I'm going to be immortal!" Or do we say, "I hope I survive this operation; I want to see a new day, and a new year, and a new decade. I want to go to bed tonight confident that I'll see the sun rise tomorrow, just as I saw it rise yesterday."

What should we tell people who say, "But if medicine can make you young again, aren't you immortal?" There are several answers, but the simplest is just: "Not if you keep driving a car!" There is a serious point beneath the humor here: unless the chance of accidental death can be driven to almost zero, we're not immortal. And there are many, many things that have a non-zero chance of killing us, not all of which we know about yet.

But let's remember the central point. We have to survive the next century or two if we're to enjoy the luxury of facing the problems that lie beyond. Right now, that's a major problem, a problem in which technology is only one factor (and probably not the most important factor). Today, pre-mortem suspensions are illegal. This has more to do with people's attitudes than any technical factor. To change this, we must persuade people that cryonics is a reasonable activity pursued by reasonable people with reasonable motives.

Today, coroners can autopsy us unless they can be persuaded (perhaps just by talking, or perhaps by the courts, or perhaps both) to refrain. Today, physicians might cause great grief and difficulty if "their" terminal patient is going to be suspended unless we can persuade them that it's better to help. Today, government agencies can cause many problems unless they can persuaded otherwise. And today, judges can decide against us in cases that are crucial to our survival unless we can persuade them to rule in our favor.

All these people must be persuaded that cryonics should at least be tolerated and perhaps supported. One of the most effective strategies for doing this is to convey one simple message: cryonics can save lives.

This is a powerful message. For best results it should be conveyed clearly and simply, without distraction.

Words are important, and the words we use to describe ourselves and our objectives can help or hinder us, save or doom us. So let's think about our choice of words, and what they mean not only to us but to the world at large.

And please, when someone asks you what cryonics is all about, tell them it's about saving lives, not about immortality.

Trying to be immortal could kill us. ■

THE ROAD LESS TRAVELED: ALTERNATIVES TO CRYONICS, A VERY PRELIMINARY SURVEY

BY R. MICHAEL PERRY, PH.D.
Cryonics, 3rd Quarter, 2007

Introduction

A man lies critically injured on the highway, one leg pinned under his battered Harley-Davidson. He had just passed a car while approaching an intersection, but he couldn't quite make it around the pickup stopped in the road just ahead. The man is alive but unconscious; blood dribbles from his mouth as his faltering, shallow breathing is assisted by a paramedic who has just arrived on the scene. Forty-five minutes later the man expires at a nearby hospital, the victim of a brain hemorrhage. The brain, which appears during the mandatory autopsy to be largely undamaged despite the fatal trauma, is placed in a fixative solution after some delay at mostly refrigerated temperature...

The above, true-life scenario played itself out in September, 2006 for a relative of mine who had expressed interest in cryonics but not completed any arrangements. He had, however, signed a "Declaration of Intent" expressing a wish to be cryopreserved. Unfortunately, with only that single signed document in place, the usual cryonics procedures could not be applied and the best that could be attempted was a "salvage job." The brain, as I write this, still rests in a refrigerated (liquid) fixative bath where it is undergoing a slow diffusion of cryoprotectant, after which it will be cooled and placed in liquid nitrogen for long-term care.

Tragic events involving persons who are interested in cryonics but who have not signed up furnish the type of case where an alternative to the usual procedures is needed, at least for the all-important preliminary stages. This presumes that funding can be arranged as needed for the long-term, cryogenic care. However, there are also many cases where there simply is not enough funding, and something entirely apart from expensive cryonics is desired.

The reasons for considering an alternative to cryonics include the potential for much easier, cheaper long-term care and thus greater security against future contingencies such as social unrest, energy and materials shortages, or economic hardships affecting the cryonics provider. Doubts have been expressed that alternative procedures would be adequate for the goal of eventual revival of the patient, given the exacting requirements that must be met versus the state of the art in current fixation technology. But this is not enough reason to give up. A thorough study of existing fixation methods, such as that used in my relative's case, is called for, along with attempts to develop better methods.

What follows is a very preliminary report. I have looked into various possible fixative techniques and their effects. Much further work is called for, both in surveying existing research and, eventually, in pursuing new research. Of what I have been able to study so far, some approaches show interesting success. As an overall impression: tissue ultrastructure, which is thought to be critical to the problem of revival (particularly for brain tissue), appears to be well-preserved by a number of different methods that start with aldehyde fixatives such as formaldehyde and glutaraldehyde. Some difficulties with fine-scale preservation have been noted. But these methods, I think, strongly merit further investigation and, in some cases at least, provisional use by cryonics providers when standard cryonics procedures are unavailable and the only alternative is to decline the case.

Philosophical Issues

A basic question in cryonics is whether preservation is good enough to offer a reasonable prospect of eventually restoring a preserved patient to full health and vigor. At minimum there should be enough structural preservation so that the healthy state of the patient can be inferred from the remains. If the healthy state can be known then it should be possible, using future technology, to make appropriate repairs to bring about the desired recovery so the patient will return to consciousness and full functionality. The repairs could be extensive, so if, for example, only the brain was preserved the entire rest of the body would need to be replaced. Repairs to the brain, too, could be substantial. The issue will arise, for some more acutely than for others, of whether the resulting patient, even if similar to the original in every respect, really would "be" that original person or, perhaps, just a faithful copy.

While I think there are reassuring answers for issues such as these, the subject is beyond the scope of this study. Instead, I will be mainly concerned with the ability of the various preservation techniques to achieve quality structural preservation. My "gold standard" will be based on an information-theoretic criterion: The healthy brain should be inferable from the state or condition of what is preserved—this I sometimes refer to as a *favorable* preservation.[1] In practice it is presently unknown whether *any* preservation should be considered favorable in this sense, including standard cryopreservations. But we can at least look at the results and see, in the case of brain tissue, whether basic structures such as neuron cell bodies, axons, dendrites, and synapses seem well-preserved (See Figures 1 & 2).

---

1   This essentially is the point of view expressed in Merkle R, "The Technical Feasibility of Cryonics," *Medical Hypotheses* 39 6–16 (1992).

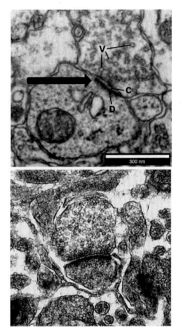

I think, too, that with our present ignorance of the limits both of preservative methods and of future resuscitation technology, together with philosophical uncertainties, we should not be too hasty in dismissing any preservative technology. Instead we should be willing to grant some benefit of doubt. Imperfect or unfavorable preservation could result both from the methods used and from the condition of the patient at the time a procedure is started. But even cases where significant information loss occurs the results could be worth the effort. We must keep in mind that future repair technology, though it too will have limitations, will be powerful in ways hard to appreciate today. Debilities other than amnesia should be fully curable, for example, while even amnesia could be mitigated through use of historical records or in other ways.

On this ground, then, I favor a "no patient left behind" policy in which preservation is attempted even when certain, expensive methods are out of reach and some damage has occurred such as through autopsy or warm ischemia.[2] (My relative here is an obvious case in point.) The brain, as the seat of the personality, is the primary focus of this article, although some interesting studies of other tissues also show details at the cellular level, particularly some work with ancient fossils.

Unintentional and Contingency Preservation

The world of nature may seem an unlikely place to look for high-

Figure 1 (top) & Figure 2 (bottom):

Figure 1 (courtesy of Narayanan Kasthuri and Kenneth Hayworth) shows a 38-nanometer-thick tissue slice of aldehyde- and osmium-fixed mouse brain cortex embedded in epon resin and sectioned and collected on Harvard's Automatic Tape Collecting Lathe Ultramicrotome (ATLUM). This scanning electron microscope (SEM) contrast-reversed image shows synapse (large arrow), synaptic vesicles (V), synaptic cleft (C) separating presynaptic and postsynaptic membranes, and postsynaptic density (D). Brain ultrastructure, including synapses which are believed important for encoding memory, appears to be well-preserved. Figure 2 (courtesy of 21st Century Medicine), showing a SEM image of a rabbit brain synapse perfused with M22 for 60 minutes and cryopreserved, shows comparable, not obviously much better, ultrastructure preservation.

---

2   For a discussion of this issue from a cryonics perspective (omitting but applicable to other forms of preservation) see Wowk B, "Ethics of Non-Ideal Cryonics Cases," Cryonics 27(4) 10-12 (Fall 2006), available online at http://www.alcor.org/cryonics/cryonics0604.pdf and reprinted in this book.

quality, long-term preservation of biological tissues, yet something of this sort does occur, relatively speaking, in such remains as natural frozen mummies and specimens embedded in amber. Here I include a very brief summary of some of these unintentional preservations, then consider a more recent, intentional but "contingency" preservation in which fixation was applied only after long delay. These cases are important, if for no other reason than because they show that surprising amounts of fine structure can be preserved under adverse circumstances, suggesting that the goal of favorable preservation may be reachable through a variety of approaches, not necessarily cryogenic.

Tyrolean Ice Man. The 5,200-year-old Tyrolean Ice Man discovered in a glacier in 1991 is the oldest known frozen human mummy. Although frozen at high subzero-Celsius (non-cryogenic) temperature for most of the five millennia since his death, it is clear that some thawing and refreezing occurred, including an incident immediately following discovery. Despite the adverse circumstances, a 1998 study reports interesting findings for many parts of the anatomy, in which many details at the cellular level can be seen, albeit with substantial loss. In the brain there was preservation of the myelin sheaths of axons, even though the material of the axons and the neuron cell bodies was mostly obliterated.[3] Details of the myelin sheaths were discernible down to 10 nanometers, or about 65 carbon atom-diameters.

Peat Bog Burials. In addition to glaciers, peat bogs have furnished surprising examples of preservation. One such location, a swampy pond near Windover, Florida, was excavated in the 1980s. Remains of several individuals with recognizable if greatly shrunken brains were found. While there was much damage, definite cellular remnants could be seen on light and electron microscopic examination: axons; cerebellar purkinje cells in approximately their original spatial configurations, and what appeared to be remnants of neurons. DNA was also recovered. The estimated age of this material was 7,000-8,000 years. The preservation, limited though it was, is all the more striking since it involved above-freezing storage under water, which normally results in rapid decomposition. Apparently the lack of oxygen and neutral pH in the water-soaked peat greatly slowed the normal processes of breakdown, leaving us this tantalizing, if fleeting, glimpse of ancient humans.[4]

Amber Fossils. Turning to something much more ancient still, study was made in 2005 of a cypress twig preserved in Baltic amber for 45 million years. As reported in the *Proceedings of the Royal Society*, the "Transmission electron micrographs revealed

---

3   Hess M W, Klima G, Pfaller K, Künzel K H, Gaber O, "Histological Investigations on the Tyrolean Ice Man," *Am. J. Phys. Anthr.* 106(4) 521-32 (1998).

4   Doran G H, Dickel D N, Ballinger W E, Agee O F, Laipis P J, Hauswirth W W, "Anatomical, Cellular and Molecular Analysis of 8,000-Yr-Old Human Brain Tissue from the Windover Archaeological Site," *Nature* 323, 803-06 (30 October 1986).

highly preserved fine structures of cell walls, membranes and organelles" with cells more or less normal-appearing. Earlier studies of amber-preserved material also showed fine details of cell structure in both animal and plant tissues. The new study used a novel, resin-embedding technique to prevent breakup of the extremely fragile ancient tissue under microtome sectioning, allowing full cross sections to be prepared for microscopic examination. DNA and RNA were not detected but hopes were raised that these species-specific macromolecules were present at least in inferable form and might be deciphered with suitable techniques.[5]

A Recent Case. I conclude this section with a case of recent, intentional preservation that occurred under adverse circumstances. The body of a woman was kept in a mortuary for 2 months at 3°C with no fixation, then the brain was removed and fixed in a phosphate-buffered formaldehyde solution (4.5%) for 9 weeks. Subsequent examination of the brain showed macroscopically visible surface deterioration; histologically, however, normal brain structures were preserved including all important cell types (neurons, astrocytes, oligodendrocytes, microglia), neuropil, axons, and myelin sheaths. From a cryonics standpoint the preservation was not good but, I would say, not negligible either.[6]

Basic Fixation: Theory, Materials, and Methods[7]

When a patient undergoes cardiac arrest, blood no longer circulates and cell metabolism is compromised. Without special intervention, deterioration of the tissues soon sets in. Cryonics protocols are designed to halt this deterioration by placing the patient's tissues in a condition of *biostasis*, in which biological and chemical activity is halted. More specifically, biostasis (1) halts any biological activity within the tissues, (2) protects the tissues from attack by microorganisms such as bacteria, and (3) stabilizes the tissues so that long-term care in an unchanging state is practical. Biostasis in this case is achieved through use of low (cryogenic) temperature, -100°C or lower.

An acceptable substitute for a cryonics protocol, a non-cryogenic fixation procedure, must likewise accomplish the goals of biostasis and permit long-term care of the patient or the patient's brain in an unchanging state. There are several possibilities.

Cross-linking fixatives use covalent chemical bonds to tie down the normally reactive molecular components such as proteins and peptides that make up tissues. The

---

5   Koller B, Schmitt J M, Tischendorf G, "Cellular Fine Structures and Histochemical Reactions in the Tissue of a Cypress Twig Preserved in Baltic Amber," *Proc. R. Soc. B* (2005) 272, 121–26, http://www.journals.royalsoc.ac.uk/content/k6y5c74pbp4g21mf/fulltext.pdf

6   Gelpi E, Preusser M, Bauer G, Budka H, "Autopsy at 2 Months after Death: Brain Is Satisfactorily Preserved for Neuropathology," *Forensic Sci Int.* 24;168(2-3):177-82 (May 2007).

7   This section is based in part on the Wikipedia article Fixation (histology), http://en.wikipedia.org/wiki/Fixation_(histology), accessed 26 Aug. 2015.

most widely used fixative, formaldehyde, is of this type, as is another popular fixative, glutaraldehyde. The two are sometimes used in combination to achieve what is thought to be a better result than either alone would accomplish. Formaldehyde has one aldehyde group per molecule to accomplish the crosslinking, whereas glutaraldehyde has two and also a longer molecule and thus is able to bond more securely by stretching its bonding over greater distances. However, the extra power of glutaraldehyde comes at a cost: its molecules are larger and thus do not penetrate into tissue as fast. Using it in combination with formaldehyde means getting what is actually a good fixative, formaldehyde, in fast while the even-better fixative, glutaraldehyde, can move in at a more leisurely pace and make its extra contribution. As one case in point, my relative's brain was preserved in a solution of 2% formaldehyde, 4% glutaraldehyde.

Formaldehyde is the most widely used fixative for the various requirements outside of cryonics; it and glutaraldehyde have also been most used in cryonics when called for by special circumstances. Other fixatives have more specialized uses, which still may have importance. *Precipitating fixatives* such as acetone, ethanol, methanol, and acetic acid achieve their effects by reducing the solubility of the proteins that largely comprise the tissues. *Oxidizing fixatives* use oxidation to crosslink proteins; osmium tetroxide is one fixative in this class that has uses connected with high-magnification microscopy.

Fixation of a tissue sample requires a reliable method of delivery. With a whole organ such as the brain it may be possible to use perfusion or pumping the fixative solution into the organ through the vascular system. The alternative is to immerse the sample in a fixative bath, during which the fixative penetrates the tissue more slowly through simple diffusion. For my relative, diffusion was used since the brain's vascular system had been traumatized; probably several days of diffusion was adequate for nearly complete penetration under refrigerated, above-freezing conditions.

When the sample—a brain, say—is fixed, we must ask (1) whether the preservation of detail is adequate and (2) whether the sample will remain stably fixed long enough to accomplish the desired purpose. These are demanding requirements for alternative procedures. Since decades or centuries may be needed to develop technology to attempt resuscitation, long-term stability becomes an especially important issue. As with cryonics itself, the basic answers are unknown. Some encouragement is provided by the high level of detail seen in preserved brain samples using, for example, formaldehyde fixation. Ultrastructural details under the high magnification of electron microscopy (10,000x plus) are quite clear, though this alone is not a demonstration that all the details one would like are present. However, the same problem exists with tissue preserved cryogenically—the answer to whether the preservation captures fine enough details is unknown though there are at least some encouraging signs along with reasons for concern.

To return to the problem of long-term stability, one consideration is whether the fixative is uniformly distributed throughout the sample. Preservation could be compromised if there are "islands" of tissue that were not properly fixed. (A somewhat analogous, though possibly less serious, problem occurs with cryopreservation. If cryoprotectant is not uniformly distributed in the tissue prior to lowering the temperature to the cryogenic range there could be freezing damage in the "islands" of tissue not protected, even though the cold penetrates uniformly everywhere and will prevent deterioration.) So far we have considered "wet" preparations only, in which the sample is to be kept immersed in a liquid bath. Water molecules in particular are small and move rapidly, and their constant, reaction-prone hammering in, say, a specimen preserved in an aqueous aldehyde solution could have unwanted long-term effects. For greater stability and durability it would thus be desirable to have some form of dry preparation for long-term care; this will now be considered.

Dry Preparations for Biostatic Care

A number of techniques, some dating back more than a century, have been developed for dry storage of preserved biological specimens. One motivation for developing these techniques has been to provide specimens, such as whole, human organs, as a teaching aid. The aim here is to render the organ in a lifelike but inert and touchable form for macroscopic or gross anatomical study or exhibits. One is not concerned with microscopic details but only those features visible to the unaided eye.

Another, very different application, for which different embedding methods have been developed, is to render specimens in a form that can be cut into thin sections for microscopic study. Here the focus is on capturing fine structure but not with preserving the whole mass intact. In cryonics, of course, we are interested in both the fine structure and in preserving the whole specimen intact, though not for either gross anatomical study or microscopic study requiring fine slicing. These differences need to be borne in mind in the short survey that follows. The techniques discussed next look promising in some cases but could be improved for our purpose.

Desiccation.[8] Nature has pioneered various forms of preservation through desiccation. In addition to amber fossils (normally quite dehydrated), natural mummies found in desert environments capture such detail as DNA and large anatomical features, though brain tissue is poorly preserved. For scientific purposes, desiccation in the form of freeze-drying has been used to preserve anatomical specimens in a lifelike, inert form for study or exhibits. The specimen is first frozen, then allowed to dry out at below-freezing temperature, generally under high vacuum to accelerate the process. As the ice evaporates, the structural shapes remain largely unchanged, even

---

8   This paragraph is based on Hower R O, *Freeze-Drying Biological Specimens: a Laboratory Manual*, Washington, D. C.: Smithsonian Institution Press (1979).

though the final result is delicate and will need protection from oxidation and moisture. Human brain tissue in large sections (order of 200g or about 15% of a whole brain) has been freeze-dried after formaldehyde fixation and shows some structural details such as capillaries under the scanning electron microscope, though much damage has occurred. Some of the damage resulted from freezing itself and might be mitigated through use of cryoprotectants; as usual, the potential of this process is unknown.

Early Embedding Techniques.[9] More than a century ago paraffin embedding was used to preserve biological specimens in a form that would be amenable to fine sectioning for microscopic study, and it is still used. In one procedure from a 1902 reference, small tissue samples fixed in formaldehyde and dehydrated with ethanol are embedded in melted paraffin, a white or colorless, tasteless, odorless, water-insoluble, solid substance not easily acted upon by reagents, which reaches a temperature of 55°C (131°F). The melt is rapidly cooled to reduce crystallization and improve transparency in the resulting solid embedding. A related technique in the same reference uses a plastic-like material, celloidin, in place of paraffin. This permits embedding at room temperature through use of an ether-ethanol solvent; it is more suited to larger specimens, though also requiring full dehydration.

Plastination. An embedding technique developed by Gunther von Hagens in Germany in the 1970s,[10] plastination starts with a previously fixed biological specimen in an aqueous medium. Water and fats (lipids) are then replaced with a liquid plastic resin monomer, which is hardened or cured by polymerization. The resulting, resin-impregnated specimen is dry, odorless, and durable. Silicone resin yields a flexible or rubbery specimen suitable for macroscopic study or exhibits; epoxy resin can be used to produce thin, rigid sections suitable for microscopic study. Silicone impregnation has also been adapted to microscopic study, with good results.[11] Other desired effects are possible using different polymers,[12] and substantial further adaptations might be feasible.

A possible drawback of this approach, from the standpoint of preserving the fine structures that are especially important from a cryonics standpoint, is the relatively harsh regimen needed to produce the finished product. Typically, the process starts with an aldehyde-fixed specimen in aqueous solution. The specimen is placed in acetone, and successive changes of the bath remove water and fats. Finally the resin

9   This paragraph is based on Hardesty I, *Neurological Technique*, Chicago: University of Chicago Press (1902).

10   von Hagens, G, "Impregnation of Soft Biological Specimens with Thermosetting Resins and Elastomers," *Anat. Rec.* 194: 247-56 (1979).

11   Grondin G, Grondin G G, Talbot B G, "A Study of Criteria Permitting the Use of Plastinated Specimens for Light and Electron Microscopy," *Biotech. Histochem.* 69(4) 219-34 (Jul. 1994).

12   For an older but interesting, informative survey see von Hagens G, Tiedemann K, Kriz W, "The Current Potential of Plastination," *Anat.and Embr.* 175(4) 411-21 (Mar. 1987).

monomer is introduced, the remaining acetone is removed by vacuum, and induced catalysis yields the desired polymerization. Concerns have been raised about whether defatting would obliterate important brain information, though there does not appear to be strong evidence of this. (Here it is appropriate to mention that lipids nevertheless could contain important information; preservation of lipids is a difficult process that has not been covered in this preliminary survey but deserves consideration.)

Polyethylene Glycol.[13] "Polyethylene glycol" (PEG) is actually a family of water-soluble polymers of ethylene glycol in which the molecules form long, linear chains. A typical batch will contain a mixture or distribution of polymer chains of varying lengths. Longer chains result in a PEG with a higher melting point, which is a waxy solid at room temperature or below. Its water solubility and other characteristics make it possible to introduce PEG into tissue without using dehydration, defatting, heating, or additional polymerization, suggesting that PEG could overcome possible problems encountered with many other forms of embedding. PEG, however, does not seem much used for biological embedding and may not be as satisfactory as other methods even for the special requirements that relate to cryonics. As usual, there are important unknowns here and further investigation is called for.

Discussion and Conclusions

The agonizing question will continually arise of what to do in an emergency where cryonics is desired but arrangements are not in place. An alternative to just giving up is to consider some non-cryonics procedures, such as chemical preservation of the brain, as a temporary solution until cryopreservation can be arranged or, if this eventuality is not feasible, as a long-term option itself.

In such a case, the question arises of whether the preservation is adequate to meet the unknown, presumably demanding requirements if the patient is to be repaired without deficits by future technology. Revival in such a "perfect" form will happen only if enough identity-critical structure is present in some inferable form. The high degree of structural preservation seen in some fixation methods raises hopes that in fact such a degree of preservation is achievable through non-cryogenic means.

In addition to the (by appearance) encouraging results obtainable with water-based fixatives in a liquid bath, there is the prospect of embedding the specimen (normally the patient's brain) in a solid matrix for long-term care. Certainly there are unknowns with such an approach but one finds this in the standard cryonics procedures too.

The alternatives discussed herein offer the additional advantage of more security per unit cost for conditions of social unrest or economic hardship which may occur over the long interval before revival will be attempted. In addition, there is reason to

---

13   This paragraph is based on Gao K (ed), *Polyethylene Glycol as an Embedment for Microscopy and Histochemistry.* Boca Raton, Fla.: CRC Press (1993).

consider preservation methods that knowingly fall short of the best methods currently possible, when, for example, the cost of better treatment is prohibitive. The alternatives must be taken seriously, then, for a number of reasons, and more work is needed to both assess and enhance their potential. Along with this, so long as invalidating difficulties are not discovered, it is imperative that such alternatives become more readily available—through some appropriate organization—and widely advertised. ■

I thank Greg Jordan, Aschwin de Wolf, Chana de Wolf, Hugh Hixon, Jennifer Chapman, and Brian Wowk for their generous assistance in tracking down references, proofreading, and/or obtaining material for illustrations.

THE MYTH OF THE GOLDEN SCALPEL

BY MICHAEL DARWIN
Cryonics, January, 1986

Both Robert Ettinger's *The Prospect of Immortality* and the cryonics movement as a whole have been accused of being unscientific, of offering unrealistic hope. In view of the history of cryonics since *The Prospect*, this criticism appears justified. Ettinger wrote *The Prospect* as an extrapolation of research observations, without further recourse to experiment. The cryonics community *The Prospect* has spawned has continued to act on the basis of that original hypothesis. Historically, we have been more concerned with preserving hope than with real examination of the problem of preserving biological structure.

A major reason why nine patients were allowed to thaw out and rot in Chatsworth was because the relatives (and in some instances the patients themselves) were more interested in buying hope than in buying a real chance at revival. In hospitals, nursing homes, and other agencies where people are cared for in a framework where they cannot speak out for or defend themselves, society at least attempts to set up feedback mechanisms in the form of watchdog agencies and ombudsmen to set standards and evaluate care. In the absence of such precautions, anyone can claim anything, and it becomes impossible to sort out reality from fantasy.

One of the most difficult and dangerous aspects of cryonics has been the absence of feedback. If you enter a hospital for surgery, take your car in for repair, or contract for the addition of a room to your home, you will have little doubt as to the quality of the work or the desirability of the outcome. The reason this is so is because of feedback. The task undertaken yields results in a meaningful time frame—and the results can be evaluated. This has not been the case with cryonics. We have proceeded by speculation in a time frame of hundreds of years. In consequence, our society (which is not composed of total fools) has peered around the edges of our hope and speculation, noted the absence of substantial evidence, and dismissed cryonics as a viable alternative to death. To put it mildly, the absence of feedback on our procedures, in the form of real research results, has created a severe marketing problem.

This lack of feedback has affected every technical question in cryonics. Which freezing technique is best? What is the safest temperature to store at? How much and which kind of cryoprotective agent should be used? How can "outsiders" verify that a patient is really being maintained in storage and that the quality of that storage is adequate and everything it was promised to be? These are serious questions and they cut to the core of our program and often are at the root of divisions and dissension within the cryonics community.

There is a significant and growing contingent of people who accuse Alcor and "Southern California cryonics" of being "too high tech" or more precisely too "chauvinistically high tech." John de Rivaz, commenting in the September, 1985 issue of *The Immortalist* has stated that "the organizers of cryonics and other immortalist societies should offer members as many options as are conceivable, from high technology, high-cost, California-style cryonics on one hand, right down through interment in the Arctic or peat bogs or storage in a deep freeze as practiced by Dr. Martinot in France on the other." The thrust of this kind of commentary is that cryonics and hope ought to be affordable to everyone. A noble sentiment, and one which we share. But the question is how do we rationally, realistically get there? Are we just trying to provide hope or are we trying to do something that will realistically result in our continued survival?

Cryonic suspension as practiced by Alcor is expensive because we are trying to offer more than empty hope. We know what our objective is: to preserve structure and viability under the best possible conditions. To this end we spend a fair amount of time and energy trying to insure that the care given meets our objectives. Tossing someone into a peat bog or dropping them into a vat of formaldehyde on the grounds of providing some hope not only isn't going to work—it is cruel and immoral as well. Proposals such as Mr. de Rivaz's cross our desk all too often. What about freeze-drying people? What about chemical fixation? What about any alternative to spending time, effort, and money? In short, what about a Cosmic Automatic Road to Immortality?

The fact of the matter is that techniques other than cryogenic storage following "high tech" perfusion may offer some hope, may even be superior to cryonics, but we don't know this! We selected cryonic suspension on the basis of conservative criteria because we don't know how memory is stored or how much molecular structure needs to be preserved to conserve identity or allow for reanimation. We chose cryonic suspension because, on the basis of the best available evidence, it is the best technique around for achieving biopreservation.

Alcor has not been content to let the matter rest there. We realize that Ettinger's original hypothesis needs a great deal of additional evidence before we can rest comfortably or even be assured that cryonics is good enough to achieve the goal of continued survival. It was nearly 20 years after publication of *The Prospect* that Alcor undertook the first basic research to examine the premise of cryonics. That research consisted of systematic electron microscopy to evaluate the extent of cryoinjury both under "optimum" conditions and after 24 hours of death with simple refrigeration. In 1983, Alcor performed the first postmortem examination of frozen-thawed suspension patients' remains (following conversion to neuropreservation) and discovered the presence of massive fracturing in most organs—including the central nervous system. For nearly 20 years patients have been suspended without anyone doing evaluations on animals, let alone on people, to determine what even the simplest gross effects of cooling to liquid nitrogen temperature were. For 20 years we've been freezing people without really knowing what kind of damage we were doing, or how we might improve things to minimize that damage!

Using conservative criteria, such as state-of-the-art medical and cryobiological technology, provides us with a benchmark and a framework against which we can measure progress. Such technologies are "expensive" because they involve feedback. When we suspend someone at Alcor we conduct sophisticated laboratory evaluation of every step of the procedure. We do bacterial cultures on our perfusates and perfusion circuits to act as a check that good sterile technique is being employed (not only to protect the patient, but to protect the staff as well—contamination goes both ways!). We run chemical analyses on the perfusate to make sure that it was mixed and formulated properly. We also take tissue, blood, and perfusate samples to evaluate the state of the patient before, during, and after suspension. In cryonics we don't have the "luxury" of waiting a few weeks to see if our patients recover from the surgery, or develop an infection from "sloppy" technique. Unless we provide the feedback in the form of quality control and laboratory evaluations, there just won't be any.

And, as the history of cryonics has sadly shown, without both positive and negative feedback there is no way to know whether you're on the right track. Opinions then hold the same weight as facts, and anyone is free to speculate and peddle false hope and empty promises. And empty promises can kill.

Not very long ago, I spoke with the family of a suspension patient who was unable to afford continued whole-body cryogenic care (the patient was suspended before current funding criteria were in place). They had been told and apparently believed that simply removing their relative from suspension and immersing the patient in formaldehyde solution promised some chance of eventual revival. No amount of trying to explain that the brain would be completely autolyzed and digested before formaldehyde (or peat bog acids, for that matter) could diffuse in was of any avail. We have actually conducted experiments to evaluate this, and we could thus speak with certainty that the brain would be decomposed long before formalin could diffuse through many millimeters of skin and bone and reach even the surface of the cerebral cortex. Despite the fact that neurosuspension was offered free of charge, they preferred to believe that chemical preservation "offered some chance."

This same kind of attitude characterizes many of the people who have accused Alcor of wielding a "golden scalpel" and of being unwilling to offer a family of low-cost alternatives or even "anything the customer wants." What they fail to understand is that, in the absence of the same kind of evidence that exists for cryonics, the various low-cost options they tout might be simply no better than empty ritual or hopeful prayer. If it doesn't matter how effective the preservation is, or even if it works at all (such as in the case of the peat bog suggestion), then why even bother with the business of preservation at all? Why not just believe in a merciful God and a bountiful Heaven and be done with it? Why even go to the inconvenience of opening a hole in the moss of a bog?

Offering ineffective or totally unsubstantiated forms of treatment just because a patient cannot afford cryonic suspension is not something that Alcor (or any cryonics organization) should rationally be expected to become involved with. An instructive analogy would be a hospital which offered to have a witch doctor chant over a cancer patient because he couldn't afford chemotherapy, or to offer to remove someone's gall bladder using kitchen utensils and no sterile technique because they cannot afford state-of-the-art surgery. For anyone who is truly in need, Alcor has been and is willing to go out of the way to be accommodating and hold costs down. But we also realize that any procedure costs something, and that those now in suspension as well as those who have made suspension arrangements with Alcor depend on us. Our first responsibility is to them. That means that standards will have to be set and operating criteria established to protect everyone from litigation and false expectations, as well as false promises.

There may be adequate or superior alternative techniques to cryogenic storage. But it is going to cost something to investigate them and to establish quality control and other criteria to see to it that they are adequately administered. 20 years after cryonics was suggested we are just now beginning to put into place the framework to demonstrate whether or not existing freezing techniques are effective in preserving most of the molecular structure of the patient. It has been a long, hard battle to lay that framework. We are heavily committed to it, and our expertise is in that area. Those who would rush into chemically fixing patients or storing them in department store freezers should be prepared to do the groundwork themselves to establish the safety and reliability of those techniques in preserving ultrastructure over long periods of time. And they should not expect us to follow until this has been done.

Even so, the fact is Alcor has had a long standing commitment to the pilot evaluation of fixatives and embedding schemes for preserving structure. As far as we know, we are the only organization in the world which has already examined tissue at intervals after fixation at room temperature to evaluate loss of structure. (We've looked at brain tissue stored in aqueous fixative for up to three years and the results are not good.) We are also storing embedded tissue (which has all its water replaced by plastic compounds, and which should minimize entropic damage) and will be examining that at intervals as well. In the meantime, we have no intention of offering any preservation procedure which we do not have reasonable confidence in, and we are not about to abandon costly quality control and feedback for wandering around idly and "hoping" everything went as we intended.

Our commitment to quality control and feedback has already paid off. In a recent suspension we discovered that a potentially serious error had been made in perfusate preparation, an error which fortunately did not result in harm to the patient. We also detected a break in sterile technique during pump set-up as a result of doing perfusate cultures. This kind of feedback alerts us to trouble spots and helps ensure that a consistent and high quality of care is delivered. The majority of cryonics organizations have conducted suspensions in the past without reference to or even concern about quality control or good care. We have been told over and over again that it doesn't matter how you get frozen as much as if you get frozen—all the errors on this end will be sorted out on the other. This kind of attitude has resulted in patients being perfused under filthy conditions with embalming equipment or not being perfused at all and with patients being stored at high subzero temperatures while armchair arguments are advanced to wish away objections and information that contraindicate this approach.

These advocates of hope and hype, no matter how good their intentions, sooner or later will confront the fact that this a rather inflexible and altogether too real world in which we live. If we are to survive we must keep our eyes open and never lose sight of the hard realities. Cryonics cannot and will not save everyone. Money, circumstances, and just plain bad luck have and will result in some painful defeats. For the time being we have to learn to live with that. Retreating into fantasy or becoming merchants of empty hope is not going to result in our long term survival. Progress will come only through feedback and rigorous reexamination of our premises and practices in the light of growing knowledge. ■

HAS CRYONICS TAKEN THE WRONG PATH?

THE UNNOTICED CONFLICT BETWEEN RESCUE TECHNOLOGY AND FUTURIST PHILOSOPHIES.

BY STEPHEN W. BRIDGE

This article was written in April, 2006, published on the Alcor News Blog on August 15, 2006, and republished in Cryonics February 2014.

A Quiet Hero

A friend of mine died this winter. He wasn't interested in cryonics, but what he didn't do is not the point of this essay. What he did do has saved uncounted lives, maybe including yours. The way this man went about his life has given me a clue to what I think is a major hidden problem with cryonics.

Douglas Crichlow was a year behind me at DePauw University (Greencastle, Indiana) when he arrived as a freshman in 1967. We all thought he was interesting but overly obsessed with fire trucks and ambulances. In my mind, he was just a kid who hadn't grown out of a childhood excitement, unlike me in my sophomoric sophistication. Most of Doug's conversation was about fire departments, emergency medical services, and disaster preparedness. It turned out he was amazingly well read in these subjects. Remember, in 1967 there were few EMTs, the concept of paramedics was brand new, and CPR was only a few years old. A national training program for EMTs and paramedics didn't begin until 1970. Disaster management was not yet even a concept.

In 1967 ambulance services in all but the largest cities were provided not by hospitals or fire departments. They were provided by the local funeral homes. If you were injured in an automobile accident, the hearse took you to the hospital. The driver had no oxygen, no CPR, no remote understanding of trauma treatment. If you didn't make it to the hospital, well, you were already in the hearse. And in these days, before airbags, shock-absorbing body frames, and high seatbelt use, there were a LOT of fatalities.

Doug was a bit overweight, walked with a limp from a childhood injury, was kind of a nerd, and was a freshman who thought he knew how the world needed to be changed. But he was also amiable, a persuasive speaker, religious without being a pest about it, and well read in a wide variety of subjects. In his favorite subjects, he seemed to have read everything in print.

Doug's enthusiasm about emergency services was contagious with many students, including his roommate, Steve Collier, and several other older students, notably Derrick Warner. The three of them and several other students formed the DePauw Volunteer Fire Brigade. They even talked me into it. The local fire department scoffed at these students—until the local newspaper caught on fire and threatened to burn down Greencastle's entire downtown. 20 DePauw students showed up to haul and man hoses, fetch food for the firemen, and stayed to clean up. That made a BIG impression.

By the time Doug was a senior, the DePauw Fire Brigade was an ongoing organization working on fires on campus and around the city. (It still exists today, and this initial cooperation between "town and gown" was so successful that every DePauw student now has a requirement of community service.) By this time Derrick had graduated and was living in Greencastle, so he, Steve Collier, and Doug turned their attention to the problem of no ambulance service in Putnam County. When they could not persuade the City Council, the fire department, or the hospital to begin ambulance service, they bought an ambulance on credit and started their own service, showing up at accidents. When they began saving lives, other people noticed. The organization they started, Operation Life, still provides ambulance service in Putnam County. Doug was obsessive about the details. He wrote SOPs (Standard Operating Procedures) for everything his team did. When he couldn't find training manuals for his EMTs, he called experts all over the country, and then typed up his own manual.

After the Blizzard of 1978, Doug moved to Indianapolis to become Director of Emergency Management and Civil Defense. In 1983 he formed his own consulting company and became a nationally known expert in the field of emergency preparedness. In 1985 his company organized and hosted in Indianapolis the first World Conference on Disaster & Emergency Management which attracted government, fire, police, and medical leaders from all over the United States and 20 other countries to discuss the planning, coordination, and response to major disasters such as hurricanes, earthquakes, floods, and terrorism. Unfortunately, emergency medicine wasn't able to save Doug himself. He died suddenly of cardiac arrest this year, just a week after his mother had died of cancer.

You won't find much about Doug Crichlow on the internet, although one important summary of modern disaster management approaches is available in his article "Taking a comprehensive approach to handling disasters."

However, hundreds of people influenced by Doug are now fire fighters, EMTs, emergency room physicians, and emergency management directors for towns and cities all over America. He didn't invent emergency services; but if you are ever injured with your life in danger, and an ambulance with trained EMTs or paramedics shows up to rescue you—instead of a hearse and mortician, you can thank Douglas Crichlow and a handful of others like him.

Comparing EMS and Cryonics

Although I helped on the student fire department, I wasn't much under Doug's influence at college. At the time, I was deeply into my major of theatre and just not that interested in fighting fires and saving lives. In retrospect, I think I was also too ignorant about the world and not ready to notice what needed to be changed.

I wasn't open to ideas about changing the world until 1976 when I met a somewhat similar missionary for saving lives—Mike Darwin. Like Doug, Mike was well read in many areas and intensely well read in the things that interested him most: cryonics/cryobiology and emergency medicine. He had a reserve of energy that seemed inexhaustible and he could argue his points persuasively. And by 1976, there had been a couple of deaths in my family, and my mother and both grandmothers would die in the next year and a half. Mortality was sitting on my couch staring at me every night and I was ready to listen to Mike telling me there was a solution.

Today emergency medical services are available just about everywhere in the United States. Most fire fighters in Indiana are also EMTs and trained to save lives. If you want to do emergency medical work for a living, there are dozens of programs ready to give you the chance to learn. Every large city and most medium-sized ones have a disaster plan and do disaster drills. Doug and his peers have had an obvious and lasting effect on the world.

Cryonics, on the other hand, is in some ways still stuck in the 1960's. It's not popular and still looks like a cult to many people. So far it does not appear to be on its way to having a lasting effect on the world. A handful of people have labored mightily to bring forth a lot of suggestive evidence but not much proof that they can achieve what they plan. Why did EMS succeed while cryonics success has stalled?

Emergency Medical Services have not been around too much longer than cryonics, yet the idea of EMS quickly moved into the mainstream of American life. The most important reason is obvious—EMTs, paramedics, ambulances, and trauma centers get immediate results. It doesn't take long to prove that the medical model saves more lives than the mortuary model. After 40 years of emergency work, EMS personnel can point to millions of rescued people, living witnesses to the success of the model. It is straightforward, easy to understand, easy to assimilate into your life. Yes, these people will still die anyway, just at older ages, unless technologies like cryonics can intervene. But cryonics has no rescued patients going on television talk shows to show that cryopreservation rescued them, and we won't have any such witnesses for decades at least. "Hey, guys, we can now preserve cells a whole lot better than we did last year," just doesn't have the same effect as living people telling how they were "miraculously" saved by the paramedics.

There is another very subtle difference that might play into the different levels of success, however—a difference in the main players. As unusual as Doug

Crichlow seemed to me at that youthful stage of our lives, he was still much more in the mainstream of American life than was anyone in cryonics then—and few, if any, cryonics leaders could be said to be part of the American mainstream since that time. Doug was a moderate Republican and he became a respected and successful government leader and businessman. He had a long, loving marriage to his wife and was the devoted father of two daughters. He was a sincere Christian without being confrontational about it. He had no goal for his work other than to save lives. He treated emergency medical services as the standard service every community should provide and he didn't load the idea down with considerations of politics, religion, or race. There were no Bible verses printed on the sides of the ambulance; no "free Gospel reading with every rescue." It was just good medicine.

In contrast, just about all of the early leaders of cryonics had some combination of extreme minority views and were "outsiders" in many ways. Most could be labeled as rebels—atheist or agnostic, libertarian or Randian or even anarchist, and they usually had family relationships outside of what most Americans consider the "ordinary" way to live (one-partner, heterosexual marriage with children). A large percentage of cryonics leaders and cryonics members have been childless couples, long-term singles, or homosexual.

Even more importantly, Robert Ettinger and many others of the early advocates for cryonics proclaimed that cryonics was part of a radical change in human nature, that humans would eventually turn into something "beyond" human—immortal, omniscient, space traveling super-beings, maybe in the form of robots or computer software. The concept of cryonics as an especially advanced form of emergency rescue service became clouded in a fog of transhumanist evangelism. I have even heard people argue that they support cryonics because they think it will help to overturn religion. For an immense percentage of Americans, these concepts are bewildering or even terrifying. "Our grandchildren are not going to be human? And these people want to destroy our religion? What kind of crazy people want that?" How could we expect that people turned off by what they see as weird or offensive futurist ideas would be turned on to the concept of cryonics? Who wants to be part of a future that will be inhospitable to their beliefs and ideas—led by the people who are often gleefully telling them this?

While this was certainly not the intent of Robert Ettinger, cryonics may have veered from being a mainstream medical rescue technology almost from the beginning. "Like calls to like." Perhaps the personalities and attitudes of cryonicists in the beginning actively put off the mainstream and only appealed to other people swimming down a narrow waterway off to the side.

It would be interesting to replay history and see what would have happened had, say, Doug Crichlow and Mike Darwin met at the right time in their lives. Would they have bonded and worked together in their common interest in saving lives? Their combined knowledge and drive could have had a dynamic effect on others. Or would their personalities and very different philosophical views have bounced them apart like the opposing poles of magnets? Would a more mainstream, Christian, family-oriented approach to cryonics have made a difference to the early success of cryonics? If Robert Ettinger had been a religious, observant Jew, could this idea have become a part of general medical culture, or even become popular with a particular sub-group of American Jews? Or is the concept itself too far beyond the mainstream to have ever appealed to the people that Doug Crichlow got involved in his grand idea? Could anyone with a personality and background much different from Robert Ettinger have even come up with the concept of cryonics?

We were who we were, of course, and we can't go back and change that; we can only go forward from where we are. But we can become more aware of where we are. The really interesting thing is that these options still face us; although I don't think we have ever called these choices "options" before. We can still choose where we will place our focus for the next two decades — how much emphasis to place on medical rescue, how much to stick with our appeal to futurists and computer technicians, how much to appeal to the mainstream culture.

Note that these choices we have to make are not mutually exclusive. We must increase our understanding and ability to handle the medical end of cryonics. If we wish to attract more mainstream members, we want to do so without losing the futurists among us. But we need to make these decisions consciously and be aware that they are decisions.

Transhumanists, futurists, and cryonics

Would a greater emphasis on medical rescue have made cryonics more popular? How much was the public and medical involvement with cryonics damaged by its association with the concepts of physical immortality, future superhumans, expansion into space, libertarianism and anarchy, and an underlying antagonism toward religion and "traditional family values"? Would ambulance-based rescue services have been given a chance if presented with such philosophical baggage?

Mike Darwin and others liked to shock friends with scenarios of what options might exist for future humans: group sex in free fall; the ability to change genders daily or to choose the "hermaphrodite option"; the ability to make immense changes to one's brain, like implantable language chips or pleasure switches; the ability to make startling changes to one's body, like functional wings, blue fur, or replacing your skull and other bones with titanium. Keith Henson's favorite scenario was making ten thousand duplicate copies of himself and sending them out into the galaxy to explore. They would all meet in a few millennia for a party on the far side of the galaxy to share information, swap tales, and plan their move to other galaxies. It was interesting to watch the division at parties, as some people moved toward Mike, Keith, and others and as just as many moved into other rooms completely.

Of course, these very ideas attracted many people to cryonics in the early years. Many of these people didn't care about or even completely understand the basic purpose of cryonics—to save lives. They simply saw it as part of something that was interesting to talk about, or possibly just as a tool that they might be able to use to get them to a future that interests them more than today's reality. And since they were most interested in the future, they often did not spend enough time in the present to focus on the hard tasks of learning physiology and chemistry, getting EMT/paramedic training, writing technical reports, evaluating procedures, doing both laboratory and literature research, and the other nitty-gritty daily details necessary to make cryonics a survival technology where success means "saving lives." Instead, too many of them (including me) focused on how to make cryonics popular, where success means "gaining members."

Now I must admit that some of these visions of the future attracted me to cryonics: Even though I had read science fiction for many years, this was the first time that I actually envisioned myself as part of the future. And in 1977, it was easy to get into cryonics "on the ground floor," to see that I could be a major part of changing the world. Cryonics was not only a solution to a problem of life and death; it was a grand adventure and a chance to defy authority (that was my generation, remember).

So I am stuck here with contemplating whether or not another pathway would have been better for the success of cryonics, while acknowledging that that pathway might well have not attracted me to cryonics at all. And I must contemplate how much the choices of my friends and myself over the past 25 years have prevented or delayed the success of cryonics, as well as how they have advanced it.

And I must further admit that an over-emphasis on future technology is probably inherent in the very concept of cryonics. We cannot rescue our cryonics members now. That can only be done by medical personnel of the future. We are attempting to move these patients through time to a hospital of the future. Before we invest our money, our time, and our very lives in such a speculative pursuit, we have to imagine the kinds of futures that will allow for success. For the limited technological and scientific understanding of most humans, however, these futures do not appear to be in any conceivable straight line from today's reality. And most people simply do not have the imagination to conceive of how the world could change in 100 years or more. Even the writers of science fiction and futurist speculation, whom one would think would have a better grasp on the future, have trouble developing a plausible, coherent vision of a future reality, with rare exceptions.

EMS only has to rely on 30 minutes into the future, the time for transportation and for the hospital to be ready for the patient. They don't concern themselves with 100 years in the future. Perhaps we are at a point in the development of cryonics where we should put more emphasis on the first 30 minutes and less on the next 100 years.

Where are the medical personnel?

We understand — or should understand — that cryonics is not about saving "dead people." It is about redefining the limits of "death." Cryonics is the last step of medical technology, not an alternate type of storage of the dead. "Death" means a permanent cessation of life. If a comatose patient is labeled as "brain dead" by physicians, yet eventually wakes up and resumes his life, the newspaper headline should not be, "Brain-dead patient revives!" It should be, "Patient mistakenly labeled as brain-dead revives!" Likewise, if cryonics works and these patients are eventually resuscitated to their conscious existence, then we can show that they also were "mistakenly labeled as dead."

So, where are the medical rescue personnel in cryonics? Over the past 40 years of this endeavor, perhaps no more than a dozen people who had a deep scientific understanding of the principles of cryonics have actually committed themselves to the scientific research or medical rescue aspects of cryonics. And only three of them (Jerry Leaf, Mike Darwin, and Steven Harris) started from a physical medicine background (and only Harris had an M.D.). Yes, other physicians have been members or board members, but most have had specialties in psychiatry and were involved much more in the business and promotion side of cryonics than the medical side. (Alcor has had other paramedics and nurses as employees and volunteers; but none have stayed involved long enough to provide many solid long-term contributions.)

Why have the medical people avoided cryonics? Certainly there has been little money in cryonics, especially compared to medicine. Leaf, Darwin, and Harris accumulated a lot more stress than wealth from their involvement in cryonics (approximately Stress = 100; Wealth = 0). And most medically-trained people, like most other mainstream-focused, educated people, don't want to be involved in something as "socially unacceptable" as cryonics has been over the years. The publicity for being involved in cryonics cases has been risky for several medical professionals. But this cannot explain it all. I have met many paramedics, EMTs, nurses, and physicians over the years and quite a few of them were willing to take chances in other areas of their lives, taking business risks, publicly supporting unpopular causes. Cryonics is about saving lives. Why haven't more of these people jumped into helping us?

It's a long list:

1. We still haven't done a good enough job explaining how cryonics fits into the field of medicine. Too many medically trained people don't "get" cryonics, don't see where the "life-saving" comes in.

2. Even for those medically trained people who do "get cryonics," we haven't placed our focus on the medical requirements, so these bright people don't see where their niches are.

3. Cryonicists on average have not been nearly as welcoming of medically trained people as we would like to think we have. Some Alcor administrators over the years have been actively hostile to medical people or generally hostile to bright people with new ideas. Yes, these ideas are often naive and simplistic, but none of us automatically understood the subtleties of cryonics the first time we heard about it, either. Others gave us the chance to learn. Can we do less for physicians and nurses?

    Even worse in some ways may have been people like me when I was Alcor's President. Under my leadership, we talked about needing medical personnel; but we weren't ready to receive medical volunteers and employees because we had no plan for using them. We certainly missed out on people who could have helped us. Active hostility can be attributed to the problems of an individual. But lack of preparation and the lack of a plan for bringing in new technical volunteers or employees lower the reputation of the entire organization and even cryonics in general.

4. The very fact we can't show that cryonics produces "survivors" removes some of the excitement and motivation for why most emergency personnel choose their jobs—saving lives is exciting and gives the rescuer a strong sense of pride. Many medical personnel in general get much of their sense of self-worth from helping people recover. A patient saying "thank you for helping me" is a motivation as strong as income. Waiting a century or two for the thank-yous is probably not going to provide the same emotional rush. As one medical student said to me, "I just can't get excited about patients who don't talk back."

5. Several people have written in the past that one of the biggest problems with improving cryonics techniques is that we can get very little feedback. We can't show better survival results from changing techniques, even if we tried them on animals, because the set of processes of dying, fluid replacement for cryoprotection, and cool-down to storage temperature has so many variables. And since we don't know how to revive even animals from cryopreservation, the end result of one research project can look pretty much like another. (Yes, we can show small incremental improvements in certain narrowly-defined details, but

nothing that will impress people outside of cryonics.) In medicine, success or failure can be measured in terms of "who survives and for how long." We don't have that in cryonics, and it is frustrating for everyone. Why become a medical rescue person in cryonics if you can't tell if you are making a difference with your knowledge and your presence?

6.   We only do 2-5 cryopreservations a year. Rescue workers can do that many rescue cases on one busy day. Emergency room physicians can have that many cases going on at the same time. Even if we had rescue personnel as full-time or part-time employees, how do we keep them busy? Giving tours? Measuring chemicals? Since we have too few suspensions, we would have to do animal research to keep people usefully occupied and to learn techniques and build teams—which is expensive and uncertain and maybe pretty useless unless you already have the medical/scientific people in place doing the planning. Many people have told cryonicists that they need to do more animal research, like Mike and Jerry used to do.

　　　　The expense of research is a major difficulty, of course, but the costs may not be where you think they are. We could find the money for any individual experiment. But the federal and practical requirements for doing animal research are much more difficult to follow than they were 25 years ago. You pretty much need a full-time person just to make sure you are following all of the reporting and filing requirements, plus the requirements for animal care and handling, medical waste handling, and security of your medications. Many cities are hostile to animal research and will add extra requirements or simply refuse to permit it all. And we must not forget that doing animal research in the same facility in which you care for your patients will subject those patients to higher risk from animal research protestors.

　　　　Mike Darwin once pointed out, quite rightly, that our need to protect our patients has made cryonics organizations much more conservative and less likely to take risks than we were 25 years ago. It may be time to increase the further legal and physical separation between patient care, suspension rescue teams, and research. In order to make progress, someone has to be able to take risks.

7.   Cryonics' dependence on future technologies—that might take a century or more to develop—distances the result from the action so far that the results are beyond the manageable limit of most people's imaginations. It becomes hard to take the concept seriously, and this distance probably works to take away the sense of urgency for the younger cryonicists and younger medical personnel alike.

8.   Cryonics organization staff are also distanced from the results and may be willing to make and tolerate more mistakes because "our friends in the future" will take care of everything.

9. Our emphasis on telling everyone how great things will be in the future both chases people away by making us sound like a cult and takes energy and time away from what our focus should be—making sure that we are doing well enough with rescues, perfusion, and cool-down today that we can be confident we ARE saving individual lives and not merely DNA for cloning.

10. I'm not sure if this one is more cause or more effect. Jerry Leaf and Mike Darwin also had that incredibly valuable obsession with soaking up knowledge and with getting the details right that the best medical personnel have. Such obsessions are time-consuming, expensive, and annoying to those who are not similarly obsessed. This approach doesn't make for big jumps in capability because it focuses on small steps—a thousand preparations before the first small step, and a thousand more for every step after that. It's not sexy; it doesn't make for good public relations stories; it doesn't get the non-medical people excited and involved. It's hard work. I see a severe shortage of these obsessions in cryonics organizations today.

    It's the sort of thing that Doug Crichlow did well. And in the EMS field, it eventually impressed the medical personnel and government officials.

11. And finally, there is one possible reason that is so big that "Number 11" is inadequate to label it. This may be a difficult truth for some of us to accept—we may chase away medical personnel and other helpful people because we are so focused on ourselves.

Almost everyone who has committed themselves to working in cryonics has done so because they wanted this idea to work for them—they wanted to save their own lives. Sure, they were willing to let other people get their lives saved, too; but they didn't get involved in order to do good for others. And therefore many cryonicists, and even cryonics organization staff, may stop well short of the maximum effort needed to make this idea work. Doug Crichlow was primarily motivated by saving the lives of other people. So are most emergency medical personnel. They never run out of people who need help and so they never run out of motivation to keep going.

We may not be able to get many medical people involved in cryonics if it remains primarily about saving ourselves. I still maintain that the decision makers, public speakers, and Directors for cryonics organizations should be suspension members of that organization. But we need to make room in cryonics for medically trained people whose major motivation is to help others. They may be the ones who bring new knowledge and innovations and who care about the details, because it is the right way to do things. And to get these people, we must change our approach to the other problems I listed above.

Where do we go from here?

I am not trying to promote one cryonics organization over another in this article. I write more about Alcor because I know it best. But I want to emphasize that there has never been a cryonics organization with more than 3-4 people at one time actively promoting and developing medical and scientific improvements. Even today, after four decades, no organization is better than one traffic collision away from a major loss of biomedical understanding and capability. No current organization looks marginally competent when compared to even a tiny hospital in a rural town.

Most employees and directors of all of the cryonics organizations are people who became interested in cryonics because they are interested in the future and want to stay alive as long as possible. They became actively involved because they are responsible people and they didn't see anyone else stepping forward. But they are typically writers, computer programmers, business owners, attorneys, accountants, life insurance sales people, etc. with the occasional engineer (and one librarian) tossed into the mix. They are not medically inclined and may not appreciate the medical issues and the need for detail involved.

Today's organizations must take the initiative to make cryonics not just popular, but to make cryonics WORK. This might mean turning down interviews, spending money on research instead of ads, maybe even placing less focus on membership growth because management time and financial resources are going into upgrading our rescue capability instead.

Our Choices

I expect a lot of disagreement with my proposition and I encourage you members to express your opinions. We must have that discussion now. If no one is interested in follow-up to this article, then I may as well devote the rest of my days to gardening, home repair, and dusting my book collection. I always thought that my cryonics participation would return results in an increased chance of a long lifespan and adventures in the future. But I'm no longer so confident, and I'm no longer sure that I made the best decisions when I had the opportunity to lead.

Let's look at one key decision that was made a year ago as an example of the confusion we are faced with. Alcor hired a promotion/production company to produce a DVD for Alcor. It is called *The Limitless Future: A documentary exploring mankind's quest for a long and healthy life*. This effort is basically a well-produced infomercial about cryonics; very obviously aimed at making a more mainstream audience comfortable with the basic concept. I (not being mainstream) felt very uncomfortable after I saw it the first time but I didn't know why. I showed it to a young friend who had just been introduced to cryonics and who had watched the Discovery Channel documentary (*Immortality on Ice*) a couple of weeks previously. She put her finger on the problem right away—it was an attempt to appeal to the people least likely to be interested in the concept. She said that even with all of the fine camera work, narration, and intelligent heads on view, it was less interesting than one live lunch with a real cryonicist. Where was the sense of adventure, of changing the world?

So here I am in this article arguing against too much emphasis on that futurist radicalism that got me involved in the first place. But that doesn't mean I am now happy with the focus of *The Limitless Future.* I am still uncomfortable with it; but I have added a second reason—it doesn't make a good case for cryonics being a workable part of emergency medicine. But then we as cryonicists haven't given the producers anything in that direction to promote, except for a vague dream of the future.

What do you say, Alcor members (and other cryonicists)? Do we put our energies into medical rescue? Do we push back all of our talk about transhumanism, uploading, the Singularity, politics, and conflicts with religion? Or do we focus on the high tech community and talk more about the future? Do we try to appeal to the mainstream of the English-speaking world? Do we try to broaden our focus beyond ourselves?

Remember, the question is not, "What do you want us to do?" The question is something that should be much more important to you—"What approach will be most effective in saving lives?" ∎

AFTERWORD

BY ASCHWIN DE WOLF

When Michael Darwin and Steve Bridge launched the *IABS Newsletter* in 1977 that later became *Cryonics* magazine, Alcor barely existed and magazines were the product of typewriters, time-consuming layout, and (hand-written) letters to the editor. As I write this in September 2014, Alcor employs 7 full-time staff members and 1 part-time staff member and has over 1,000 members with cryonics arrangements. And perhaps most importantly, Alcor has introduced a number of major technological advances that push the organization further in the direction of human suspended animation. These developments raise an important question. What is the role of *Cryonics* magazine today, and what can we expect from Alcor in the next 40 years?

It is undeniable that with the rise of the Internet and the widespread adoption of smart phones (a development anticipated in Frederik Pohl's 1969 cryonics novel *The Age of the Pussyfoot*) *Cryonics* magazine has changed as well. As important news and new developments in cryonics can now be disseminated to Alcor members in real-time, the importance of a (paper) magazine to keep members informed about these things appears to be lessened, especially for younger- and computer-savvy people. But just like newspapers, magazines, and books continue to be published, publication of *Cryonics* magazine remains important for a number of reasons.

First of all, a formal publication can play an important role in the documentation and preservation of institutional knowledge (technological, logistical, and legal). The requirement of publishing all important (proposed) changes at Alcor in the magazine ensures a sense of continuity and facilitates member involvement. Secondly, the structured and serial nature of a publication allows it to be used to drive progress at the organization. When the editor, an Alcor official, or member believes in a specific improvement, a case can be made for it in the magazine that can be scrutinized and endorsed by other Alcor members and officials. And last but not least, a (paper) magazine remains a popular format to publish long (technical) articles and highlight the human aspects of cryonics (such as member profiles). I will also add that I personally think that publication of a paper magazine is particularly important for Alcor because of its unique aspiration to both preserve and renew. Just think of the "magic" of being able to present a resuscitated patient with the latest paper issue of *Cryonics* magazine!

Not only has the production and presentation of the magazine changed, so has the content. As a general rule we should expect the contents of the magazine to reflect the current direction of the organization and it usually has done this. How do we conceptualize cryonics? How do we promote it? To what extent do technological advances change our perception of the feasibility of this endeavour? Can we be more specific about resuscitation and reintegration of our patients? Should we be satisfied with the current number of members? Have the demographics of cryonics changed, and what does this mean for how we present cryonics to the general public? Just think of all the articles you have read in this book with these questions in mind and it should have become evident that Alcor has evolved and will continue to evolve.

As was indicated in the Introduction, the articles collected in this book are not a "neutral" selection of writings that have appeared in the magazine over the last 40 years. While ensuring not to omit any classic and important writings, we have deliberately selected those articles that reflect the current perspective on cryonics that guides Alcor. In a nutshell, this means a strong emphasis on cryonics as an evidence-based extension of medicine, and less emphasis on any associated philosophies or grandiose visions. This does not mean that we do not recognize the value of such writings, but we think it evident that the widespread adoption of any new medical technology requires that it should be presented in a manner that is non-objectionable to most people. As I have said on occasion, "cryonics is controversial enough; let's not make it more controversial."

So what can we expect in the next 40 years of Alcor? I am not a big proponent of making bold predictions but I think it reasonable to expect that we will see a further increase in membership (provided costs are kept under control), a more diverse membership, new advances in cryopreservation technologies, changes in long-term care conditions, and a much stronger emphasis on resuscitation and reintegration.

Although the envisioned, almost limitless, capabilities of future medicine sometimes weakens the desire to make rapid technological progress in our field, cryonics needs an ideal to aim for. That ideal is human suspended animation. If the process of cryopreservation (or any credible preservation technology) can prevent a patient from deterioration without adding further injury, the only technical objection to cryonics would be to claim that a disease can never be cured in the future, and who could reasonably claim that? Human suspended animation remains a formidable challenge; but now that we are on the path of eliminating ice formation and fracturing, the remaining scientific, technological, and logistical challenges can be identified, i.e. conducting our procedures in an environment that excludes further ischemic injury (something we already know how to do in ideal circumstances), designing vitrification solutions with negligible toxicity that avoid excessive dehydration, and developing safe re-warming technologies. The ultimate goal of Alcor aiming at human suspended animation provides an important benchmark to measure our progress and to identify future "repair" scenarios.

I will close this afterword on the topic of resuscitation and reintegration. While Alcor undoubtedly remains the leading cryonics organization in terms of advancing new technologies, there has been an increasing recognition that most people reject cryonics for personal and social reasons—as opposed to scientific and technological ones. To some extent we have ourselves to blame for this because we have not devoted a whole lot of time to specific resuscitation scenarios and the great benefits of remaining alive and reaching the future. One thing I expect to see more in the magazine, and other Alcor media, is a stronger engagement with concerns about loss and alienation. Clearly, we cannot promise that all will be well in the future; but we can offer a counter-weight to the often dystopian discourse about human enhancement and paradigm-shifting technologies. Most of all, it is important to convey that cryonics is not just a technology to avoid individual oblivion but a means of families, friends, and loved ones to remain together. When people read our magazine, or peruse the Alcor website, we do not only want them to think that human cryopreservation is a good idea, but that we have also put a lot of work into giving members the legal and technological tools to preserve their memories, assets, and most of all, the people dear to them in order to head into this future prepared and together. And what a future it will be! ■

BIOGRAPHIES

Gregory Benford is an emeritus professor of physics at the University of California, Irvine. He is a Woodrow Wilson Fellow, was Visiting Fellow at Cambridge University, and in 1995 received the Lord Prize for contributions to science. A fellow of the American Physical Society and a member of the World Academy of Arts and Sciences, he continues his research in both astrophysics and plasma physics and biotech. He was a staff member at the Livermore Laboratories 1967-71 and has founded three biotech companies, including Genescient. He has published 31 novels, including the bestseller *Timescape*.

Stephen W. Bridge became involved in cryonics in 1977 and was the co-founder and original co-editor of *Cryonics* magazine. He was the President of the Alcor Life Extension Foundation from 1993 to 1997. He led Alcor's move to Scottsdale, Arizona in 1994 and was the chief architect of Alcor's Patient Care Trust. Bridge is currently an Alcor advisor and a Co-Manager of Cryonics Property, LLC, which owns the building that houses Alcor and its patients. He is a graduate of DePauw University and Indiana University. Bridge is a recently retired librarian in Indianapolis, Indiana, where he lives with his family.

Fred Chamberlain III and **Linda Chamberlain** are the co-founders of Alcor, which was incorporated in California in 1972. Linda was the first president and Fred the second. Fred and Linda are also the co-producers/writers of the first manual on how to place humans into cryostasis as well as developing the first special purpose equipment for that purpose. In the 1980s, Linda and Fred relocated to Lake Tahoe, CA and started giving annual cryonics conferences. In the 1990s, the Chamberlains once again headed up Alcor after it relocated to Arizona. Fred went into cryostasis at Alcor in 2012. Linda is retired and living near Alcor.

Michael G. Darwin was the President of the Alcor Life Extension Foundation from 1983 to 1988 where he led the initial expansion of Alcor's capabilities and stabilized its policies and financing. He was Research Director until 1992. He was also President of BioPreservation, Inc. and Director of Research of Twenty-First Century Medicine from 1993 to 1999. Darwin was the co-founder of *Cryonics* magazine and has participated in many cryopreservations. He is currently an independent consultant in the field of critical care medicine.

Aschwin de Wolf is the CEO of Advanced Neural Biosciences, Inc., a neural cryobiology company in Portland, Oregon. Before that, he was employed at the cryonics stabilization services company Suspended Animation, Inc. An active Alcor member since 2003, he is an Advisor to the Board of Directors, and also a member of its Research and Development committee. In 2007, he founded the Institute for Evidence-Based Cryonics, a tax exempt non-profit organization aimed at educating the general public about the benefits of human cryopreservation. De Wolf has been the Editor of Alcor's *Cryonics* magazine since 2008.

Thomas K. Donaldson was a mathematician and well-known cryonics advocate. He received his Ph.D. from the University of Chicago in 1969. He lived in Sunnyvale, California, and for many years in Canberra, Australia, where he taught mathematics at Australian National University. He founded both the Cryonics Association of Australia and the Institute for Neural Cryobiology, which has funded ground-breaking research in cryopreservation of brain tissue. Donaldson also maintained an avid interest in biomedical gerontology, self-publishing the book *A Guide to Anti-aging Drugs* in 1994. In 1988 he was diagnosed with an inoperable brain tumor and sought the right, in California courts, to a premortem cryopreservation, reasoning that it would be better than letting nature run its course until his cardiac arrest. Though he lost the case, it helped spur interest in the rights of patients to end-of-life choices as well as publicizing cryonics. Donaldson's tumor was in remission for many years and he was active in cryonics and life-extension causes until he finally relapsed and was cryopreserved in 2006.

Gregory Fahy earned his Ph.D. in pharmacology from the Medical College of Georgia (graduating with a 4.0 GPA), working under the supervision of organ cryopreservation specialist Dr. Armand Karow, Jr., in 1977. He worked at the American National Red Cross in the laboratory of cryobiology luminary Dr. Harold T. Meryman from 1977 through 1995, conceiving of the concept of organ cryopreservation by vitrification in 1980 and publishing the first proof of principle in Nature in 1985 with W.F. Rall. He moved to California in 1997 and became the scientific leader of 21st Century Medicine not long thereafter. In 2009 he published the first report of the in vivo survival of a vascularized organ after vitrification and transplantation, and in 2013 he presented evidence showing that ice damage seen in the earlier report can be avoided. In 2014 his achievements were recognized by the Society for Cryobiology, which named him a Fellow, the highest honor the Society can convey.

Robert A. Freitas Jr. is Senior Research Fellow at the Institute for Molecular Manufacturing (IMM) in Palo Alto CA (USA) and was a Research Scientist at Zyvex Corp. during 2000-2004. He wrote the first detailed technical design study of a medical nanorobot ever published in a peer-reviewed mainstream biomedical journal, and authored *Nanomedicine*, the first book-length technical discussion of the potential medical applications of molecular nanotechnology and medical nanorobotics. The first 2 volumes of this 4-volume series were published in 1999 and 2003 by Landes Bioscience. He co-authored *Kinematic Self-Replicating Machines* (2004), another first-of-its-kind technical treatise, and has 53 refereed journal publications or contributed book chapters. Freitas won the 2009 Feynman Prize in Nanotechnology for theory, the 2007 Foresight Prize in Communication, and the 2006 Guardian Award from Lifeboat Foundation, and was awarded the first patent on diamond mechanosynthesis in 2010. His home page is www.rfreitas.com.

Steven B. Harris earned his B.S. degree in chemistry (A.C.S.) and his M.D. from the University of Utah. He has been licensed to practice medicine in California since 1984, and has been board-certified in internal medicine and geriatrics. He studied gerontology with Roy Walford, M.D., at UCLA. Harris is currently Director of Research at Critical Care Research (Rancho Cucamonga, California). He is presently engaged in the development of resuscitation physiology involving delivery of lipid-soluble drugs to the resuscitated brain (dog model), and also experimental hypothermia induction for resuscitation and cerebral protection using post-resuscitation hypothermic perfluorocarbon lung lavage (also dog model). He is also Alcor's Chief Medical Advisor.

Hugh L. Hixon, Jr. began working at Alcor in 1982 as the Facilities Engineer, where he currently has the title of Research Fellow. He is in charge of technology application and development, systems maintenance, and institutional memory research applications. Hixon has participated in a record number of cryopreservations. He is the inventor of the "crackphone," a device which determines cracking temperature and degree of cracking during cryogenic cooling of patients. He is the initial fabricator of the Bigfoot Patient Pod System and modified the MVE Bigfoot dewar design for simpler manufacture. Hixon designed and was instrumental in constructing the Alcor Patient Care LN2 Bulk Fill System, in addition to conceiving, designing, and constructing the LN2 Vacuum Transfer System and the LN2 Vapor Cloud Extractor. He is the designer and builder of the Mobile Advanced Rescue Cart (MARC). Before coming to Alcor, Hixon served as a Captain in the United States Air Force from 1965 to 1972 as an Aerospace Munitions Officer. He earned a B.S. in Chemistry from the University of Redlands and an M.S. in Biochemistry from California State University at Long Beach. His father was one of Alcor's first neuropreservation patients.

Tad Hogg is an Institute for Molecular Manufacturing Research Fellow, and was a member of the research staff at Hewlett-Packard Laboratories and the Xerox Palo Alto Research Center (PARC). Hogg holds a Ph.D. from Stanford and B.S. from Caltech, both in physics. He holds over 20 patents and his research includes studies of medical applications of microscopic robots, designing distributed controls for reconfigurable robots, and defect-tolerant architectures for molecular electronics.

Tanya Jones is the Co-founder and Chief Executive Officer of Arigos Biomedical, a startup that is developing a method for the long term banking of organs for the transplant industry. She recently resigned as the Chief Operating Officer of SENS Research Foundation, a nonprofit working to research, develop, and promote comprehensive regenerative medicine solutions for the diseases of aging. As the CEO of Arigos, Jones secured early funding for the company, including becoming the first organization funded by Breakout Labs, the Thiel Foundation's most recent effort to effect disruptive innovation in science and technology. Jones was employed by Alcor in a number of positions from 1991 to 2009 (not all consecutively), including COO and CEO.

Saul Kent has been a member of the Alcor Board since 2001. In 1965, he was one of the founders of the first cryonics organization, the Cryonics Society of New York. Kent is CEO of Suspended Animation, a research company in Boynton Beach, Florida that offers cryonics services to members of cryonics organizations. Kent is co-founder of the Life Extension Foundation, a non-profit organization in Ft. Lauderdale, Florida, which offers information about the latest advances in the biomedical sciences and dietary supplements for health and longevity. Kent is also co-founder and director of three research companies: 21st Century Medicine, Critical Care Research, and BioMarker Pharmaceuticals, as well as co-founder of the Timeship Project.

Theodore (Ted) C. Kraver was born (1938) and reared on a farm in a utopian, small-town, Medina, Ohio community by his librarian mother, entrepreneur father, machinist-inventor grandfather, and serf-master grandmother. His formal education included honors program Aero-Astro B.S. and M.S. degrees from MIT, 20 years later an innovation and organizational design M.B.A. from UCLA, and 20 more years later a Ph.D. in Aero-Mech Engineering from Arizona State University. With emerging Arizona supporting a fervent career environment, Kraver contributed as researcher-engineer-manager in thirteen different industries including bio-med, gaming, aerospace, software, electronics, ed-tech, cryogenics, and automotive. His public sector successes include founding state-level teams to bring gifted education, broadband telecommunications, data systems, and educational technology to Arizona school systems.

Rebecca Lively is an attorney in Texas. Lively is a graduate of St. Mary's Law School where she graduated Summa Cum Laude in the top 2% of her class. At St. Mary's, she was an Associate Editor of the *St. Mary's Law Journal*, member of Phi Delta Phi, and Vice President of the Technology and Intellectual Property Association. Prior to St. Mary's, Lively received her B.B.A. in Information Systems from the University of Texas at San Antonio where she graduated Magna Cum Laude with Tier Two Honors from the Honors College. She is licensed to practice before the Western District of Texas and the Texas Supreme Court.

Ralph Merkle received his Ph.D. from Stanford University in 1979 where he co-invented public key cryptography. He joined Xerox PARC in 1988, where he pursued research in security and computational nanotechnology until 1999. He was a Nanotechnology Theorist at Zyvex until 2003, when he joined the Georgia Institute of Technology as a Professor of Computing, remaining there until 2006. Merkle is now a Senior Research Fellow at the Institute for Molecular Manufacturing, on the faculty at Singularity University, a director of Alcor, and a co-founder of the Nanofactory Collaboration. He chaired the Fourth and Fifth Foresight Conferences on Nanotechnology. He was co-recipient of: the Feynman Prize for Nanotechnology for theory, the ACM's Kanellakis Award for Theory and Practice, the IEEE Kobayashi Award, the RSA Award in Mathematics, the IEEE Hamming Award; a Fellow of the IACR, a Fellow of the Computer History Museum, and a National Inventor's Hall of Fame Inductee. Merkle has fourteen patents, has published extensively and has given hundreds of talks. His home page is at www.merkle.com.

Michael B. O'Neal is a professor and former Chair of the Computer Science Program at Louisiana Tech University, where he holds the Larson Endowed Professorship. O'Neal received his B.S. (Magna Cum Laude, 1982) and M.S. (1984) from Louisiana Tech, and his Ph.D. (1989) from the University of Louisiana, Lafayette. He was Co-Founder and CTO of OneNetNow.com, a community-based web portal focused on the urban community, which was acquired by EarthLink in 2001. O'Neal is also the Founder and Chief Scientist of Network Foundation Technologies. His academic research interests include distributed online broadcast technologies, behavioral biometrics based active authentication, and computer science education. O'Neal has been a cryonicist for many years, joining Alcor in the late 1980s.

R. Michael Perry is Alcor's Care Services Manager and also Treasurer. He has been a member of Alcor since 1984, the same year he obtained a Ph.D. in Computer Science at the University of Colorado, Boulder. Perry has worked at Alcor since 1987 where he has contributed to automated systems for cooling patients and writes articles for

Cryonics magazine among other duties. Among his interests are cryonics history and the possible application of mathematics to the problems of personal identity, death, and survival. Perry was a cofounder in 1986 of the cryonics-promoting Society for Venturism, and has been active in fundraising by them to assist with cryopreservations for hardship cases. Perry has written an immortalist philosophical treatise, *Forever for All: Moral Philosophy, Cryonics, and the Scientific Prospects for Immortality* (Universal Publishers, 2000). A revised edition is in progress.

Brian Wowk, Ph.D., is a biophysicist employed as a Senior Scientist at 21st Century Medicine, Inc., a company specializing in low temperature preservation of tissue and organs for medical applications. He holds M.Sc. and Ph.D. degrees in medical physics, specializing in radiation oncology physics and magnetic resonance imaging. He is a leading expert in cryopreservation by vitrification. Wowk has maintained an interest in cryonics since 1986. He has served on Alcor's board of directors since 2004.